D0457569

THE IDENTIFICATION OF TREES & SHRUBS

By the same author:

BRITISH TREES IN WINTER

THE IDENTIFICATION OF TREES & SHRUBS

HOW TO NAME ANY WILD OR GARDEN TREE OR SHRUB LIKELY TO BE MET WITH IN THE BRITISH ISLES WITH 2,500 DIAGRAMS MADE BY THE AUTHOR

BY

F. K. MAKINS, M.A., F.L.S.

SECOND EDITION

LONDON
J. M. DENT & SONS LIMITED
1948

J. M. DENT & SONS LTD.
Aldine House · Bedford St. · London

Made in Great Britain
by
The Temple Press • Letchworth · Herts.
First published 1936
Reprinted (with corrections) 1944
Reset 1948

INTRODUCTION

It is not the purpose of this book to compete with the many excellent works on the selection and cultivation of trees and shrubs, but to provide the amateur without previous knowledge of the subject with the means of identifying any tree or shrub he is likely to meet with, growing in the open in any part of the British Isles. The explorations of Wilson, Henry, and others, have resulted in such a large addition to our shrub flora in recent years that even the experienced professional gardener is often at a loss when confronted with many of the newer kinds. As, however, there can be few parts of the world left unexplored by collectors, it is probable that the limit has now been reached in the case of hardy trees and shrubs; and the time has arrived to place before the public a tree and shrub flora of these islands in a readily accessible and inexpensive form, and with some prospect of completeness.

The most popular method of identification is by means of illustrations. In this book will be found illustrations of 1,311 species, belonging to 534 genera. As the total number of genera described here is 552 it will be seen that nearly every genus of tree or shrub native to the British Isles or cultivated in our gardens has been figured. To illustrate every species, amouting to 1,732 in all, would have made the book too bulky and expensive. It should not, however, be difficult to name any species, first, by comparing it with the illustrations of others in the same genus, and then by referring to the descriptions given in the later part of the book.

As this book could not have been produced without special facilities for examining private collections of exotic trees and shrubs, it remains for the author to express his thanks to all those owners who have so kindly placed their collections at his disposal, and particularly to the Rt. Hon. Henry Hobhouse; to his son, Mr. A. L. Hobhouse (whose head-gardener, Mr. E. W. A. King, has been of the greatest help); to Sir Henry Hoare, Bart.; and to Mr. A. Lewingdon, who is in charge of the Earl of Ilchester's fine collection of sub-tropical plants at Abbotsbury in Dorset.

Valuable help has been freely and generously given at all times by the Directors and Staff of the Botanical Gardens at Kew and Cambridge, especially by Messrs. W. J. Bean and V. S. Summerhayes; by Messrs. D. Stewart & Sons Ltd., Ferndown Nurseries, Wimborne; and by Messrs. John Scott & Co., The Royal Nurseries, Merriott, Somerset.

Apart from local floras the works most frequently consulted have been Rehder's *Manual of Cultivated Trees and Shrubs Hardy in North America* and Bean's *Trees and Shrubs Hardy in the British Isles.* Also the excellent catalogue issued by Messrs. Hillier & Sons, Winchester, has largely influenced the scope of this work.

F. K. M.

September 1935.

INTRODUCTION TO THE SECOND EDITION

THE first edition was perhaps too sanguine in holding out hopes to the amateur that he would be able, without previous knowledge of the subject, to identify any tree or shrub growing in the open in any part of the British Isles. It is not easy to write for those amateurs—and they form the majority—who object to the use of technical terms. Nevertheless, the temptation to use them in the second edition has been resisted. In some other respects, however, an attempt has been made to render the book of more value to the serious student. Descriptions of families and genera have been amplified with the object of bringing to the front the affinities of whole groups of plants. The importance of the vegetable kingdom has been stressed by the addition of notes on timber and other economic products. The authors of the Latin names have been given in the text and the Latin names brought up to date as far as possible. Many species have been added to the descriptions, thus rendering the book less susceptible to the charge of important omissions. A list of accessible reference books has also been added, and the index enlarged to include species as well as genera.

F. K. M.

September 1946.

CONTENTS

HOW TO USE THE BOOK

If the plant to be identified is entirely unknown the first thing to do is to turn to the

KEY

on page 12, and decide in which figure or group of figures it is most likely to be found. (By a tree or shrub is meant a plant with a woody stem, part of which, at least, does not die back every winter. It is no use, therefore, looking for herbaceous perennials, many of which have, when fully developed, the appearance of shrubs. On the other hand, many low-growing plants, more suitable for the rockery than the shrubbery, will be found. Generally speaking, everything described in this book would be included in their tree and shrub catalogue by most nurserymen. All other terms used in the key and elsewhere in this book are fully explained on pages 4 to 10.)

Having found the most likely group turn to the Figures indicated on the right-hand side of the key and run through the

DIAGRAMS,

marking those which are most like the specimen it is desired to identify. The illustrations are somewhat diagrammatic; superfluous shading and other details not necessary for clarification or determination having been omitted for the sake of clearness. Nor have the illustrations been drawn to a definite scale. Apart from the difficulty of making exact scale-drawings in a book of this size, they would serve no useful purpose owing to the great variation in the size of leaves on one plant. The relative sizes of leaves on different species have, however, been indicated as far as possible; for example, where the average leaves of one species are about three times larger than those of another figured on the same page, they have been drawn three times larger wherever space permits. In the case of flowers shown separately from the plant to which they belong the size is governed solely by the need for displaying their structure. In any case, the average dimensions of leaves, flowers, and fruits are given in the descriptive section.

The drawings have mostly been made from living (in a few cases from dried) material; where they have not, the source has been acknowledged in brackets.

The different species illustrated in one figure are given letters: A, B, C, and so on. (There may be several drawings for one species, when arrows indicate to which species they belong.) Now refer to the text at the bottom of each figure. Each letter is followed by the popular name, if any, and then by the Latin (botanical) name in italics. (Notice that the Latin name of the genus is not repeated in full unless the sequence is interrupted by the name of a different genus.) The numbers in brackets refer to the pages on which the

DESCRIPTIONS

will be found. Turn to the appropriate page and see if the description there given agrees with the actual specimen. To make sure of the species run through all the descriptions given under one genus. This is not so tedious as it sounds, for the largest genera have been split up into groups, each with a different characteristic.

The purpose of the descriptions, therefore, is to supplement the illustrations and to carry the identification as far as the species where that has not already been done. With these objects, and also to save space, the descriptions have been confined to the salient points of difference between the species.

The arrangement of families is approximately that of Bentham and Hooker, the system in use at Kew.

The name of the family is followed by the floral formula (see page 5). After the floral formula is given a short list of the salient characters, to which is sometimes added a few notes of general interest such as economic uses and well-known herbaceous plants, if any, belonging to the family.

The genera belonging to one family and the species to one genus follow each other in alphabetical order, unless the family or genus has been subdivided, in which case the alphabetical order is limited to each subdivision.

An asterisk (*) indicates that the plant is not hardy at Kew, though successfully grown in the open throughout the year near the south and west coasts of the British Isles.

The generic name precedes the specific name or 'specific epithet' as it is called, and the latter is followed by the author's name, often abbreviated but given in full on pages 346 to 349. The synonyms, which are not necessarily obsolete, are enclosed in brackets. As far as possible, the international rules of botanical nomenclature have been observed; that is to say, the earliest published name since the appearance of *Species Plantarum* by Linnaeus in 1753 is the valid one. When a species has been transferred to another genus the specific name is kept and the name of the first author appears in brackets followed by that of the second. Owing to difficulty in keeping up with research on priorities it is not possible to guarantee the validity of every name used. Indeed, too frequent changes of name are confusing and irritating to those who have to deal with living plants and is to be deprecated even at the risk of consigning the original author to oblivion. On the other hand, a little trouble and inconvenience may reasonably be demanded. There is no sense in a few people perpetuating a name that every one else knows has been obsolete for a hundred years. The common habit of beginning all specific epithets with a capital letter is bad because it is incorrect; a specific epithet never begins with a capital unless it is a personal name (*Henryana*, *Henryi*, *Hermanniae*) or is also the name of a genus (*Abies*, *Cerasus*) or other noun (*Barba-Jovis*, *Crista-galli*, *Granatum*). Adjectival place names do not take a capital (*europaea*, *japonica*, *hupehensis*).

The popular name comes next, followed, when known, by a figure showing the maximum height in feet which the plant is expected to reach in these islands, given favourable conditions. The months of flowering follow next; these cannot always be relied upon, particularly in species from the southern hemisphere where the seasons are reversed. In mild seasons such species may flower at any time; and the flowering of native species is often abnormal for the same reason. Where no information under this head has been given the species has either not been known to flower in the British Isles or reliable information has not been forthcoming. Subsequent figures give dimensions in inches, unless hyphened.

At the end of each description appears the country of origin. It is interesting to observe that out of every hundred species dealt with in this book twenty-nine are natives of China or Japan, twenty-one of North America, twenty of Europe, seven of the Himalayas, six of New Zealand, five of South America, four of north and west Asia, four are hybrids, three are natives of Australia or Tasmania, while only one is of African origin.

It is possible that the plant looked for may be one that is unknown to the writer or, if known, omitted for lack of space. In either event there can, of course, be no clear identification. In deciding what to omit the question has always been asked : Is it worth growing or likely to be met with? Sometimes there have been other considerations : for instance, a species may owe its inclusion to the part it has played in the production of well-known hybrids, or to its botanical interest, or to the mere chance that the writer happens to be more familiar with it than with some other which may have equal claims to notice.

EXPLANATION OF THE TERMS USED

A. See *Floral Formula* and *Stamens*.

ALTERNATE. Used of leaves or other parts when each one arises from a different level on the stem from the next.

ANTHER. The terminal and pollen-bearing part of the stamen, usually yellow. (Fig. 82 C.)

APEX. The top. In the case of leaves the end furthest from the point of attachment.

AWL-SHAPED. Tapering evenly from base to apex, and not narrowing at the base. (Fig. 43 G.)

AXIL. The upper angle formed by a leaf or branch with the stem, or by a side vein with the main vein.

AXILLARY. Used of flowers borne in the axil of a leaf. (Fig. 78 A, H–K, and M.)

AXIS. An imaginary line running through the centre of a plant or any part of a plant. Also used generally of any structure on or immediately around the axis.

BASE. The bottom. In the case of leaves that part of the blade nearest the point of attachment. (*Heart-shaped* base, Fig. 78 C; *straight*, Fig. 78 K; *rounded*, Fig. 78 E and L; *tapering* or *wedge-shaped*, Fig. 78 A, D, F–J, and M.)

BRACT. Any leaf-like structure on the flower-stalk outside the sepals and petals. (Fig. 82 C.) Also used of the small leaves from the axils of which the flowers arise. (Fig. 86 G.)

C. See *Floral Formula* and *Corolla*.

CALYX (K). The outermost parts of the flower, usually green, and resembling a ring of small leaves enclosing the petals and internal organs. (Fig. 82 C.) The separate parts are known as the *sepals*. Denoted in the floral formulae by the letter K (from the Greek word *kalyx*, cover). Note that in the Compositae (Daisy family) there is a false calyx composed of bracts, and that what appears to be one flower is really a composite head of small highly specialized flowers. (Fig. 99 L.)

CAPSULE. A dry splitting fruit made up of more than one carpel. (Fig. 84 E.)

CARPEL. One or more special ovule-bearing structures which will be seen in the centre of most flowers (considered by some botanists to be originally a leaf which has become changed and specialized for the production of seed). After fertilization the carpel usually enlarges and becomes the fruit. (Figs. 112 and 113.)

CATKIN. A tail-like or brush-like collection of small unisexual and usually stalkless flowers without petals, but with scale-like bracts, the whole falling as one, e.g. the 'lambs' tails' of hazel. (Figs. 106 to 111.)

CLUSTER. When two or more leaves, flowers, or fruits arise from the same point at the end of the main stem or of a side shoot (often very short and scarcely perceptible), they are said to be in a cluster. (Fig. 94 H and J.) A flower-cluster of this kind is called an *umbel*, a term not used in this book. (Fig. 120 A shows a *compound umbel*.) To avoid technicalities the term *branched cluster* is applied generally in this book to any group of flowers having a common stalk, but not coming under the definition of a raceme or panicle.[1]

Compound Leaf. When the blade of a leaf is divided into two or more separate leaflets, each with its own stalk or independent base, the leaf is said to be compound. That the leaflets themselves are not leaves is shown by the absence of buds in their axils; also the whole leaf can be pulled off as one, leaving a well-defined scar on the stem. (Figs. 1–23.)

Corolla (C). The petals taken together. Denoted in the floral formulae by the letter C.

Deciduous (D). Falling off, not persistent. A deciduous tree or shrub is one which normally loses all or most of its leaves, i.e. becomes bare, during a definite season of the year, usually the winter.

Dicotyledon. See page 143.

Digitate. Used in this book of a compound leaf of 2, 4, or more leaflets, which all arise from approximately the same point at the end of the common stalk. (A leaf of 3 leaflets can also be digitate, but the distinct term *3-foliolate* has been used here for such leaves owing to their large number.) (Figs. 4–6.)

Embryo. The rudimentary or 'unborn' plant tucked away inside the seed before germination.

Entire. Without teeth or lobes.

Evergreen (E). Clothed with leaves throughout the year, not deciduous. Plants that are normally leafless are also described as evergreen when the branches or any other parts assuming the functions of leaves remain green throughout the year, e.g. gorse and broom.

Flaccid. Not stiff or rigid.

Floral Formula. A method of compressing information, used by botanists for many years. K stands for the calyx, C for the corolla, A for the stamens, and G for the pistil. $\underline{G}$ means that the pistil has a superior ovary (see *Ovary*), $\bar{G}$ an inferior ovary, $\underline{\bar{G}}$ that both superior and inferior ovaries may be present. The figure after each indicates the number of parts of which it is composed; if the figure is enclosed in brackets the parts are all joined together, i.e. they cannot be pulled off separately without tearing. For instance, the floral formula of the family Diapensiaceae is K (5), C (5), A5, $\underline{G}$ (3), which means that the flowers of this family have 5 united sepals, 5 united petals, 5 separate stamens, and a superior pistil formed by the union of three originally separate parts (carpels). Other symbols used are : P (perianth), ∞ for numerous or an indefinite number, and + inserted between figures to show the separation of the parts into two or more layers or whorls.

G. See *Floral Formula* and *Pistil*.

Genus. Plural *genera*, adjective *generic*. The genus of a plant is indicated by the first of its two Latin names, e.g. in *Quercus coccinea* the tree belongs to the genus *Quercus*. *Quercus* is the generic name, *coccinea* the specific name (see

[1] A branched cluster, in which the central flowers open first, is known as a *cyme*. (Fig. 65 H.) When the outer flowers open first it is a *corymb*. (Fig. 93 H.) These terms have not been used in this book, for they are often difficult to determine.

Species). There is no absolute rule as to what constitutes a genus. All that can be said is that species which show several distinct characters in common are usually grouped together in one genus. In *Quercus* (Oak) the most easily recognizable common character is the acorn. Allied genera are grouped into *Families*, families into *Orders* (not referred to in this book), orders into *Sub-classes*, sub-classes into *Classes*, and classes into *Subdivisions*. (For convenience Gymnosperms and Cryptogams are ranked as Classes in this book, though they are really subdivisions.)

GLAND. A small swelling often found on leaves or other parts of plants, and usually secreting oil or some other substance.

GLAUCOUS. Covered with bloom (like a plum) or grey or white substance as distinct from hairs.

GRAFT. The artificial union of two different kinds of tree or shrub by making an incision in one and inserting a small branch of another. In the vast majority of cases the two kinds thus united retain their distinctive characters. Where they do not, the result is known as a *graft hybrid*. The best-known instance of this is the Purple Laburnum, which is the result of grafting the Purple Broom on the Common Laburnum.

HEAD. A dense cluster of flowers or fruits.[1] (Figs. 14 E and 30 A and B.)

HYBRID. When the flowers of one kind of tree or shrub are fertilized by the pollen from another kind—it may be a different variety, or species, or even genus—the resulting offspring, if any, is termed a hybrid. Hybrids, while usually combining the characters of both parents, often reveal entirely new characters, such as more luxuriant growth, or showier and more abundant flowers; on the other hand, they seldom breed true, if they breed at all, and have to be increased by division. Most of the hybrids included in this book are important enough in the garden and field to be treated as separate species, though botanically they cannot be regarded as such. A *natural hybrid* is one produced without the conscious agency of man; they are very common, for instance, among the willows, poplars, elms, and veronicas, and make it much more difficult to sort out the species belonging to these genera.

K. See *Floral Formula* and *Calyx*.

LANCE-SHAPED (lanc.). Shaped like a lance head, i.e. with curved edges narrowing at the base and apex and much longer than broad. If a leaf is at least three times longer than broad, it can be taken as lance-shaped for the purposes of this book, regardless of its actual outline (but see *Linear* and *Ovate*). (Figs. 40 and 58 D.)

LATERAL. At the side, as opposed to terminal.

LEAFLET (lflt.). See *Compound Leaf*.

LINEAR. Long and very narrow, with nearly parallel margins and narrowing at the base, e.g. a blade of grass. (Figs. 50–53.)

LOBED. Divided into segments the spaces between which do not reach the axis or centre. There is no hard and fast distinction between lobes and large teeth. (Figs. 23–36.)

[1] A head formed of stalkless flowers borne on the swollen end of the axis is known as a *capitulum*. (Figs. 67 D and 99 L.)

Midrib. The largest vein of a leaf, usually running lengthwise along the axis from base to apex.

Monocotyledon. See page 321. As the term is used in the key to the illustrations, a few words here may not be out of place. The term covers a large class of closely allied plants. Every gardener knows how the seeds of grasses, onions, and leeks send up a single narrow leaf instead of the double and multiple leaf of most other seeds. It is this character which gives the class its name (*mono*, one; *cotyledon*, seed leaf). Monocotyledons can be recognized in later life by the leaves or leaflets being usually long and narrow, and nearly always without a conspicuous network of veins. Very few are trees or shrubs. Not one of the trees is a native of Europe, and only two shrubs: Butcher's Broom and Asparagus. Not more than twenty genera of monocotyledons have been included in this book, and most of these are unmistakable on account of their tropical or grass-like appearance. Of the remainder *Smilax* and *Lapageria* are climbers, while only *Philesia* and the Alexandrian Laurel, in addition to those already mentioned, are shrubs. (All except the palms and banana are illustrated in Figs. 38–40, which should be referred to in cases of doubt.)

Nerves. The chief veins.

Ob-. When the half towards the apex is broader than the half towards the base, as in the pear or fig. *Oblance-shaped* (oblanc.) and *obovate* (obov.) mean, therefore, inversely lance-shaped and inversely ovate, i.e. the narrow end is towards the point of attachment. (Fig. 74 L.)

Oblong. Ovate or lance-shaped with sides nearly parallel, except at the base and apex. Used also of fruits with approximately straight sides, i.e. neither egg-shaped nor pear-shaped. (Figs. 40 D and 88 L.)

Opposite. Arising in pairs from the same level, but on opposite sides.

Ovary. The hollow chamber formed by the growth of the basal part of the carpel, and completely enclosing one or more ovules. An ovary may be formed by one carpel or by the union of several. It is said to be *superior* (Fig. 82 C) or *inferior* (Fig. 94) when it is in a position above or below the insertion of the stamens and other floral parts. Usually there is no difficulty in deciding this; but sometimes, and particularly in the rose family, the ovaries may be borne in a hollow cup, above or outside which the other floral parts are inserted. Where the cup is definitely hollow, i.e. where there is a clear space between the ovary and the sides of the cup, as in the plum and cherry (Figs. 90 and 91), the ovary must be treated as superior. Where there is partial (Fig. 58 A) or complete (Fig. 58 D) fusion, the ovary must be treated as inferior.

Ovate (ov.). Shaped like an egg, i.e. with curved sides narrowing at the base and apex. In this book any leaf narrowing to the stalk and less than three times longer than broad, regardless of its actual outline. For example, 'Leaf ov., 3–5-lobed' means that the leaf is less than three times longer than broad, and would be egg-shaped if the spaces between the lobes were filled up. The same applies to leaves described as lance-shaped or linear. (Fig. 35.)

Ovules. Tiny seed-like bodies, which may be seen when the ovary is dissected or cut through (in conifers and shrubby horsetails the ovules are not enclosed in an ovary; in the tree fern there is none). It is from the ovules, after they have been fertilized by the pollen, that the seeds develop. (Fig. 82 C.)

P. See *Floral Formula* and *Perianth*.

PALMATE. Arranged like the fingers of a hand, i.e. arising from approximately the same point and spreading outwards.

PALMATELY LOBED. Where the midribs of the lobes are palmately arranged. (Fig. 23.) This is an important point in the key. For example, the leaf of the Wild Service Tree (*Sorbus Torminalis*) appears at first sight to be palmately lobed, and is so described in some books, but a reference to Fig. 36 K shows that the midribs of the lobes are not palmately arranged; the leaf is therefore pinnately lobed. (Figs. 23–31.)

PALMATELY VEINED. Where the chief veins of the leaf are palmately arranged. (Fig. 38 G.)

PANICLE. A branched raceme, i.e. a raceme in which the common stalk sends off lateral branches, which may themselves branch. The largest branches are usually at the base, giving the panicle a roughly pyramidal shape. (Fig. 69.) A flattened panicle becomes a *corymb* (see footnote on page 5). A group of flowers may take the form of a panicle without being a branched raceme, e.g. in the Privet. The term panicle, therefore, can be taken to mean any loose and open group of flowers, which has a roughly pyramidal outline, and this is the sense in which it has been used in this book.

PELTATE. Attached to the stalk by the centre or one face, and not by the end, as in the leaf of a nasturtium. (Figs. 31 B and 44 H.)

PERIANTH (P). The outermost floral parts, or floral envelope, i.e. the calyx and corolla, especially when there is no clear distinction between the two, or when one or the other is absent. (Figs. 113 D and 127 A–D.) Denoted in the floral formulae by the letter P.

PERSISTENT. Remaining attached, not falling off.

PINNATE. Arranged like the divisions of a feather or herring-bone, i.e. arising from opposite sides of a common axis. Used of compound leaves with pinnate leaflets. If the leaflets of a pinnate leaf are themselves simple, the leaf is said to be *simple pinnate*. (Figs. 7–17.) If, however, they are divided into secondary pinnate leaflets, the leaf is *2-pinnate*. (Fig. 18 F.) If these secondary leaflets are again divided, the leaf is *3-pinnate*.

PINNATELY LOBED. Where the midribs of the lobes are pinnately arranged. (Figs. 32–36.)

PINNATELY VEINED. Where the chief side veins arise at intervals from opposite sides of the midrib. (Fig. 58 D.)

PISTIL (G). The organs in the centre of the flower, from which the seed and fruit directly develop, i.e. the carpel, or carpels taken together, the female organs. The pistil includes the ovary, style, and stigma, but not the stamens. (Fig. 82 C.) Denoted in the floral formulae by the letter G (from the Greek word *gynoecium*, female part).

POLLEN. The yellow dust-like grains that are produced by the stamens (male organs), and fertilize the ovule. They are usually conveyed to the pistil by wind or insects.

PROSTRATE. Lying on or near the ground.

RACEME. A group of flowers on a common axis, each flower being stalked and generally in the axil of a bract. The oldest (fully open) flowers will be found near the bottom of the axis, and the youngest (unopened buds) at the top. It follows that the common stalk of a raceme can be clearly traced through the group as a more or less straight line from base to apex. (Fig. 90 F.) See also *Panicle*.

RADIAL. Spreading outwards on all sides at approximately the same level like the spokes of a wheel.

RECEPTACLE. The swollen head of the flower-stalk, on which the floral organs, or in the case of a capitulum the flowers, are inserted. In the rose, plum, and cherry family the receptacle is converted into a cup enclosing the pistil, while the sepals, petals, and stamens grow from the rim.

RECURVED. Curved downwards or backwards. Also *reflexed*.

ROUND. Shaped like a ball or a circle.

SIMPLE. Not compound. A leaf is simple when it is not divided into leaflets.

SOLITARY. When one flower only is found in the axil of a normal leaf or at the end of a shoot.

SPECIES. Plants which, given the same conditions of growth, show no structural difference from one another usually belong to the same species. Also, if the seed is sown, the vast majority of the offspring will be practically the same as the parents. Occasionally, however, there may be a marked difference in one or two individuals. If these hand on their peculiar features to their offspring, a new species is formed; if they do not, we call the new kind a *variety*. Generally speaking, therefore, a species breeds true, while a variety does not. Sometimes, however, it is not easy to say whether a plant should be considered a variety or a separate species. Moreover, a too literal interpretation of the breeding rule would lead to a vast number of new species which to the ordinary man would be practically indistinguishable from one another. The whole question of species, varieties, and *forms* (differences due to differing conditions of growth) is largely a matter of opinion. When different species hitherto isolated by distance or environment are brought together, they may lose their specific characters and behave as varieties, or even forms. On the other hand, we know that there is some factor in the seed, seemingly independent of outside circumstances, which causes like to breed like, though exactly what it is no one knows. In this book the number of species has been kept as small as possible by classing the minor differences as varieties and generally ignoring the scientific arguments for ranking them as species.

SPIKE. Used generally for a long and narrow raceme, but strictly speaking a raceme in which the individual flowers are stalkless. (Fig. 66 A.)

STAMENS (A). The special (male) organs of the flower concerned with the production of pollen. They usually consist of several to many thread-like bodies, each bearing at its end a pair of small yellow lobes (the anther), which contain the pollen. At the time of fertilization the anther lobes split open and discharge the pollen, or, as in the heath and rhododendron family, the pollen is discharged through apical pores. The stalk is known as the filament. (Fig. 82 C.) Denoted in the floral formulae by the letter A (from the Greek word *androecium*, male part).

STIGMA. The extreme outer end of the style. (Fig. 82 C.) When the flower is ripe for fertilization, the stigma is often sticky or feathery for the purpose of catching and retaining the pollen. (Fig. 82 C.)

STIPULE. An appendage at the base of the leaf-stalk, usually one on each side and often leaf-like. The small scar left by its fall is an important point in identification. (Figs. 11 A and 90 A.)

STYLE. An extension upwards of the ovary for the purpose of exposing the stigma for the reception of pollen. (Fig. 82 C.)
SUB-OPPOSITE. Nearly but not quite opposite. (Fig. 69 A.)

TENDRIL. A coiled thread by which a climbing plant grasps an object for support.
TERMINAL. At the end, as opposed to lateral.
THREE-NERVED (3-nerved). A 3-nerved leaf is one in which three of the chief veins, usually the midrib and two side veins, are much larger than all the others. (Figs. 65 C and 68 J.) It is usually palmately veined, but not always so. (Fig. 126 C and H.)
TOOTHED. Evenly (Fig. 83 A and B). Unevenly (Figs. 82 H and 83 K). Closely (Fig. 83 B). Distantly (Fig. 83 E and G). Finely (Fig. 83 J). Coarsely (Fig. 83 G). Minutely (Fig. 83 E). Round- (Fig. 93 B). Double- (Fig. 92 J). Sharp (Fig. 94 C and K). Blunt (Fig. 94 F).
TRIFOLIOLATE (3-fol.). A compound leaf with three leaflets.

UNDULATING. When the outline of a leaf is curved into a series of shallow bays not pronounced enough to be called teeth or lobes. (Fig. 98 B.)
UNISEXUAL. Of one sex only. A flower or catkin with stamens, but without, or with rudimentary pistil is called *male* (Fig. 81 B); one with a pistil, but without, or with rudimentary stamens is *female* (Fig. 81 A). A flower possessing both is *bisexual* (Fig. 81 E).

VARIETY. See *Species*.

WAVY. When the margin of a leaf is crinkled or folded in a vertical plane, as distinct from undulating, where the curvature is in a horizontal plane. (Fig. 120 M.)
WHORL. A group of three or more stems, leaves, or flowers arising from the same level on all sides of the main axis. (Fig. 55.)

DIAGRAMS

DIAGRAMS

KEY

Note: The number in brackets after the name of each species at the foot of pages 131–40, denotes the page on which a description of the species will be found.

Trees and shrubs with *compound* leaves.	FIGS.
3-foliolate leaves :	
Opposite leaves	1 A–J
Alternate leaves	1 K–3
Digitate leaves	4–6
Pinnate leaves :	
Simply pinnate leaves :	
Opposite leaves	7–9 D
Alternate leaves	9 E–17
2- or 3-pinnate leaves (sometimes simply pinnate) . .	18–23
Trees and shrubs with normally *simple* or no leaves (if the leaves are compound, they are very small beyond the seedling stage).	
Lobed leaves :	
Palmately lobed leaves :	
Opposite leaves	23–26 C
Alternate leaves	26 D–31
Pinnately lobed leaves	32–36
Leaves normally *absent* or nearly so [1]	37
Monocotyledons with simple leaves	38–40
Conifers (resinous plants with needle-like or scale-like leaves, including pines, firs, yews, cedars, cypresses, and junipers) .	41–47
Non-coniferous *heath-like* shrubs with leaves not usually longer than ¼ inch	48–49
Trees and shrubs with simple *linear* leaves, not included in any of the above groups	50–53
Trees and shrubs with simple *opposite* or *whorled* leaves, not included in any of the above groups :	
Prickly or spiny	54
Toothed leaves :	
Leaves in whorls	55
Leaves in opposite pairs	56–64
Entire leaves	65–77
Trees and shrubs with simple *alternate* leaves or leaves in *alternate clusters*, and not included in any of the above groups :	
Toothed leaves	78–111
Entire leaves [2]	112–128

[1] Deciduous trees and shrubs can only be tested in the leaf-bearing season.
[2] See also Figs. 79 K and L, 95 G, and 97 M.

FIG. 1

A. *Clematis montana* (144)
B. *Acer griseum* (181)
C. Box Elder, *A. Negundo* (181)
D. *Acradenia Frankliniae* (167)
E. Mexican Orange Blossom, *Choisya ternata* (167)
F. Winter Jasmine, *Jasminum nudiflorum* (276)
G. Primrose Jasmine, *J. primulinum* (276)
H. *Pithecoctenium muricatum* (288)
J. Leaf of *Forsythia* (see Fig. 60 A)
K. *Holboellia coriacea* (151)
L. *Anagyris foetida* (191)
M. *Lardizabala biternata* (150)
N. *Sinofranchetia sinensis* (151)

Genus not figured: *Staphylea*, see Fig. 7 E.

(Flowers and fruits of M after Le Maout and Decaisne and *Botanical Magazine*.)

FIG. 2

A. *Acanthopanax lasiogyne* (235)
B. Lawyer Vine, *Rubus australis* (203)
C. Hop Tree, *Ptelea trifoliata* (167)
D. *Sargentodoxa cuneata* (157)
E. Dewberry, *Rubus caesius* (203)
F. Fragrant Sumach, *Rhus canadensis* (183)
G. Coral Tree, *Erythrina Crista-galli* (190)
H. *Cytisus Battandieri* (186)
J. *Akebia lobata* (150)
K. *Psoralea glandulosa* (189)

(D after Hutchinson.)

Fig. 3

A. Hardy Orange, *Aegle sepiaria* (167)

B. Evergreen Laburnum, *Piptanthus nepalensis* (192)

C. Common Laburnum, *Laburnum anagyroides* (187)

D. Poison Ivy, *Rhus Toxicodendron* (184)

E. *Adenocarpus decorticans* (185)

F. *Cytisus nigricans* (186)

G. Shrubby Restharrow, *Ononis fruticosa* (188)

H. Dalmatian Laburnum, *Petteria ramentacea* (188)

J. Tick Trefoil, *Desmodium tiliaefolium* (190)

K. Moon Trefoil, *Medicago arborea* (190)

L. Bush Clover, *Lespedeza formosa* (190)

Genera not figured: *Pueraria* (189), *Rosa* (199), *Vitis* (175)

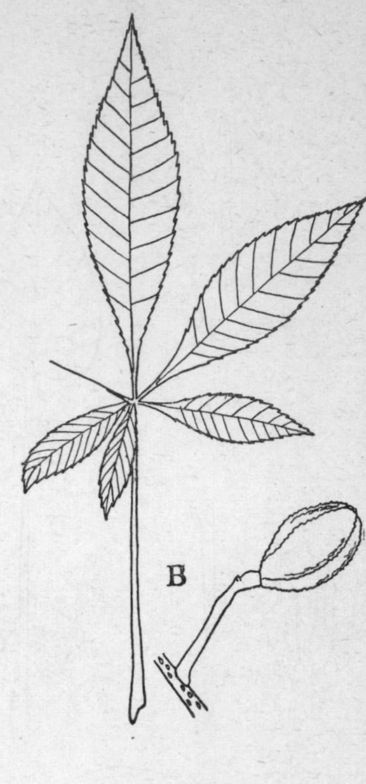

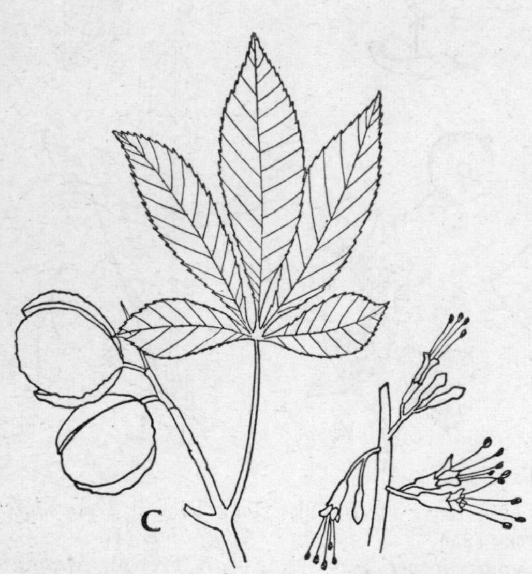

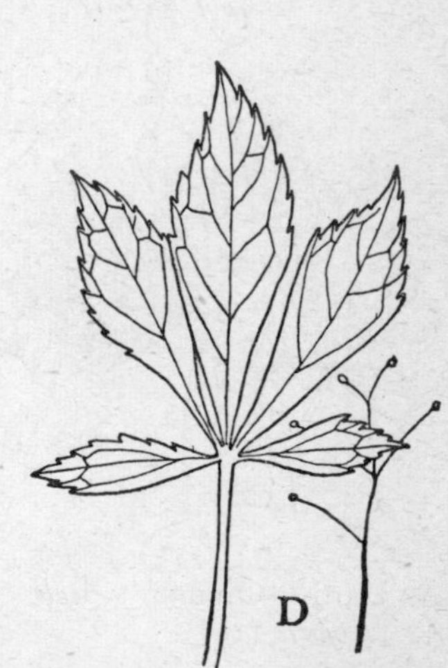

FIG. 4

A. Common Horse-chestnut, *Aesculus Hippocastanum* (176)

B. Indian Horse-chestnut, *A. indica* (177)

C. Shrubby Pavia, or Dwarf Buckeye, *A. parviflora* (177)

D. True Virginia Creeper, *Vitis quinquefolia* (*Ampelopsis hederacea*) (175)

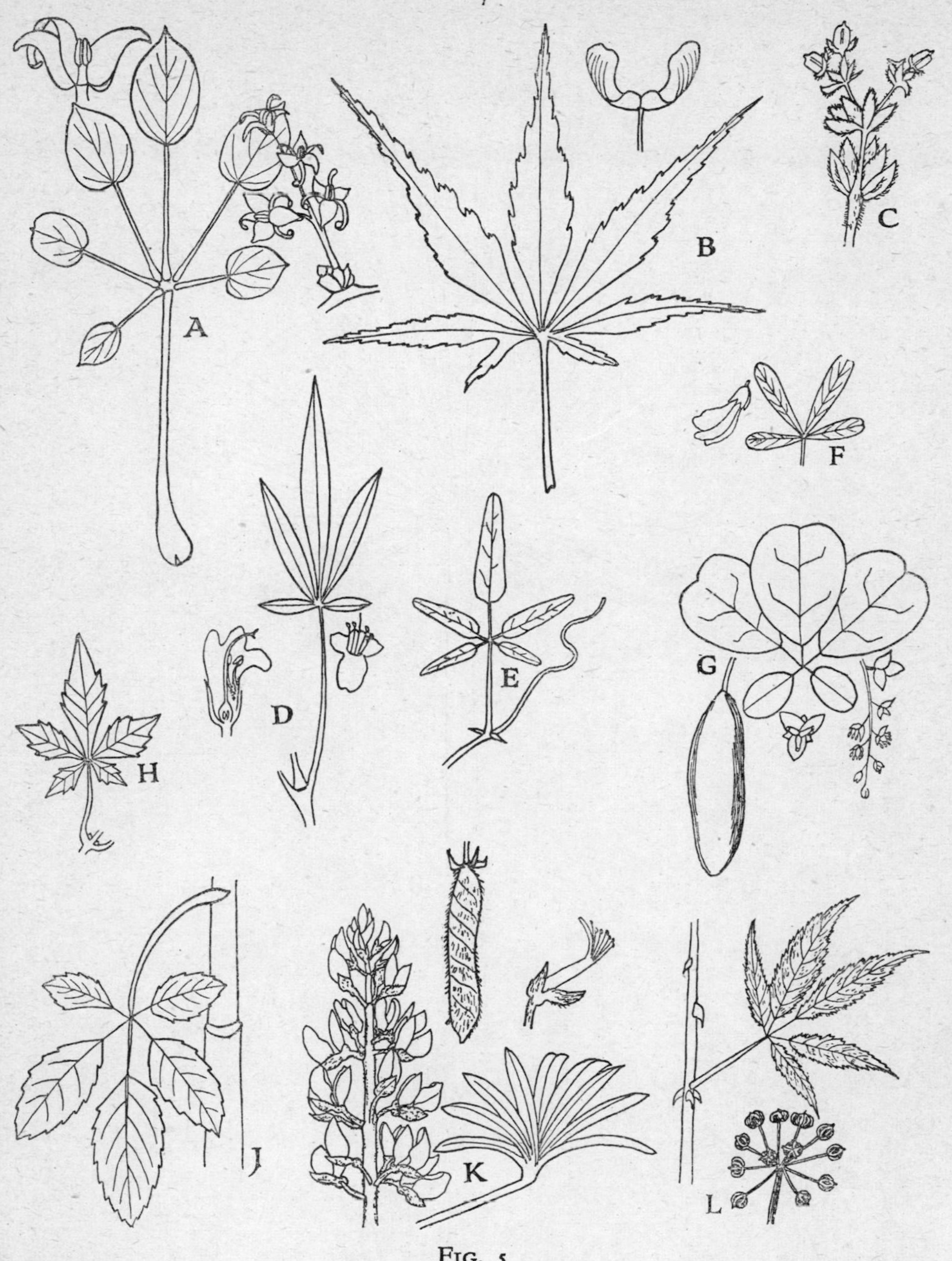

FIG. 5

A. *Stauntonia hexaphylla* (151)
B. Japanese Maple, *Acer palmatum*, var. *dissectum* (181)
C. *Dorycnium hirsutum* (190)
D. Chaste Tree, *Vitex Agnus-castus* (289)
E. *Hardenbergia Comptoniana* (190)
F. *Caragana frutescens* (188)
G. *Akebia quinata* (150)
H. *Vitex Negundo* (289)
J. *Panax arboreum* (236)
K. Tree Lupin, *Lupinus arboreus* (187)
L. *Acanthopanax Simonii* (235)

(Flowers of A after *Gardener's Chronicle*.)

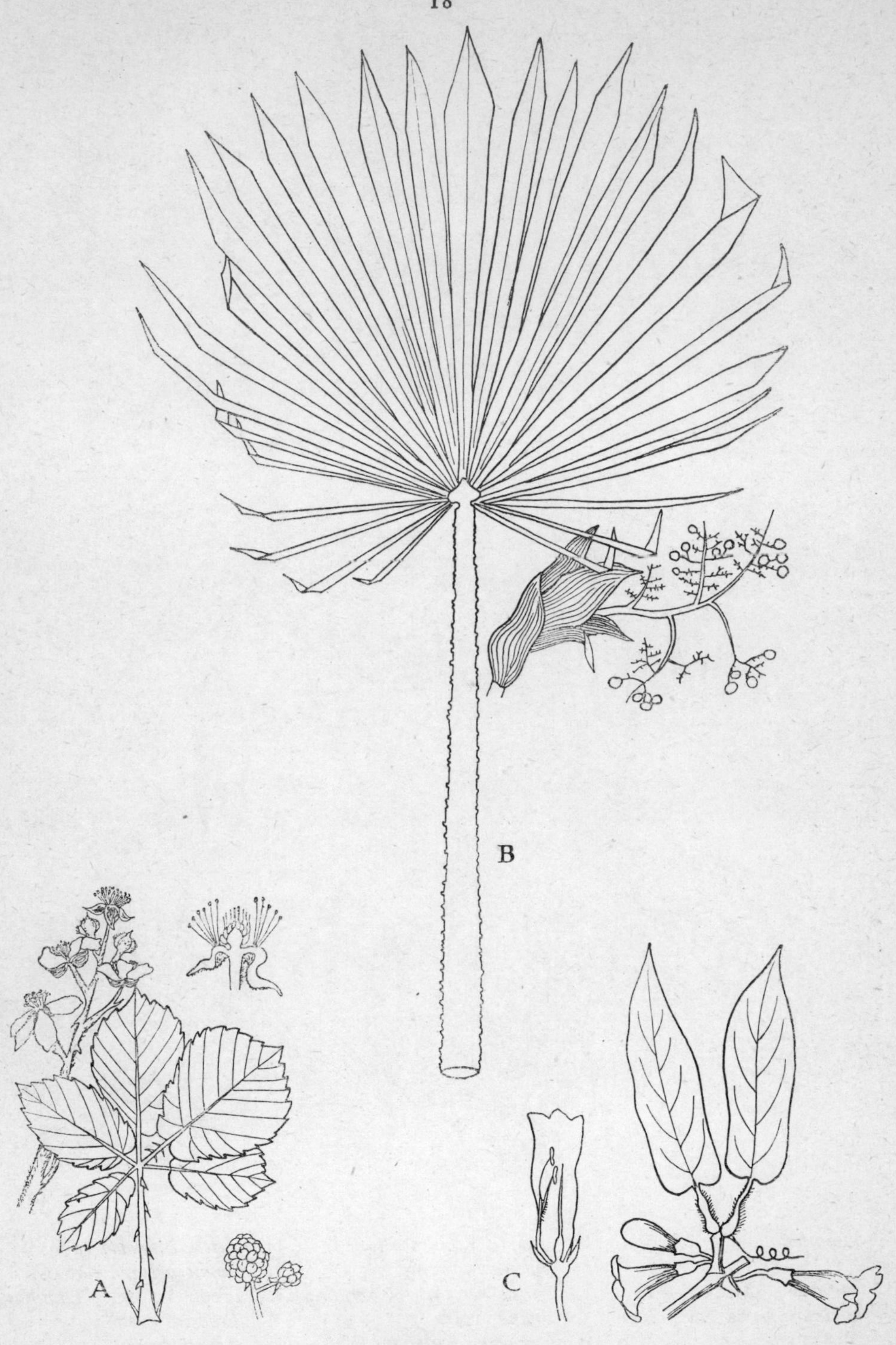

Fig. 6

A. Blackberry, Bramble, *Rubus fruticosus* (203) B. Chusan Palm, *Trachycarpus Fortunei* (324) C. Cross Vine, *Bignonia capreolata* (287)

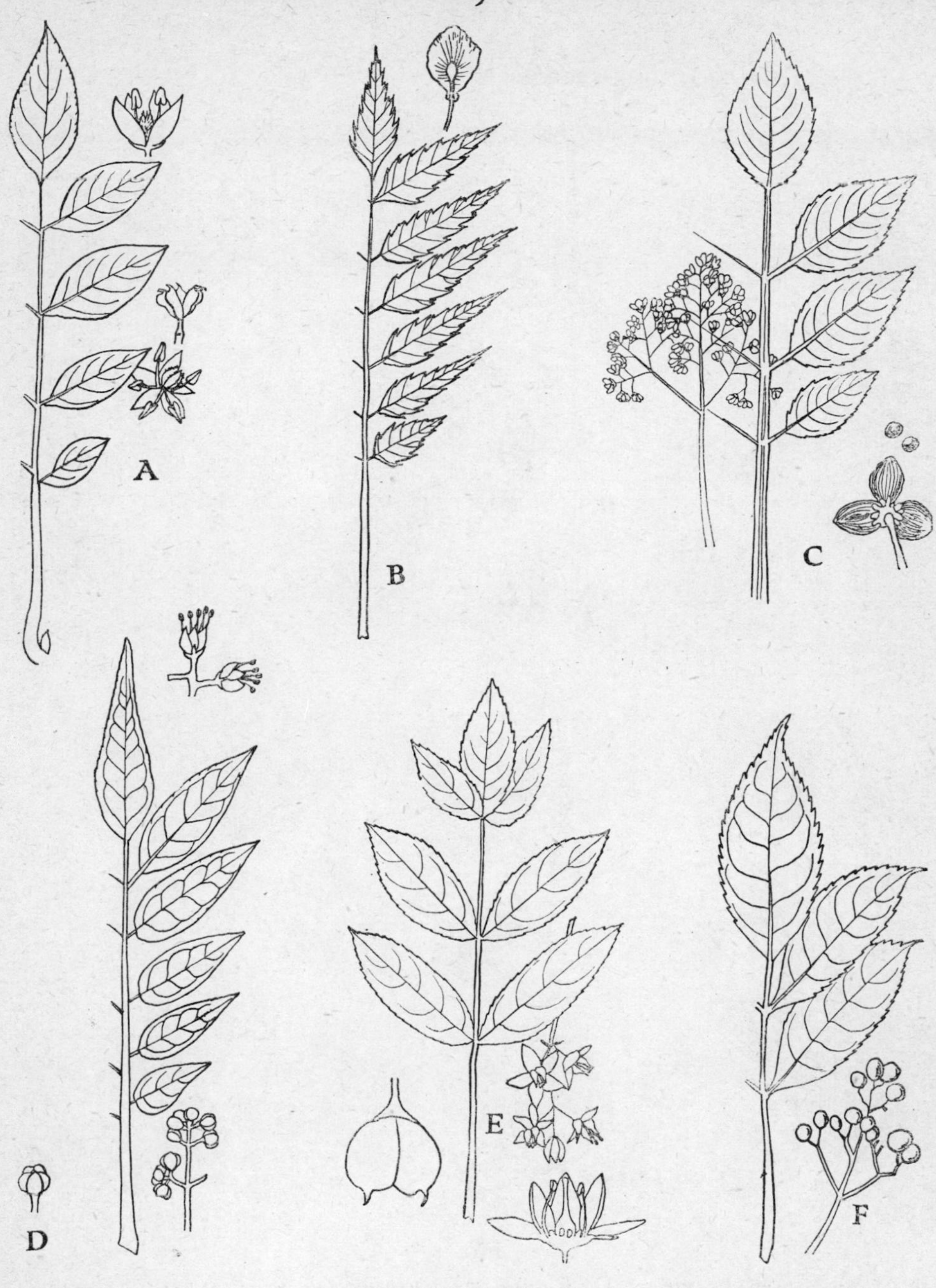

FIG. 7

A. *Evodia Daniellii* (167)

B. *Dipteronia sinensis* (181)

C. *Euscaphis japonica* (182)

D. Amur Cork Tree, *Phellodendron amurense* (167)

E. Bladder Nut, *Staphylea colchica* (182)

F. *Turpinia nepalensis* (182)

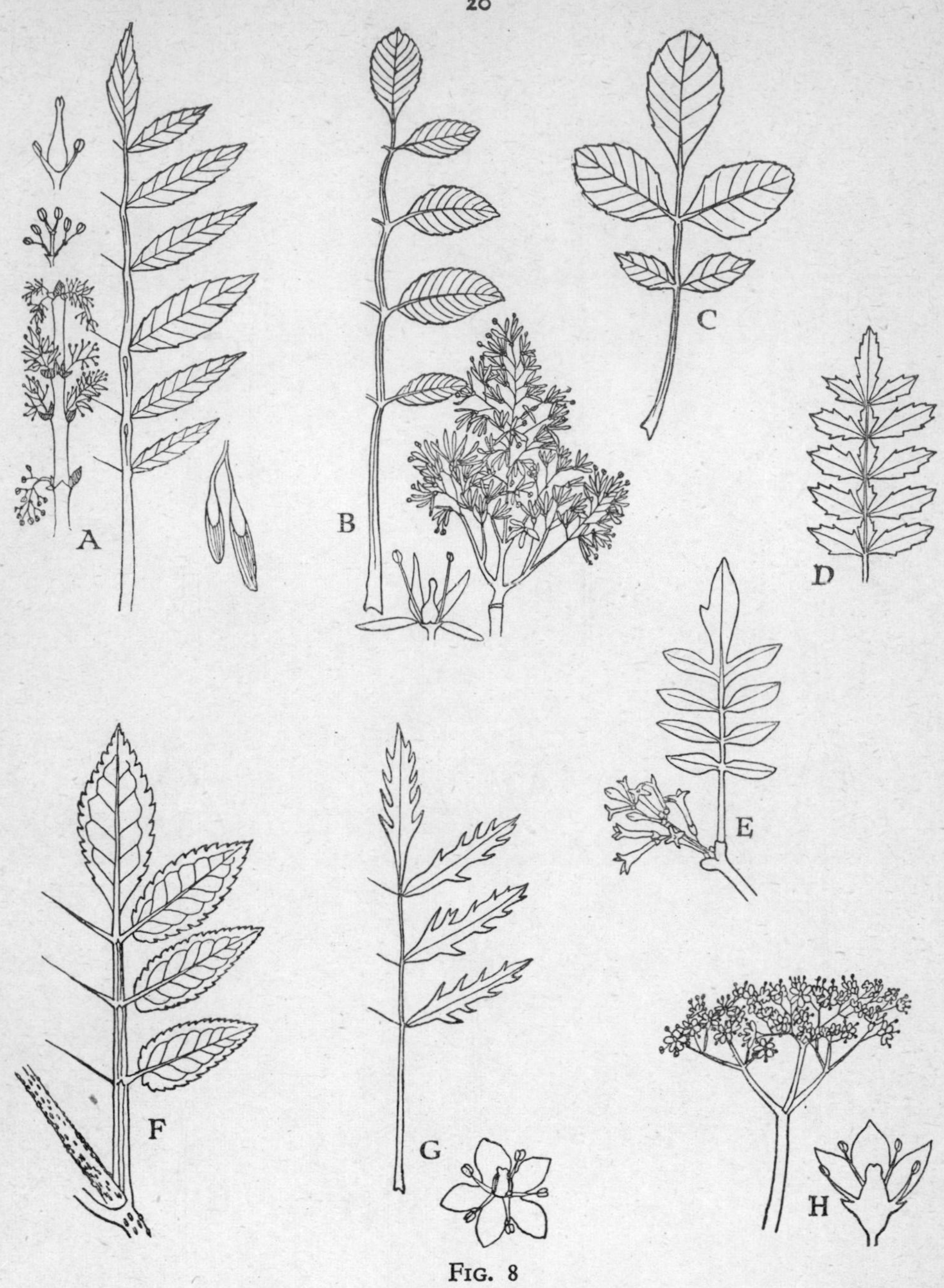

Fig. 8

A. Common Ash, *Fraxinus excelsior* (275)

B. Flowering Ash, or Manna Ash, *F. Ornus* (274)

C. Maries's Flowering Ash, *F. Mariesii* (274)

D. *Weinmannia trichosperma* (229)

E. Pinnate Lilac, *Syringa pinnatifolia* (280)

F. Common Elder, *Sambucus nigra* (245)

G. Plumed Red-berried Elder, *S. racemosa*, var. *plumosa* (245)

H. Flowers of Elder

Genus not figured: *Lyonothamnus* (195)

Fig. 9

A. Common Jasmine, or Jessamine, *Jasminum officinale* (276)
B. Brush Bush, *Eucryphia glutinosa* (195)
C. Trumpet Flower, *Campsis radicans* (287)
D. Traveller's Joy, or Old Man's Beard, *Clematis Vitalba* (145)
E. *Zanthoxylum alatum* (168)
F. Toothache Tree, *Z. americanum* (168)
G. Japan Pepper, *Z. piperitum* (168)
H. Chian Turpentine Tree, *Pistacia Terebinthus* (183)
J. *Picrasma ailanthoides* (168)

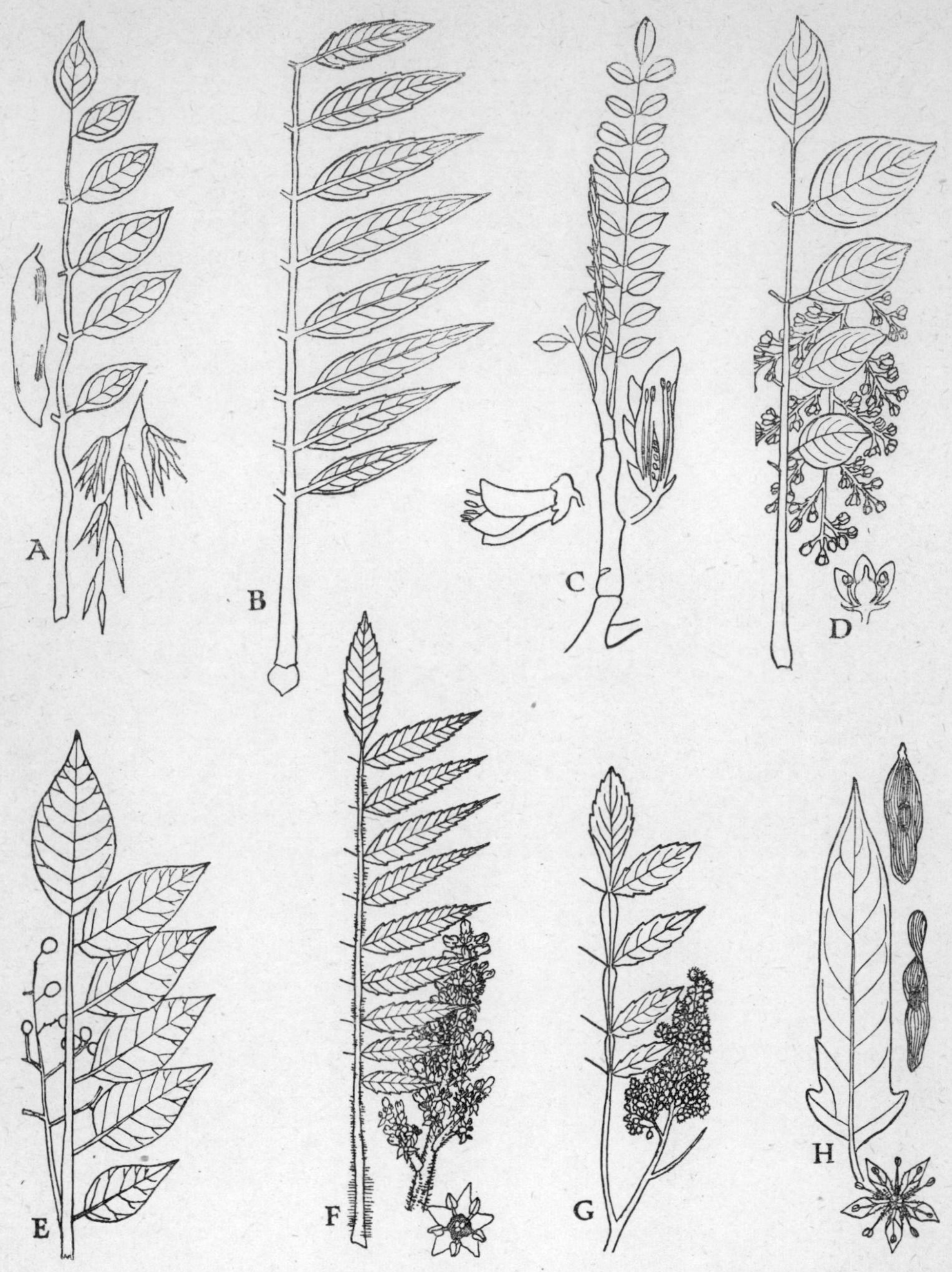

FIG. 10

A. *Decaisnea Fargesii* (150)

B. *Cedrela sinensis* (169)

C. *Sophora tetraptera* (192)

D. *Meliosma Veitchiorum* (183)

E. Lacquer or Varnish Tree, *Rhus verniciflua* (184)

F. Stag's Horn Sumach, *R. typhina* (184)

G. Shining Sumach, R. *copallina* (183)

H. Leaflet, flower, and fruits of Tree of Heaven, *Ailanthus altissima* (168)

(G after Sargent.)

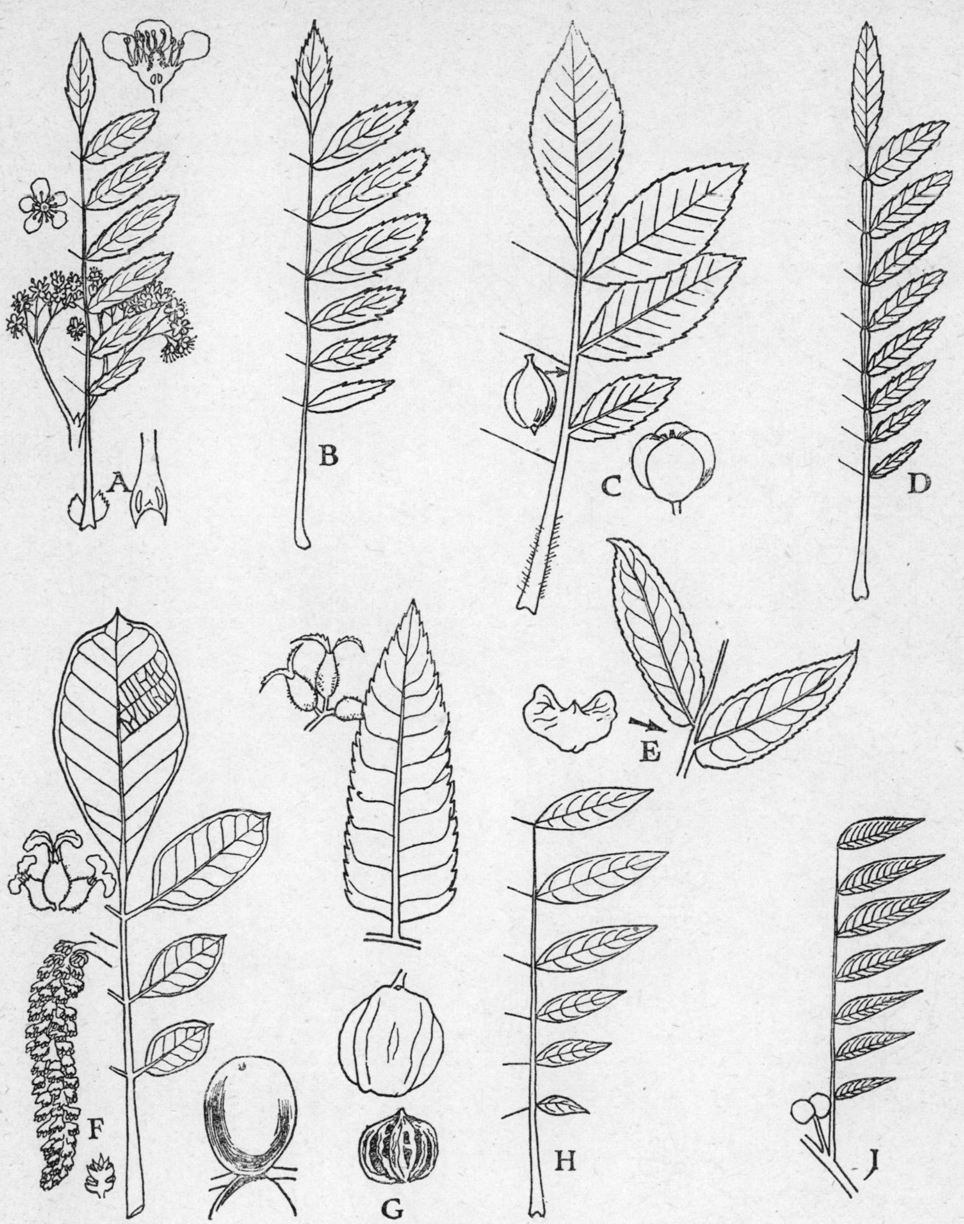

FIG. 11

A. Mountain Ash, or Rowan, *Sorbus Aucuparia* (220)

B. Service Tree, *S. domestica* (220)

C. Mocker Nut (a hickory), *Carya alba* (304)

D. Chinese Wing Nut, *Pterocarya stenoptera* (305)

E. Leaflets and fruit of Caucasian Wing Nut, *P. fraxinifolia* (305)

F. Common Walnut, *Juglans regia* (305)

G. Black Walnut, *J. nigra* (305)

H. Chinese Pistachia, *Pistacia chinensis* (183)

J. Soapberry, *Sapindus Drummondii* (177)

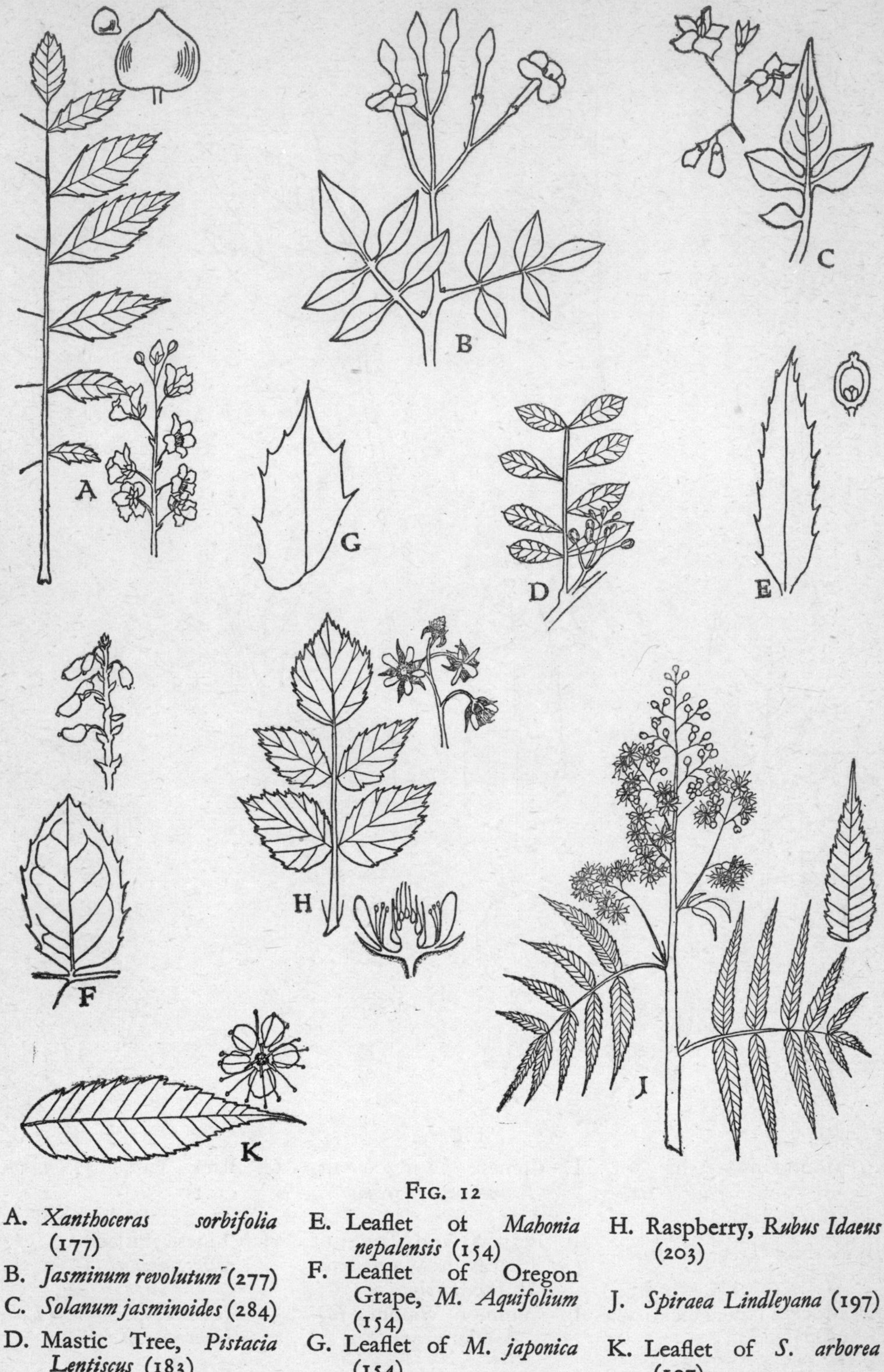

FIG. 12

A. *Xanthoceras sorbifolia* (177)

B. *Jasminum revolutum* (277)

C. *Solanum jasminoides* (284)

D. Mastic Tree, *Pistacia Lentiscus* (183)

E. Leaflet ot *Mahonia nepalensis* (154)

F. Leaflet of Oregon Grape, *M. Aquifolium* (154)

G. Leaflet of *M. japonica* (154)

H. Raspberry, *Rubus Idaeus* (203)

J. *Spiraea Lindleyana* (197)

K. Leaflet of *S. arborea* (197)

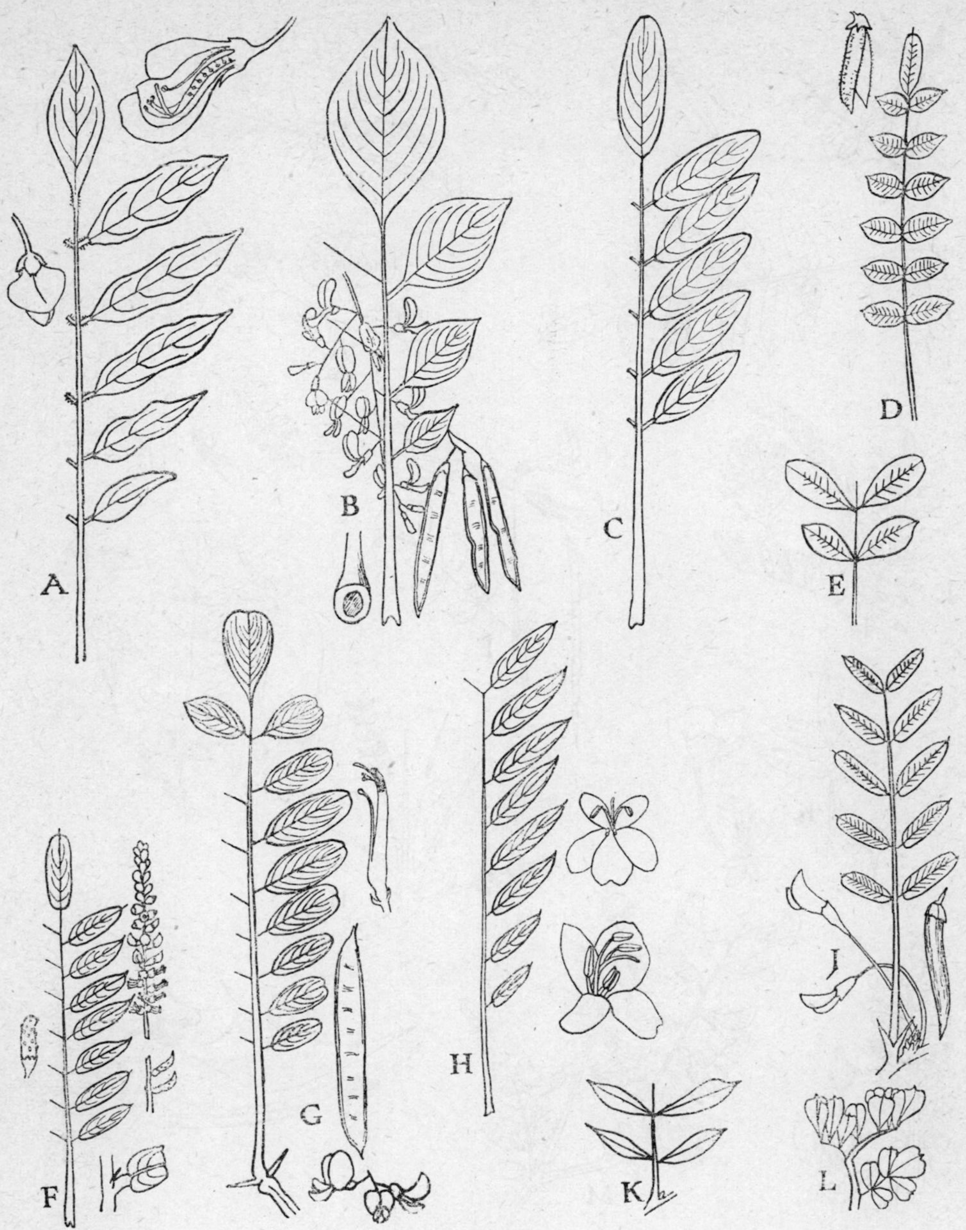

FIG. 13

A. *Wistaria sinensis* (191)
B. Yellow Wood, *Cladrastis tinctoria* (191)
C. *Maackia amurensis* (192)
D. *Calophaca wolgarica* (188)
E. *Caragana Chamlagu* (188)
F. False Indigo, *Amorpha fruticosa* (185)
G. False Acacia, or Locust Tree, *Robinia Pseudacacia* (191)
H. Wild Senna, *Cassia marylandica* (193)
J. Pea Tree, *Caragana arborescens* (188)
K. Salt Tree, *Halimodendron argenteum* (187)
L. *Coronilla glauca* (190)
Genus not figured: *Calpurnia* (191)

(Flowers of B after Sargent.)

FIG. 14

A. *Indigofera Gerardiana* (190)
B. Rose Acacia, *Robinia Kelseyi* (191)
C. Pagoda Tree, *Sophora japonica* (192)
D. *S. viciifolia* (192)
E. Jupiter's Beard, or Silver Bush, *Anthyllis Barba-Jovis* (185)
F. Scorpion Senna, or Crown Vetch, *Coronilla Emerus* (190)
G. Bladder Senna, *Colutea arborescens* (189)
H. Goat's Thorn, *Astragalus Tragacantha* (188)
J. Glory Pea, or Parrot's Bill, *Clianthus puniceus* (189)
K. Shrubby Cinquefoil, *Potentilla fruticosa* (198)
L. *Osteomeles anthyllidifolia* (217)
M. French Honeysuckle, *Hedysarum multijugum* (190)

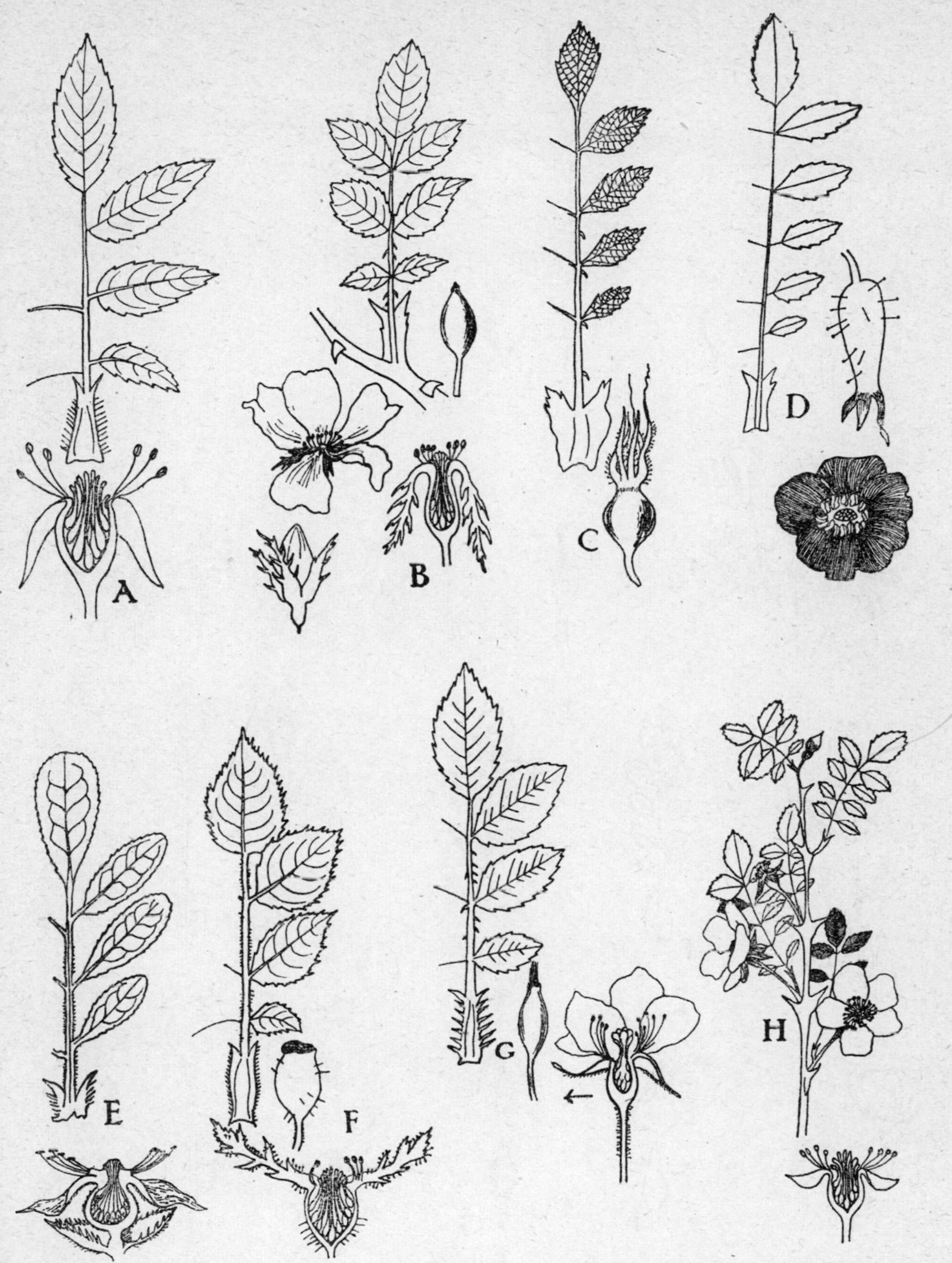

FIG. 15

A. Chinese or Monthly Rose, *Rosa chinensis* (199)
B. Dog Rose, R. *canina* (201)
C. Ramanas Rose, R. *rugosa* (202)
D. R. *Moyesii* (201)
E. Macartney Rose, *bracteata* (200)
F. Sweet Briar, or Eglantine, R. *Eglanteria* (200)
G. R. *multiflora* (199)
H. R. *Hugonis* (202)

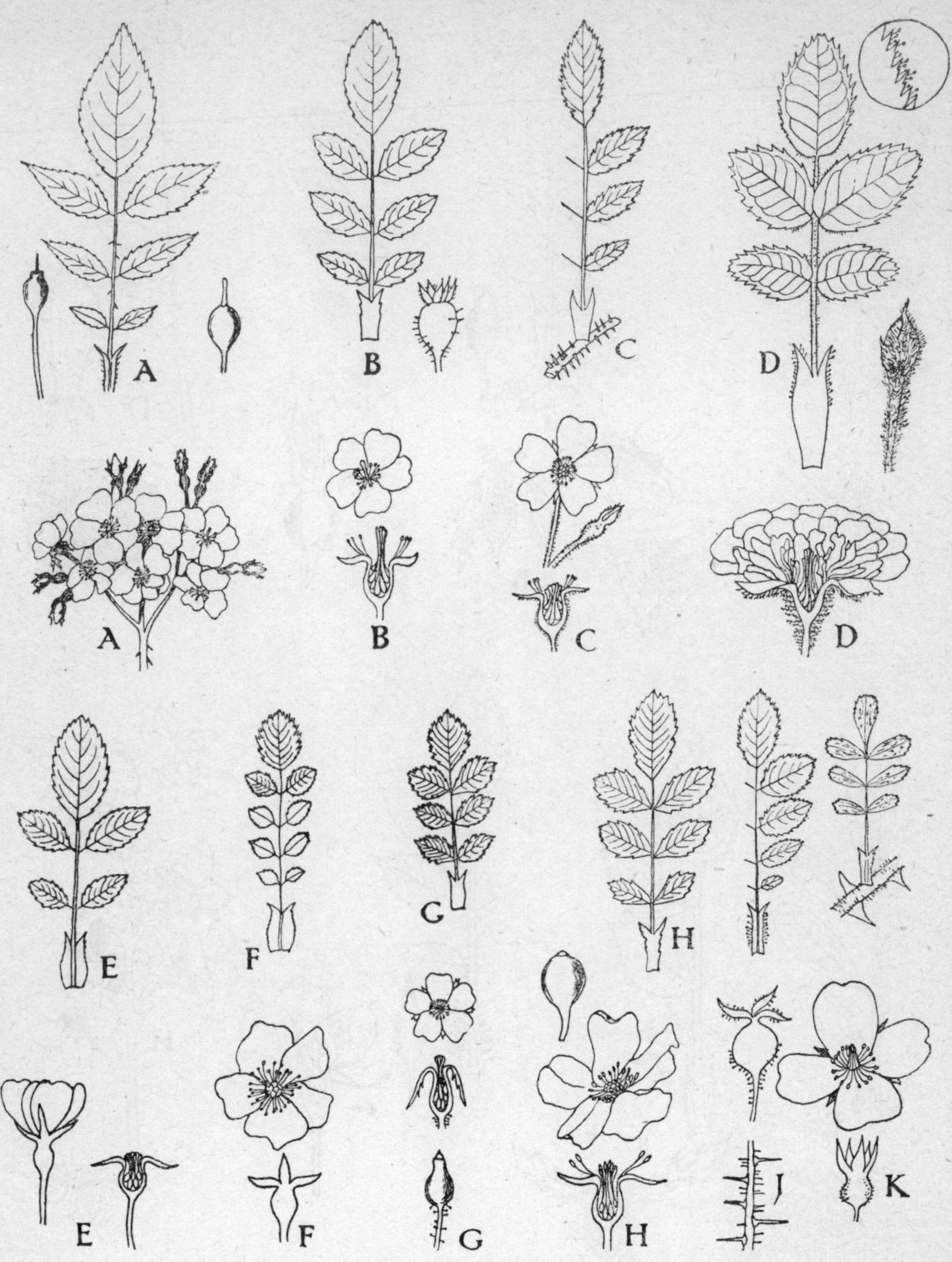

FIG. 16

A. Musk Rose, *Rosa moschata* (199)
B. Trailing Wild Rose, *R. arvensis* (199)
C. Downy Rose, *R. villosa* (201)
D. Moss Rose, *R. centifolia*, var. *muscosa* (200)
E. Irish Rose, *R. hibernica* (202)
F. Scotch or Burnet Rose, *R. spinosissima* (202)
G. Small-flowered Briar, *R. micrantha* (201)
H. Austrian Briar, *R. foetida* (202)
J. Sabine's Rose, *R. involuta* (201)
K. *R. sericea* (201)

(C after Butcher and Strudwick.)

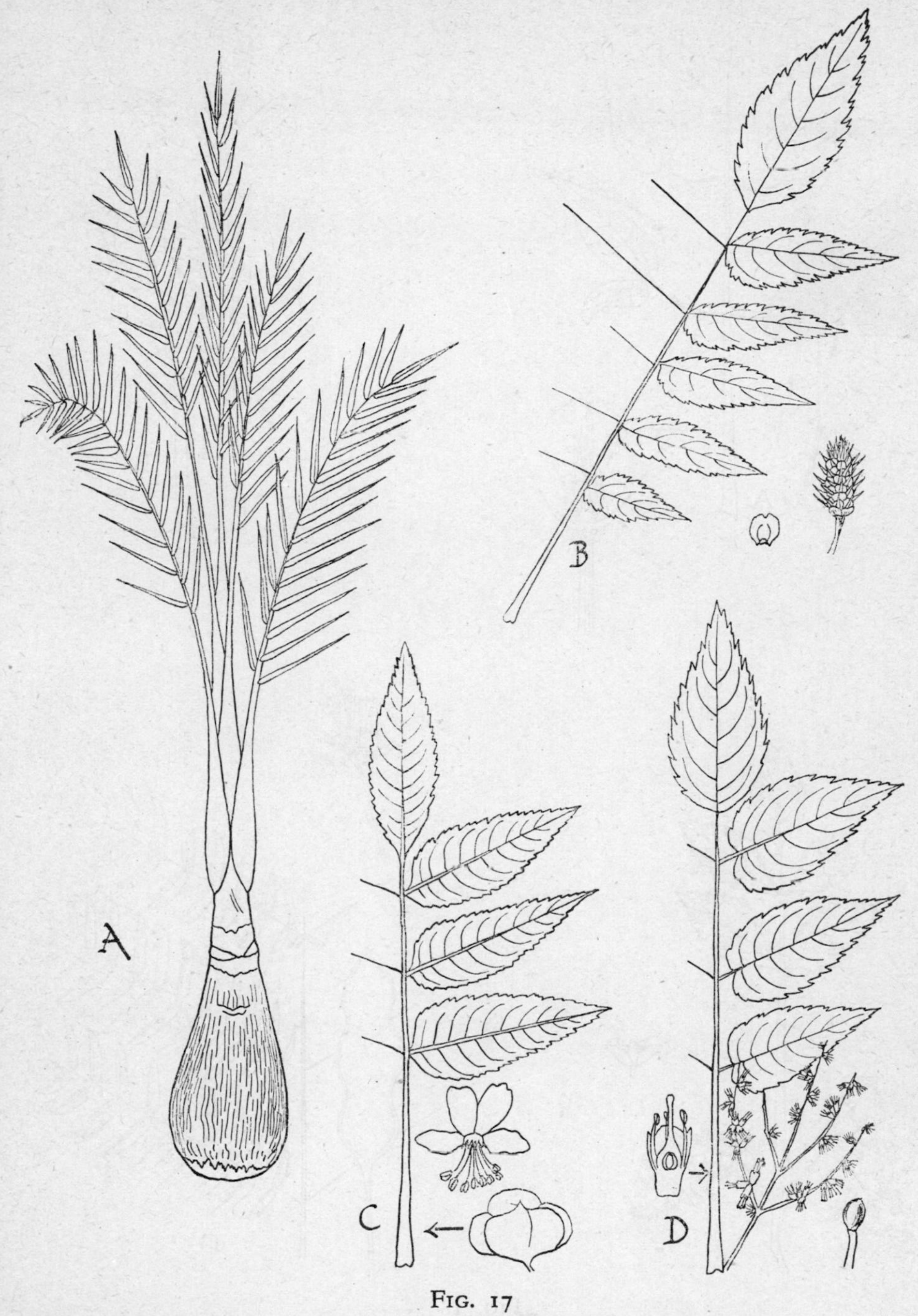

FIG. 17

A. Wine Palm, *Jubaea spectabilis* (323)

B. *Platycarya strobilacea* (305)

C. Mexican Buckeye, *Ungnadia speciosa* (177)

D. *Tapiscia sinensis* (182)

(C after *Flore des Serres*.

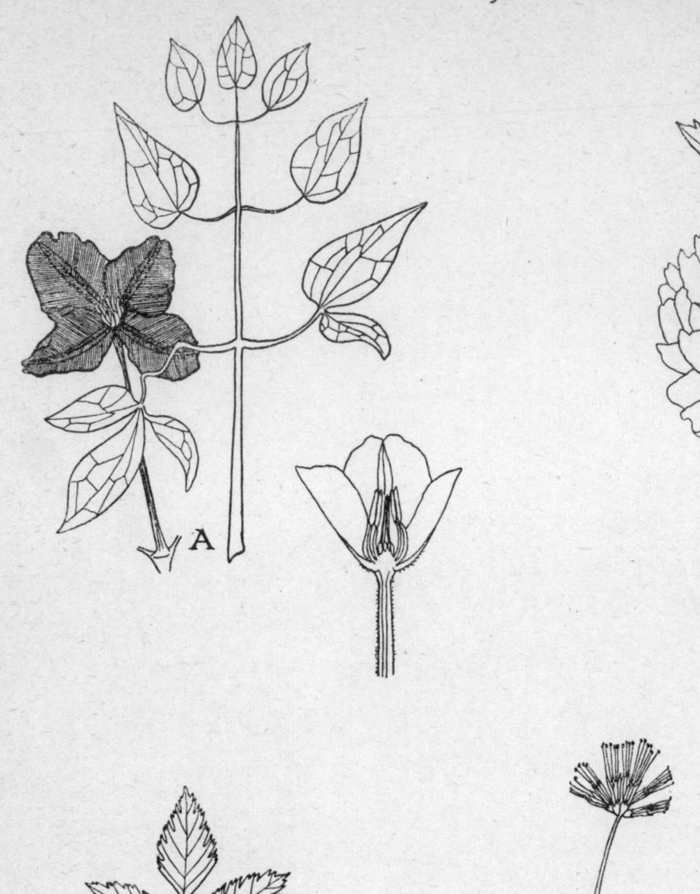

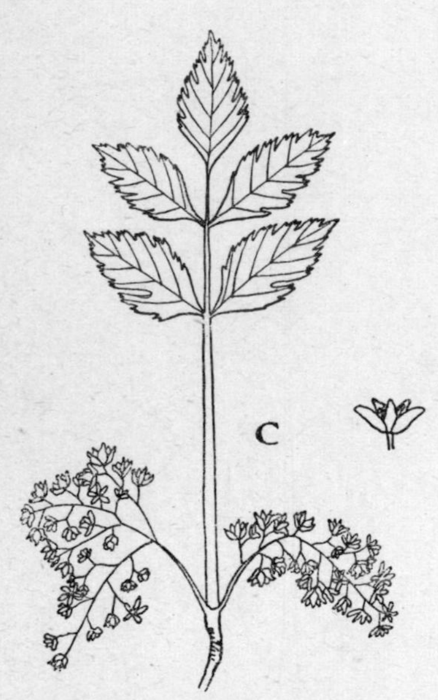

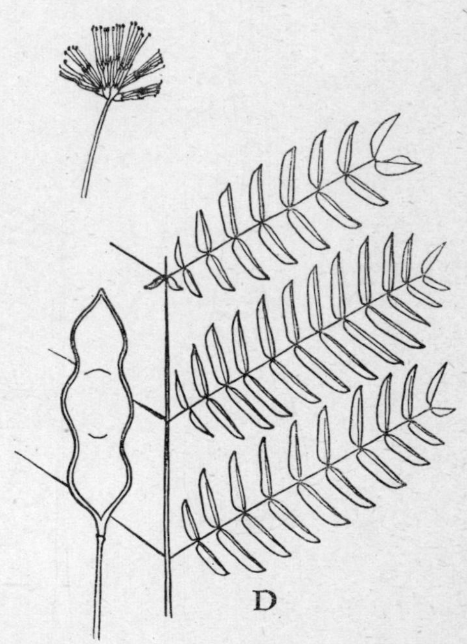

FIG. 18

A. *Clematis Jackmannii* (144)

B. Tree Paeony, *Paeonia suffruticosa* (145)

C. Yellow-root, *Zanthorrhiza apiifolia* (145)

D. Pink Siris, *Albizzia Julibrissin* (194)

FIG. 19

A. Pride of India, *Koelreuteria paniculata* (177)

B. Honey Locust, *Gleditschia triacanthos* (193)

C. Fruit of Water Locust, *G. aquatica* (193)

D. *Chamaebatia foliolosa* (198)

E. Kentucky Coffee Tree, *Gymnocladus canadensis* (193)

(Fruits of C and E after Sargent.)

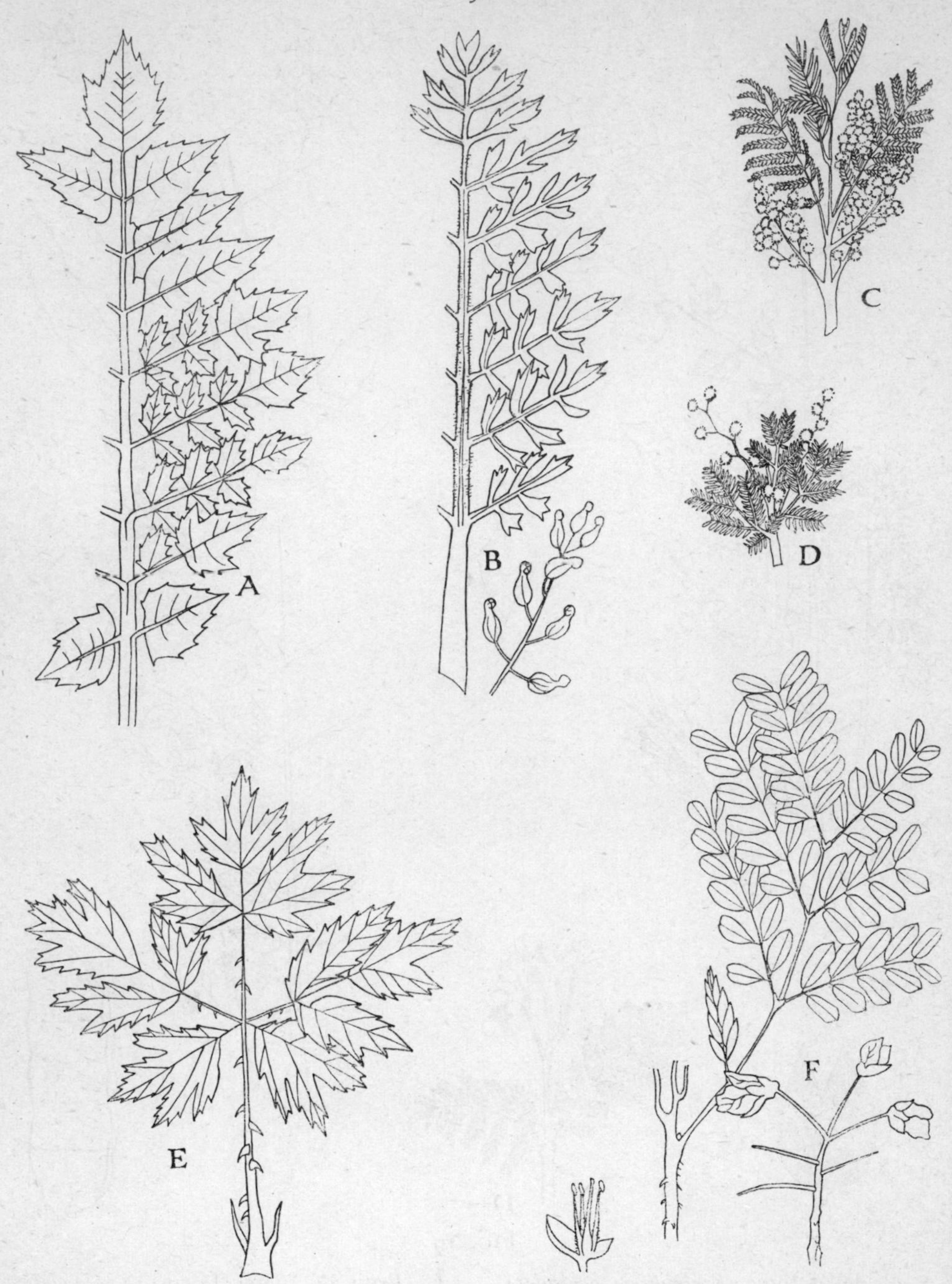

FIG. 20

A. Chilean Nut, *Guevina Avellana* (295)
B. *Lomatia ferruginea* (295)
C. Mimosa, or Silver Wattle, *Acacia dealbata* (194)
D. Bailey's Mimosa, *A. Baileyana* (194)
E. Cut-leaved Bramble, *Rubus laciniatus* (204)
F. *Caesalpinia japonica* (193)

(Flowers of B after *Gardener's Chronicle*.)

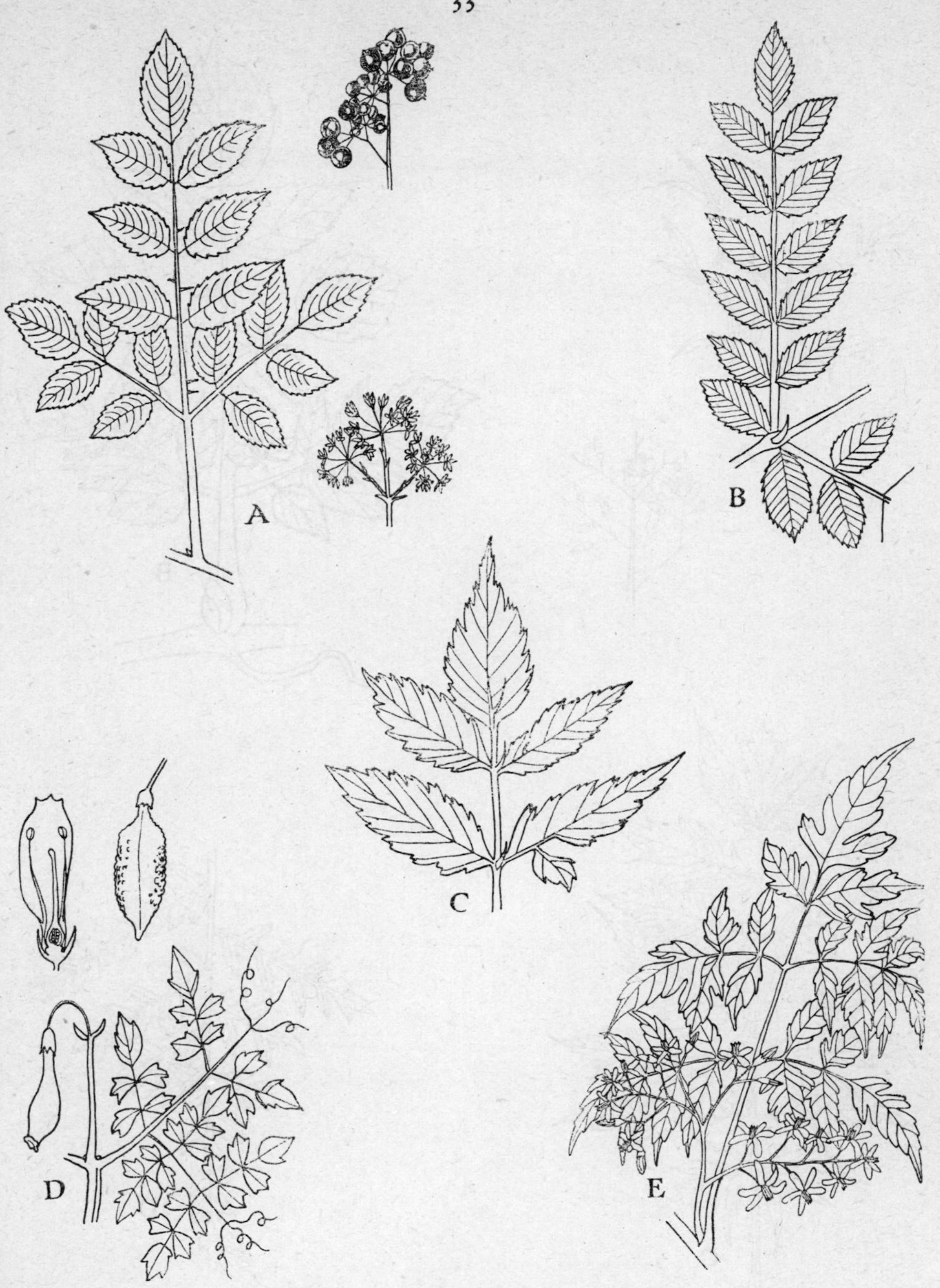

FIG. 21

A. Hercules' Club, or Devil's Walking Stick, *Aralia spinosa* (236)
B. Chinese Angelica Tree, *A. chinensis* (236)
C. Ditto, var. *mandschurica* (236)
D. *Eccremocarpus scaber* (288)
E. Bead Tree, or China Tree, *Melia Azedarach* (169)

(A after Sargent.)

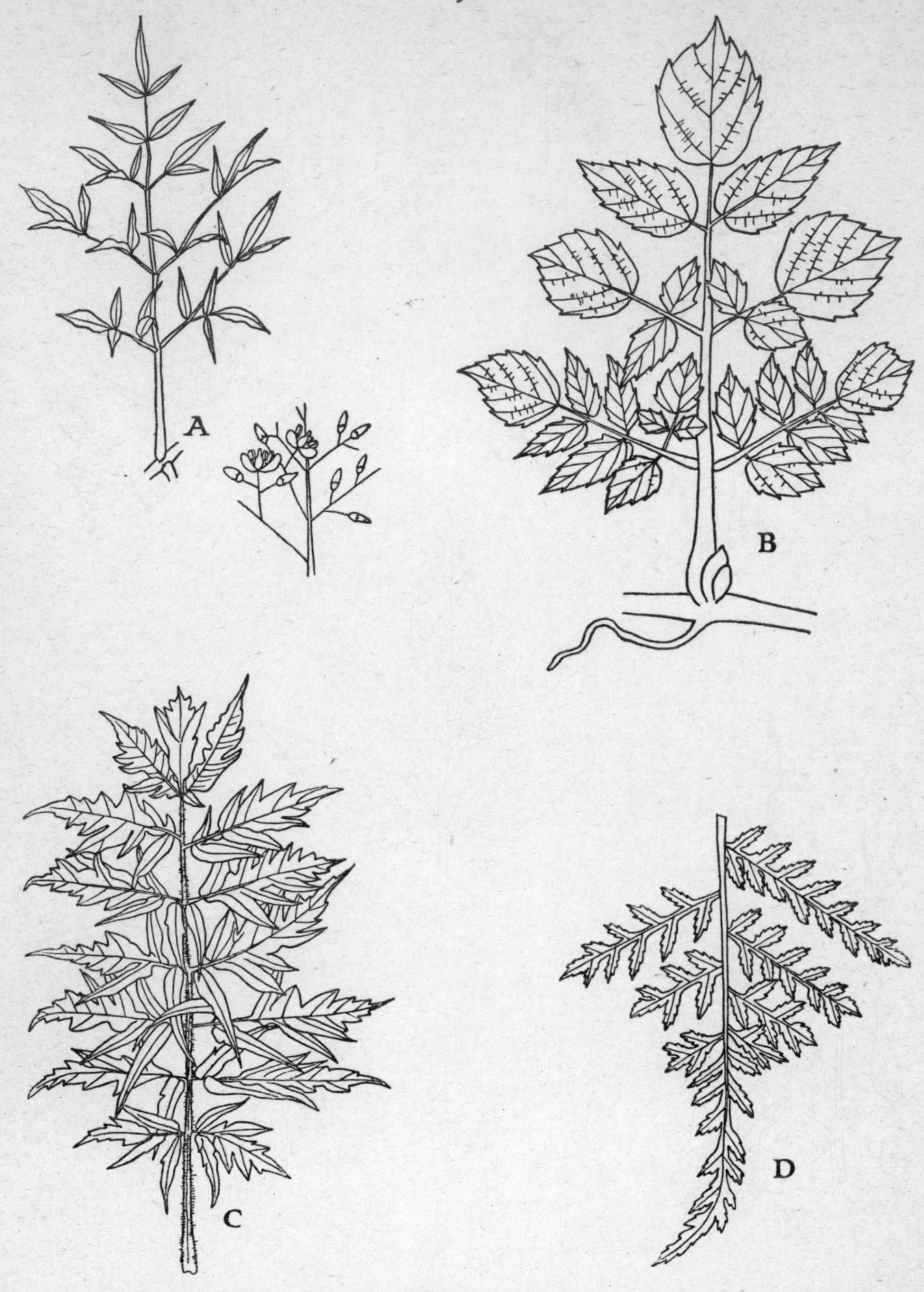

FIG. 22

A. Heavenly Bamboo, *Nandina domestica* (154)
B. *Vitis megalophylla* (176)
C. Cut-leaved Sumach, *Rhus laciniata* (184)
D. Tree Fern, *Dicksonia antarctica* (345)

FIG. 23

A. Sycamore, *Acer Pseudoplatanus* (180)
B. Norway Maple, *A. platanoides* (180)
C. Red Maple, *A. rubrum* (179, 180)
D. Common Maple, *A. campestre* (179)
E. Hawthorn Maple, *A. crataegifolium* (178)
F. *A. rufinerve* (179)
G. Montpelier Maple, *A. monspessulanum* (178)
H. Sugar Maple, *A. saccharum* (181)

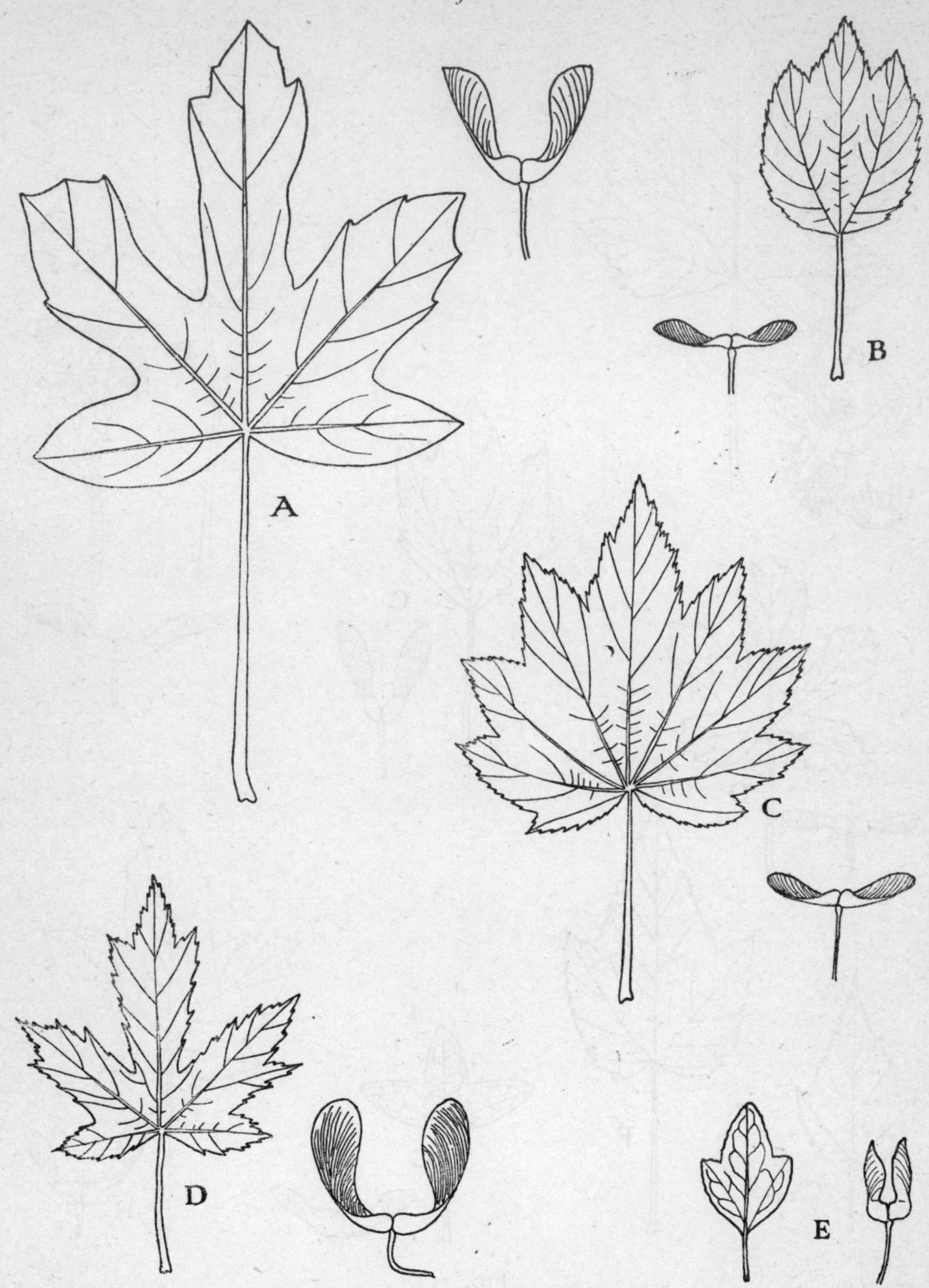

FIG. 24

A. Oregon Maple, *Acer macrophyllum* (180)
B. Moose Wood, or Snakebark Maple, *A. pennsylvanicum* (178)
C. Vine Maple, *A. circinnatum* (179)
D. Silver Maple, *A. saccharinum* (180)
E. Cretan Maple, *A. orientale* (178)

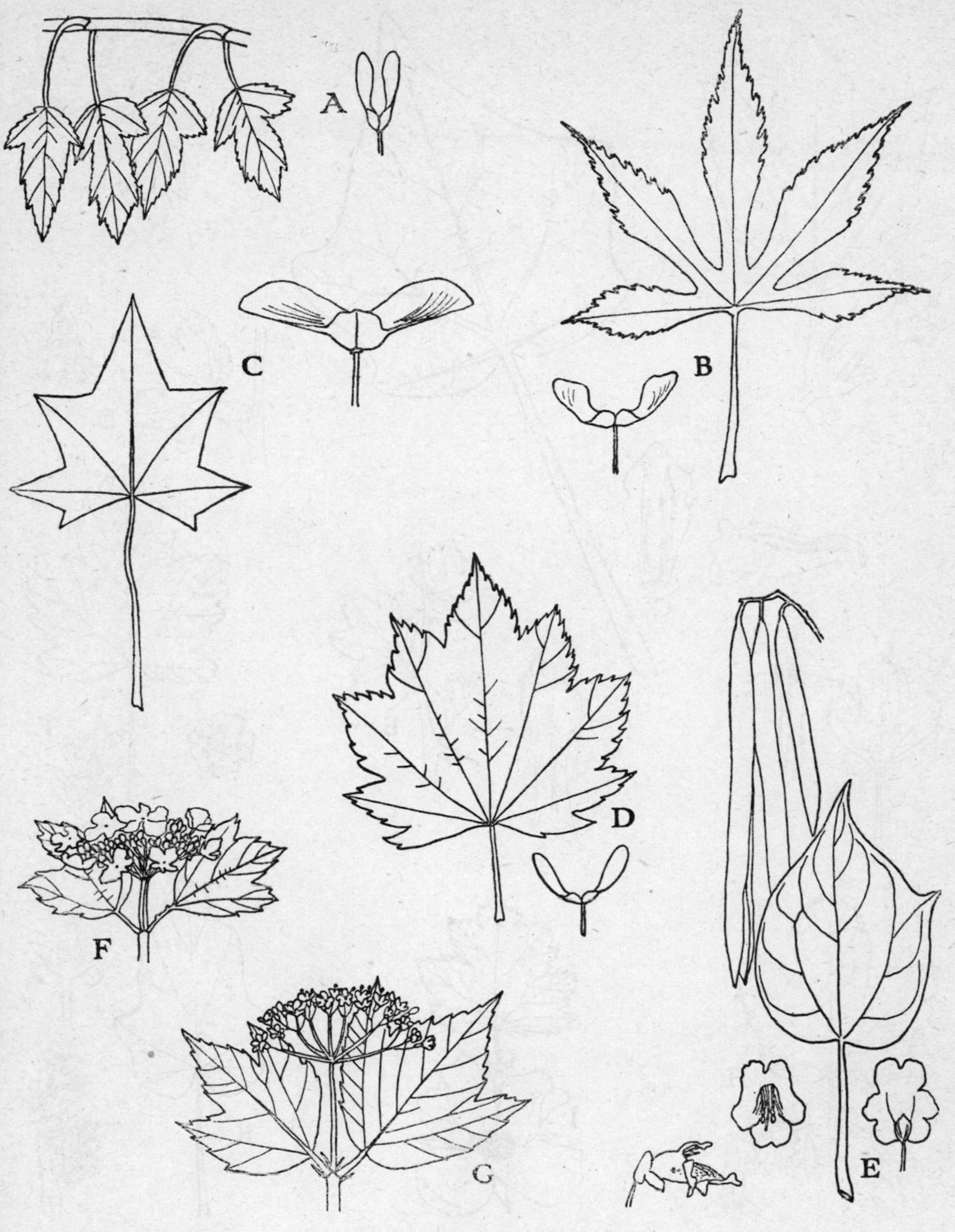

FIG. 25

A. *Acer Ginnala* (178)

B. Japanese Maple, *A. palmatum* (180)

C. *A. cappadocicum* (179)

D. *A. japonicum* (180)

E. Indian Bean Tree, *Catalpa bignonioides* (288)

F. Guelder Rose, *Viburnum Opulus* (246)

G. Dockmackie, *V. acerifolium* (246)

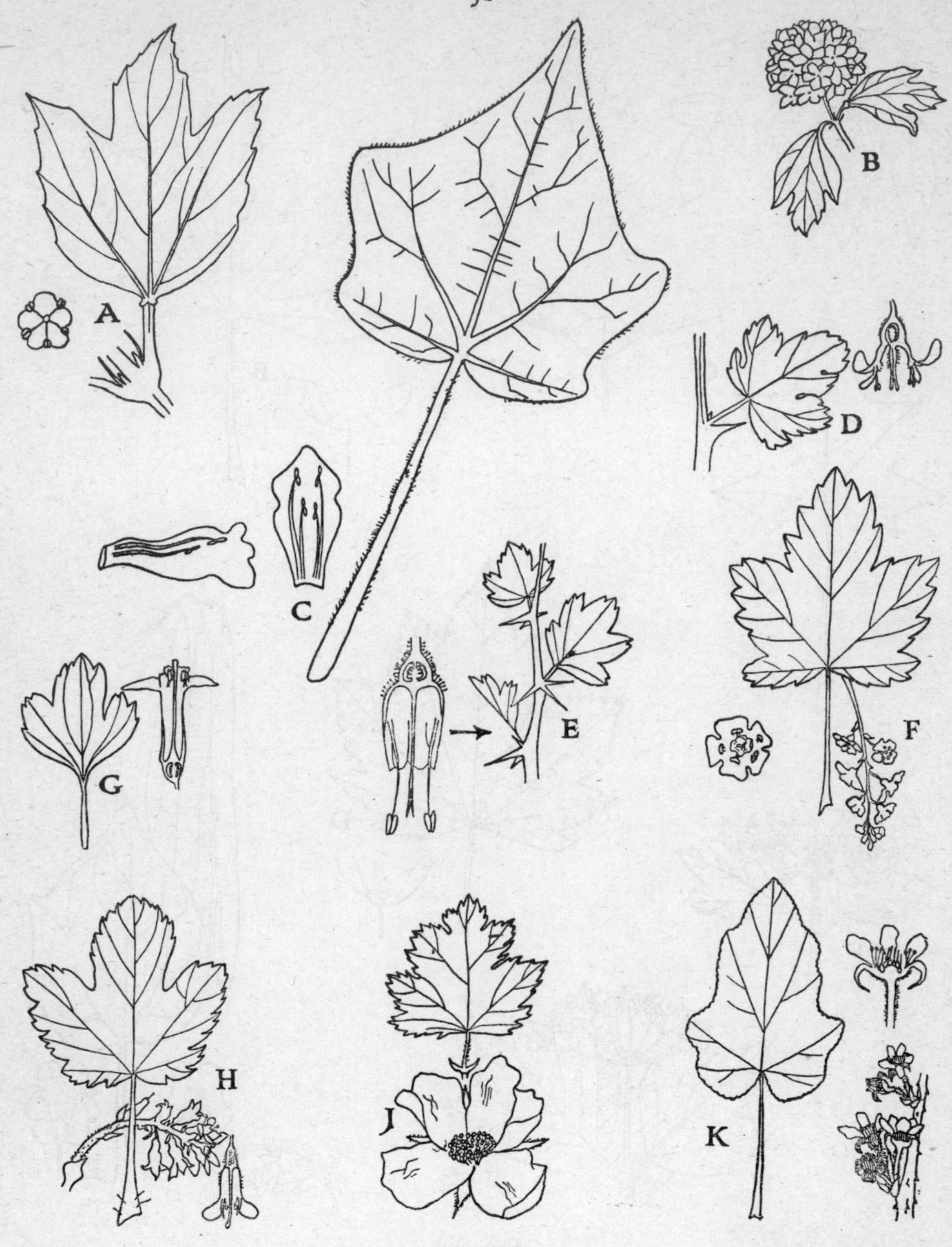

FIG. 26

A. Leaf and flower of Guelder Rose, *Viburnum Opulus* (246)
B. Snowball Tree, *V. Opulus*, var. *sterile* (246)
C. *Paulownia tomentosa* (285)
D. Common Gooseberry, *Ribes Grossularia* (227)
E. Fuchsia - flowered Gooseberry, *R. speciosum* (228)
F. Red Currant, *R. rubrum* (228)
G. Buffalo Currant, or Golden Currant, *R. aureum* (228)
H. Flowering Currant, *R. sanguineum* (229)
J. Rocky Mountain Bramble, *Rubus deliciosus* (203)
K. *R. flagelliflorus* (203)

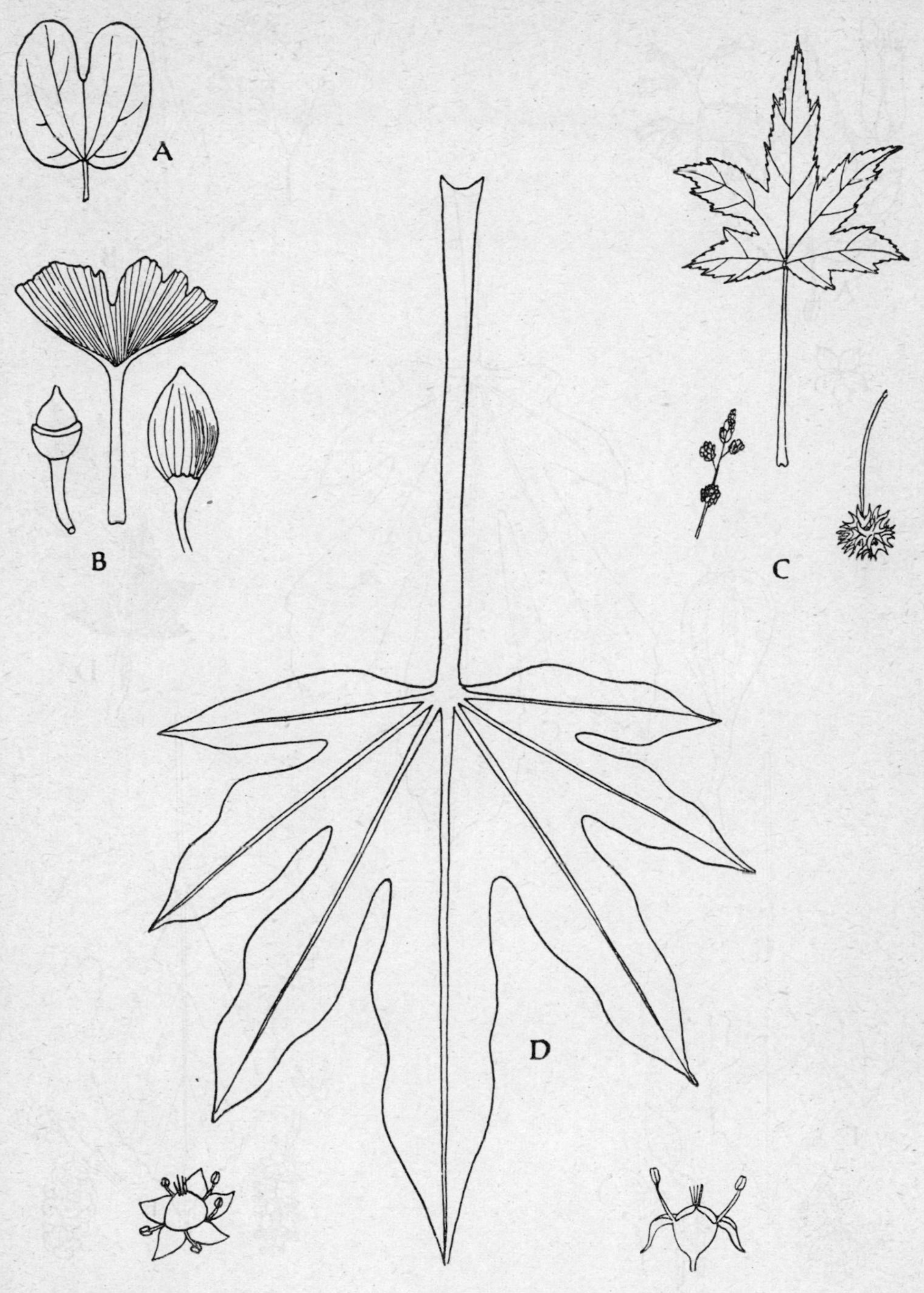

FIG. 27

A. Leaf of *Bauhinia* (192)

B. Maidenhair Tree, *Ginkgo biloba* (344)

C. Sweet Gum, *Liquidambar styraciflua* (230)

D. *Fatsia japonica* (236)

(Fruit of B after Veitch, flowers and fruits of C after Sargent, flowers of D after Bois.)

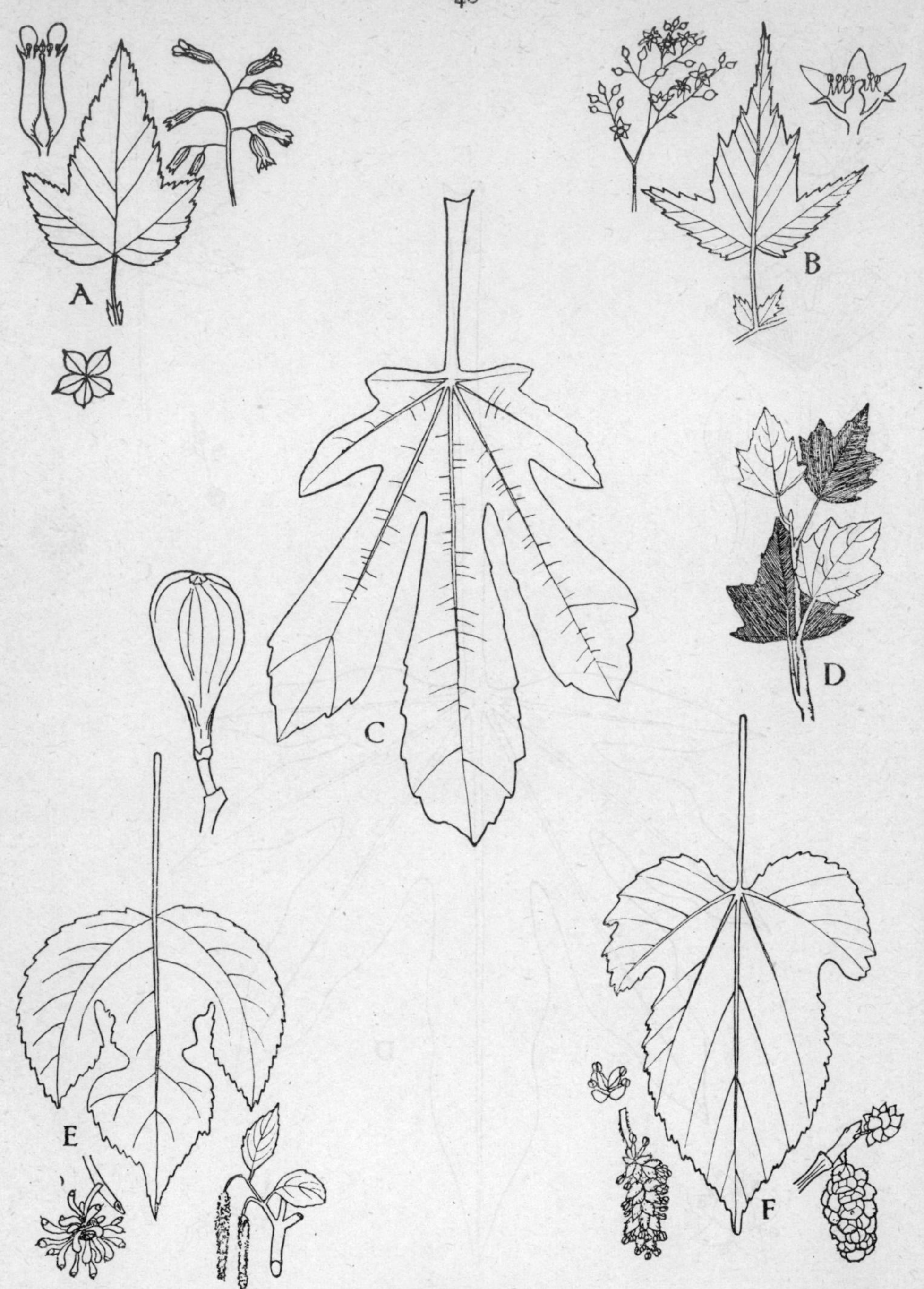

Fig. 28

A. Nine Bark, *Neillia opulifolia* (195)
B. *Stephanandra Tanakae* (197)
C. Common Fig, *Ficus Carica* (303)
D. White or Silver Poplar, *Populus alba* (316)
E. Paper Mulberry, *Broussonetia papyrifera* (302)
F. Common Mulberry, *Morus nigra* (303)

(Flowers of E after Brandis.)

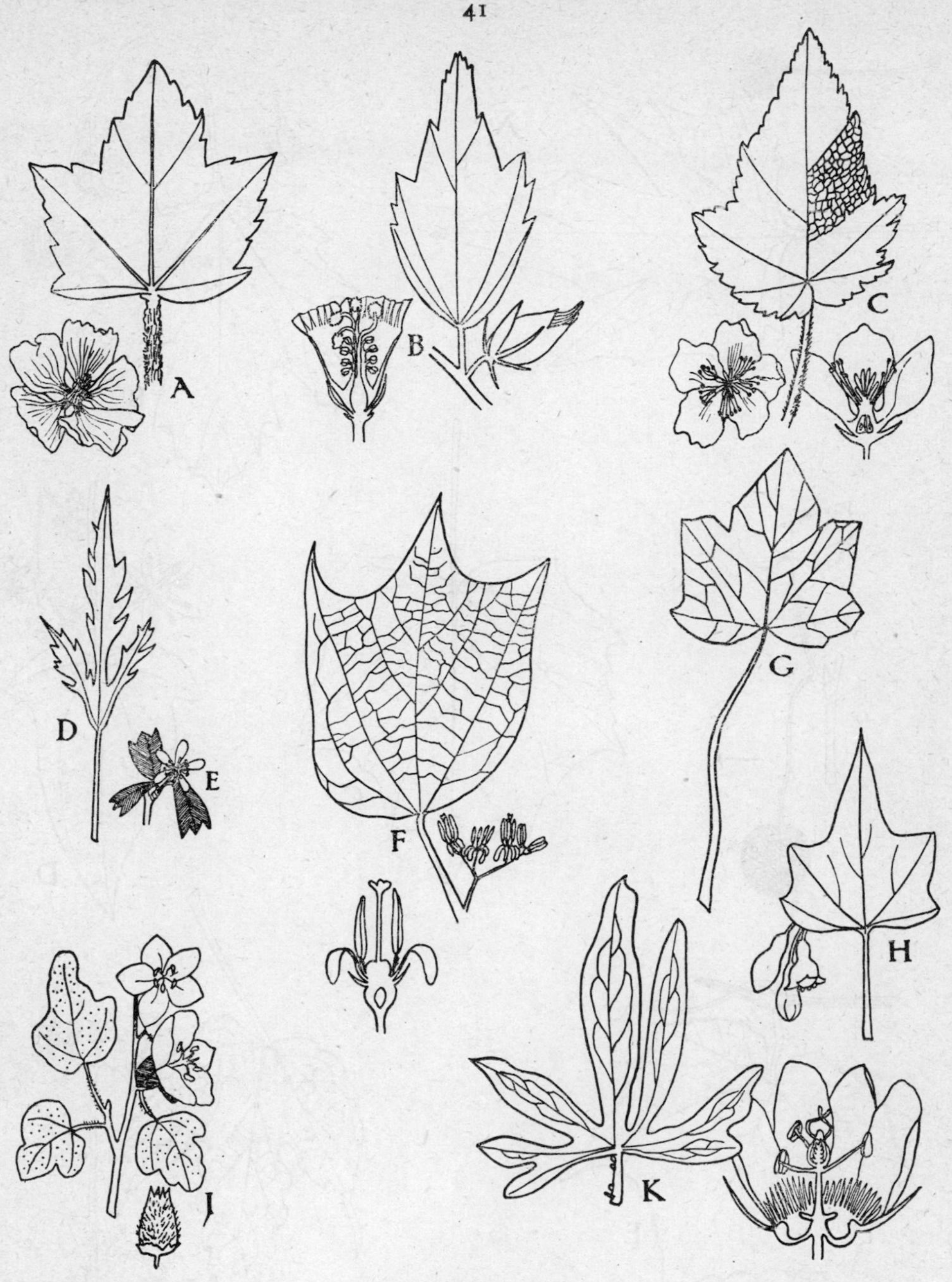

FIG. 29

A. Tree Mallow, *Lavatera arborea* (164)
B. Shrubby Althaea, *Hibiscus syriacus* (164)
C. *Abutilon vitifolium* (164)
D. Cut-leaved Lime, *Tilia asplenifolia* (165)
E. *Purshia tridentata* (199)
F. *Alangium chinense* (237)
G. Leaf of Ivy, *Hedera Helix* (see Fig. 120 B)
H. Flame Tree, *Sterculia acerifolia* (164)
J. *Fremontia californica* (164)
K. Passion Flower, *Passiflora coerulea* (234)

(Flowers of H after *Botanical Magazine*, of K after Bois.)

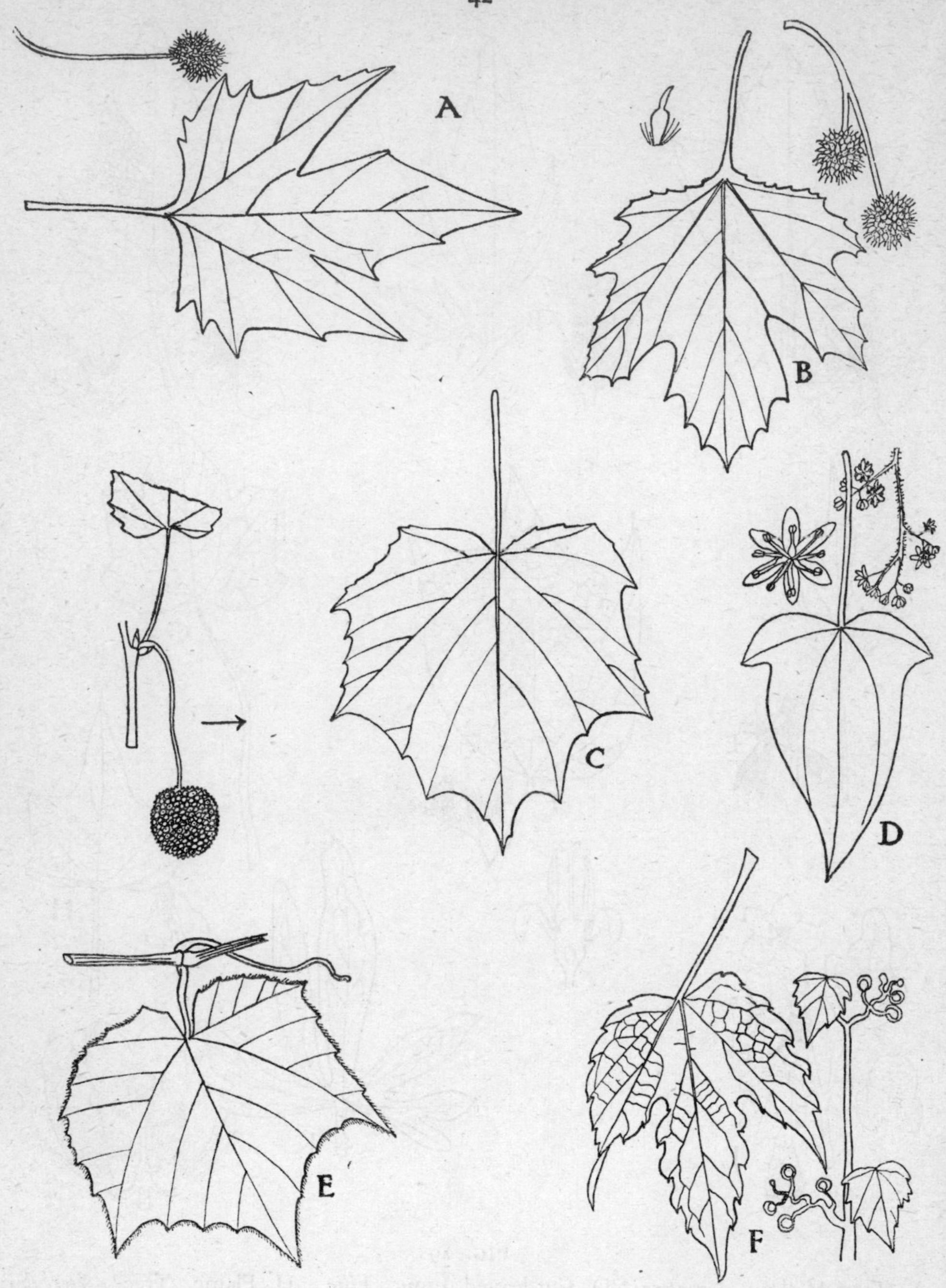

Fig. 30

A. Oriental Plane, *Platanus orientalis* (303)
B. London Plane, *P. acerifolia* (303)
C. Button Wood, *P. occidentalis* (303)
D. *Sinomenium acutum* (150)
E. *Vitis Coignetiae* (175)
F. *V. inconstans* (*Ampelopsis Veitchii*) (175)

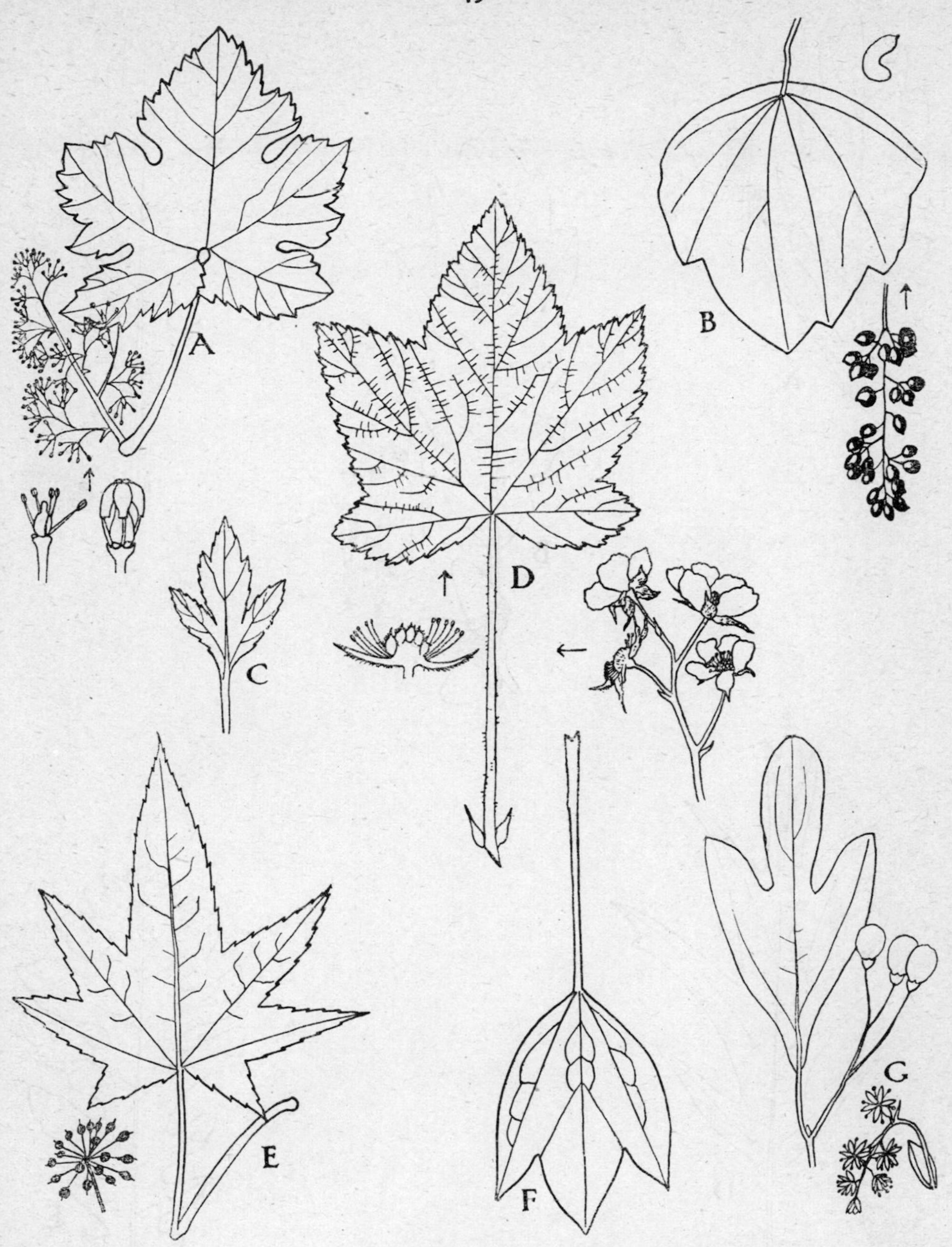

FIG. 31

A. Grape Vine, *Vitis vinifera* (176)
B. Moonseed, *Menispermum canadense* (150)
C. Leaf of *Malus toringoides* (217)
D. Salmon Berry, *Rubus parviflorus* (203)
E. *Acanthopanax ricinifolius* (205)
F. *Dendropanax japonicum* (236)
G. Ague Tree, *Sassafras officinale* (294)
Genus not figured: *Echinopanax* (236)

(Fruits of B after Le Maout and Decaisne.)

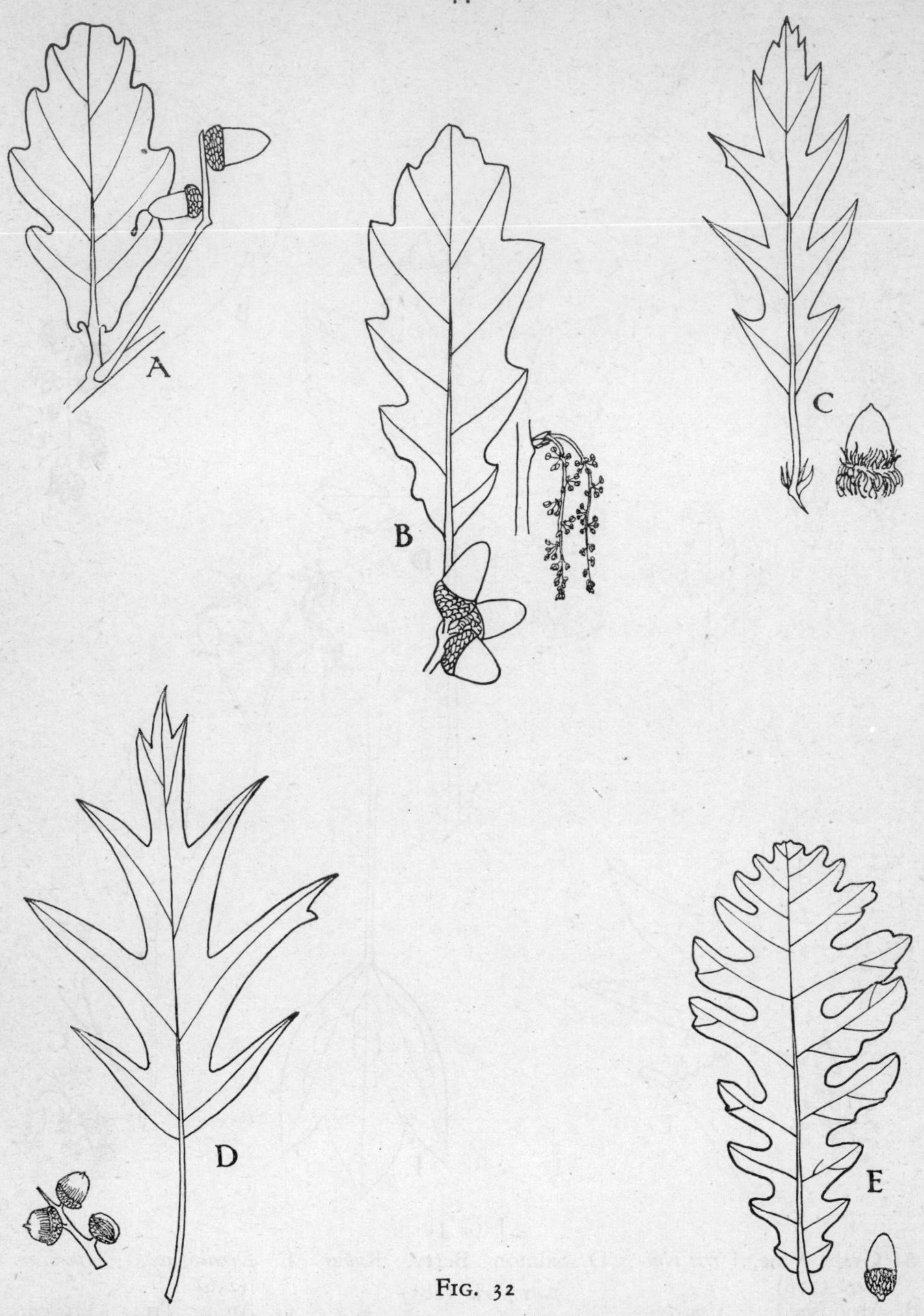

FIG. 32

A. Common English Oak, *Quercus Robur* (*pedunculata*) (315)
B. Durmast Oak, or Sessile Oak, *Q. petraea* (*sessiliflora*) (315)
C. Turkey Oak, *Q. Cerris* (313)
D. Red Oak, *Q. rubra* (314)
E. Hungarian Oak, *Q. Frainetto* (*conferta*) (314)

(D after Sargent.)

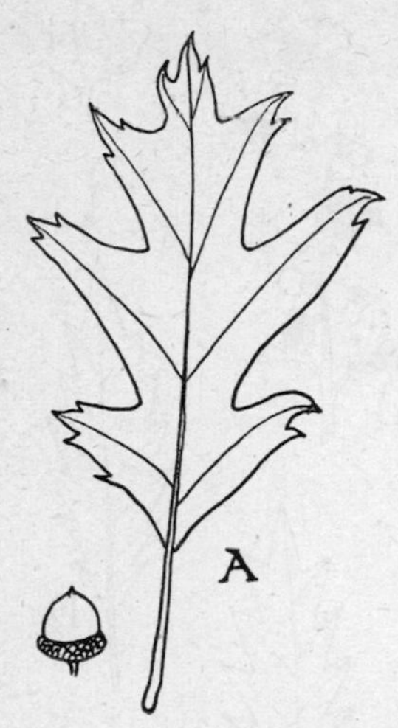

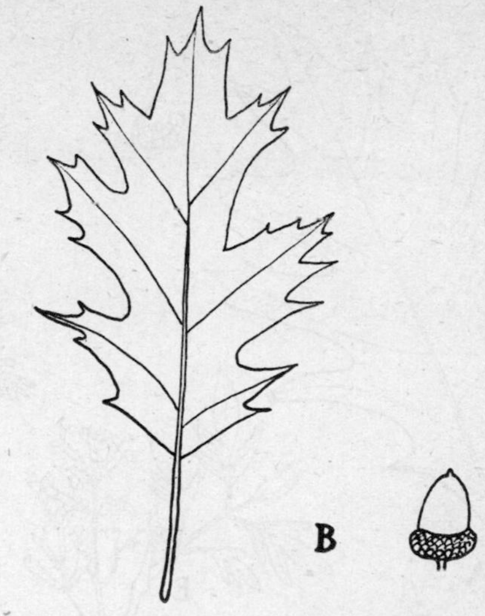

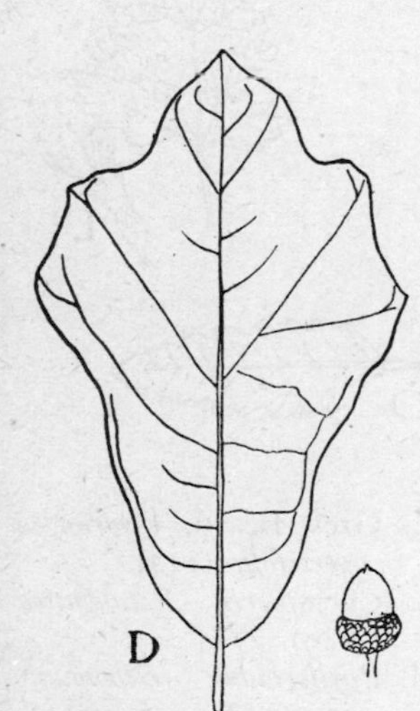

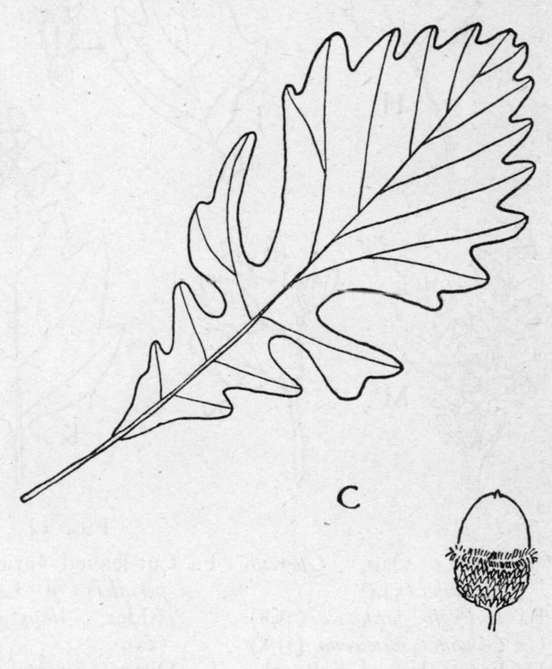

FIG. 33

A. Pin Oak, *Quercus palustris* (314)
B. Scarlet Oak, *Q. coccinea* (312)
C. Burr Oak, *Q. macrocarpa* (315)
D. Black Jack, *Q. marilandica* (314)

(All after Sargent.)

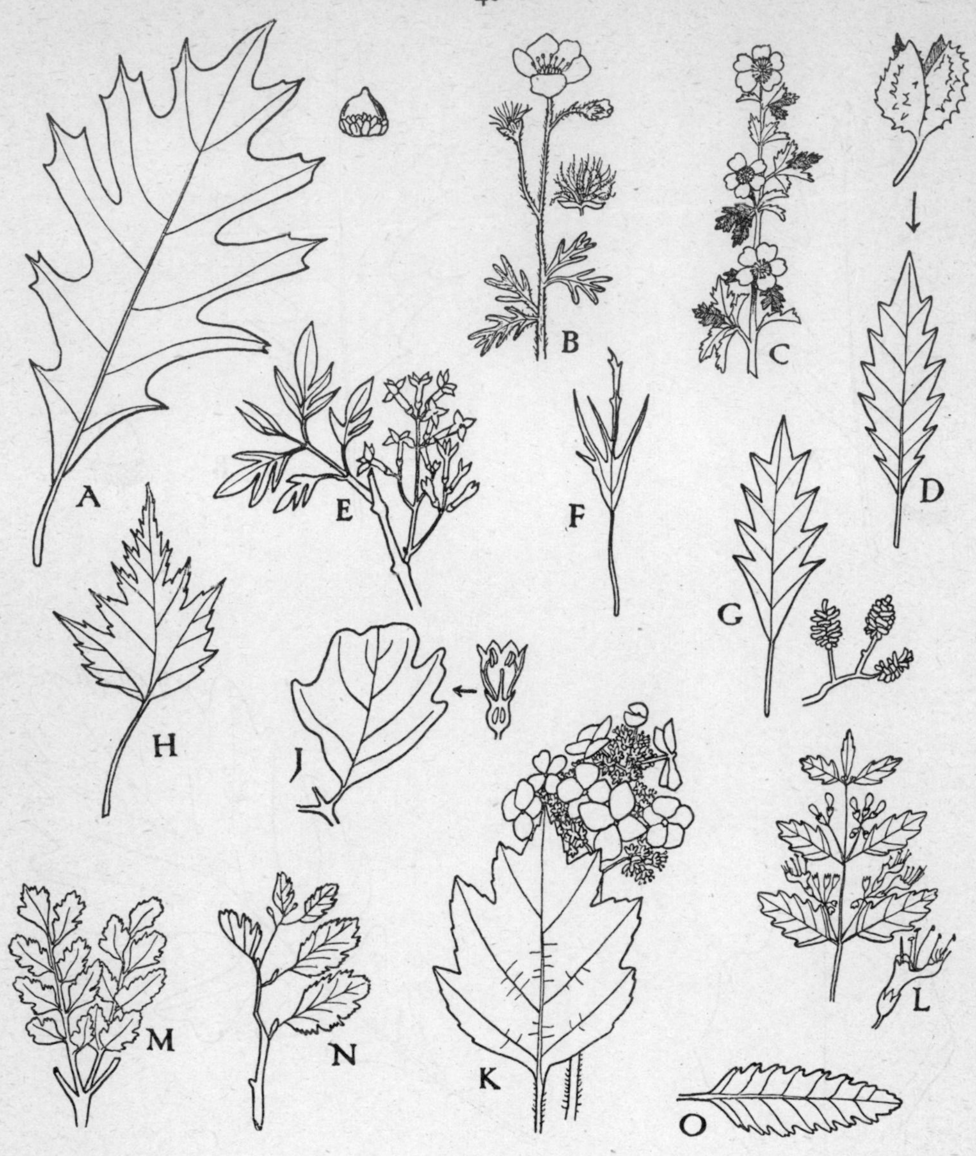

FIG. 34

A. Black Oak, *Quercus velutina* (314)
B. *Fallugia paradoxa* (198)
C. *Cowania mexicana* (198)
D. Fern - leaved Beech, *Fagus sylvatica*, var. *heterophylla* (311)
E. Cut-leaved variety of Persian Lilac, *Syringa persica* (280)
F. Cut-leaved variety (*imperialis*) of Common Alder, *Alnus glutinosa* (306)
G. Ditto (*laciniata*) (306)
H. Swedish Birch, *Betula verrucosa*, var. *laciniata* (308)
J. Snowberry, *Symphoricarpus racemosus* (245)
K. Grey Beard, *Hydrangea quercifolia* (224)
L. *Caryopteris tangutica* (289)
M. *Phyllocladus trichomanioides* (328)
N. Antarctic Beech, *Nothofagus antarctica* (311)
O. Roblé Beech, *N. obliqua* (311)

(A after Sargent, C after Loudon, M after Dallimore and Jackson.)

FIG. 35

A. *Crataegus punctata* (213)
B. Common Hawthorn or Quick, *C. monogyna* (213)
C. May, *C. Oxyacantha* (213)
D. Parsley-leaved Thorn, *C. apiifolia* (213)
E. Scarlet Haw, *C. rotundifolia* (212)
F. Hungarian Thorn, *C. nigra* (213)
G. Red Haw, *C. mollis* (212)
H. Tansy-leaved Thorn, *C. tanacetifolia* (213)
J. Azarole, *C. Azarolus* (213)
K. Washington Thorn, *C. Phaenopyrum* (212)

(D and F after Loudon, K after Sargent.)

FIG. 36

A. Lavender Cotton, *Santolina Chamaecyparissus* (251)

B. Wormwood, *Artemisia Absinthium* (251)

C. Southernwood, or Lad's Love, *A. Abrotanum* (251)

D. Tulip Tree, *Liriodendron Tulipifera* (146)

E. *Romneya Coulteri* (155)

F. Common Rue, *Ruta graveolens* (167)

G. Sweet Fern, *Myrica* (*Comptonia*) *asplenifolia* (305)

H. Leaf of *Spiraea discolor* (flowers similar to Fig. 12 J) (196)

J. Hawthorn-leaved Crab Apple, *Malus florentina* (216)

K. Wild Service, *Sorbus Torminalis* (219)

L. Bastard Service, *S. hybrida* (219)

M. *Pittosporum divaricatum* (159)

(Flower of F after Kerner and Oliver.)

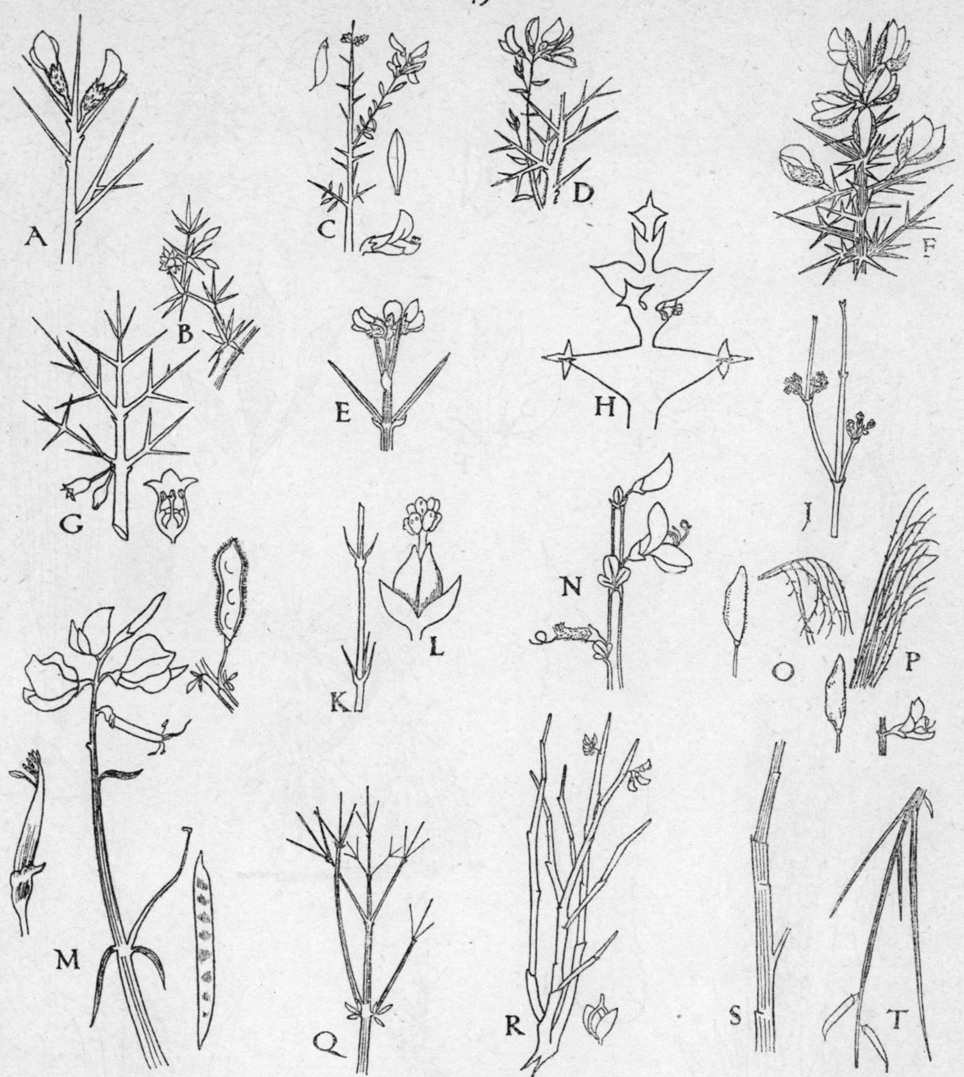

FIG. 37

A. Hedgehog Broom, *Erinacea pungens* (186)
B. *Asparagus aphyllus* (321)
C. Needle Furze, or Petty Whin, *Genista anglica* (187)
D. Spanish Gorse, *G. hispanica* (187)
E. *G. horrida* (186)
F. Gorse, Furze, or Whin, *Ulex europaeus* (188)
G. *Colletia armata* (174)
H. *C. cruciata* (174)
J. Shrubby Horsetail, *Ephedra distachya* (327)
K. *E. trifurca* (327)
L. Male flower of *Ephedra*
M. Yellow Spanish Broom, *Spartium junceum* (188)
N. Common Broom, *Cytisus scoparius* (186)
O. Diagrammatic representation of Warminster Broom, *C. praecox* (186)
P. Ditto of White Spanish Broom, *C. albus* (186)
Q. *Genista radiata* (186)
R. Lilac Broom, *Carmichaelia australis* (189)
S. Pink Broom, *Notospartium Carmichaeliae* (189)
T. Etna Broom, *Genista aetnensis* (187)
Genus not figured: *Chordospartium* (189)

(L after Le Maout and Decaisne.)

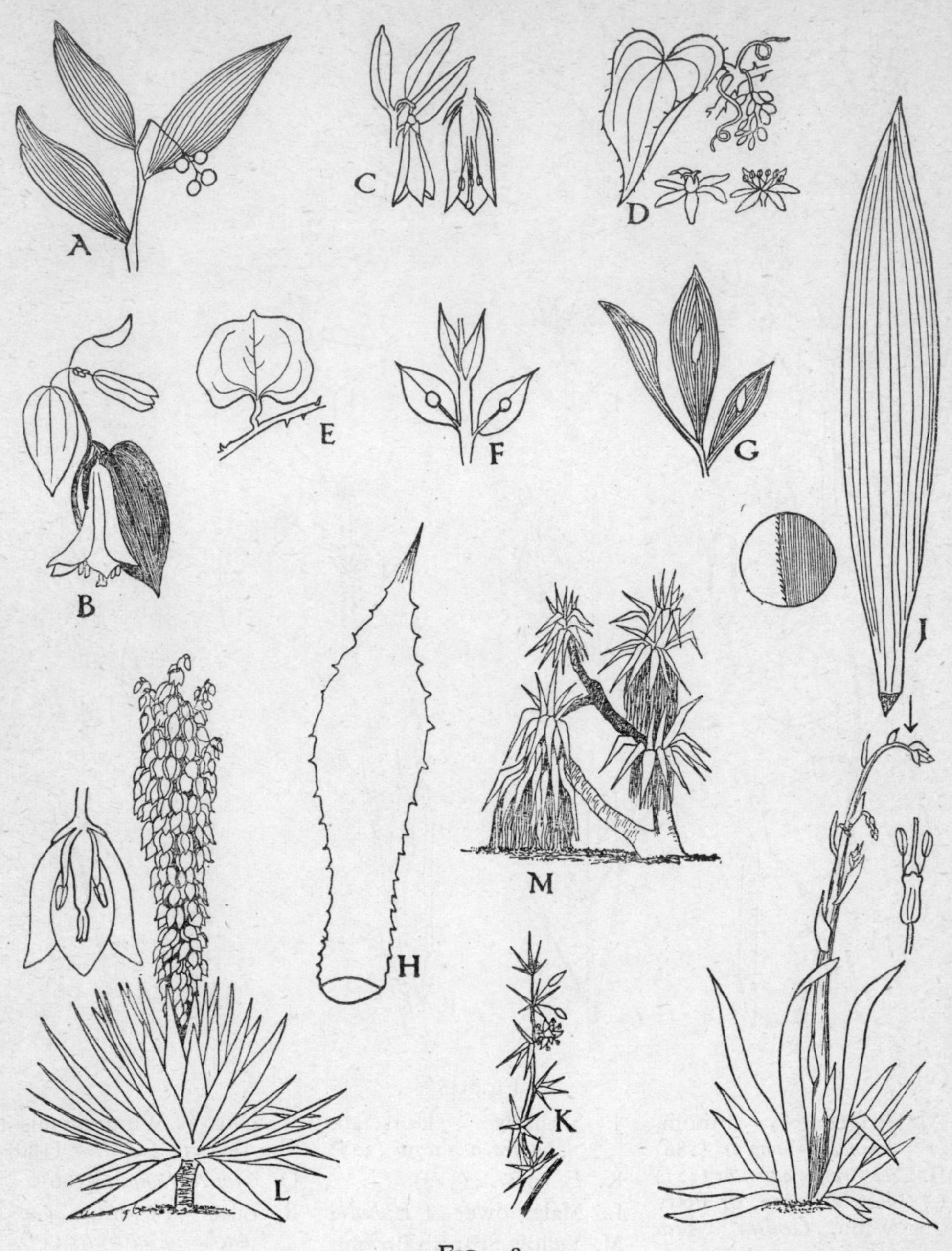

Fig. 38

A. Alexandrian Laurel, *Danaea racemosa* (322)
B. Chilean Bell Flower, *Lapageria rosea* (322)
C. Pepino, *Philesia magellanica* (322)
D. Rough Bindweed, *Smilax aspera* (323)
E. Horse Brier, *S. rotundifolia* (323)
F. Butcher's Broom, *Ruscus aculeatus* (322)
G. R. *hypoglossum* (322)
H. Leaf of *Agave* (321)
J. *Beschorneria yuccoides* (321)
K. *Asparagus aphyllus* (321)
L. Adam's Needle, *Yucca gloriosa* (323)
M. *Y. recurvifolia* (323)

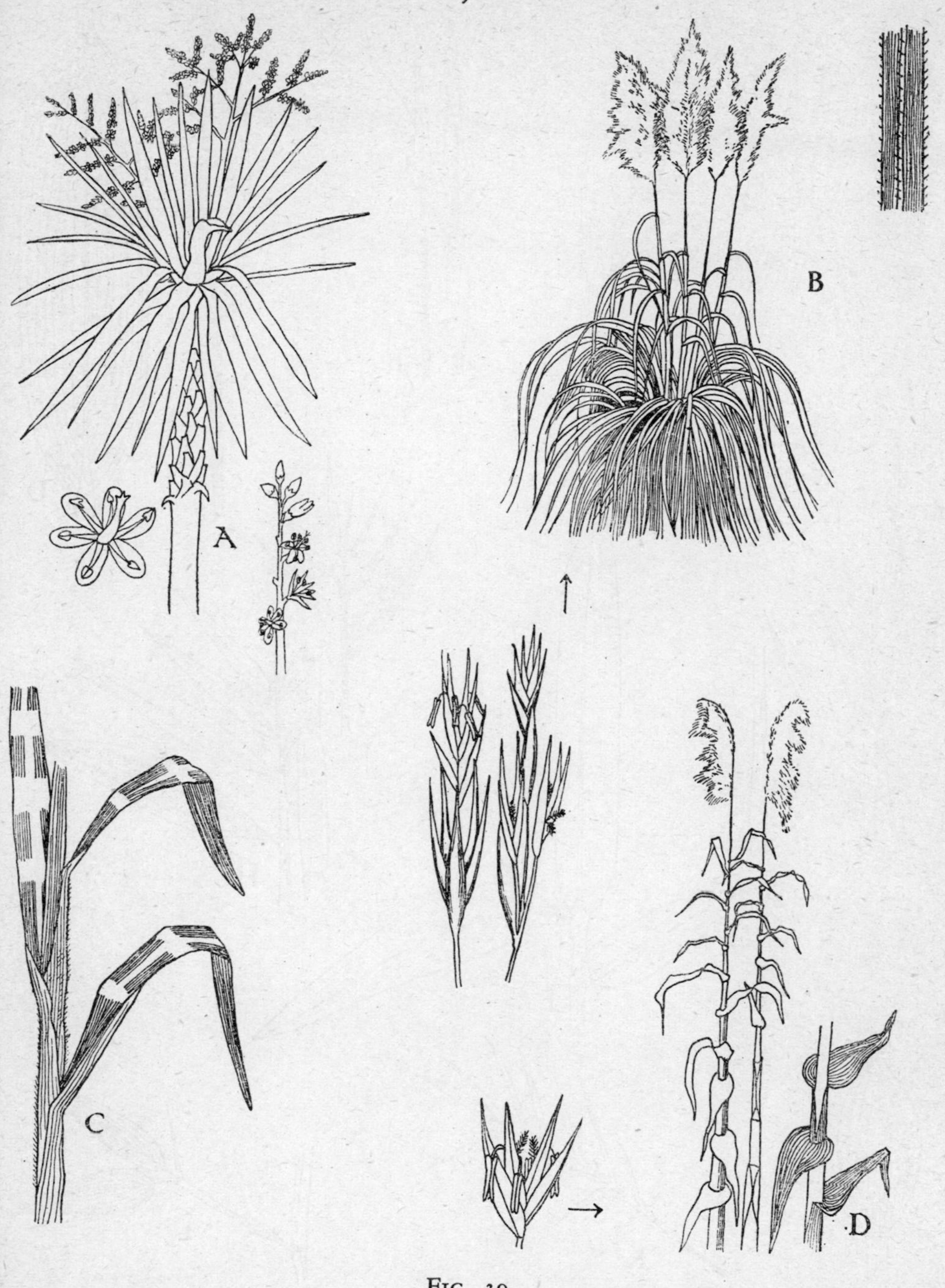

FIG. 39

A. Club Palm, or Cabbage Tree, *Cordyline* (*Dracaena*) *australis* (322)

B. Pampas Grass, *Cortaderia* (*Gynerium*) *argentea* (325)

C. *Miscanthus* (*Eulalia*) *japonicus*, var. *zebrina* (325)

D. Great Reed, *Arundo Donax* (325)

(Flowers of B after Le Maout and Decaisne, of D after Wettstein.)

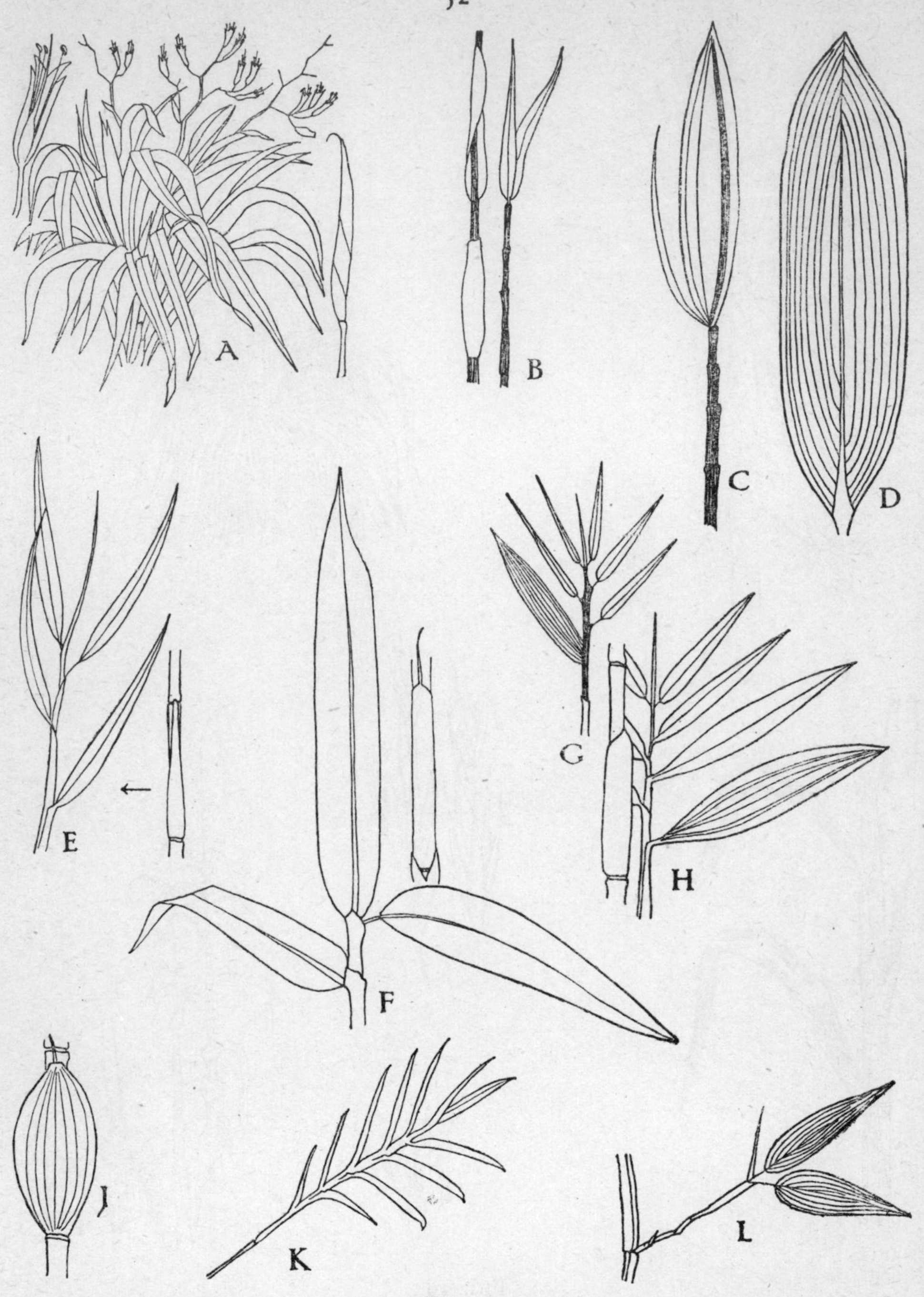

FIG. 40

A. Mountain Flax, *Phormium Colensoi* (322)

Hardy Bamboos

B. *Arundinaria anceps* (324)

C. *A. auricoma* (324)

D. *A. palmata* (324)

E. *A. falcata* (324)

F. *A. japonica* (325)

G. *A. nitida* (324)

H. *A. graminea* (325)

J. *A. fastuosa* (325)

K. *Bambusa disticha* (325)

L. *Phyllostachys* (325)

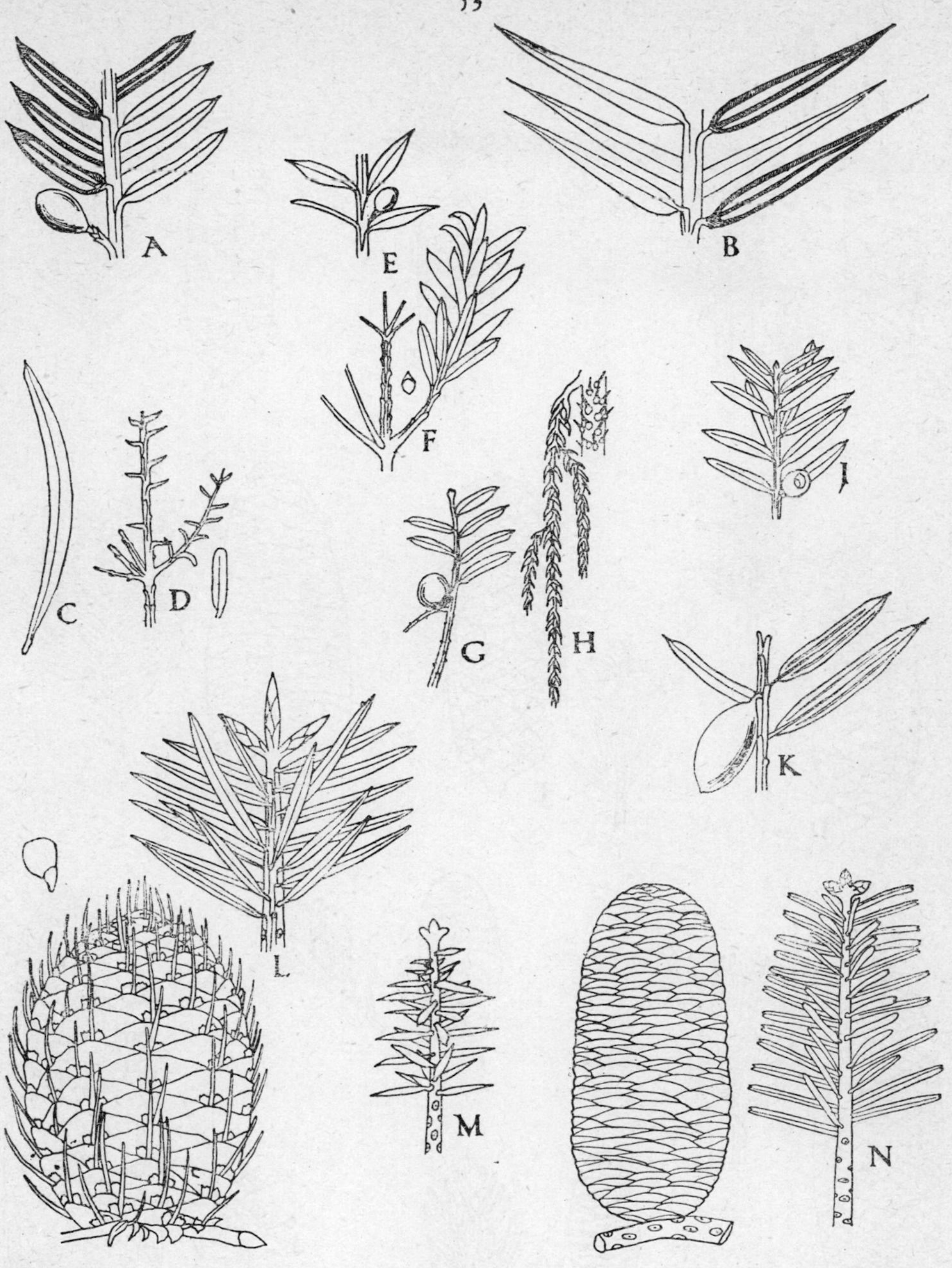

FIG. 41

A. Cow's Tail Pine, *Cephalotaxus drupacea* (327)

B. *C. Fortunei* (327)

C. Leaf of *Podocarpus saligna* (328)

D. *P. alpina* (328)

E. *P. Totara* (328)

F. Prince Albert's Yew, *Saxegothea conspicua* (328)

G. Plum - fruited Yew, *Podocarpus andina* (328)

H. Rimu, *Dacrydium cupressinum* (328)

J. Common Yew, *Taxus baccata* (328)

K. *Torreya nucifera* (328)

L. Santa Lucia Fir, *Abies venusta* (329)

M. Spanish Fir, *A. Pinsapo* (329)

N. Giant Fir, *A. grandis* (329)

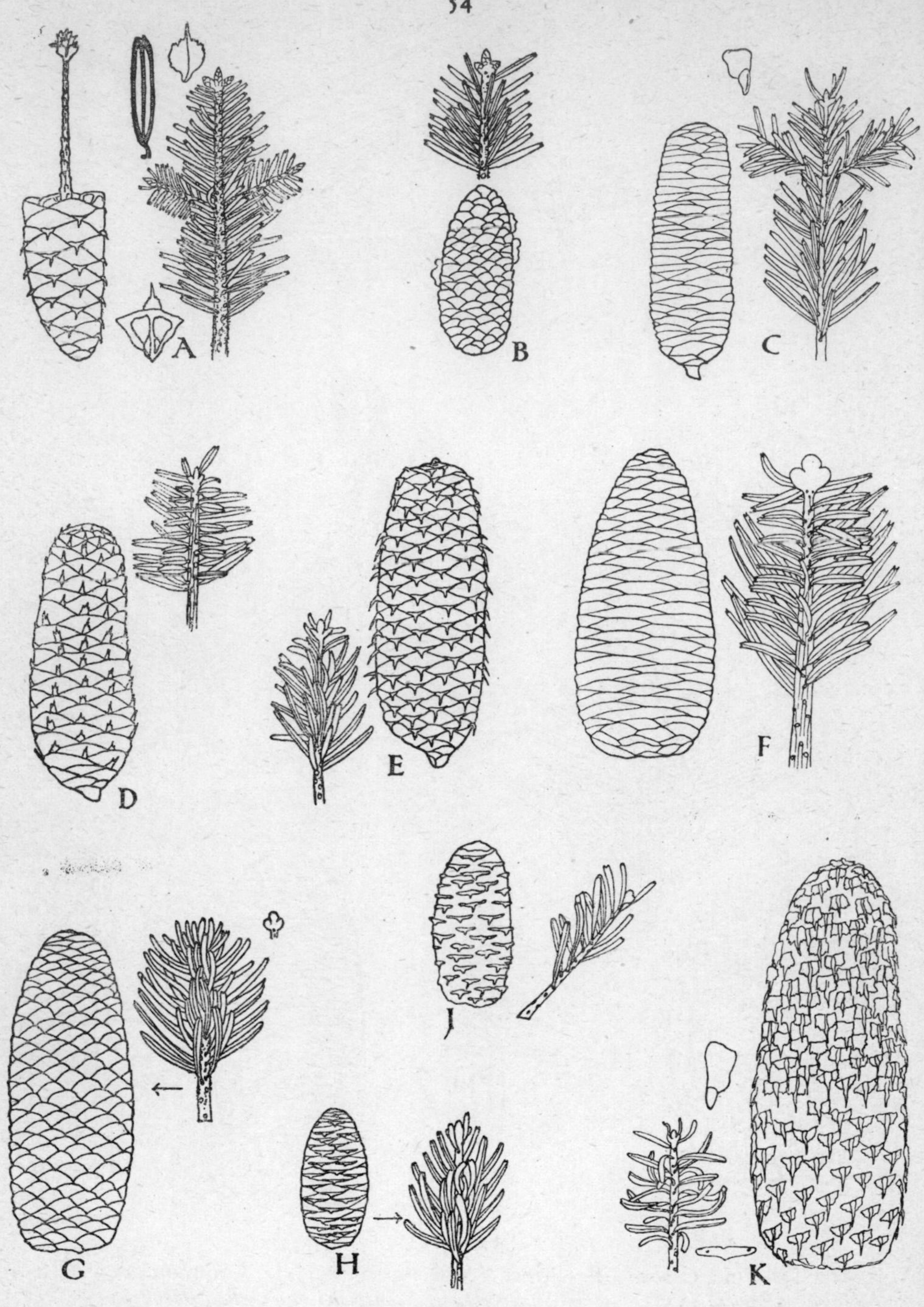

FIG. 42

A. Common Silver Fir, *Abies alba* (329)
B. Balsam Fir, *A. balsamea* (329)
C. Nikko Fir, *A. homolepis* (330)
D. Momi Fir, *A. firma* (330)
E. Caucasian Fir, *A. Nordmanniana* (330)
F. Himalayan Fir, *A. spectabilis* (330)
G. *A. amabilis* (330)
H. *A. Veitchii* (331)
J. Corean Fir, *A. koreana* (331)
K. Noble Fir, *A. nobilis* (331)

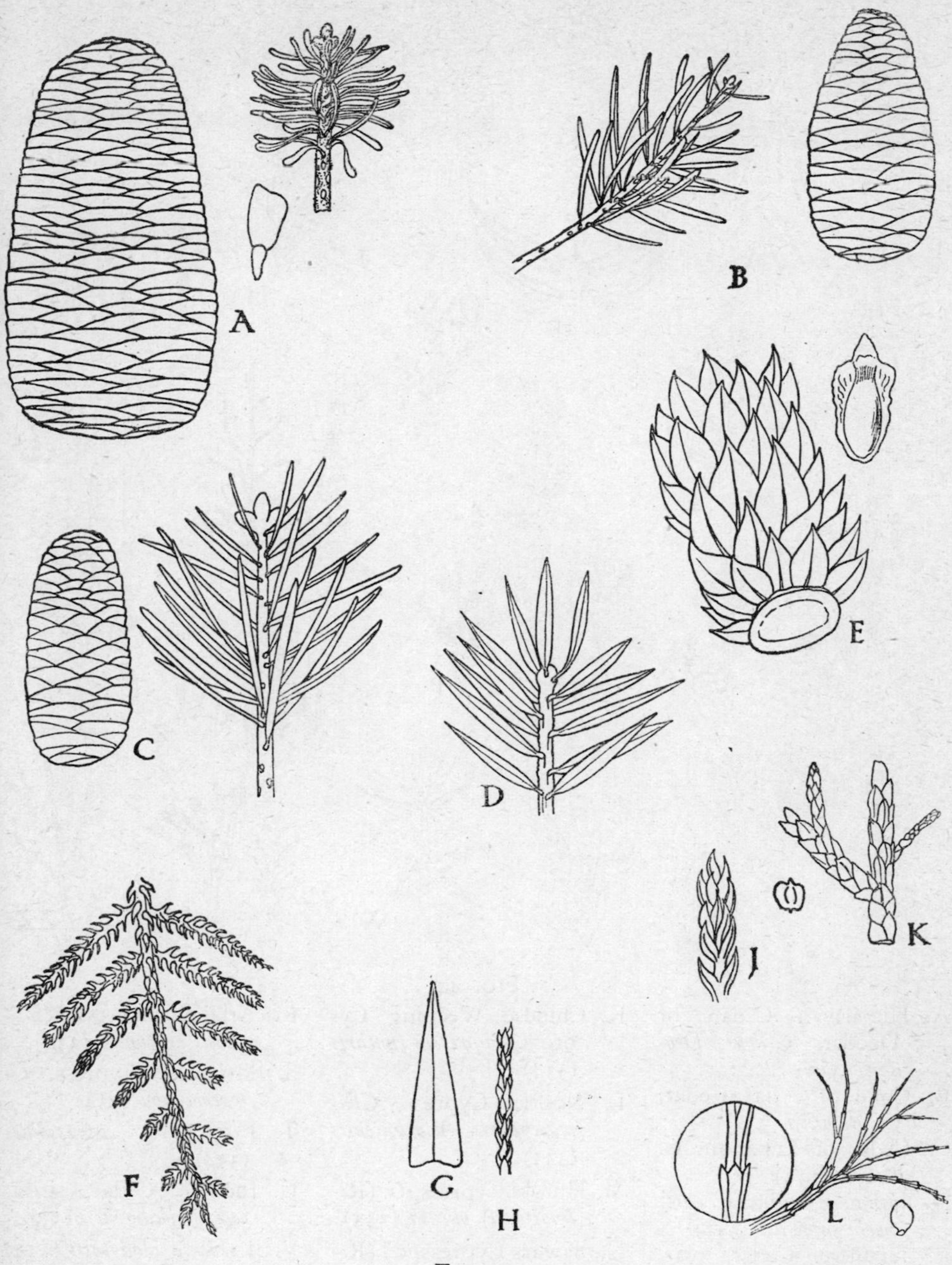

FIG. 43

A. Red Fir, *Abies magnifica* (331)

B. Rocky Mountain Fir, *A. lasiocarpa* (331)

C. Colorado Fir, *A. concolor* (331)

D. *Keteleeria Davidiana* (336)

E. Chile Pine, or Monkey Puzzle, *Araucaria araucana* (331)

F. Norfolk Island Pine, *A. excelsa* (331)

G. Diagram of an awl-shaped leaf

H. Tasmanian Cedar, *Athrotaxis laxifolia* (332)

J. King William Pine, *A. selaginoides* (332)

K. *A. cupressioides* (331)

L. Cypress Pine, *Callitris oblonga* (332)

Genus not figured: *Kalmia* (262)

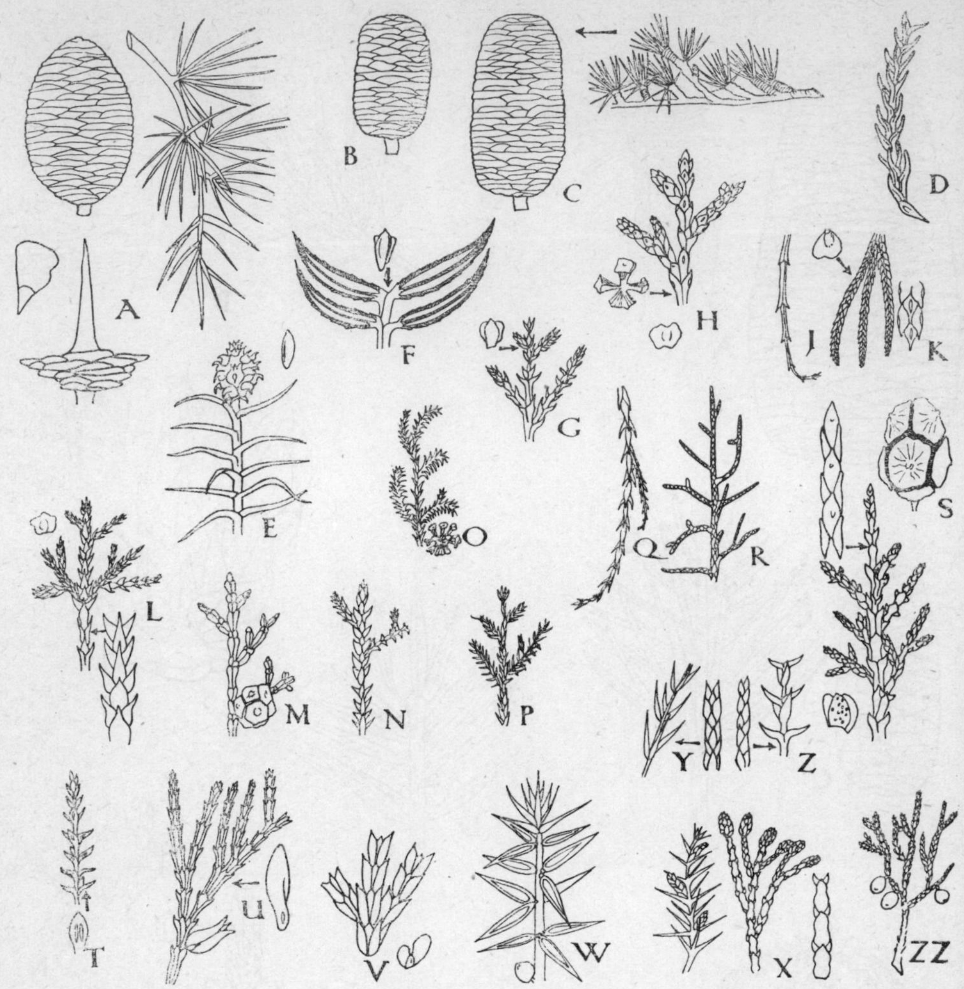

FIG. 44

A. Himalayan Cedar, or Deodar, *Cedrus Deodara* (332)
B. Cone of Atlas Cedar, *C. atlantica* (332)
C. Cedar of Lebanon, *C. Libani* (332)
D. Japanese Cedar, *Cryptomeria japonica* (333)
E. Japanese Cedar, var. *elegans* (333)
F. *Cunninghamia sinensis* (333)
G. Formosan Cypress, *Chamaecyparis formosensis* (332)
H. Lawson's Cypress, *C. Lawsoniana* (332)
J. Lawson's Cypress, var. *filiformis* (333)
K. Chinese Weeping Cypress, *Cupressus funebris* (334)
L. Nootka Cypress, *Chamaecyparis nootkatensis* (333)
M. Hinoki Cypress, *C.* (*Retinospora*) *obtusa* (333)
N. Sawara Cypress, *C.* (*Retinospora*) *pisifera* (333)
O. Sawara Cypress, var. *plumosa* (*Retinospora plumosa*) (333)
P. Sawara Cypress, var. *squarrosa* (*Retinospora squarrosa*) (333)
Q. Sawara Cypress, var. *filifera* (333)
R. Arizona Cypress, *Cupressus arizonica* (334)
S. Monterey Cypress, *C. macrocarpa* (334)
T. *Fitzroya cupressoides* (334)
U. Incense Cedar, *Libocedrus decurrens* (337)
V. *Fokienia Hodginsii* (334)
W. Common Juniper, *Juniperus communis* (335)
X. Chinese Juniper, *J. chinensis* (335)
Y. Himalayan Juniper, *J. recurva* (335)
Z. Red or Pencil Cedar, *J. virginiana* (336)
ZZ. Savin, *J. Sabina* (336)

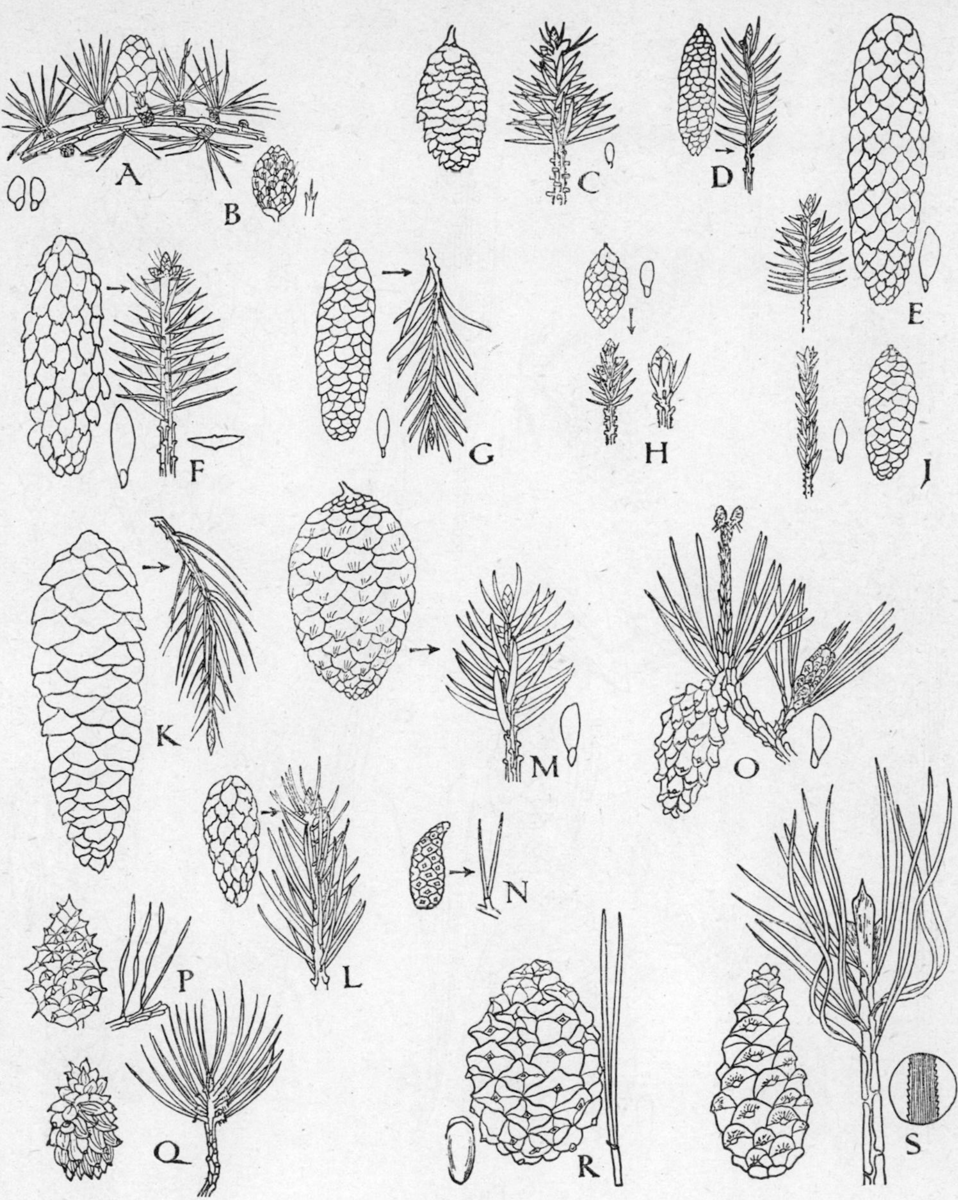

FIG. 45

A. Common Larch, *Larix decidua* (336)
B. Cone of *L. occidentalis* (337)
C. Servian Spruce, *Picea Omorika* (337)
D. White Spruce, *P. glauca* (338)
E. Common or Norway Spruce, *P. Abies* (338)
F. Sitka Spruce, *P. sitchensis* (337)
G. Weeping Spruce, *P. Breweriana* (337)
H. Black Spruce, *P. mariana* (338)
J. *P. orientalis* (338)
K. Himalayan Spruce, *P. Smithiana* (338)
L. *P. Engelmannii* (338)
M. Tiger-tail Spruce, *P. polita* (338)
N. Jack Pine, *Pinus Banksiana* (339)
O. Scots Pine, *P. sylvestris* (340)
P. Beach Pine, *P. contorta* (339)
Q. Mountain Pine, *P. mugo* (339)
R. Stone Pine, *P. Pinea* (340)
S. Corsican Pine, *P. nigra* (339)

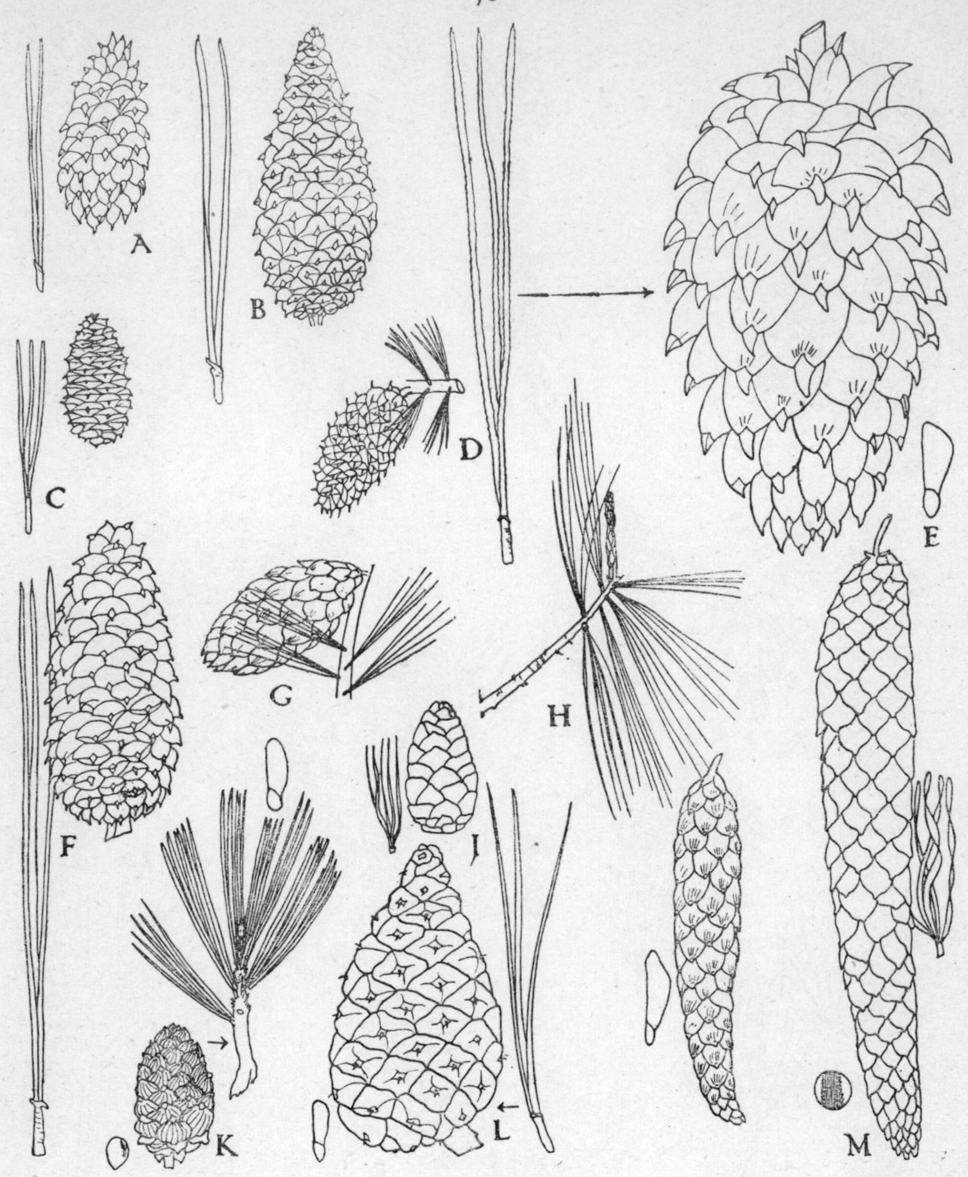

Fig.

A. Bishop Pine, *Pinus muricata* (339)

B. Maritime or Cluster Pine, *P. Pinaster* (340)

C. Northern Pitch Pine, *P. rigida* (341)

D. Bristle-cone or Hickory Pine, *P. aristata* (341)

E. Big-cone Pine, *P. Coulteri* (340)

F. Western Yellow Pine, *P. ponderosa* (340)

G. Limber Pine, *P. flexilis* (341)

H. Bhutan Pine, *P. excelsa* (341)

J. Japanese White Pine, *P. parviflora* (341)

K. Arolla Pine, or Cembran Pine, *P. Cembra* (341)

L. Monterey Pine, *P. radiata* (*insignis*) (340)

M. Sugar Pine, *P. Lambertiana* (341)

(A, C–G, and M after Sargent.)

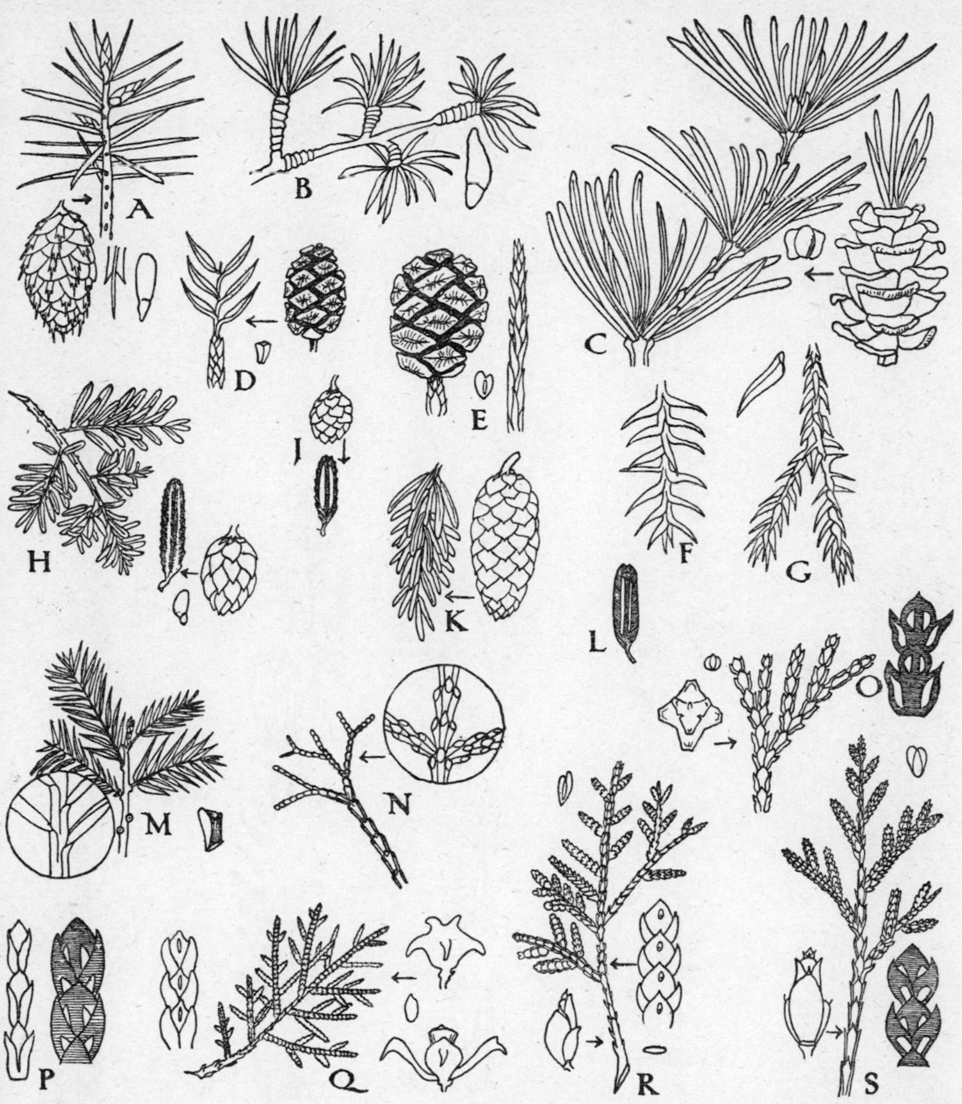

FIG. 47

A. Douglas Fir, *Pseudotsuga taxifolia* (342)

B. Golden Larch, *Pseudolarix amabilis* (342)

C. Umbrella Pine, *Sciadopitys verticillata* (342)

D. Redwood, *Sequoia sempervirens* (342)

E. Mammoth Tree, *S.* (*Wellingtonia*) *gigantea* (342)

F. Milanji Cedar, *Widdringtonia Whytei* (344)

G. *Taiwania cryptomerioides* (342)

H. Western Hemlock, *Tsuga heterophylla* (344)

J. Eastern Hemlock, *T. canadensis* (344)

K. Mountain Hemlock, *T. Mertensiana* (344)

L. Leaf of Japanese Hemlock, *T. diversifolia* (344)

M. Deciduous or Swamp Cypress, *Taxodium distichum* (343)

N. Alcerce, *Tetraclinis articulata* (343)

O. *Thuyopsis dolabrata* (343)

P. Japanese Arbor-vitae, *Thuya Standishii* (343)

Q. Chinese Arbor-vitae, *T. orientalis* (343)

R. American Arbor-vitae, *T. occidentalis* (343)

S. Western Arbor-vitae, *T. plicata* (*T. Lobbii*) (343)

Genus not figured: *Glyptostrobus* (334)

Fig. 48

A. *Phyllodoce coerulea* (264)
B. *Bruckenthalia spiculifolia* (259)
C. St. Dabeoc's Heath, *Daboecia cantabrica* (260)
D. Cornish Heath, *Erica vagans* (262)
E. Winter-flowering Heath, *E. carnea* (261)
F. *E. lusitanica* (261)
G. Scotch or Grey Heath, *E. cinerea* (261)
H. Cross-leaved Heath, *E. Tetralix* (262)
J. Fringed Heath, *E. ciliaris* (261)
K. Alpine Azalea, *Loiseleuria procumbens* (263)
L. *Coprosma Petriei* (250)
M. Crowberry, *Empetrum nigrum* (320)
N. Portuguese Crowberry, *Corema album* (320)
O. Sea Heath, *Frankenia laevis* (160)
P. Ling, or Heather, *Calluna vulgaris* (259)
Q. Himalayan Heather, *Cassiope fastigiata* (259)

(K after Butcher and Strudwick.)

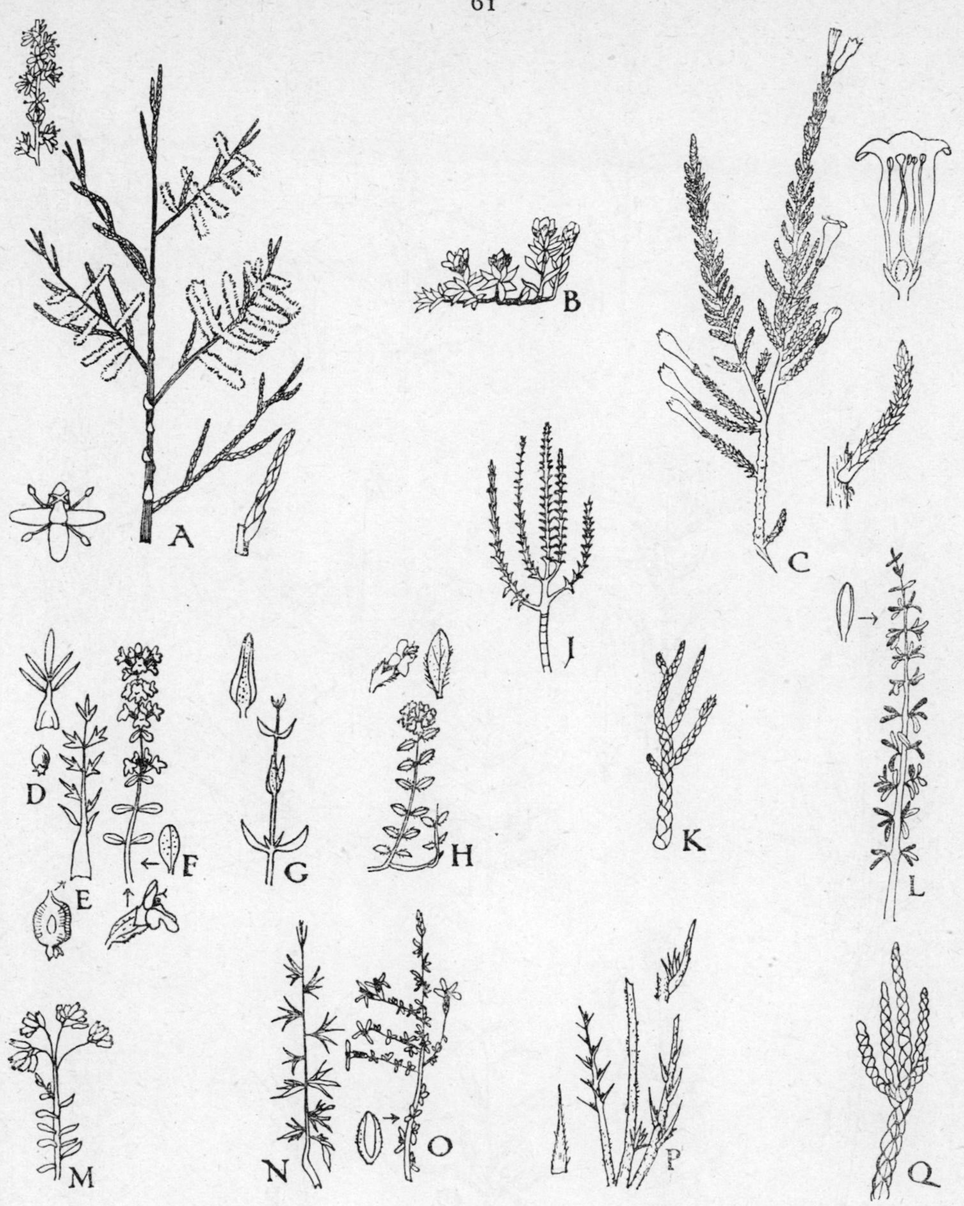

FIG. 49

A. Tamarisk, *Tamarix tetrandra* (160)

B. Flowering Moss, *Pyxidanthera barbulata* (271)

C. False Heath, *Fabiana imbricata* (284)

D. Pearl Fruit, *Margyricarpus setosus* (198)

E. *M. alatus* (198)

F. Common Thyme, *Thymus Chamaedrys* (291)

G. Garden Thyme, *T. vulgaris* (292)

H. Wild Thyme, *T. serpyllum* (291)

J. *Veronica cupressoides* (286)

K. *V. lycopodioides* (286)

L. *Olearia Solandri* (254)

M. Golden Bush, *Cassinia fulvida* (251)

N. *Aplopappus ericoides* (253)

O. *Olearia floribunda* (255)

P. *Camphorosma monspeliacum* (292)

Q. *Veronica Hectori* (286)

Genus not figured: *Myricaria* (160)

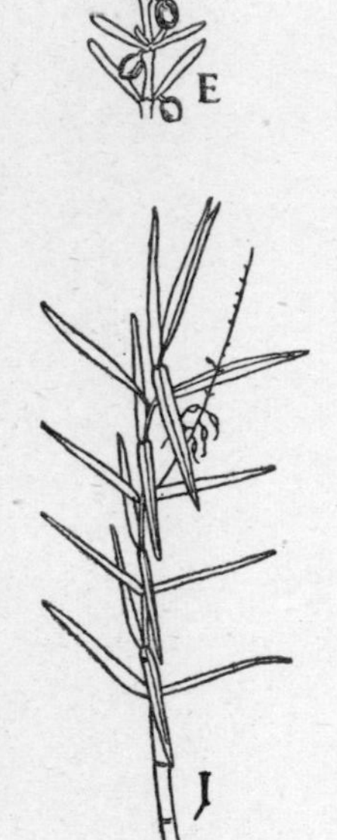
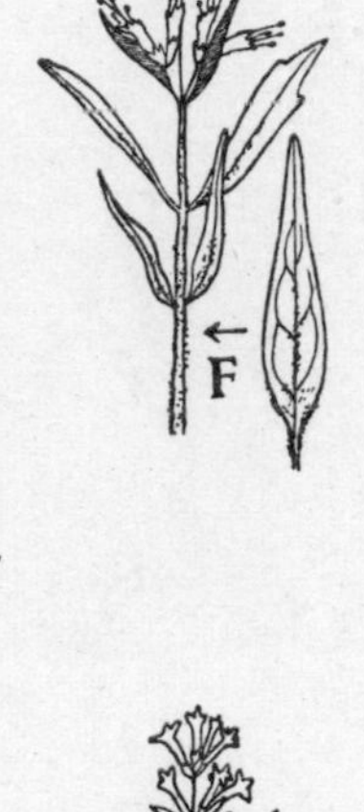

Fig. 50

A. Hyssop, *Hyssopus officinalis* (290)
B. Winter Savory, *Satureia montana* (291)
C. Rosemary, *Rosmarinus officinalis* (291)
D. Lavender, *Lavandula vera* (290)
E. *Coprosma acerosa* (250)
F. *Caryopteris mongolica* (289)
G. *Nesaea* (*Heimia*) *salicifolia* (233)
H. *Freylinia cestroides* (285)
J. *Veronica angustifolia* (287)
K. *Leptodermis Purdomii* (250)
L. *Lonicera Albertii* (243)
M. Spiny Cress Rocket, *Vella spinosa* (155)
N. *Alyssum argenteum* (155)
O. *Anthyllis Hermanniae* (185)
P. Goat Wheat, *Atraphaxis frutescens* (293)
Q. *Adenandra uniflora* (167)

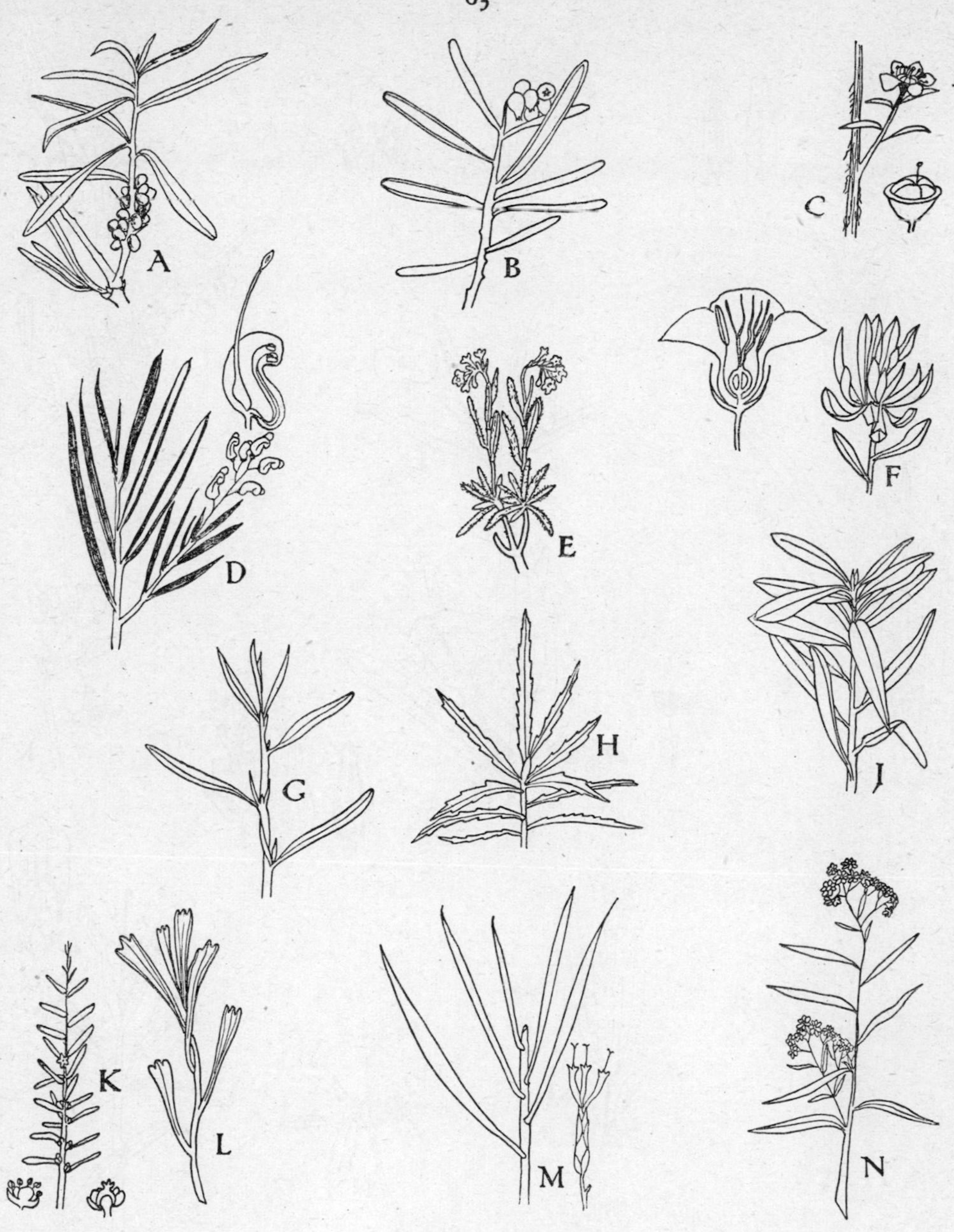

FIG. 51

A. Sea Buckthorn, *Hippophae rhamnoides* (298)
B. Bog Rosemary, *Andromeda polifolia* (258)
C. South Sea Myrtle, or New Zealand Tea Plant, *Leptospermum scoparium* (232)
D. *Grevillea rosmarinifolia* (295)
E. *Moltkia petraea* (283)
F. Tree Flax, *Linum arboreum* (166)
G. Orach, or Grey Sage Brush, *Atriplex canescens* (292)
H. *Pittosporum patulum* (159)
J. *P. bicolor* (159)
K. Shrubby Goosefoot, *Suaeda fruticosa* (292)
L. Sage Brush, *Artemisia tridentata* (251)
M. Plumed Golden Rod, *Bigelovia graveolens* (253)
N. *Helichrysum* (*Ozothamnus*) *rosmarinifolium* (252)

FIG. 52

A. Marsh Ledum, or Wild Rosemary, *Ledum palustre* (263)

B. Evergreen Candytuft, *Iberis sempervirens* (155)

C. *Cercocarpus intricatus* (198)

D. Prickly Mimosa, *Acacia verticillata* (194)

E. *Pyracantha angustifolia* (218)

F. *Hypericum Coris* (161)

G. *Acacia neriifolia* (194)

H. Shrubby Spurge, *Euphorbia Wulfenii* (300)

J. Gromwell, *Lithospermum diffusum* (283)

K. *Spiraea Thunbergii* (197)

L. *Prinsepia uniflora* (205)

M. *Phillyrea angustifolia* (278)

N. *Pentstemon Scouleri* (285)

O. *P. heterophyllus* (285)

P. *Acacia juniperina* (194)

Fig. 53

A. *Salix incana* (318)

B. Purple Osier, *S. purpurea* (320)

C. *S. rubra* (319)

D. Common Osier, *S. viminalis* (319)

E. *Olearia virgata* (254)

F. *O. odorata* (253)

G. *O. lineata* (255)

H. *Cneorum tricoccum* (168)

Genera not figured: *Berberis* (151), *Pseudopanax* (236)

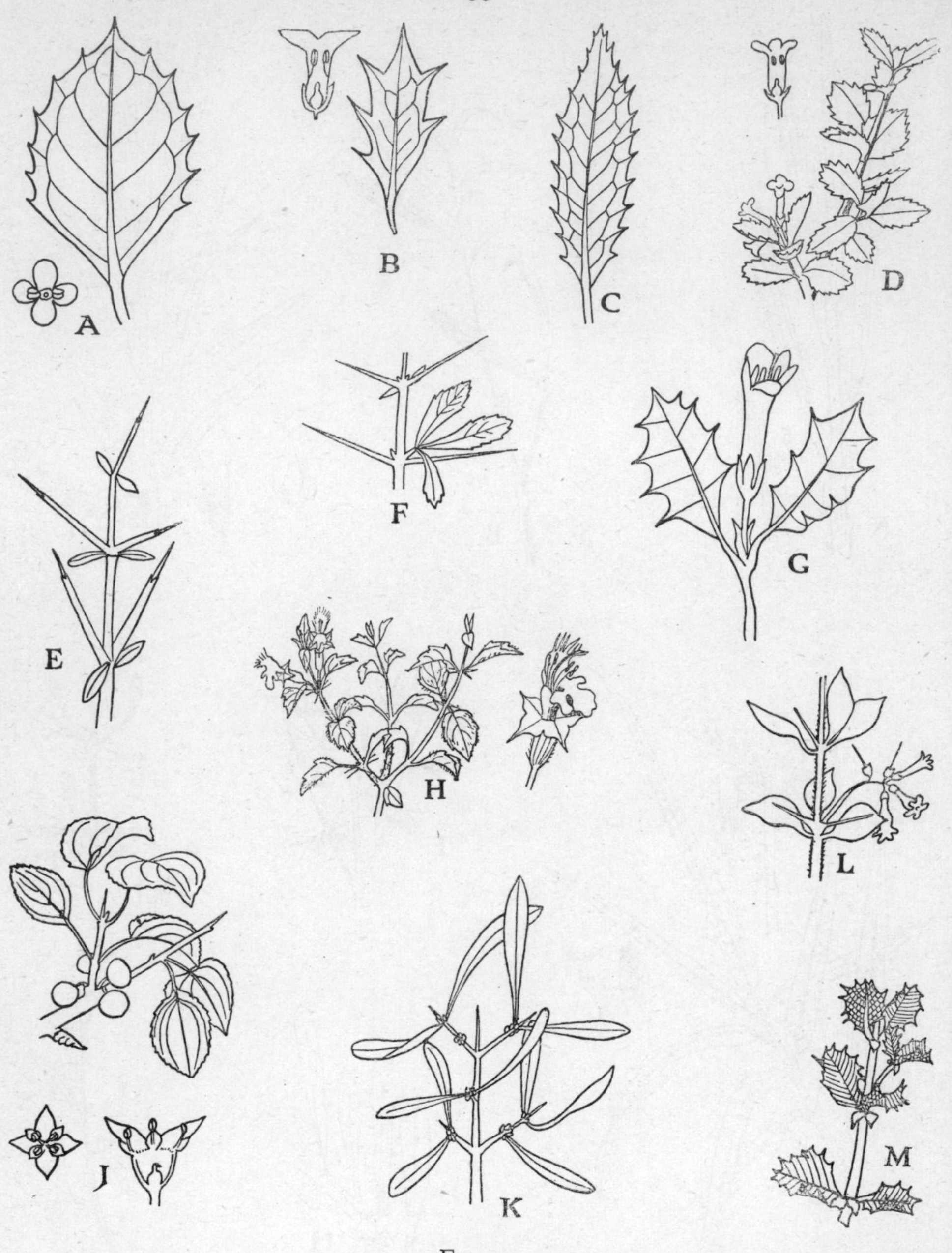

FIG. 54

A. *Osmanthus Fortunei* (278)
B. *O. Aquifolium* (278)
C. *O. armatus* (278)
D. *O. Delavayi* (278)
E. Wild Irishman, *Discaria Toumatou* (174)
F. *D. serratifolia* (174)
G. *Desfontainea spinosa* (283)
H. Shrubby Horehound, *Ballota frutescens* (290)
J. Common Buckthorn, *Rhamnus cathartica* (175)
K. Buffalo Berry, *Shepherdia argentea* (298)
L. *Raphithamnus cyanocarpus* (289)
M. *Ceanothus prostratus* (173)

(Flowers of H after Moggridge.)

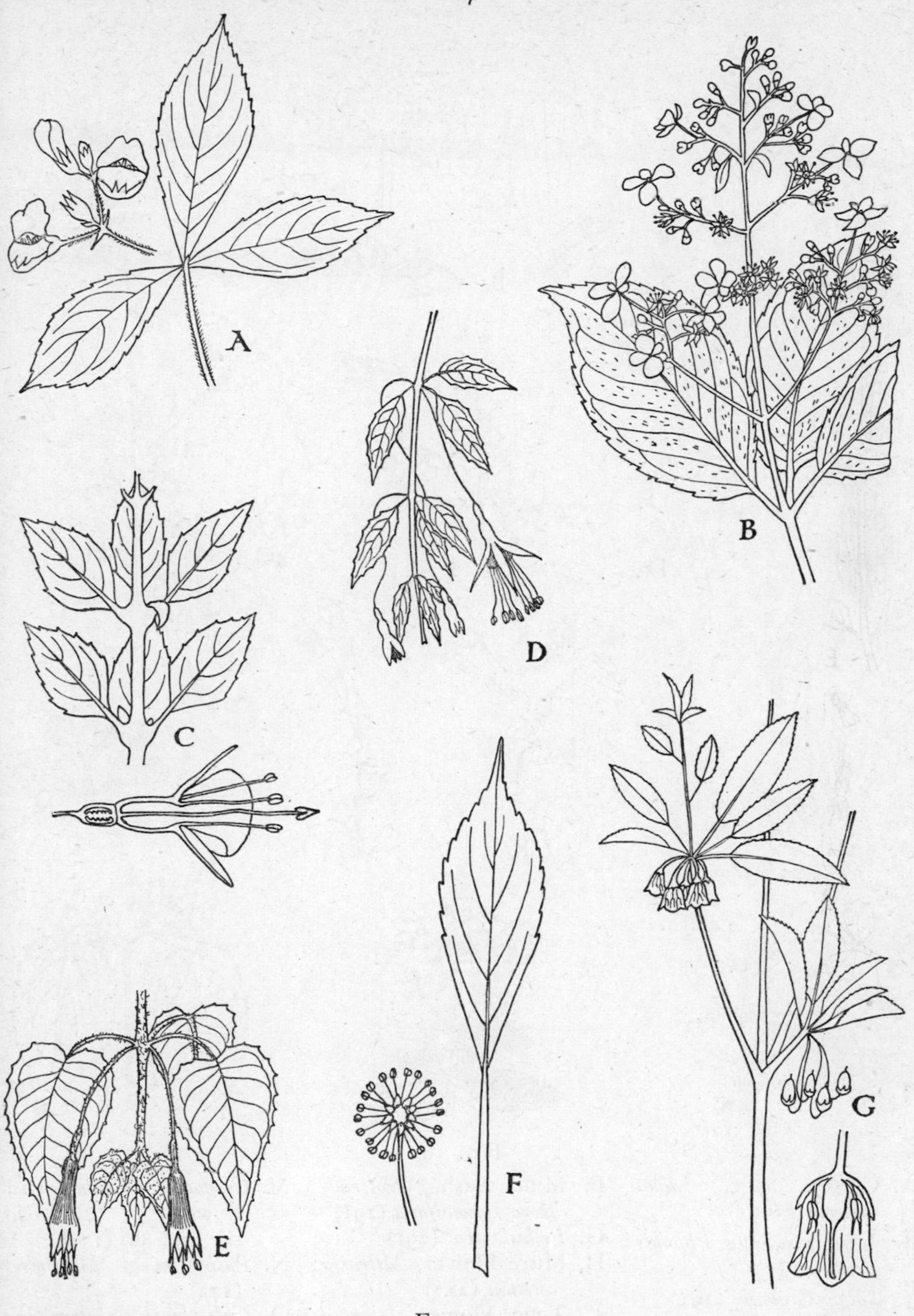

FIG. 55

A. *Bowkeria Gerrardiana* (284)
B. *Hydrangea paniculata* (223)
C. *Fuchsia macrostemma* (234)
D. *F. gracilis* (234)
E. *F. cordifolia* (234)
F. *Trochodendron aralioides* (149)
G. *Enkianthus campanulatus* (261)

FIG. 56

A. Garden Sage, *Salvia officinalis* (291)

B. Jerusalem Sage, *Phlomis fruticosa* (290)

C. *Salvia Grahami* (291)

D. Russian Sage, *Perowskia atriplicifolia* (290)

E. Germander, *Teucrium Chamaedrys* (291)

F. Mint Bush, *Prostranthera rotundifolia* (291)

G. *P. lasianthos* (291)

H. Mitre Flower, *Mitraria coccinea* (287)

J. Twin Flower, *Linnaea borealis* (241)

K. *Pentstemon cordifolius* (285)

L. *P. Menziesii* (285)

(P after *Botanical Magazine*.)

M. *Ceanothus rigidus* (for flowers of *Ceanothus* see Fig. 86) (173)

N. *Pachystima Myrsinites* (172)

O. *Calceolaria integrifolia* (285)

P. *Colquhounia coccinea* (290)

Genus not figured: *Leonotis* (290)

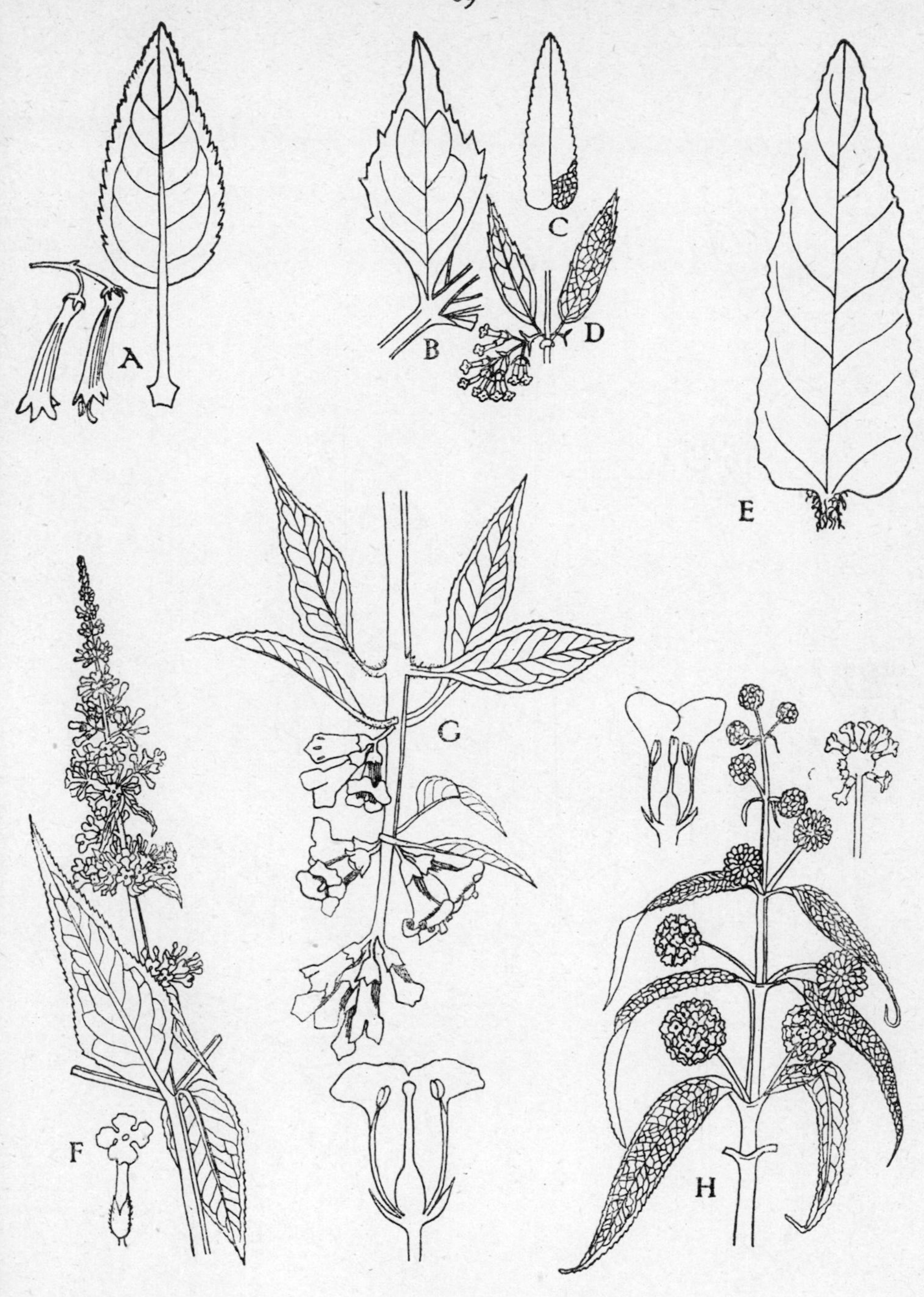

FIG. 57

A. Cape Figwort, *Phygelius capensis* (285)
B. *Buddleia Lindleyana* (281)
C. South African Sage Wood, *B. salvifolia* (282)
D. *B. auriculata* (282)
E. *B. Farreri* (282)
F. *B. Davidii* (*variabilis*) (282)
G. *B. Colvilei* (282)
H. Orange Ball Tree, *B. globosa* (282)

FIG. 58

A. *Hydrangea macrophylla* (224)
B. *H. Davidii* (224)
C. *H. petiolaris* (224)
D. *H. villosa* (225)
E. *H. Sargentiana* (225)
F. *H. Bretschneideri* (224)
G. *H. involucrata* (224)
H. *Schizophragma hydrangeoides* (229)

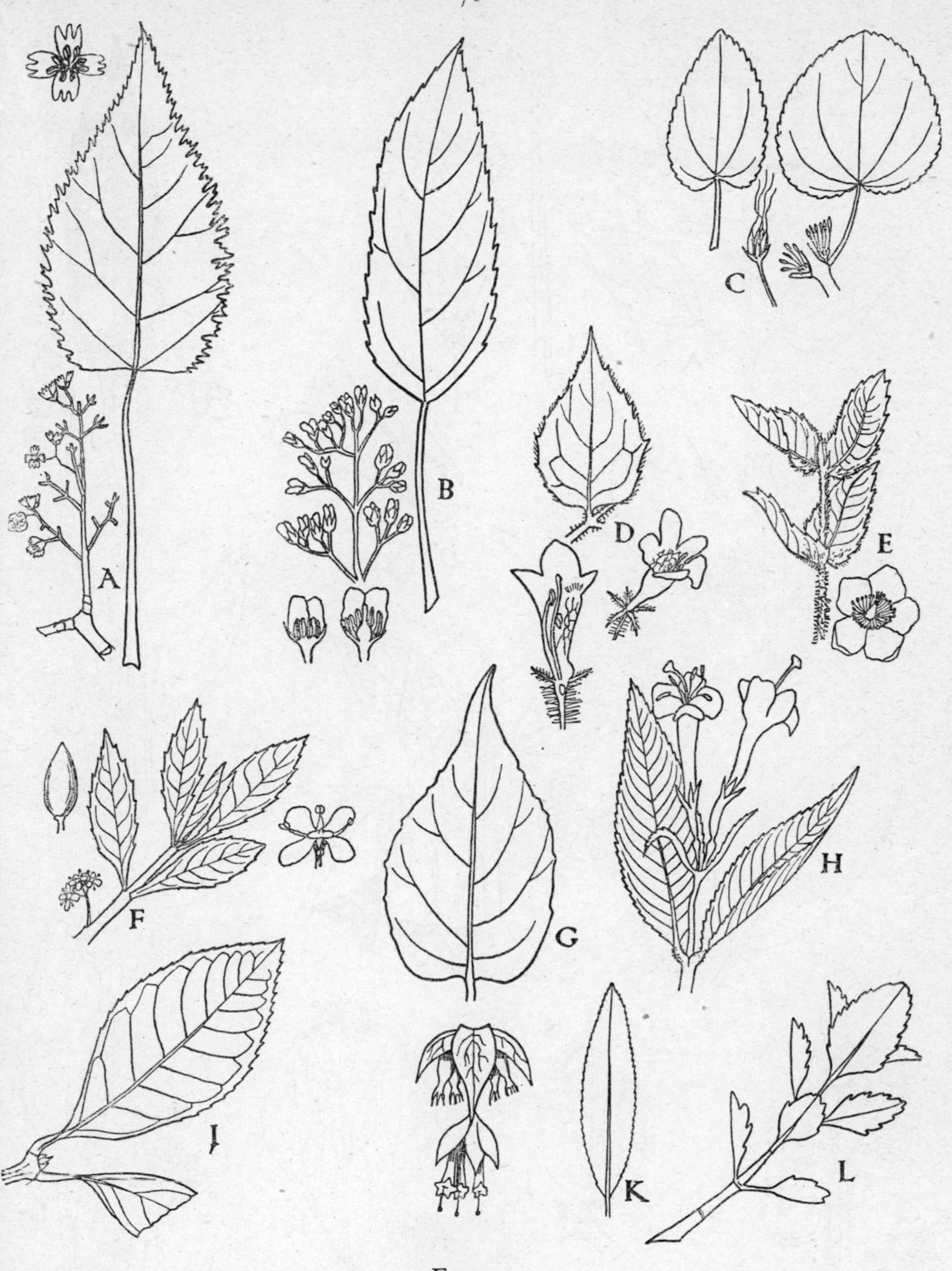

FIG. 59

A. *Aristotelia racemosa* (165)
B. *A. Macqui* (165)
C. Katsura Tree, *Cercidiphyllum japonicum* (149)
D. *Kolkwitzia amabilis* (241)
E. *Eucryphia cordifolia* (195)

F. *Elaeodendron capense* (171)
G. Flowering Nutmeg, *Leycesteria formosa* (241)
H. *Diervilla* (*Weigela*) *floribunda* (240)
J. *Olea fragrans* (278)
(F after *Botanical Magazine*.)

K. *Osmanthus serrulatus* (see Fig. 54 A–D) (278)
L. *Veronica Hulkeana* (287)
Genera not figured: *Acer* (178), *Forestiera* (274)

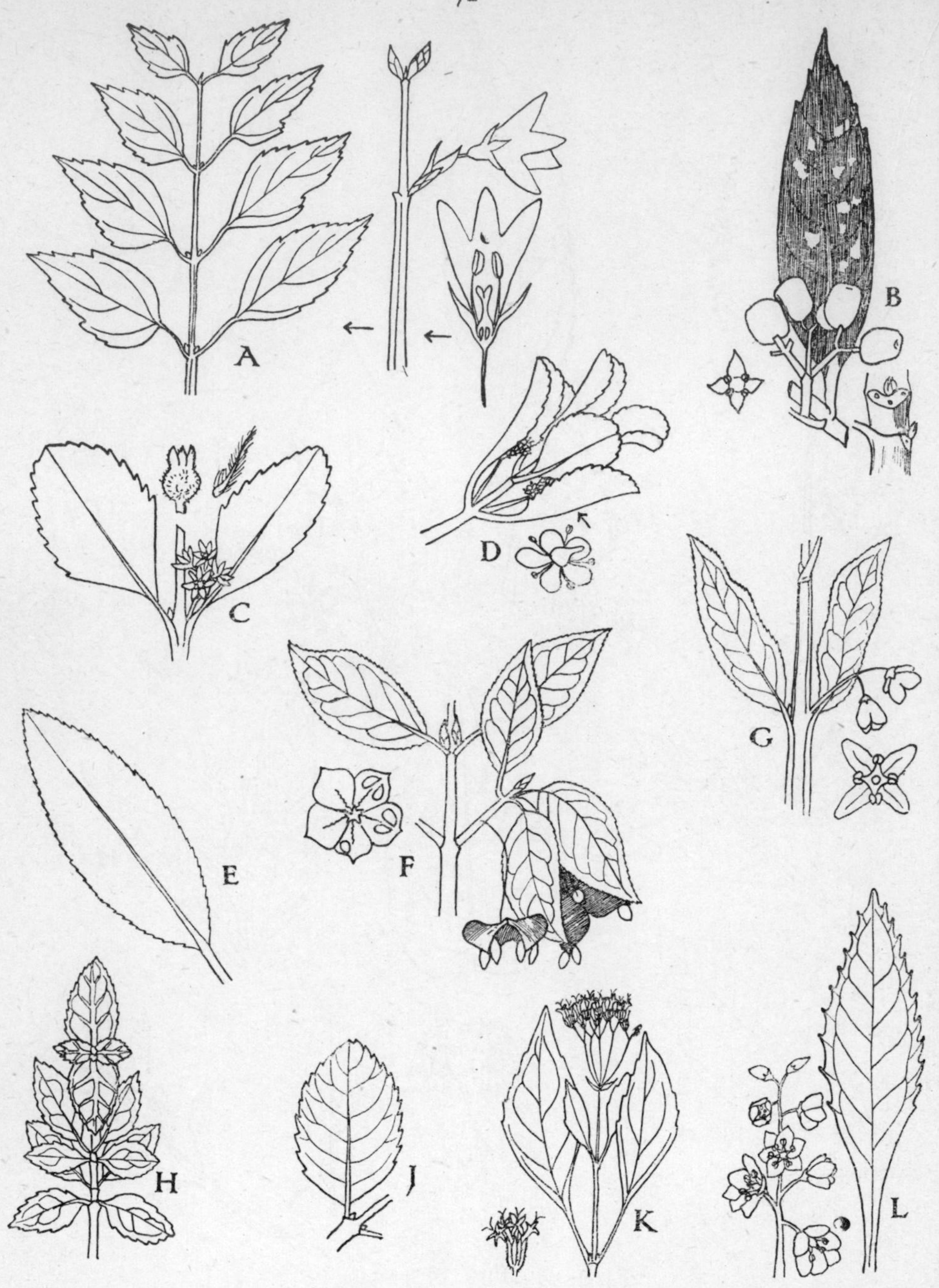

FIG. 60

A. Golden Bell, *Forsythia suspensa* (274)

B. Spotted Laurel, *Aucuba japonica* (237)

C. *Laurelia serrata* (293)

D. *Euonymus japonicus* (172)

E. *E. pendulus* (172)

F. *E. latifolius* (171)

G. Common Spindle Tree, *E. europaeus* (171)

H. *E. radicans* (172)

J. *Phillyrea latifolia* (278)

K. *Eupatorium micranthum* (252)

L. Tasmanian Laurel, *Anopterus glandulosus* (220)

Genus not figured: *Fraxinus* (274)

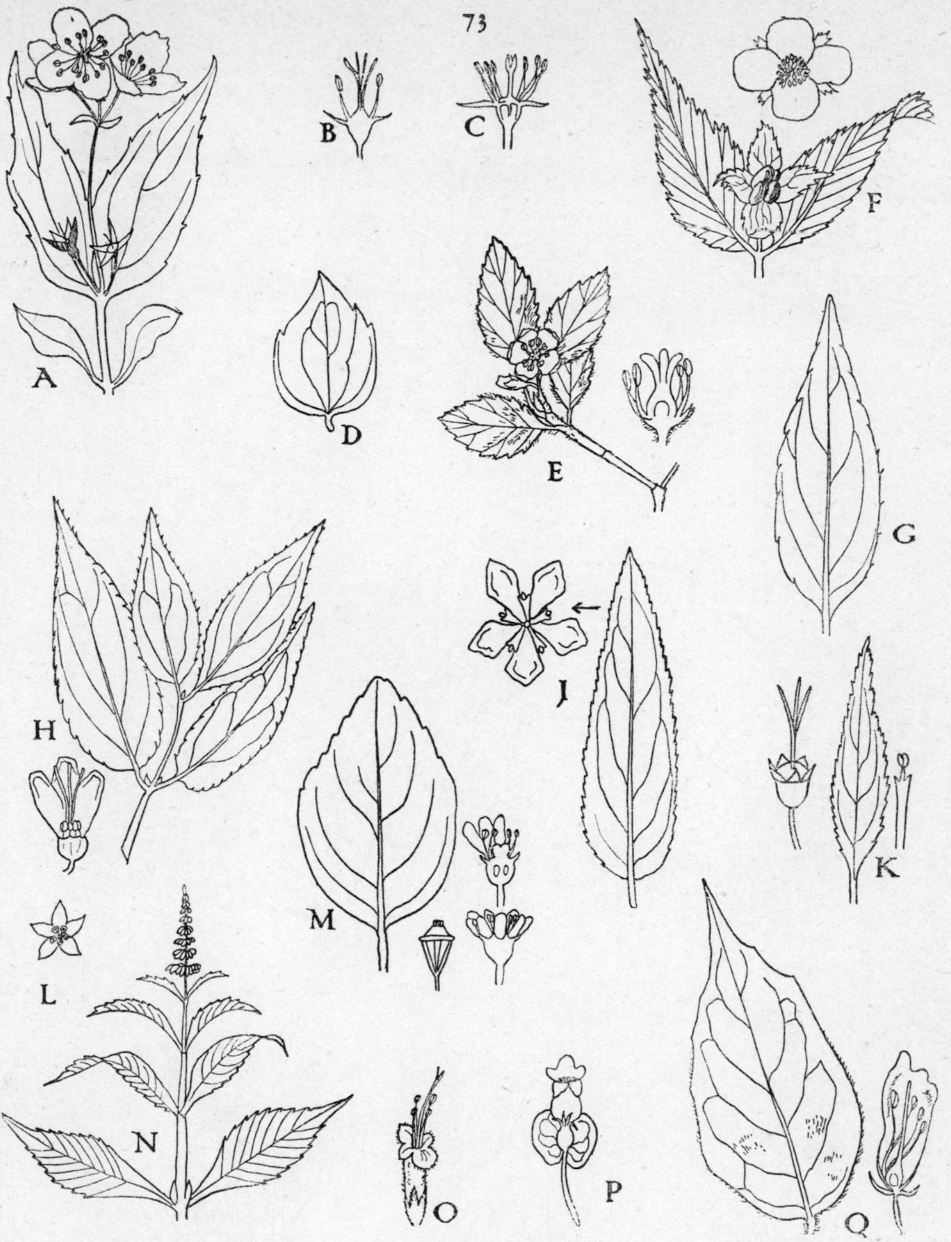

FIG. 61

A. Mock Orange, or Syringa, *Philadelphus coronarius* (225)
B. Flower of *P. Lewisii* with petals removed (226)
C. Ditto, *P. Delavayi* (225)
D. Leaf of *P. purpureo-maculatus* (227)
E. *Jamesia americana* (225)
F. White Kerria, *Rhodotypos kerrioides* (199)
G. *Deutzia discolor* (221)
H. *D. scabra* (222)
J. *D. longifolia* (221)
K. *D. gracilis* (222)
L. Flower of *D. setchuenensis* (221)
M. *Decumaria barbara* (221)
N. *Elsholtzia Stauntonii* (290)
O. Flower of *E. polystachya* (290)
P. *Dipelta ventricosa* (241)
Q. Flower of *D. floribunda* (241)

(O after Collett.)

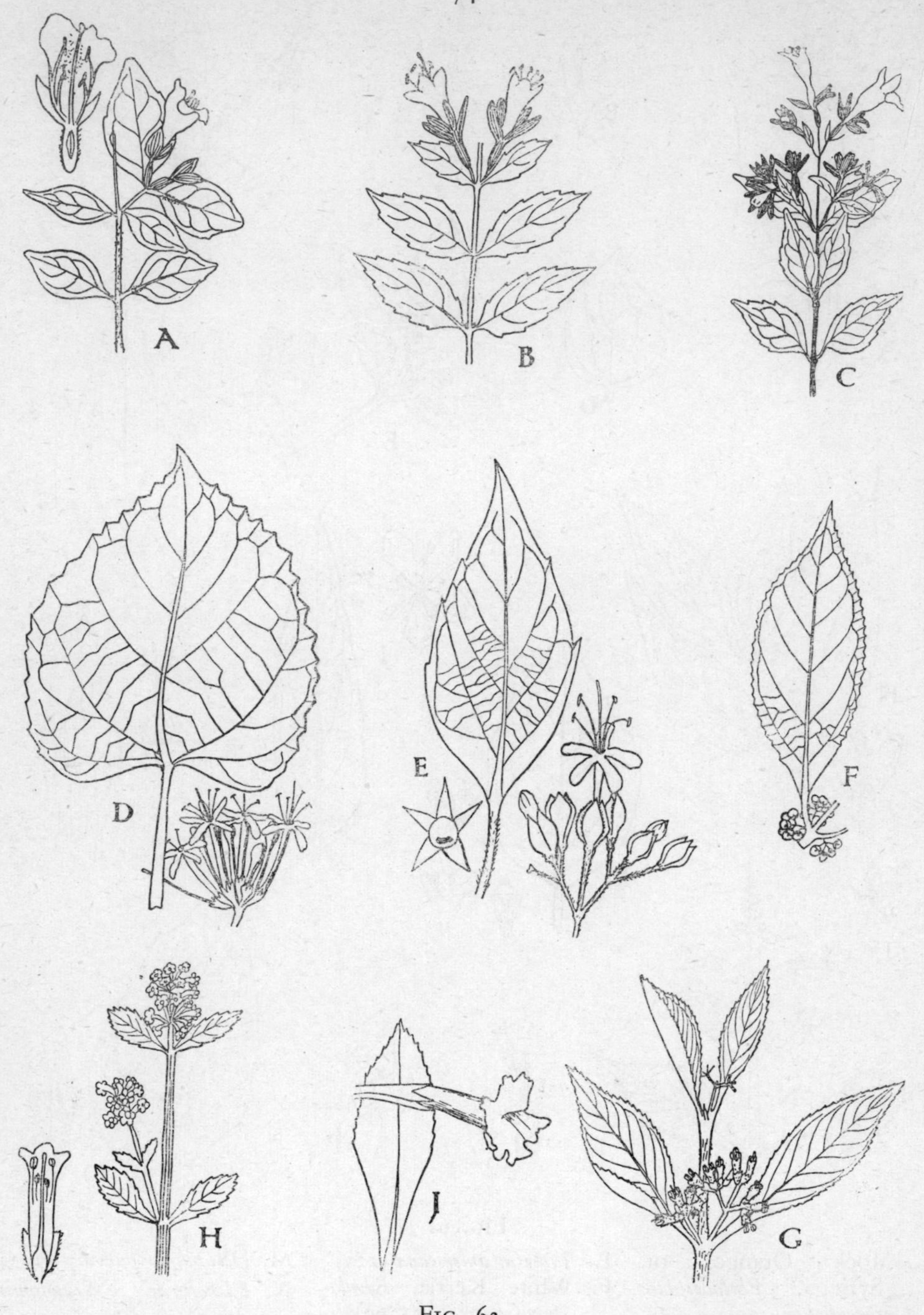

Fig. 62

A. *Abelia Schumannii* (239)

B. *A. grandiflora* (239)

C. *A. chinensis* (239)

D. *Clerodendron foetidum* (289)

E. *C. trichotomum* (289)

F. *Callicarpa Giraldiana* (288)

G. Murasaki, *C. japonica* (288)

H. *Diostea juncea* (289)

J. *Mimulus aurantiacus* (285)

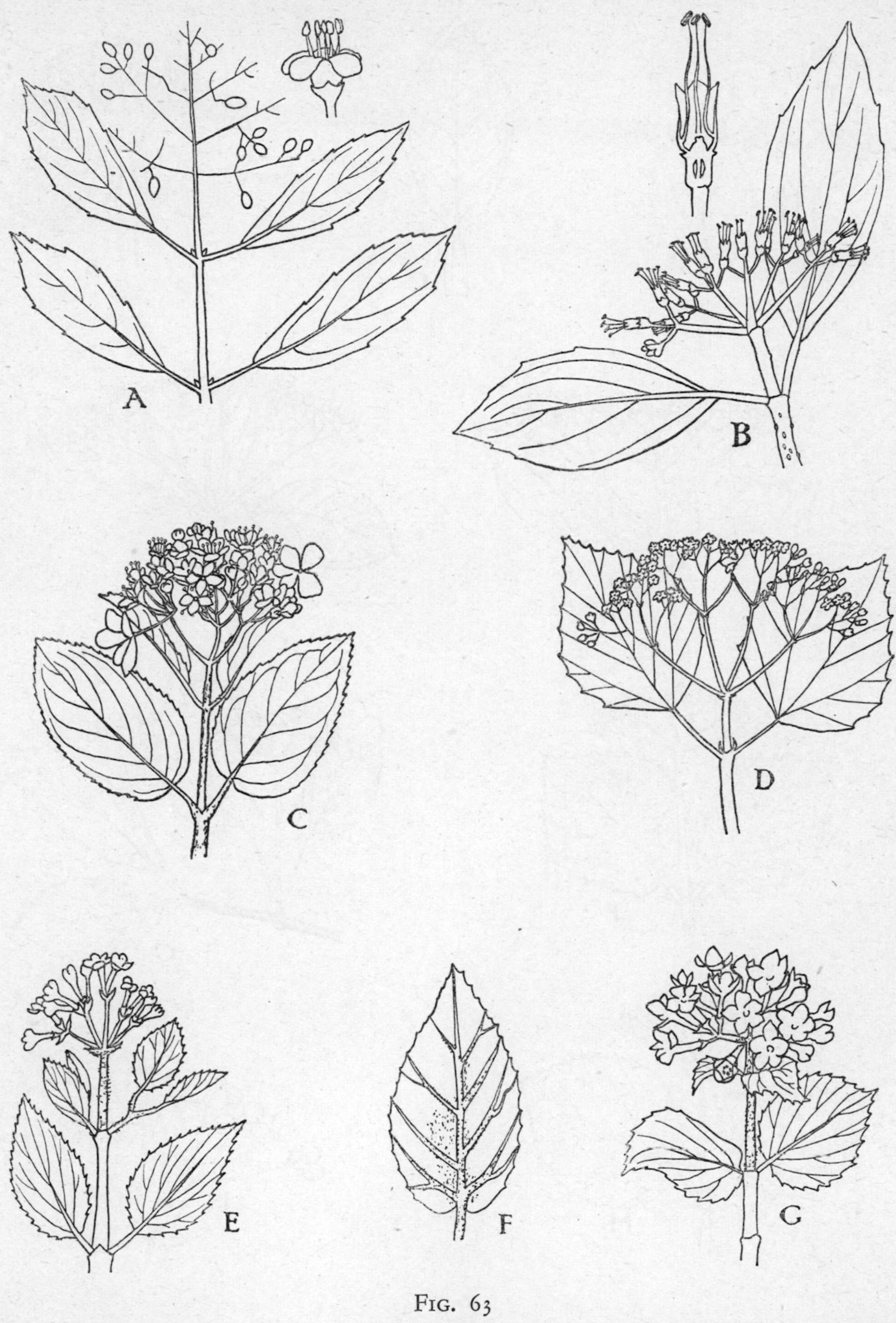

FIG. 63

A. *Viburnum Henryi* (246)
B. *V. cylindricum* (246)
C. Chinese Snowball Tree, *V. macrocephalum* (246)
D. *V. betulifolium* (248)
E. *V. bitchiuense* (247)
F. Leaf of *V. buddleifolium* (248)
G. *V. Carlesii* (248)

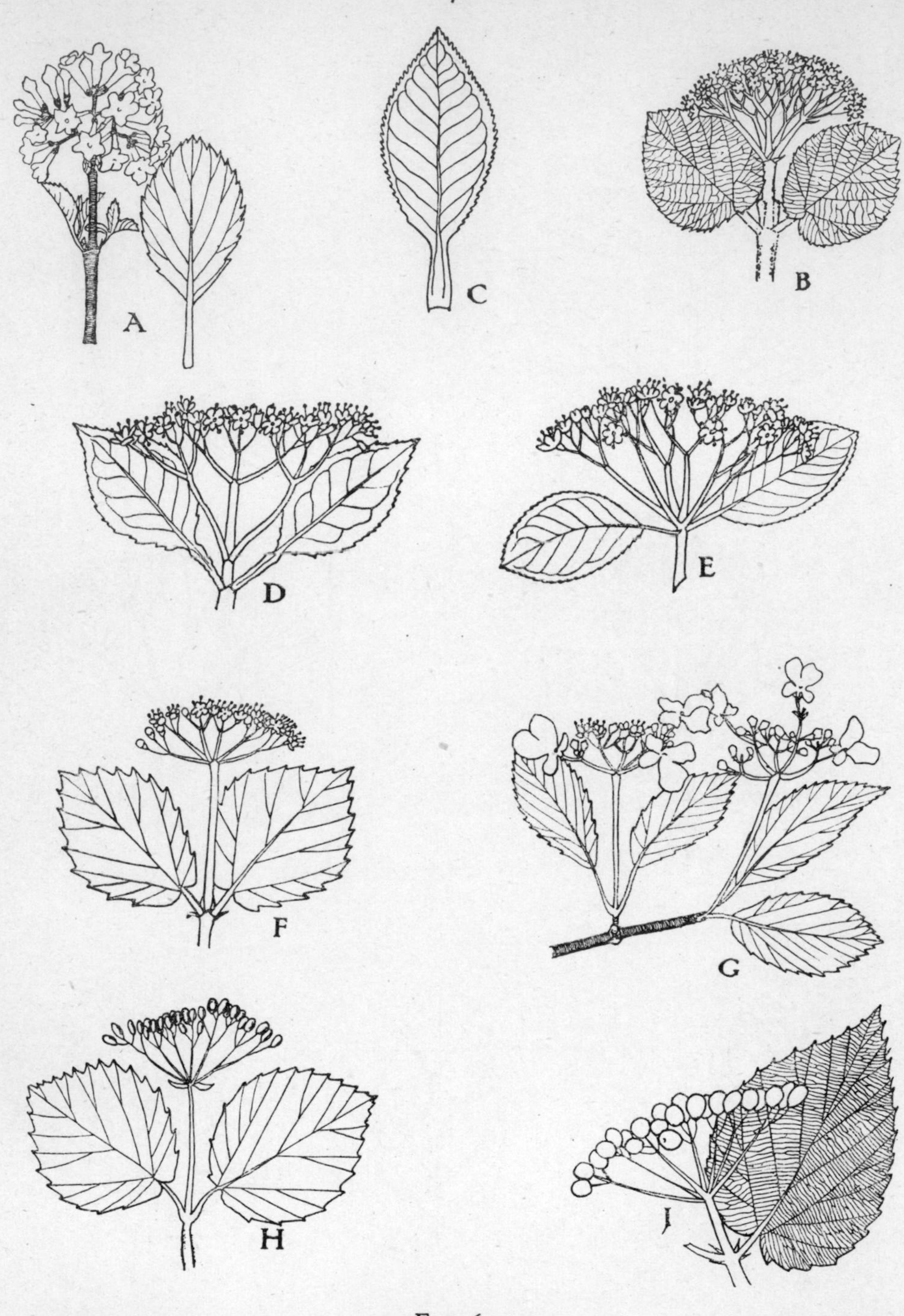

FIG. 64

A. *Viburnum fragrans* (248)
B. Wayfaring Tree, *V. Lantana* (248)
C. Leaf of Sheepberry, *V. Lentago* (247)
D. Withe Rod, *V. nudum* (247)
E. Black Haw, *V. prunifolium* (247)
F. *V. molle* (249)
G. *V. tomentosum* (249)
H. *V. pubescens* (249)
J. *V. lobophyllum* (249)

Fig. 65

A. Laurustinus, *Viburnum Tinus* (247)
B. *V. odoratissimum* (246)
C. Leaf of *V. Davidii* (246)
D. *V. rhytidophyllum* (247)
E. *V. cotinifolium* (248)
F. *V. Harryanum* (246)
G. *V. utile* (247)
H. Diagram of a cymose branched cluster (see footnote on page 5)

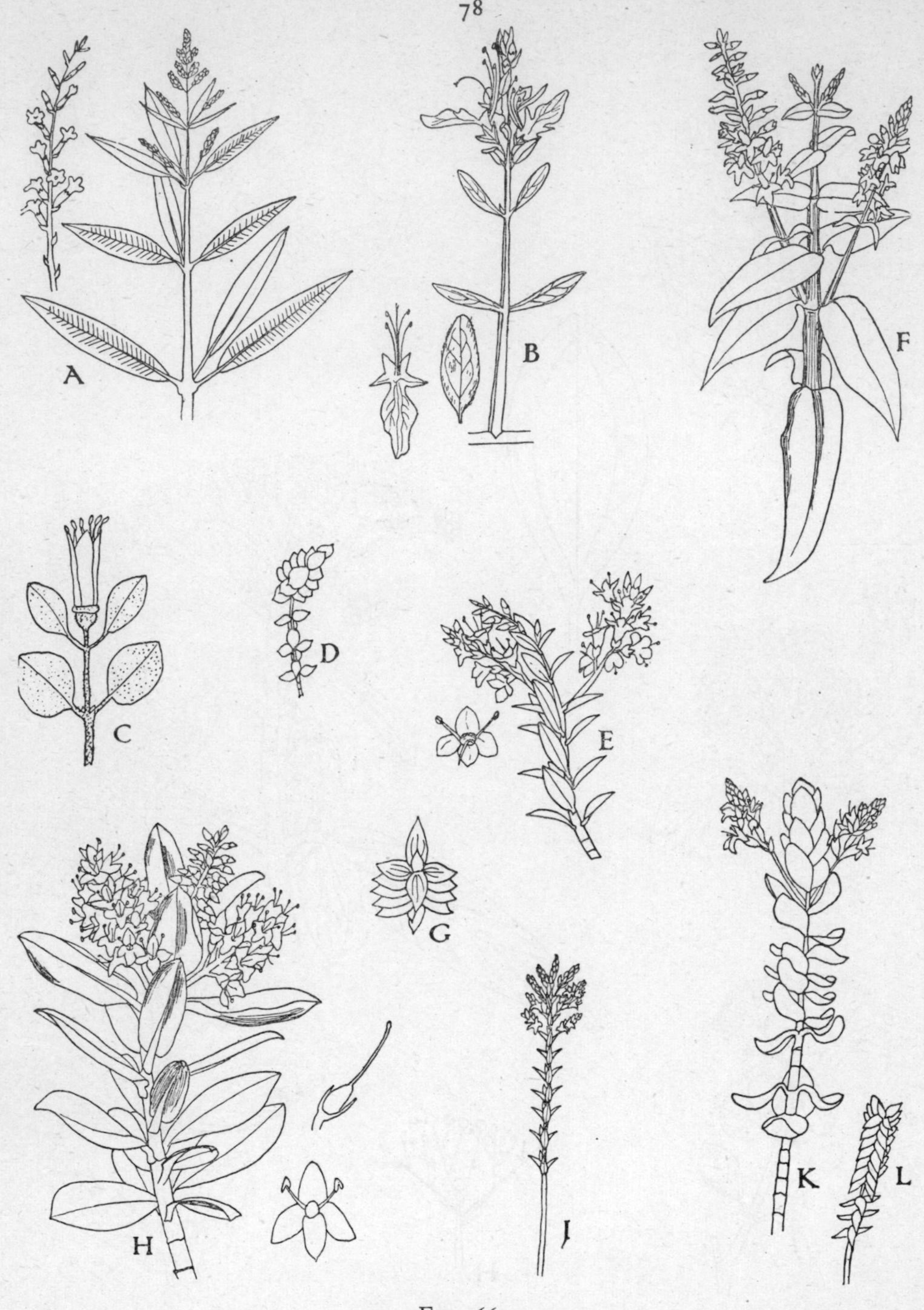

FIG. 66

A. Lemon-scented Verbena, *Lippia* (*Aloysia*) *citriodora* (289)
B. *Teucrium fruticans* (291)
C. *Correa speciosa* (167)
D. *Veronica pinguifolia* (286)
E. *V. Traversii* (286)
F. *V. salicifolia* (287)
G. *V. Colensoi* (286)
H. *V. speciosa* (287)
J. *V. anomala* (286)
K. *V. amplexicaulis* (286)
L. *V. buxifolia* (286)

Fig. 67

A. *Philadelphus microphyllus* (227)
B. *Fendlera rupicola* (223)
C. Partridge Berry, *Mitchella repens* (250)
D. *Pimelea ligustrina* (297)
E. *Diapensia lapponica* (271)
F. Sand Myrtle, *Leiophyllum buxifolium* (263)
G. *Emmenopterys Henryi* (250)
H. Common Box, *Buxus sempervirens* (299)
J. *Leptodermis lanceolata* (250)
K. *L. pilosa* (250)
L. *L. oblonga* (250)
M. *Coprosma lucida* (250)
N. *C. foetidissima* (250)
O. Button Bush, *Cephalanthus occidentalis* (249)

Genera not figured: *Luculia* (250), *Paederia* (250)

(A after Robinson.)

FIG. 68

A. Rose of Sharon, *Hypericum calycinum* (161)
B. *H. patulum* (161)
C. *H. elatum* (161)
D. Tutsan, *H. Androsaemum* (161)
E. St. Andrew's Cross, *Ascyrum hypericoides* (160)
F. *Cistus villosus* (157)
G. *C. corbariensis* (156)
H. Gum Cistus, *C. ladaniferus* (156)
J. Bush Rock Rose, *C. laurifolius* (156)
K. Hoary Rock Rose, *Helianthemum canum* (157)
L. White Rock Rose, *H. appeninum* (157)
M. Common Rock Rose, *H. nummularium* (157)

(K and L after Butcher and Strudwick.)

FIG. 69

A. Fringe Tree, *Chionanthus virginica* (274)

B. *Fontanesia phillyreoides* (274)

C. *Jasminum Beesianum* (276)

D. Olive, *Olea europaea* (278)

E. Common Lilac, *Syringa vulgaris* (280)

F. Himalayan Lilac, *S. emodi* (279)

G. Persian Lilac, *S. persica* (280)

H. *S. villosa* (279)

(Flowers of D after Berger and Schmidt.)

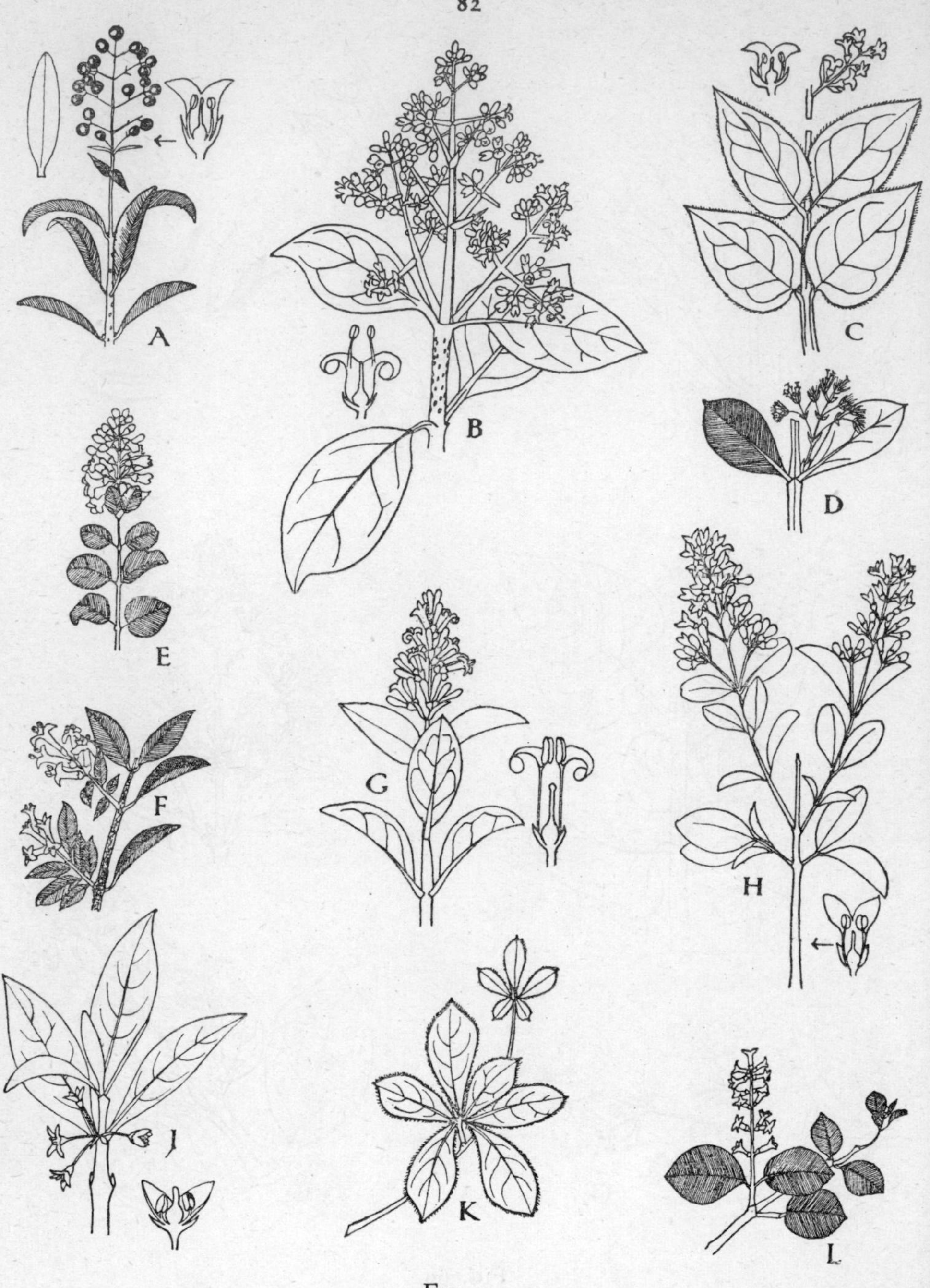

FIG. 70

A. Common Privet, *Ligustrum vulgare* (277)
B. *L. lucidum* (277)
C. *Abeliophyllum distichum* (273)
D. *Olearia Traversii* (254)
E. *Ligustrum ionandrum* (277)
F. *L. Delavayanum* (277)
G. *L. ovalifolium* (277)
H. Chinese Privet, *L. sinense* (277)
J. *Phillyrea decora* (278)
K. *Rhododendron quinquefolium* (266) (for flowers of *Rhododendron* see Figs. 122 and 123)
L. *Parasyringa sempervirens* (278)

Genus not figured: *Kalmia* (262)

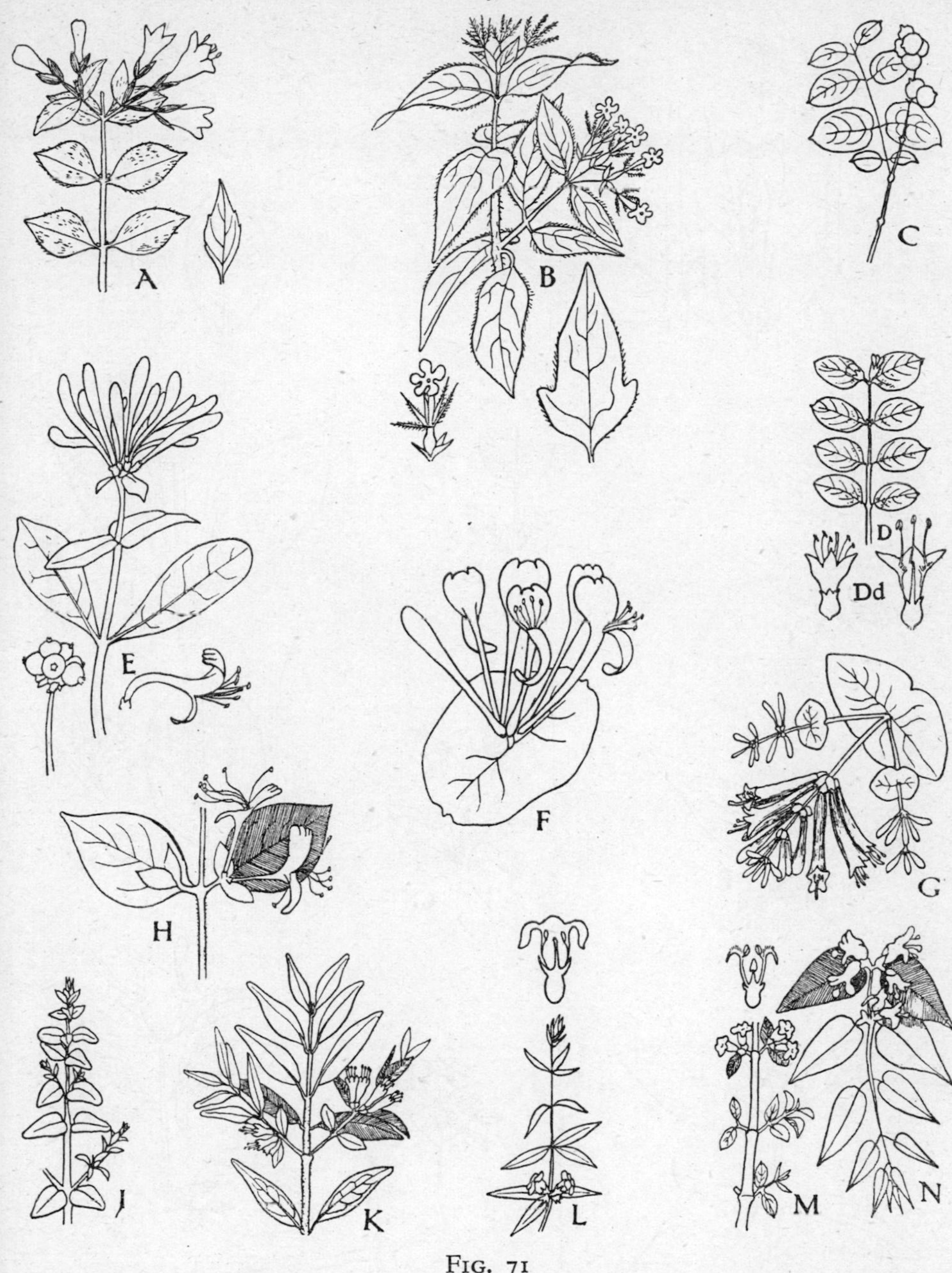

Fig. 71

A. *Abelia Engleriana* (239)
B. *A. triflora* (240)
C. Coral Berry, or Indian Currant, *Symphoricarpus orbiculatus* (245)
D. *S. mollis* (245)
Dd. Flowers of Wolfberry, *S. occidentalis* (245)

E. Common Honeysuckle, *Lonicera Periclymenum* (242)
F. Perfoliate Woodbine, *L. Caprifolium* (241)
G. Trumpet Honeysuckle, *L. sempervirens* (242)

H. *L. japonica* (241)
J. *L. nitida* (242)
K. *L. pileata* (242)
L. *L. thibetica* (244)
M. *L. Myrtillus* (243)
N. *L. tricosantha* (244)

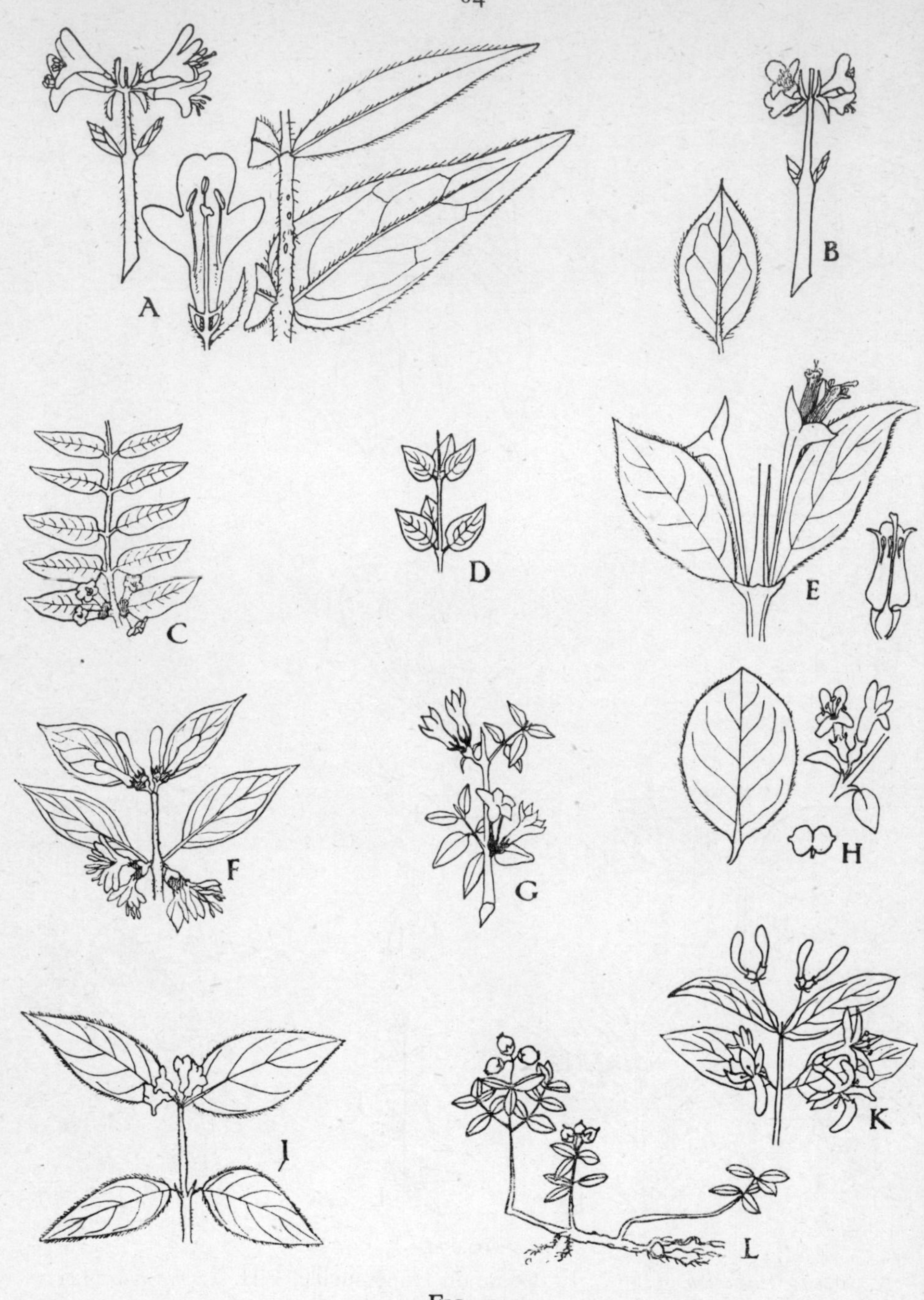

FIG. 72

A. *Lonicera Standishii* (243)
B. *L. fragrantissima* (243)
C. *L. tomentella* (243)
D. *L. rupicola* (243)
E. *L. Ledebouri* (242)
F. *L. Maackii* (244)
G. *L. syringantha* (244)
H. Fly Honeysuckle, *L. Xylosteum* (244)
J. *L. Ferdinandi* (243)
K. *L. tatarica* (244)
L. *Arcterica nana* (258)

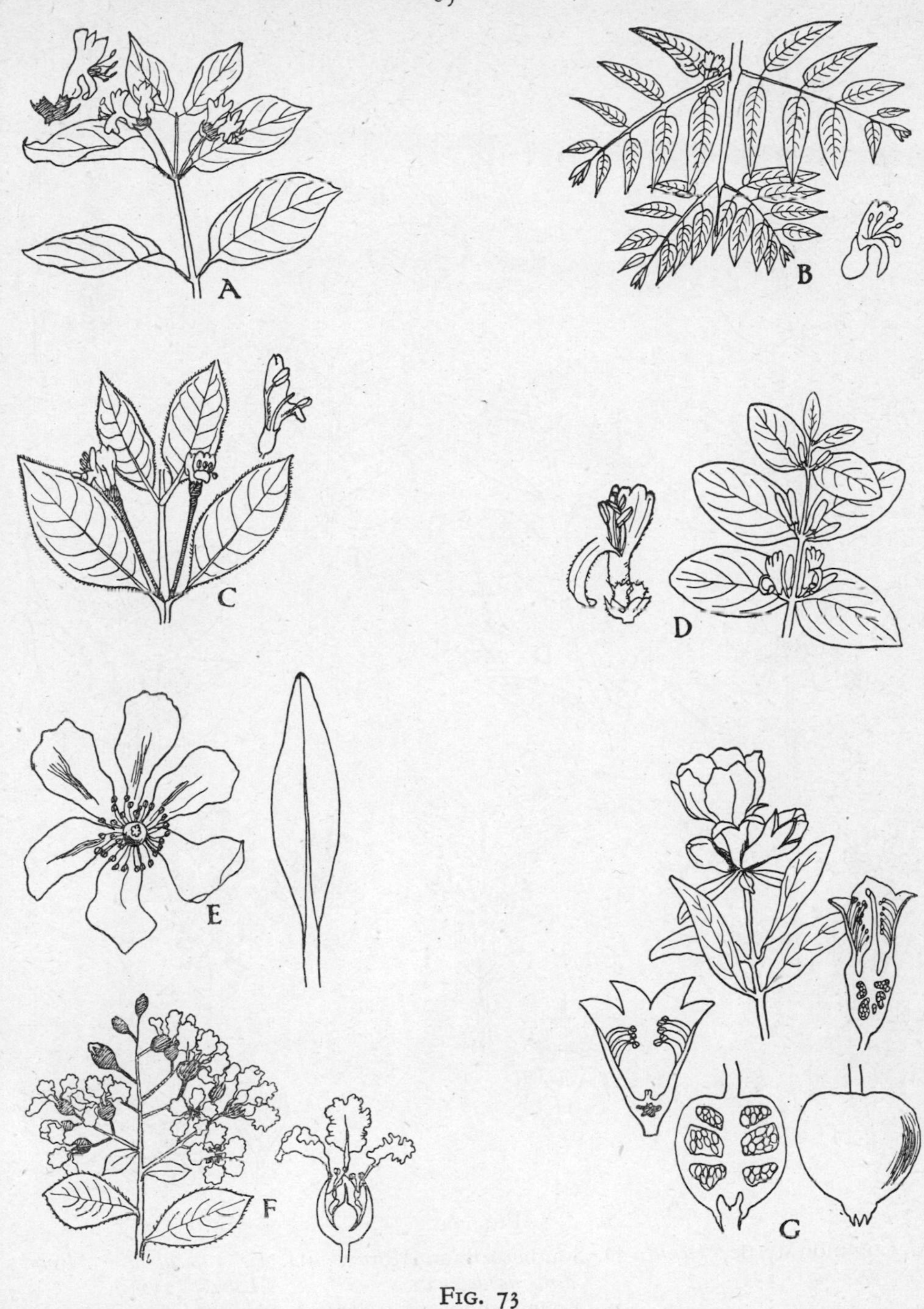

FIG. 73

A. *Lonicera chrysantha* (244)
B. *L. deflexicalyx* (244)
C. Cherry Woodbine, *L. alpigena* (243)
D. *L. quinquelocularis* (244)
E. Californian Mock Orange, *Carpenteria californica* (221)
F. Crape Myrtle, *Lagerstroemia indica* (233)
G. Pomegranate, *Punica Granatum* (233)

(Flower of E after a photograph.)

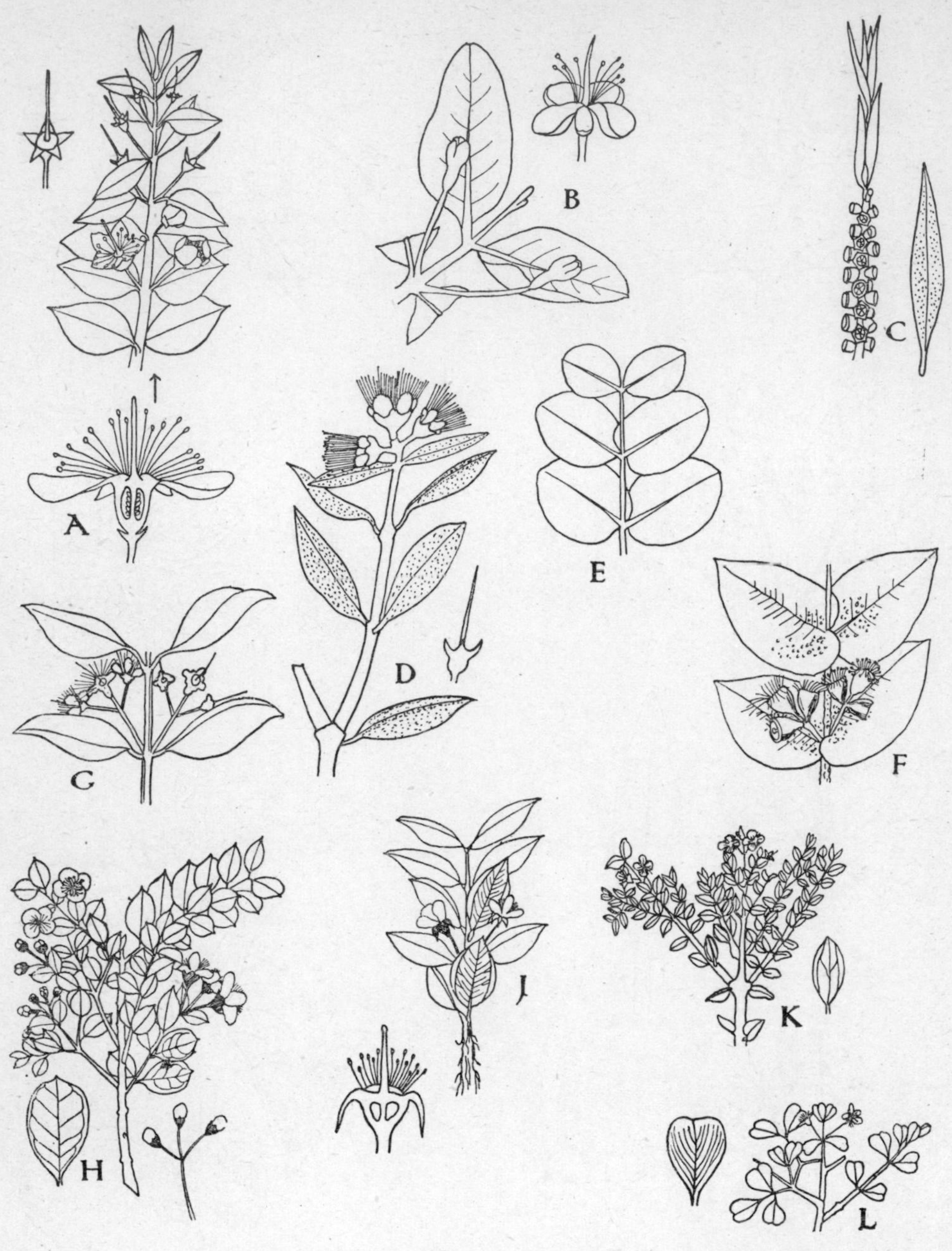

Fig. 74

A. Common Myrtle, *Myrtus communis* (233)

B. *Feijoa Sellowiana* (232)

C. Leaf and fruits of Bottlebrush Tree, *Callistemon* (231)

D. Southern Rata, *Metrosideros lucida* (232)

E. Young shoot of Cider Gum, *Eucalyptus Gunnii* (232)

F. Ditto of *E. cordata* (232)

G. *Eugenia myrtifolia* (232)

H. *E. apiculata* (*Myrtus Luma*) (232)

J. *Myrtus Ugni* (233)

K. *M. nummularia* (233)

L. *M. obcordata* (233)

Genus not figured: *Melaleuca* (232)

Fig. 75

A. Common Dogwood, *Cornus sanguinea* (238)
B. Cornel, or Cornelian Cherry, *C. Mas* (237)
C. *C. florida* (237)
D. *C. Kousa* (237)
E. *C. Nuttallii* (237)
F. *C. alba* (237)
G. *C. capitata* (237)

(G after Collett.)

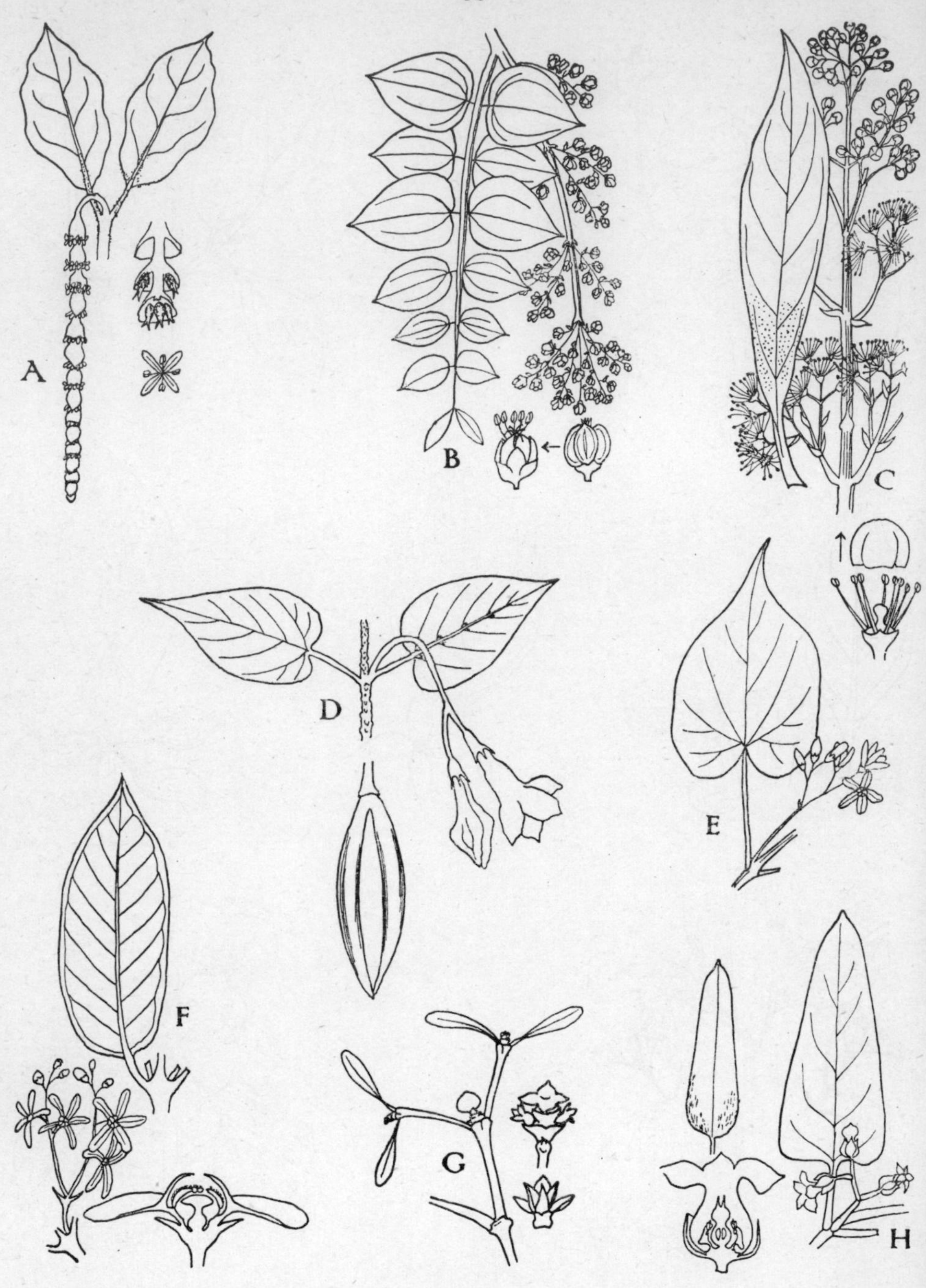

Fig. 76

A. *Garrya elliptica* (238)
B. *Coriaria terminalis* (184)
C. *Pileostegia viburnoides* (277)
D. *Mandevilla suaveolens* (280)
E. *Marsdenia erecta* (281)
F. Silk Vine, *Periploca graeca* (281)
G. Mistletoe, *Viscum album* (298)
H. *Araujia sericofera* (281)
Genus not figured: *Metaplexis* (281)

(H and flowers of F after Kirk.)

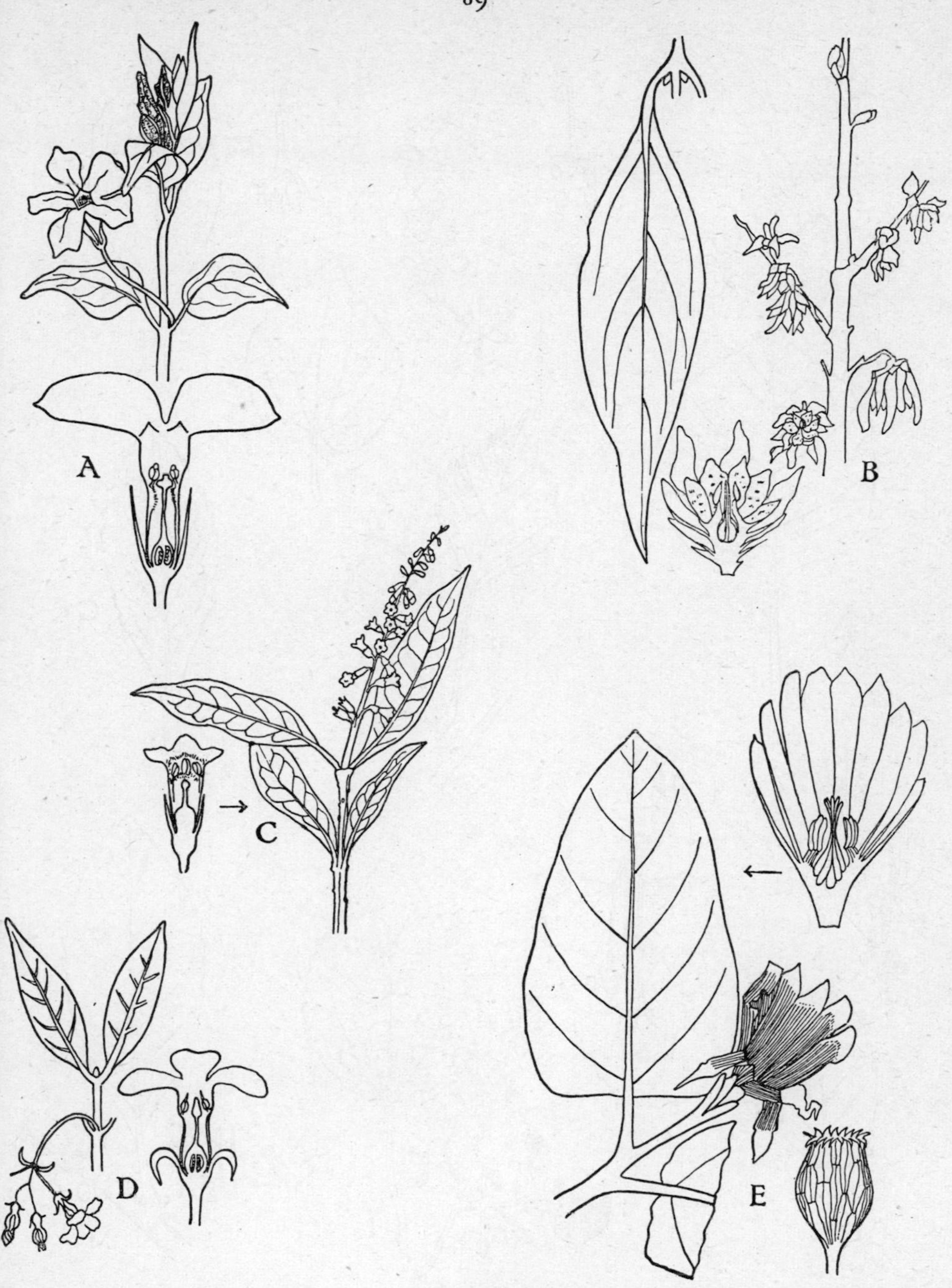

Fig. 77

A. Greater Periwinkle, *Vinca major* (281)

B. Wintersweet, *Chimonanthus praecox* (146)

C. Fiddle Wood, *Citharexylum quadrangularis* (289)

D. *Trachelospermum jasminoides* (280)

E. Californian Allspice, *Calycanthus occidentalis* (145)

Genera not figured: *Acer* (178), *Kalmia* (262)

(Section of flower of E after Le Maout and Decaisne, fruit after Kerner.)

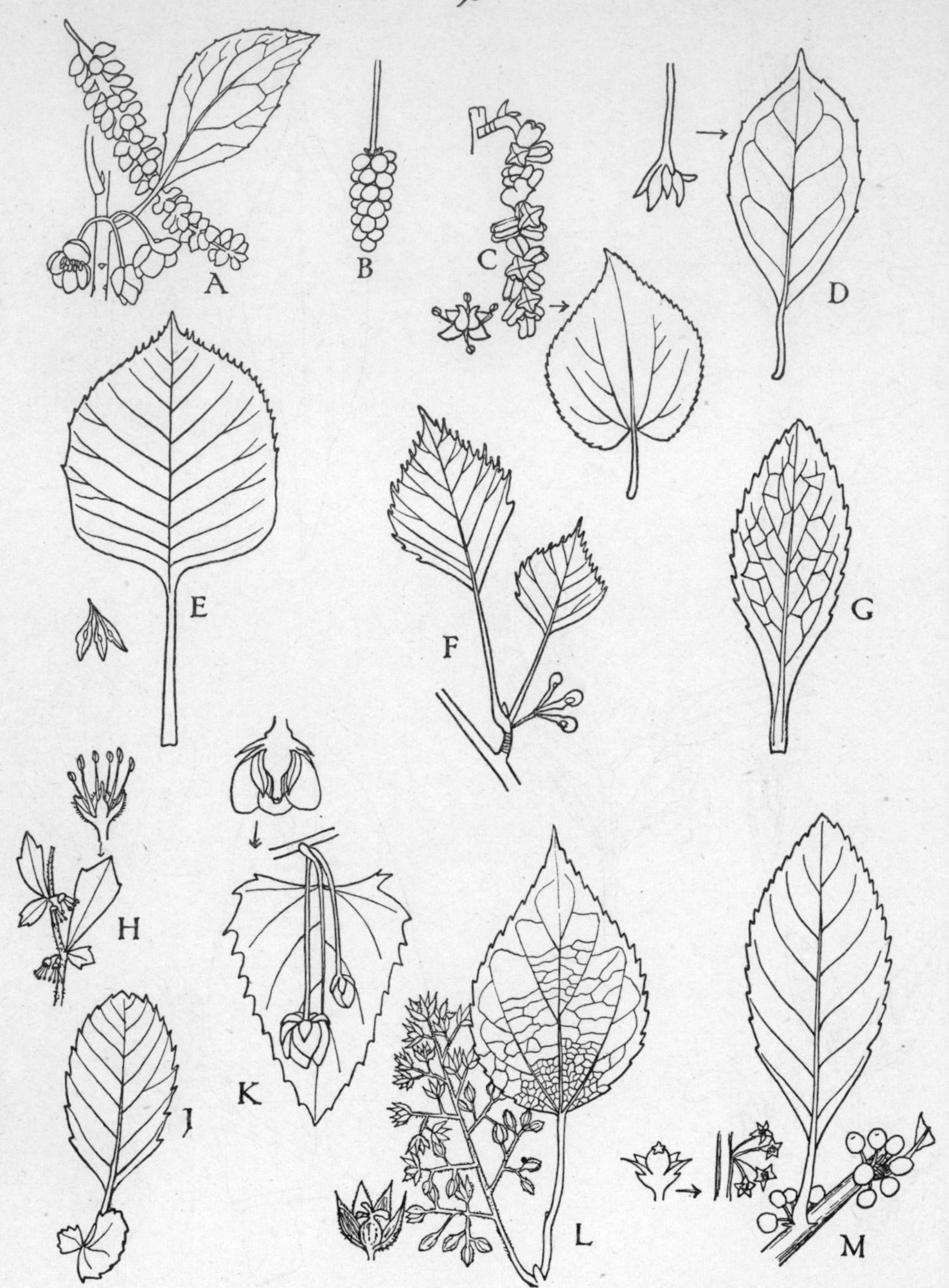

FIG. 78

A. *Schizandra chinensis* (148)
B. Fruits of *S. rubriflora* (149)
C. *Tetracentron sinense* (149)
D. *Kadsura japonica* (148)
E. *Euptelea Franchetii* (149)
F. *E. polyandra* (149)
G. Leaf of *Hymenanthera chathamica* (157)
H. *Azara microphylla* (158)
J. *A. Gilliesii* (158)
K. Strangle Bush, or Coral Barberry, *Berberidopsis corallina* (158)
L. *Poliothyrsis sinensis* (158)
M. *Melicytus ramiflorus* (157)

(Flowers and fruits of C after Hooker, fruits of E after a drawing.)

FIG. 79. DECIDUOUS BARBERRIES

A. *Berberis aetnensis* (151)
B. *B. aggregata* (152)
C. *B. aristata* (151)
D. *B. brachypoda* (151)
E. *B. concinna* (152)
F. *B. dictophylla* (152)
G. *B. diaphana* (152)
H. *B. polyantha* (152)
J. *B. Sieboldii* (152)
K. *B. Thunbergii* (153)
L. *B. Wilsonae* (153)
M. Common Barberry, *B. vulgaris* (152)
N. *B. Vernae* (152)
O. *B. yunnanensis* (153)

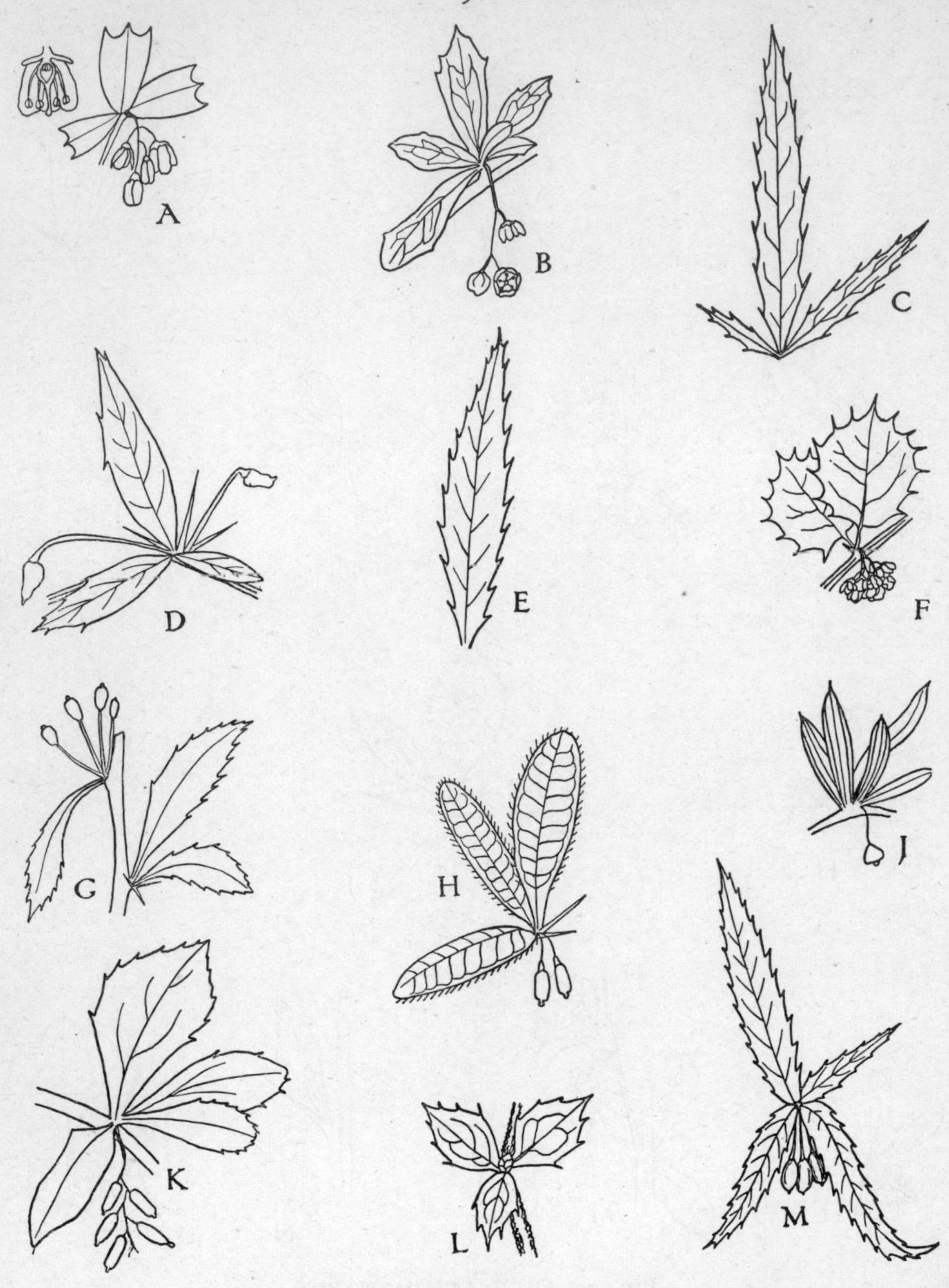

FIG. 80. EVERGREEN BARBERRIES

A. *Berberis Darwinii* (153)
B. *B. Lycium* (153)
C. *B. Gagnepainii* (153)
D. *B. Hookeri* (154
E. *B. insignis* (154)
F. *B. hakeoides* (153)
G. *B. pruinosa* (154)
H. *B. Sargentiana* (154)
J. *B. stenophylla* (153)
K. *B. chitria* (151)
L. *B. verruculosa* (154)
M. *B. Veitchii* (154)

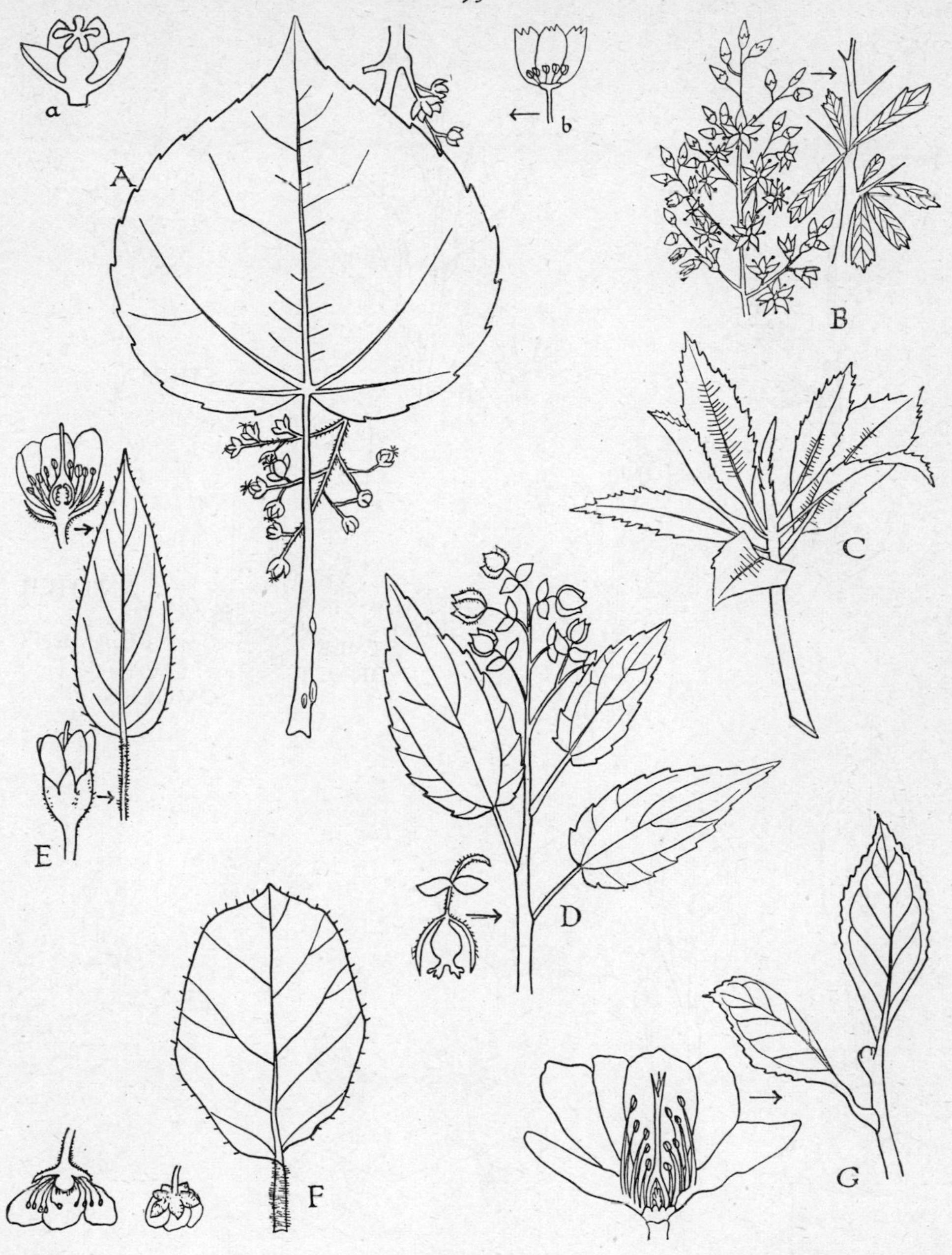

FIG. 81

A. *Idesia polycarpa* (158)
Aa. Ditto, female flower
Ab. Ditto, male flower

B. *Bursaria spinosa* (158)
C. *Pittosporum Dallii* (159)
D. *Carrierea calycina* (158)

E. *Clematoclethra scandens* (162)
F. *Actinidia chinensis* (162)
G. *Camellia japonica* (162)

C

STIGMA

B

A

PETAL
SEPAL
STYLE
BRACT
ANTHER
FILAMENT
OVARY
OVULES

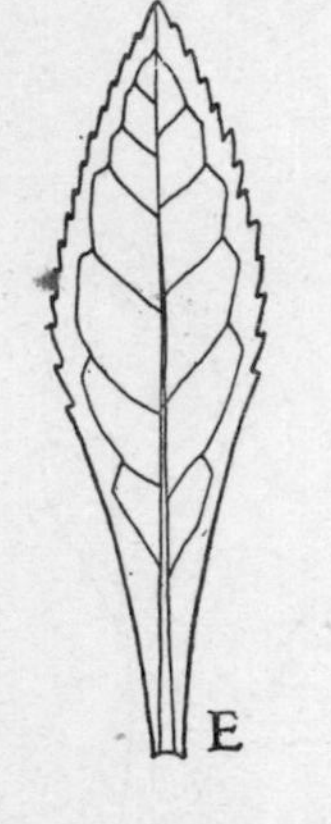

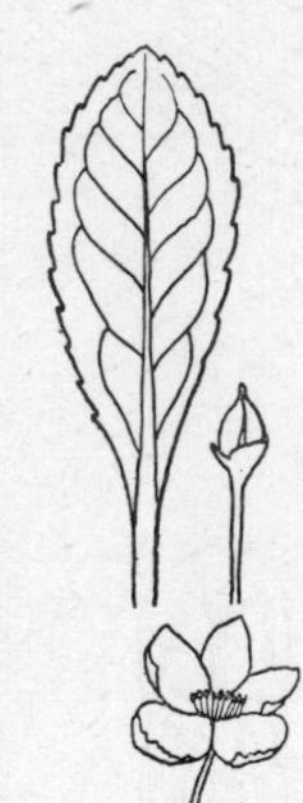

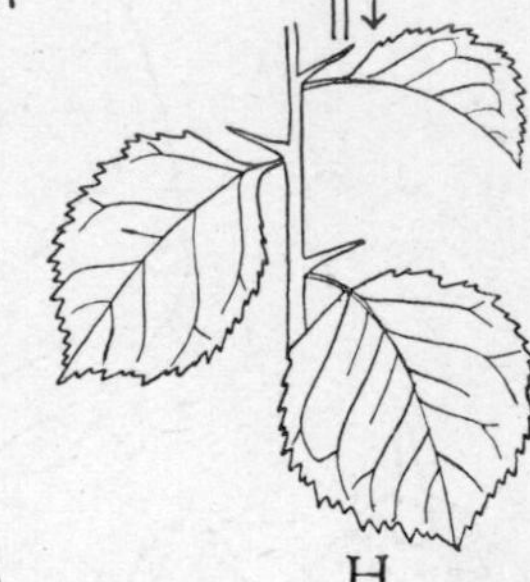

FIG. 82

A. Tea Plant, *Camellia chinensis* (162)
B. *C. Sasanqua* (162)
C. *C. cuspidata* (162)
D. *Eurya japonica* (162)
E. *Gordonia Altamaha* (163)
F. Loblolly Bay, *G. Lasianthus* (163)
G. *G. axillaris* (163)
H. Tung - Ching Tree, *Xylosma racemosa* (158)

(Flowers of A after Wossidlo, E and F after Sargent, G after a photograph, H from Kew Herbarium and after Le Maout and Decaisne.)

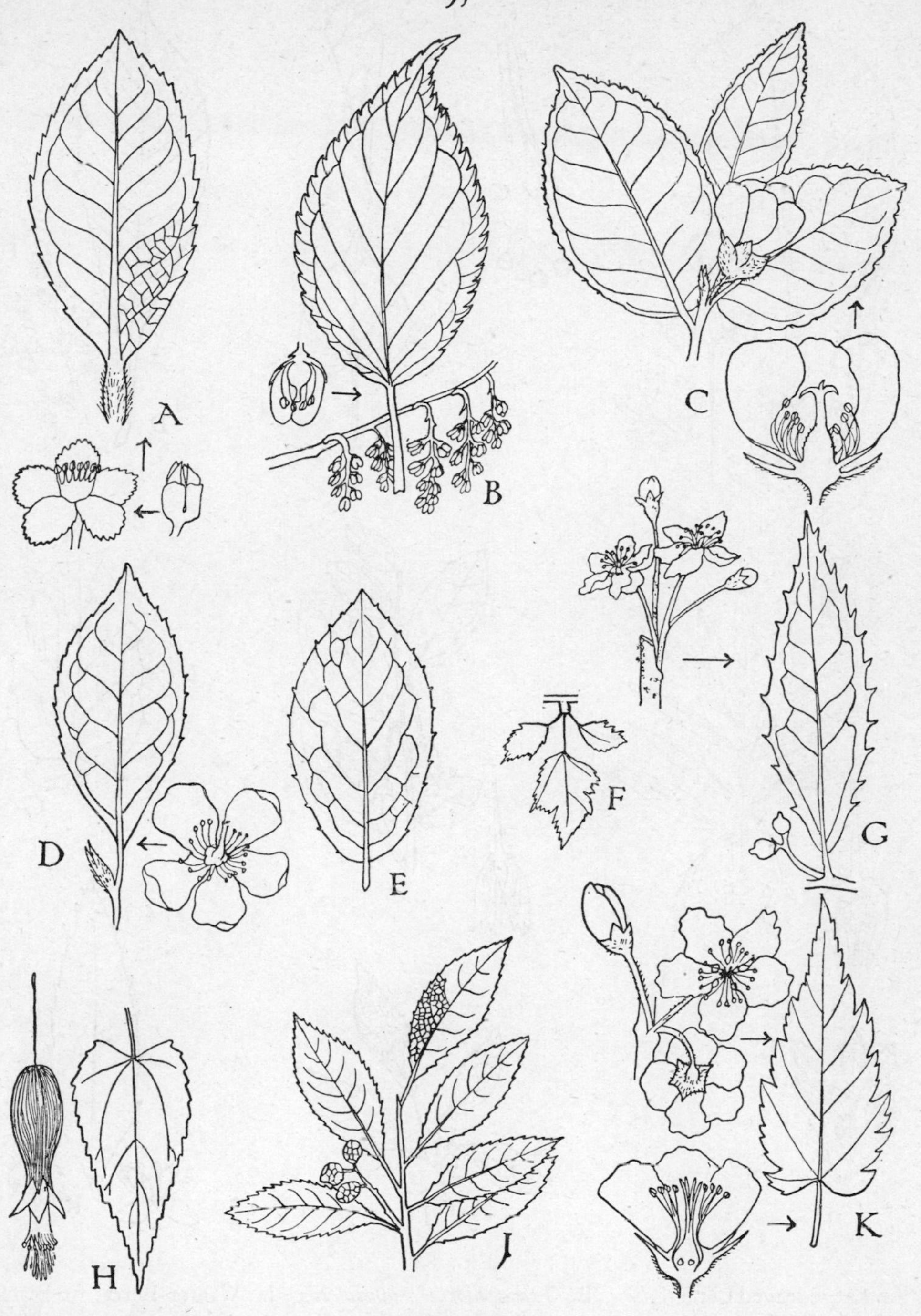

Fig. 83

A. *Hartia sinensis* (163)
B. *Stachyurus chinensis* (163)
C. *Stewartia Pseudocamellia* (163)
D. *S. Malacodendron* (163)
E. *S. pentagyna* (163)
F. *Plagianthus betulinus* (164)
G. *Hoheria populnea* (164)
H. *Abutilon megapotamicum* (164)
J. *Elaeocarpus cyaneus* (165)
K. *Hoheria* (*Plagianthus*) *Lyalli* (164)

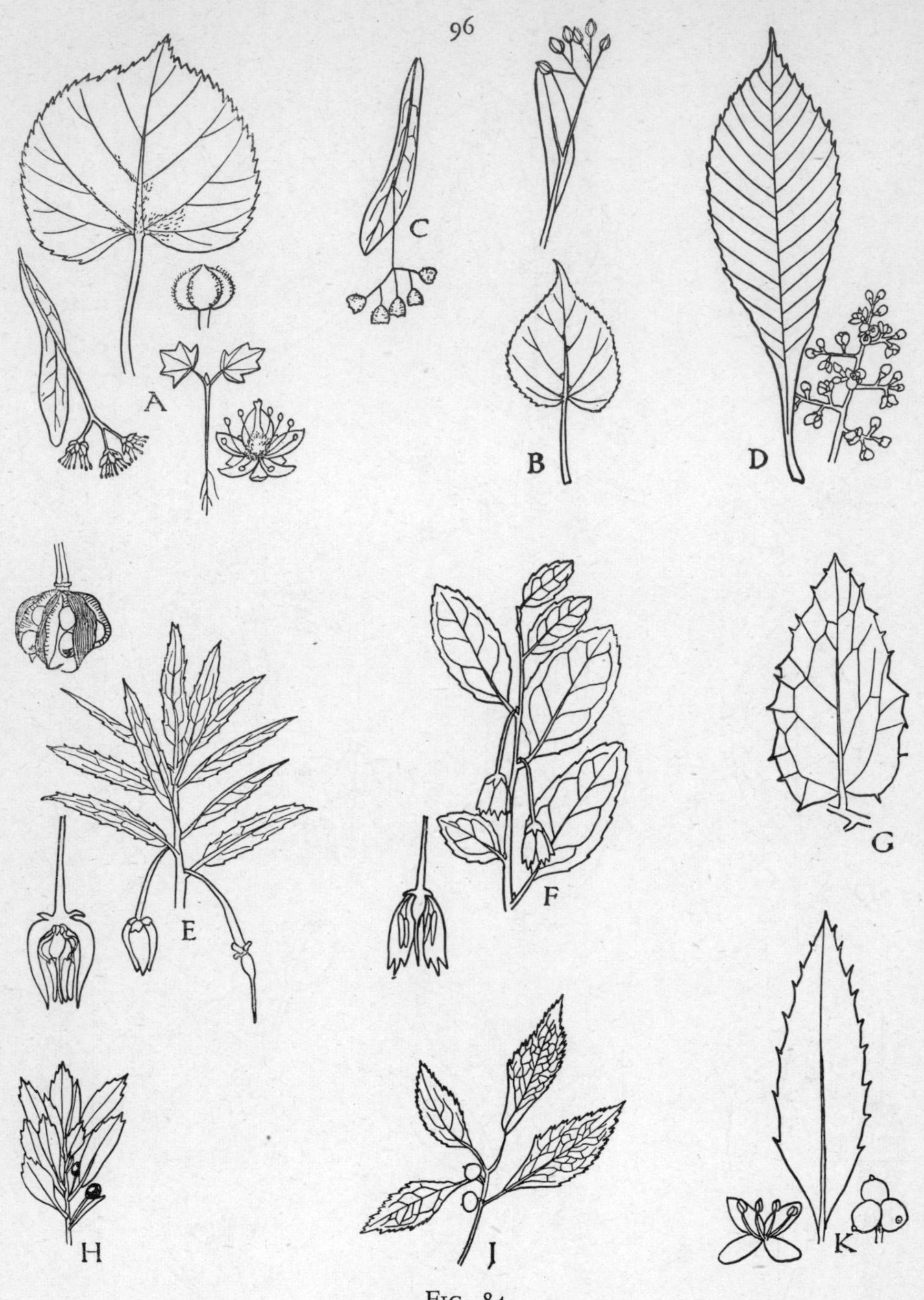

Fig. 84

A. Large-leaved Lime, *Tilia platyphyllos* (165)

B. Small-leaved Lime, *T. cordata* (165)

C. Fruits of Common Lime, *T. vulgaris* (166)

D. *Meliosma cuneifolia* (183)

E. *Tricuspidaria lanceolata* (*Crinodendron Hookerianum*) (166)

F. *T. dependens* (166)

G. *Villaresia mucronata* (169)

H. Inkberry, *Ilex glabra* (169)

J. Winter Berry, or Black Alder, *I. verticillata* (170)

K. Himalayan Holly, *I. dipyrena* (169)

Genus not figured: *Grewia* (165)

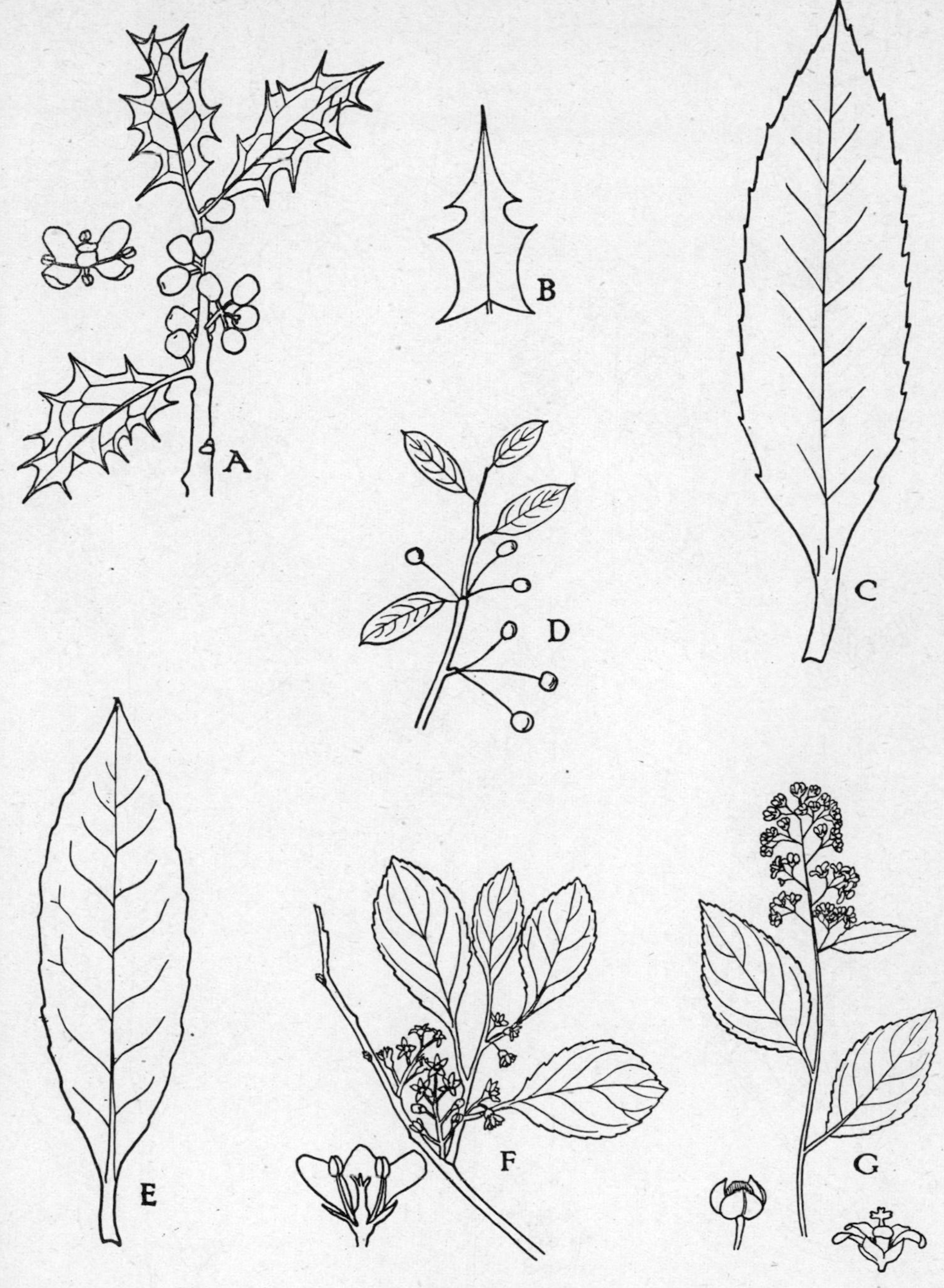

FIG. 85

A. Common Holly, *Ilex Aquifolium* (169)
B. *I. pernyi* (170)
C. Tarajo, *I. latifolia* (170)

D. Mountain Holly, *Nemopanthus mucronatus* (170)

E. *Ilex insignis* (170)

F. *Celastrus articulatus* (171)

G. Staff Tree, or Waxwork, *C. scandens* (171)

FIG. 86

A. *Maytenus chilensis* (172)
B. *Tripterygium Regelii* (172)
C. New Jersey Tea, *Ceanothus americanus* (173)
D. Californian Lilac, *C. thyrsiflorus* (173)
E. *C. dentatus* (173)
F. *C. Veitchianus* (173)
G. *C. Delilianus* (173)
H. Japanese Raisin Tree, *Hovenia dulcis* (174)
J. *Pomaderris elliptica* (174)

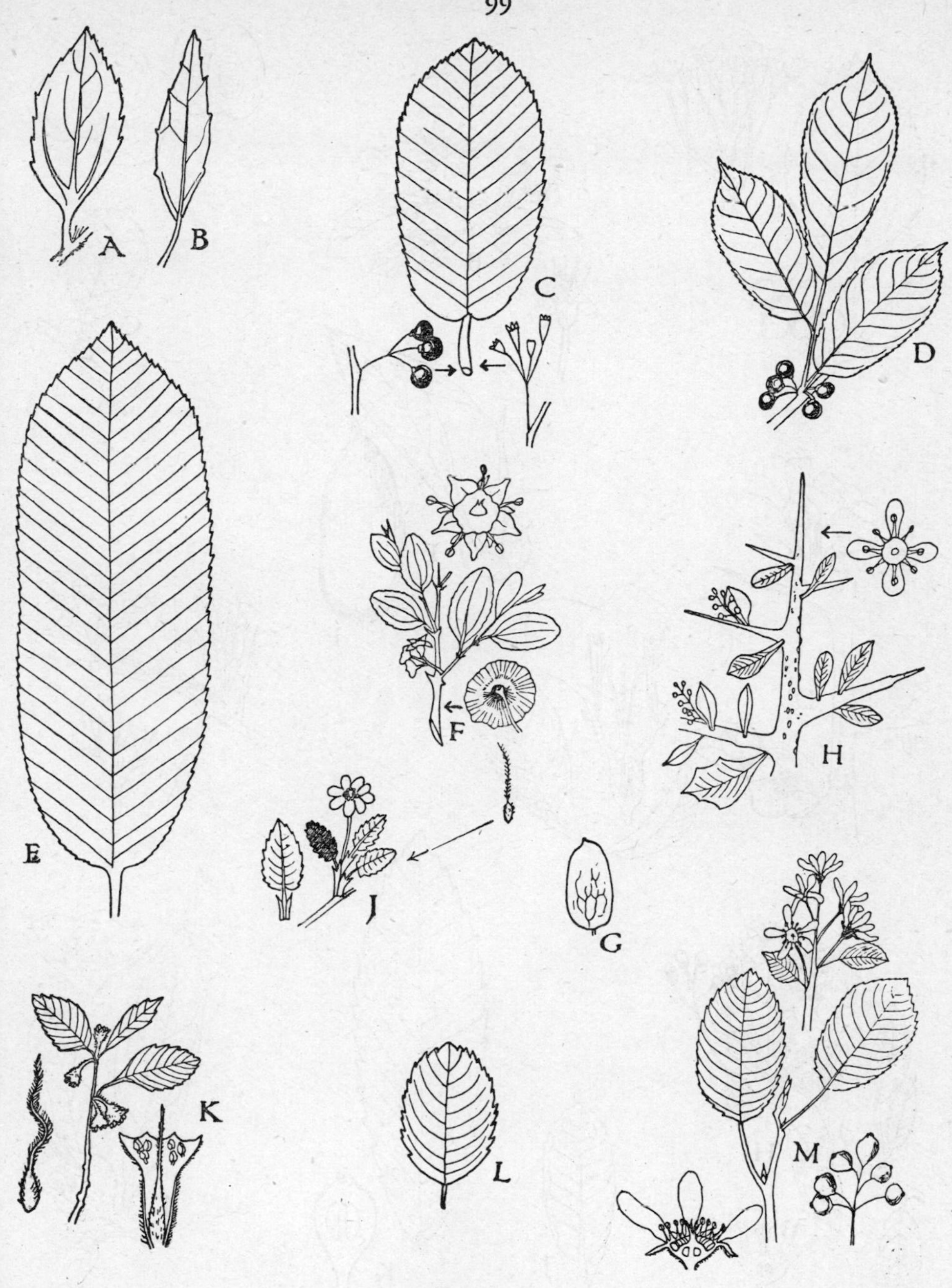

FIG. 87

A. *Rhamnus Alaternus* (174)
B. Ditto, var. *angustifolia* (174)
C. Cascara Sagrada, R. *Purshiana* (174)
D. R. *crenata* (174)
E. R. *imeretina* (174)
F. Christ's Thorn, *Paliurus Spina-Christi* (174)
G. Fruit of Jujube, *Zizyphus jujuba* (175)
H. *Schinus dependens* (184)
J. Mountain Avens, *Dryas octopetala* (198)
K. Mountain Mahogany, *Cercocarpus montanus* (198)
L. Leaf of Snowy Mespilus, *Amelanchier ovalis* (209)
M. June Berry, or Service Berry, *A. canadensis* (208)

FIG. 88

A. Cockspur Thorn, *Crataegus Crus-galli* (212)
B. *Crataegomespilus grandiflora* (211)
C. Dwarf Quince, *Cydonia japonica* (*C. Maulei*) (214)
D. Japonica, *C. lagenaria* (*Pyrus japonica*) (214)
E. *C. cathayensis* (214)
F. Fruit of Chinese Quince, *C. sinensis* (214)
G. *Pyracantha Rogersiana* (218)
H. Firethorn, *P. coccinea* (218)
J. Leaf of *P. Gibbsii* (218)
K. Loquat, *Eriobotrya japonica* (214)
L. Medlar, *Mespilus germanica* (217)

FIG. 89

A. *Raphiolepis umbellata* (219)

B. *Stranvaesia Nussia* (220)

C. Chinese Hawthorn, *Photinia serrulata* (217)

D. *P. villosa* (*Pourthiaea arguta*) (217)

E. Toyon, or Tollon, *P.* (*Heteromeles*) *arbutifolia* (217)

F. Leaf of *P. Davidsoniae* (217)

G. Jew's Mallow, *Kerria japonica* (198)

H. *Exochorda Korolkowii* (195)

FIG. 90

A. Cherry Laurel, *Prunus Laurocerasus* (205)

B. Portugal Laurel, *P. lusitanica* (205)

C. Bird Cherry, *P. Padus* (205)

D. American Wild Red Cherry, *P. pennsylvanica* (206)

E. Rum Cherry. *P. serotina* (205)

F. Diagram of a raceme

(D and E after Sargent.)

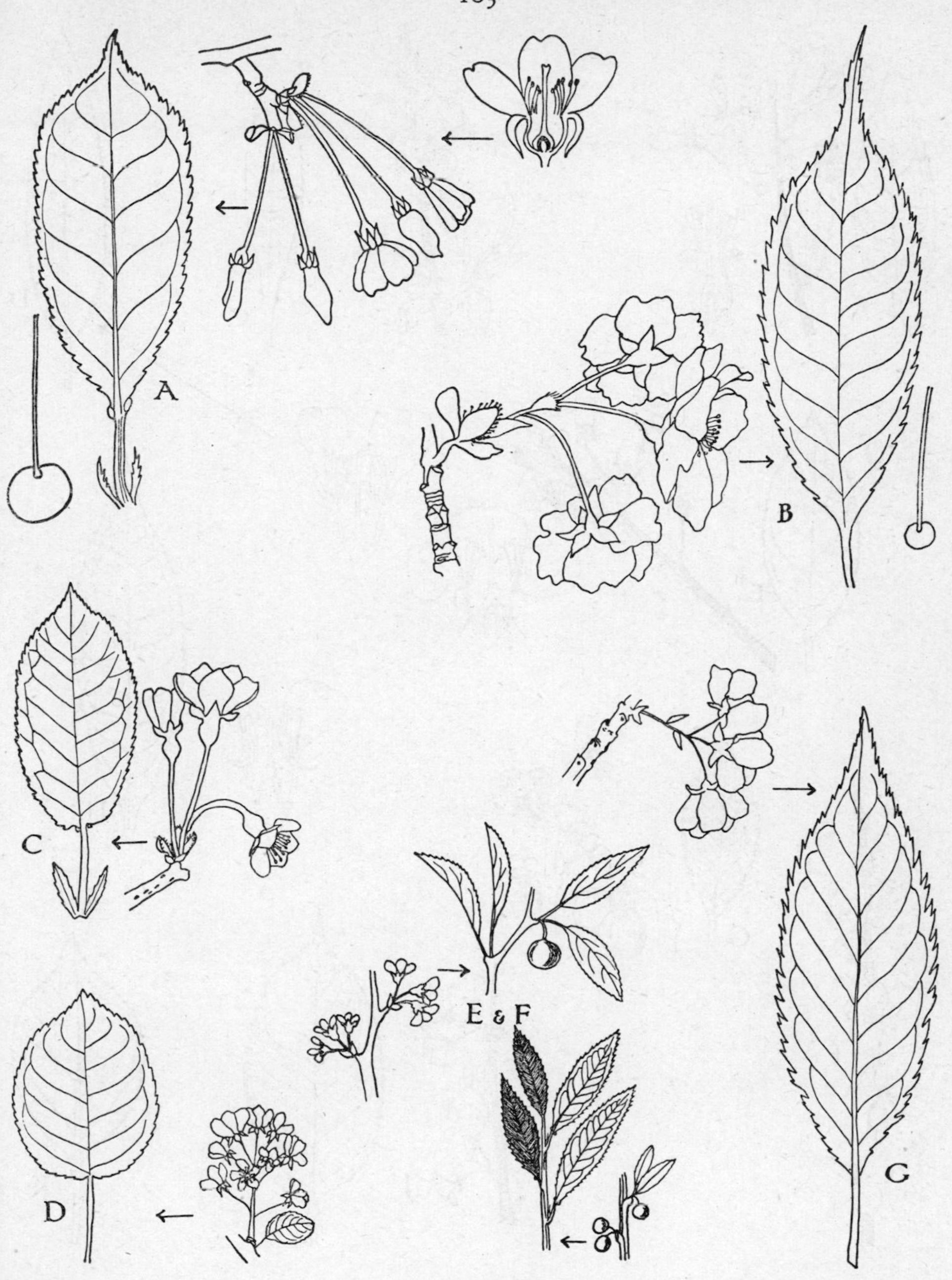

Fig. 91

A. Wild Cherry, Gean, or Mazzard, *Prunus avium* (206)

B. Japanese Double-flowered Cherry, *P. serrulata*, var. *flore pleno* (207)

C. Wild Dwarf Cherry, *P. Cerasus* (206)

D. St. Lucie Cherry, *P. Mahaleb* (206)

E. Mountain Cherry, or Chickasaw Plum, *P. angustifolia* (205)

F. Willow Cherry, *P. incana* (206)

G. *P. Lannesiana* (206)

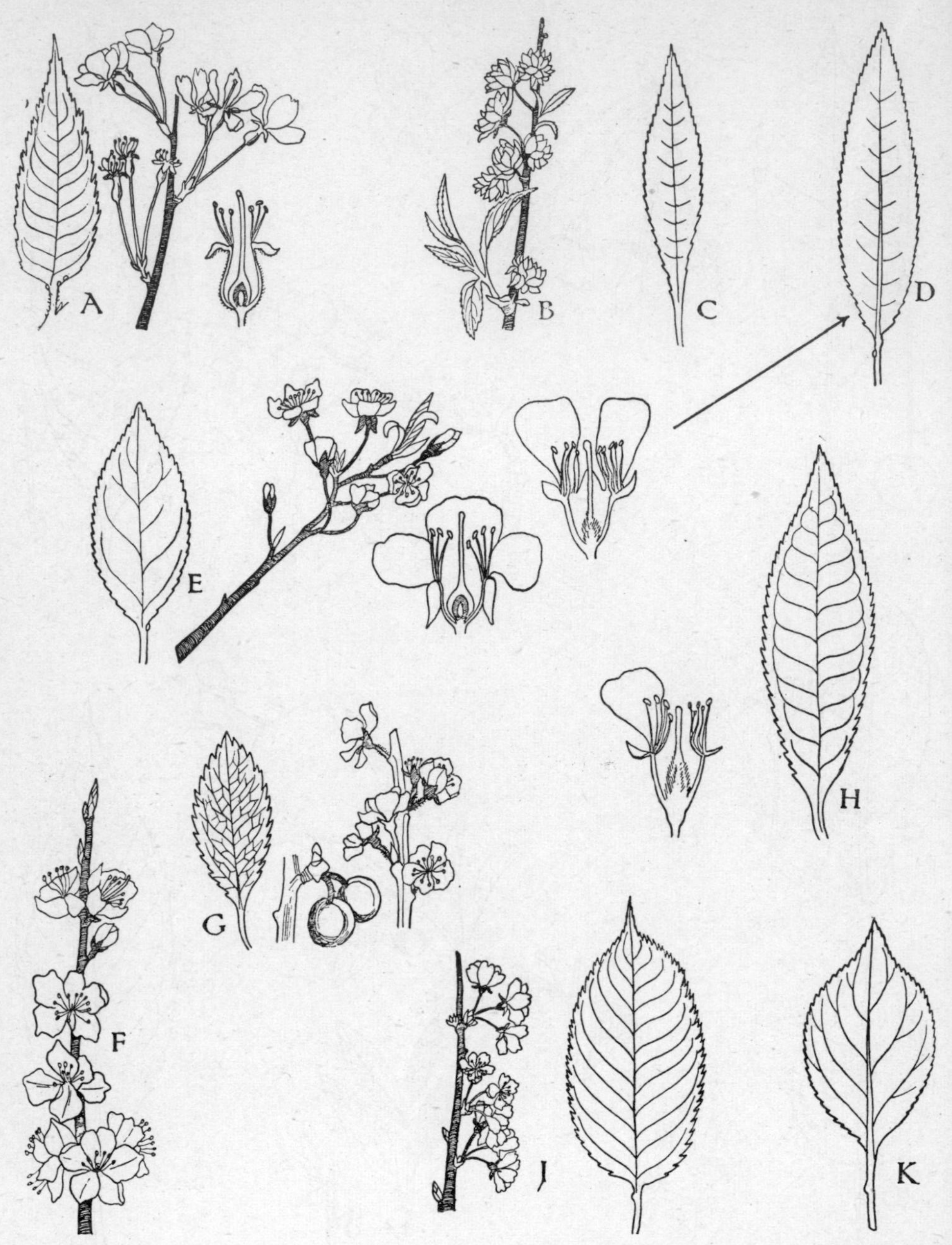

FIG. 92

A. Rosebud Cherry, *Prunus subhirtella* (207)
B. *P. glandulosa* (206)
C. Leaf of Dwarf Russian Almond, *P.* (*Amygdalus*) *nana* (208)
D. Almond, *P. communis* (207)
E. Cherry Plum, or Myrobolan, *P. cerasifera* (207)
F. *P. Davidiana* (207)
G. Bullace, *P. insititia* (208)
H. Peach, *P. Persica* (208)
J. *P. Conradinae* (206)
K. Leaf of Apricot, *P. Armeniaca* (207)

(F after Robinson, G after Butcher and Strudwick.)

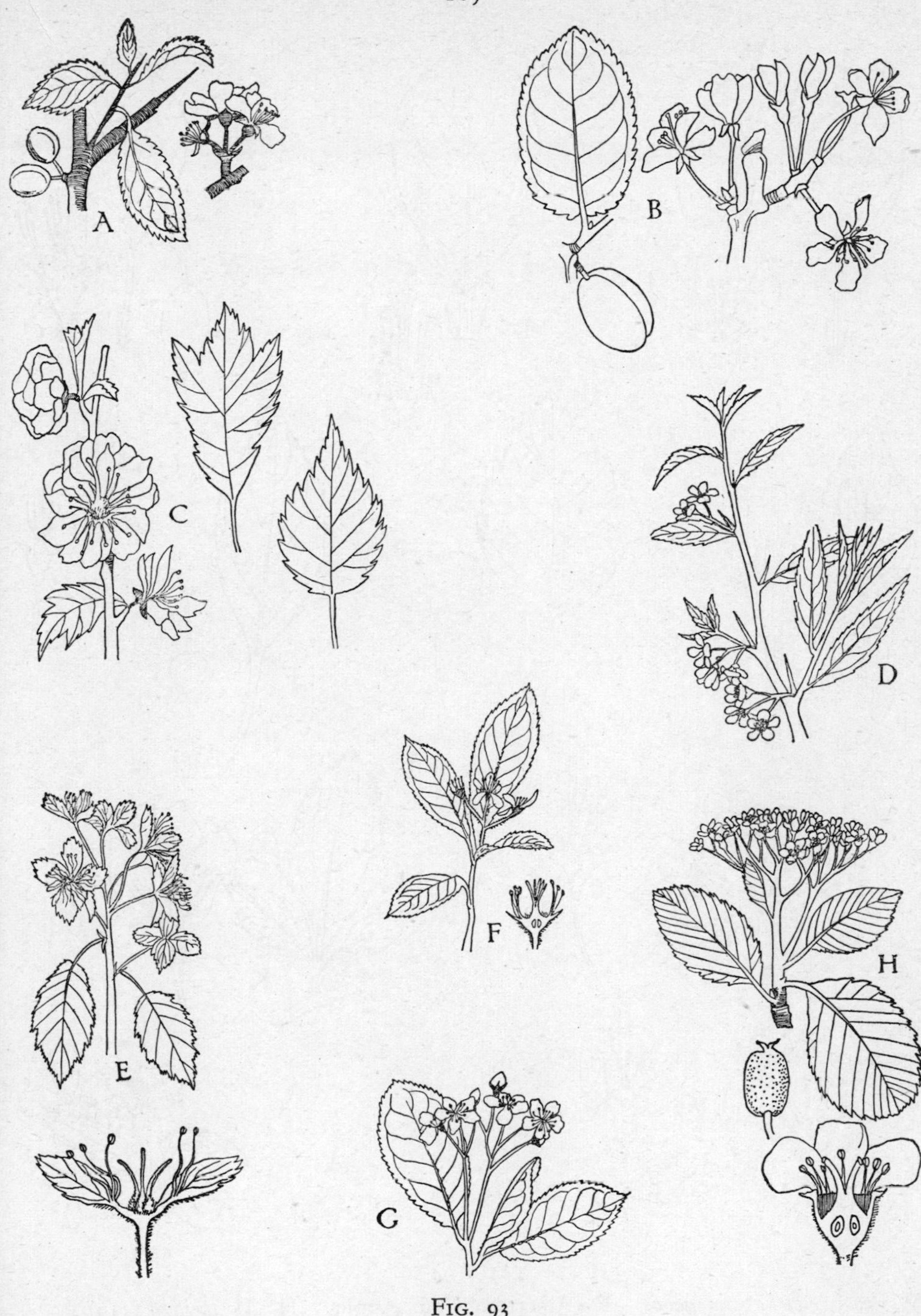

FIG. 93

A. Sloe, or Blackthorn, *Prunus spinosa* (208)

B. Plum, *P. domestica* (207)

C. *P. triloba* (208)

D. *Prinsepia utilis* (205)

E. Snow-in-Summer, *Neviusa alabamensis* (198)

F. Chokeberry, *Aronia arbutifolia* (209)

G. Black Chokeberry, *A. melanocarpa* (209)

H. White Beam, *Sorbus Aria* (219)

Genus not figured: *Peraphyllum* (217)

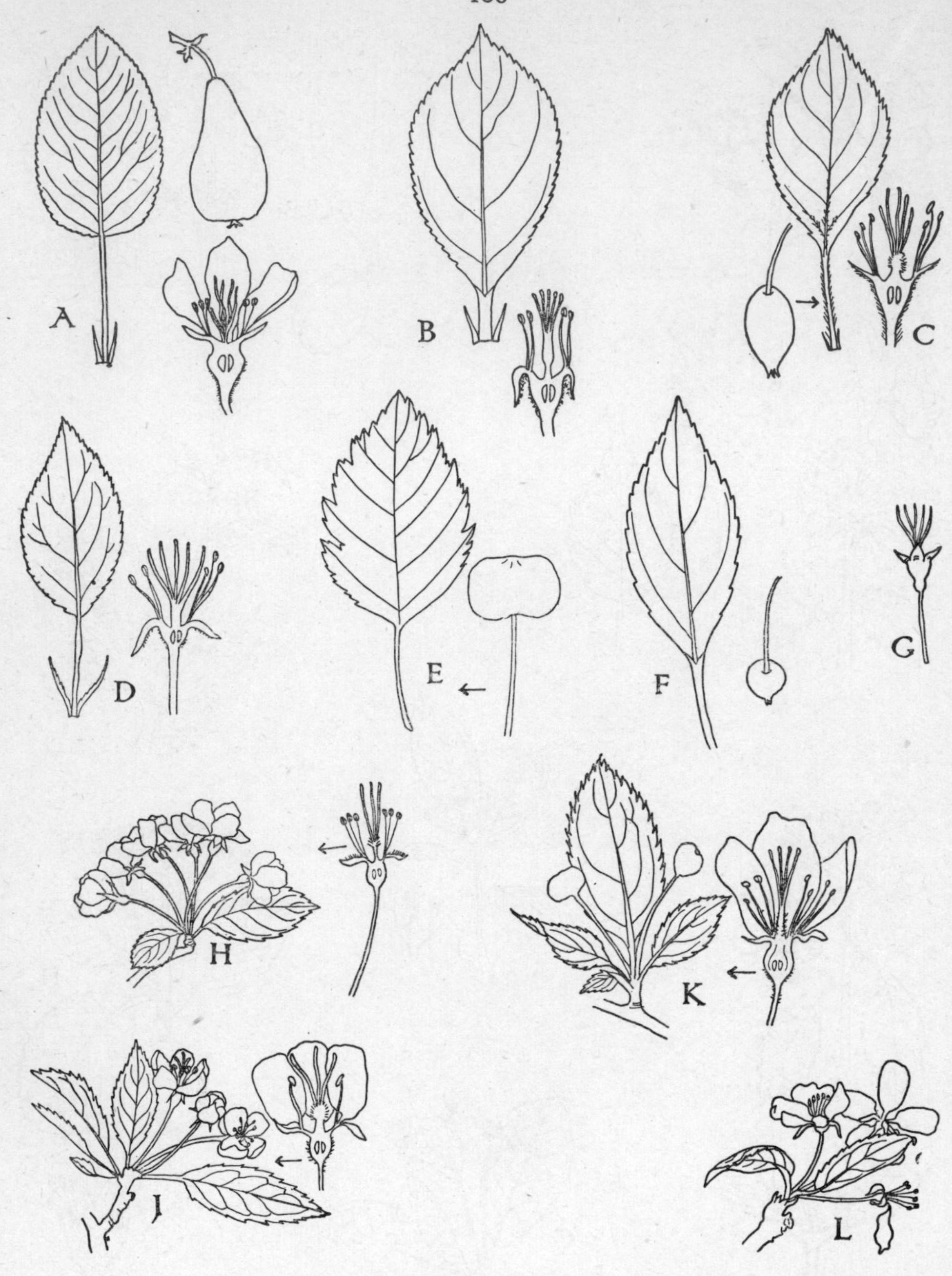

FIG. 94

A. Pear, *Pyrus communis* (218)
B. Wild Crab Apple, *Malus pumila* (215)
C. *M. Eleyi* (215)
D. Siberian Crab Apple, *M. baccata* (214)
E. American Crab Apple, *M. coronaria* (216)
F. *M. purpurea* (215)
G. Flower of *M. Halliana* (215) after petals and sepals have fallen off
H. *M. theifera* (216)
J. *M. Sargentii* (216)
K. Japanese Crab Apple, *M. floribunda* (216)
L. *M. Sieboldii* (*Toringo*) (216)

FIG. 95

A. *Spiraea arguta* (196)
B. *S. canescens* (196)
C. Leaf of *S. crenata* (196)
D. Leaf of *S. Douglasii* (196) (flowers similar to E)
E. *S. Menziesii* (196)
F. Steeplebush, or Hardhack, *S. tomentosa* (196)
G. *S. Veitchii* (197)
H. Bridewort, *S. salicifolia* (196)
(H after Fitch and Smith.)
J. *S. japonica* (196)
K. *S. prunifolia* (197)
L. *S. media* (197)
M. *S. bella* (195)
N. *S. Van Houttei* (197)

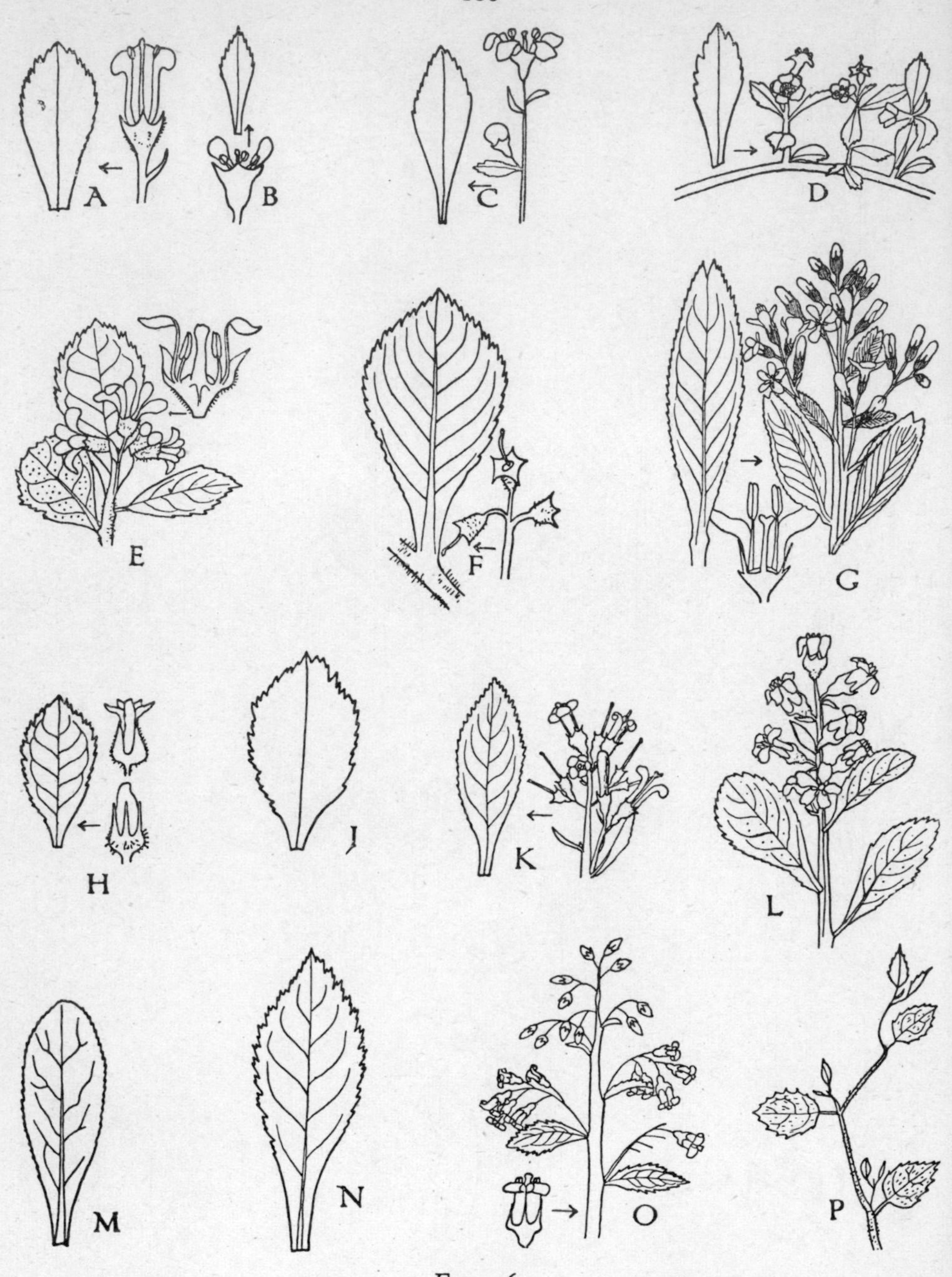

FIG. 96

A. *Escallonia exoniensis* (222)
B. *E. virgata* (223)
C. *E. edinensis* (223)
D. *E. langleyensis* (223)
E. *E. Ingrami* (223)
F. *E. macrantha* (223)
G. *E. montevidensis* (223)
H. *E. rubra* (223)
J. *E. revoluta* (222)
K. *E. illinita* (222)
L. *E. Iveyi* (222)
M. *E. viscosa* (223)
N. *E. pulverulenta* (223)
O. *E. pteroclador* (222)
P. *Carpodetus serratus* (221)

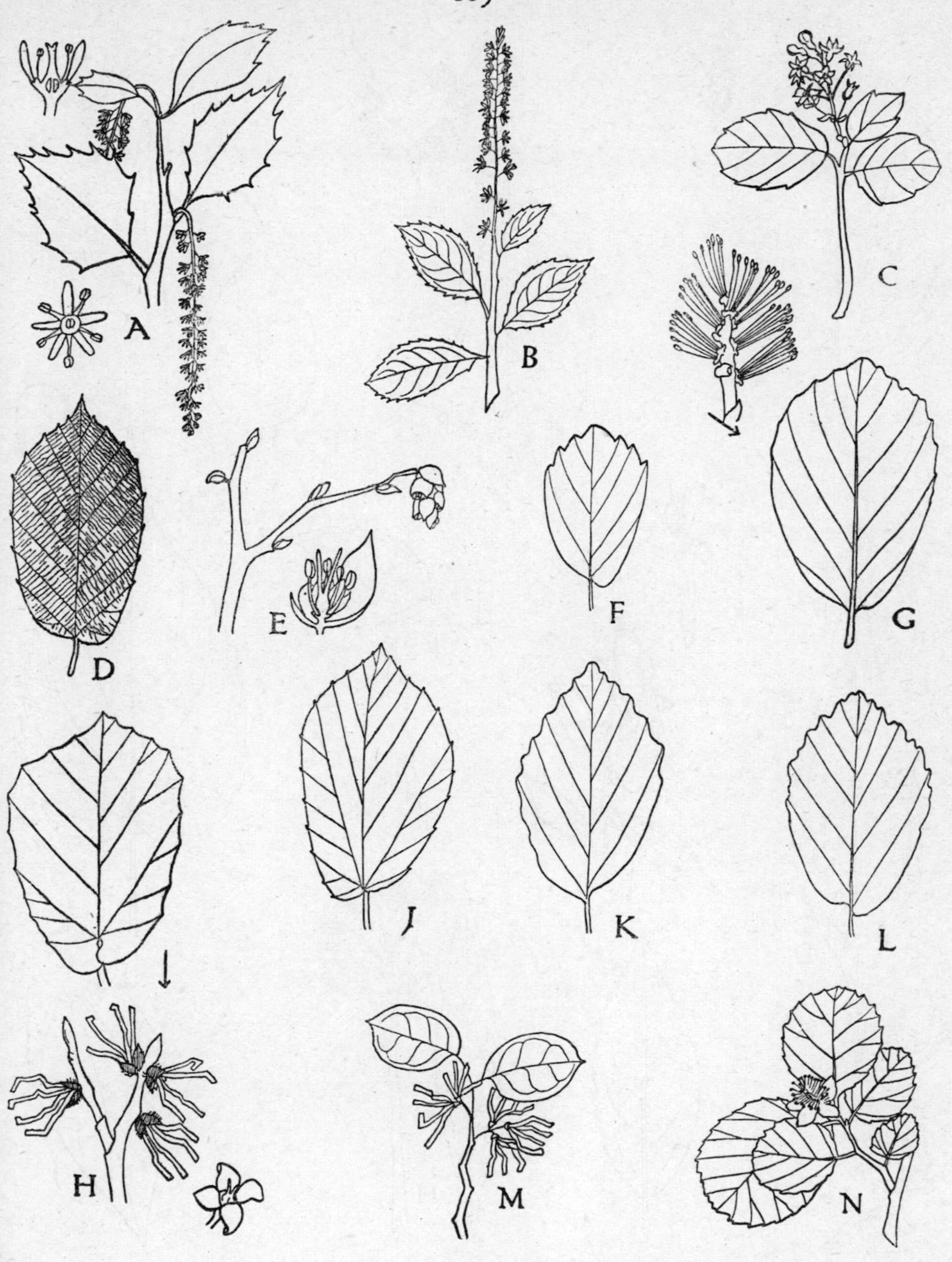

FIG. 97

A. *Itea ilicifolia* (225)
B. *I. virginica* (225)
C. *Ribes viburnifolium* (229)
D. Leaf of *Corylopsis Willmottiae* (229)
E. Flowering twig of *C. spicata* (229)
F. Leaf of *Fothergilla Gardenii* (230)
G. *F. major* (230)
H. Chinese Witch Hazel, *Hamamelis mollis* (230)
J. Leaf of Japanese Witch Hazel, *H. japonica* (230)
K. *H. vernalis* (230)
L. Virginian Witch Hazel, *H. virginiana* (230)
M. *Loropetalum chinense* (231)
N. *Parrotiopsis* (*Parrotia*) *Jacquemontiana* (231)

(N after Brandis.)

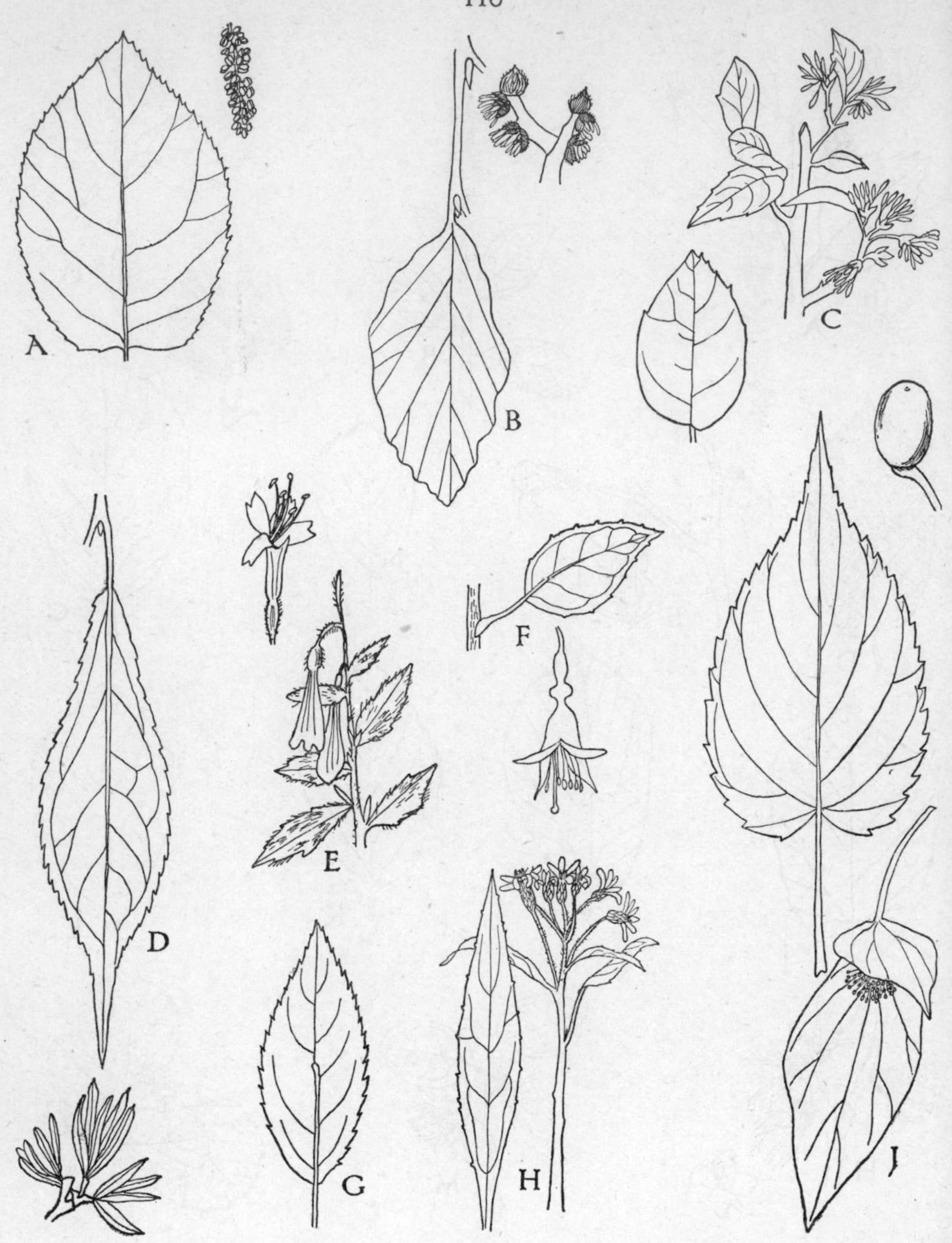

FIG. 98

A. *Sinowilsonia Henryi* (231)
B. Iron Tree, *Parrotia persica* (231)
C. *Sycopsis sinensis* (231)
D. Gutta-percha Tree, *Eucommia ulmoides* (231)
E. Californian Fuchsia, *Zauschneria californica* (234)
F. *Fuchsia excorticata* (234)
G. Leaf of *Helwingia japonica* (238)
H. *Microglossa albescens* (253)
J. Bract Tree, *Davidia Vilmoriniana* (238)

Genus not figured: *Fortunearia* (230)

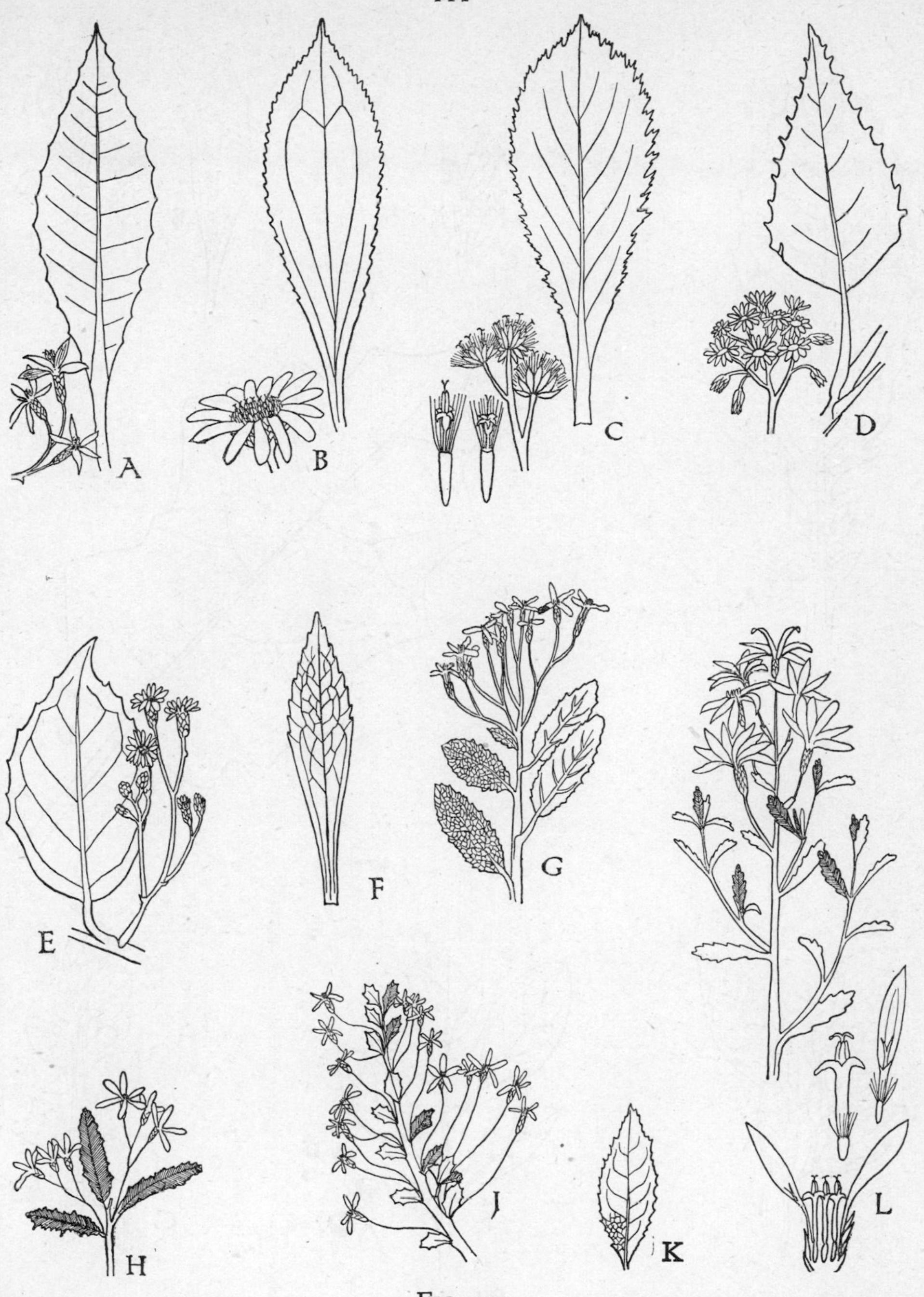

FIG. 99

A. *Olearia argophylla* (254)
B. *O. chathamica* (254)
C. *O. Colensoi* (254)
D. *O. macrodonta* (254)

E. *O. nitida* (254)
F. Leaf of *O. semidentata* (255)
G. *O. speciosa* (255)

H–K. Three forms of *O. erubescens* (254)
L. *O. Gunniana* (*O. stellulata*) (254)

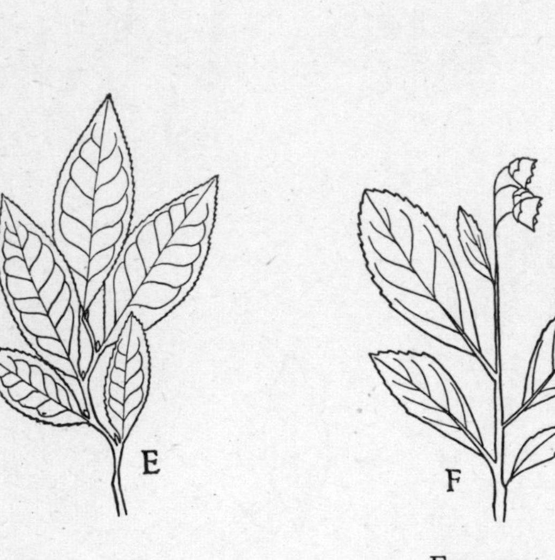

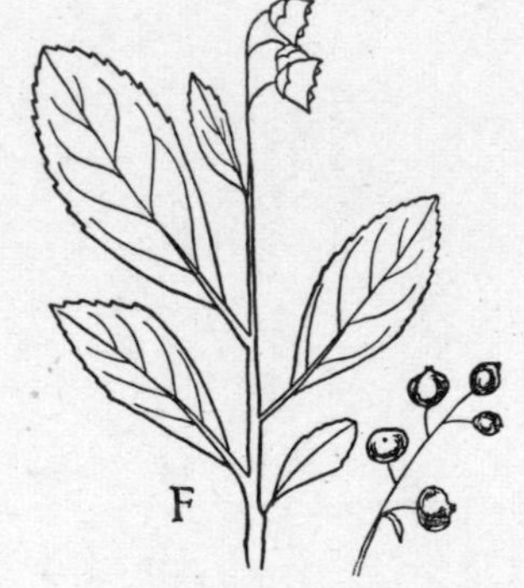

FIG. 100

A. Leaf of *Senecio Hectori* (253)
B. Groundsel Tree, *Baccharis halimifolia* (253)
C. *B. patagonica* (253)
D. Leaf of *Brachyglottis repanda* (252)

E. Shoot of Box Huckleberry, *Gaylussacia brachycera* (256)
F. Farkleberry, *Vaccinium arboreum* (257)
(F after Sargent.)

G. Whortleberry, or Bilberry, *V. Myrtillus* (257)

Genus not figured: *Grindelia* (253)

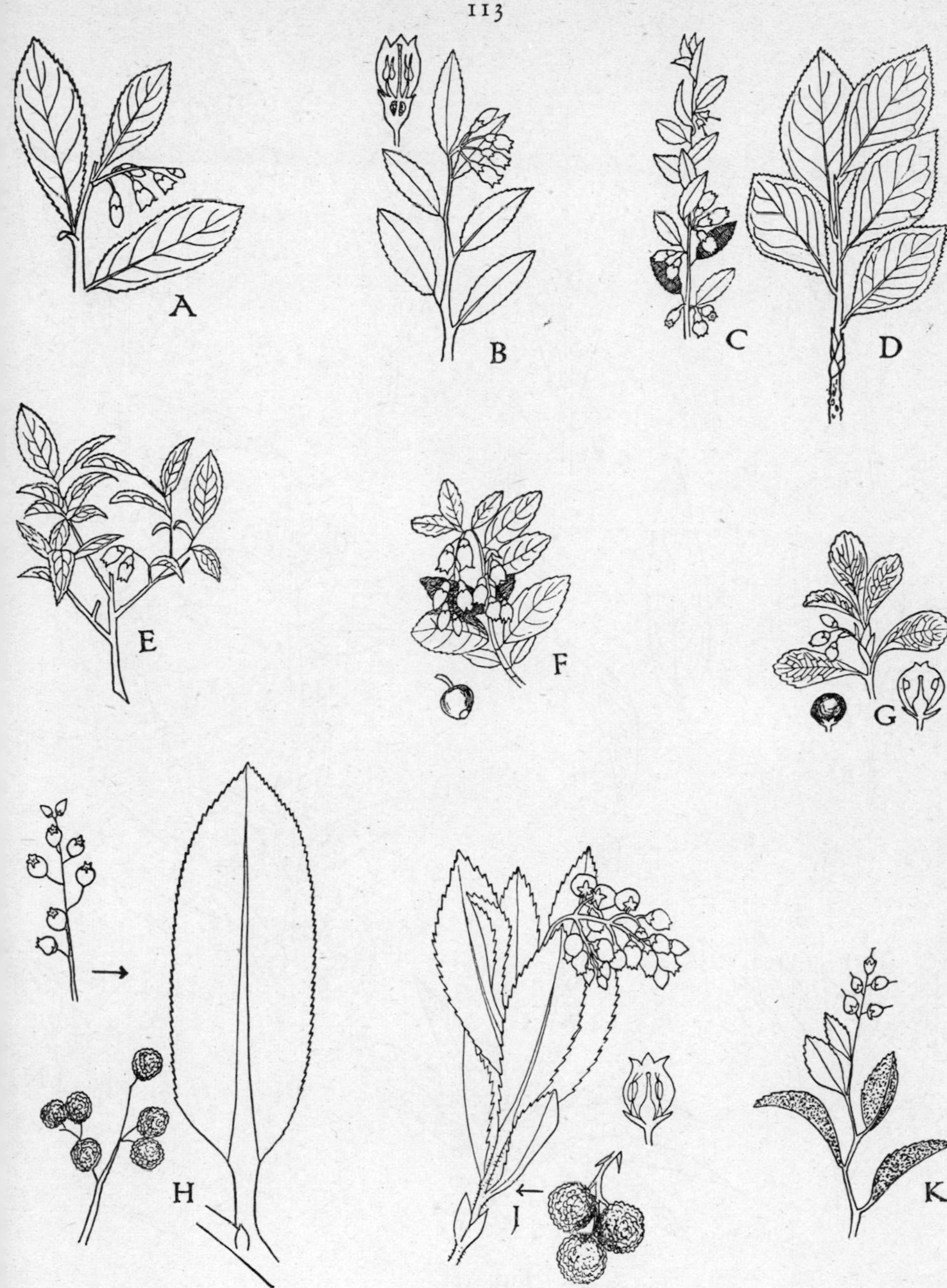

FIG. 101

A. Caucasian Whortleberry, *Vaccinium Arctostaphylos* (257).
B. *V. ovatum* (258)
C. Mortina, *V. Mortinia* (258)
D. *V. glauco-album* (258)
E. Low Blueberry, *V. pennsylvanicum* (257)
F. Cowberry, *V. Vitis-idaea* (258)
G. Black Bearberry, *Arctous alpinus* (259)
H. Madrona, *Arbutus Menziesii* (258)
J. Strawberry Tree, *A. Unedo* (258)
K. Leather Leaf, *Cassandra calyculata* (259)

(G after Butcher and Strudwick.)

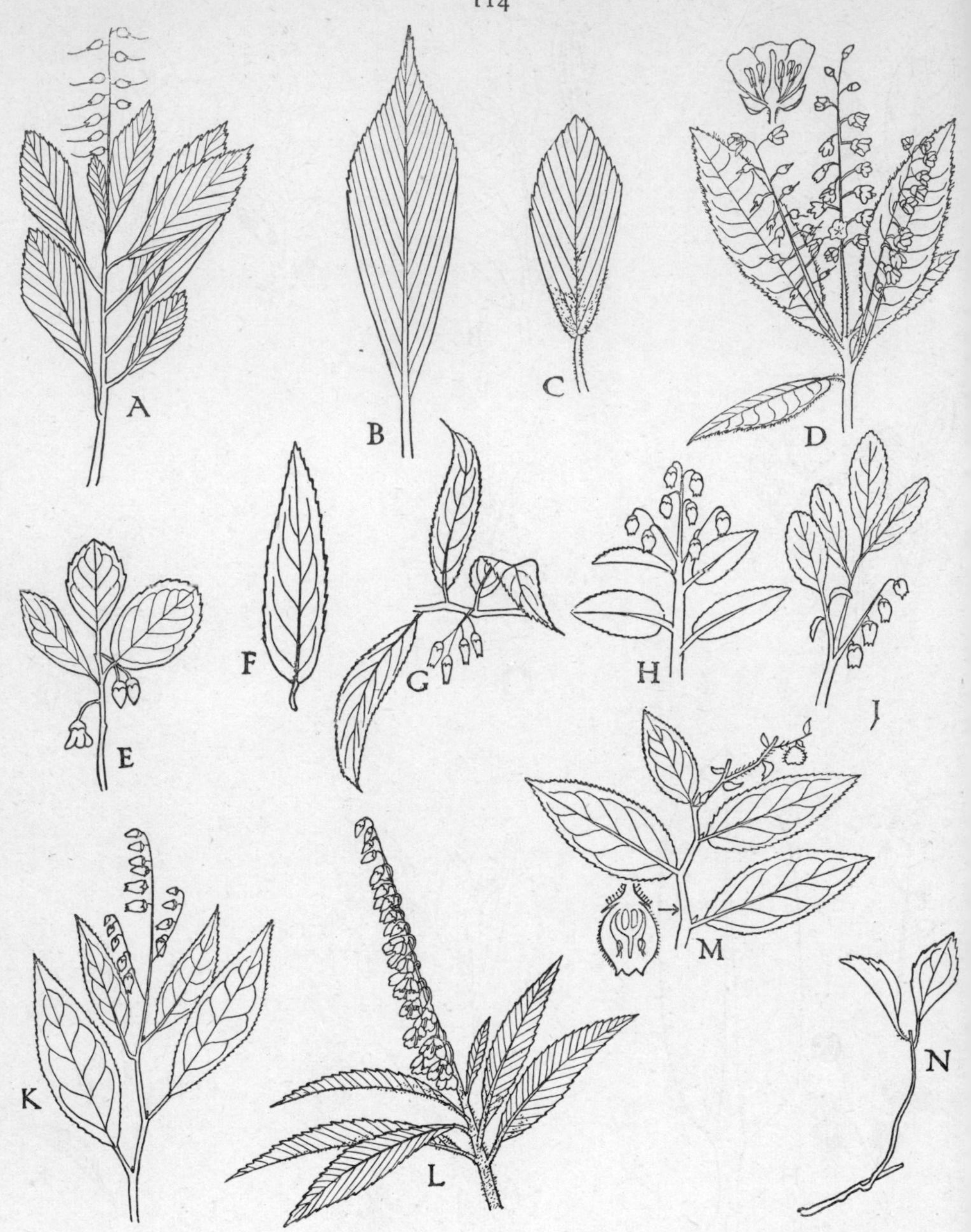

FIG. 102

A. Sweet Peppermint, *Clethra alnifolia* (260)

B. White Alder, *C. acuminata* (260)

C. *C. tomentosa* (260)

D. Lily-of-the-Valley Tree, *C. arborea* (260)

E. May Flower, *Epigaea repens* (261)

F. Leaf of *Leucothoe axillaris* (263)

G. *L. Catesbaei* (263)

H. *L. Davisiae* (263)

J. *L. racemosa* (263)

K. *Oxydendron arboreum* (264)

L. *Clethra Delavayi* (260)

M. Shallon, *Gaultheria Shallon* (262)

N. Shoot of Creeping Wintergreen, *G. procumbens* (262)

(G–J after Bean, L after a photograph.)

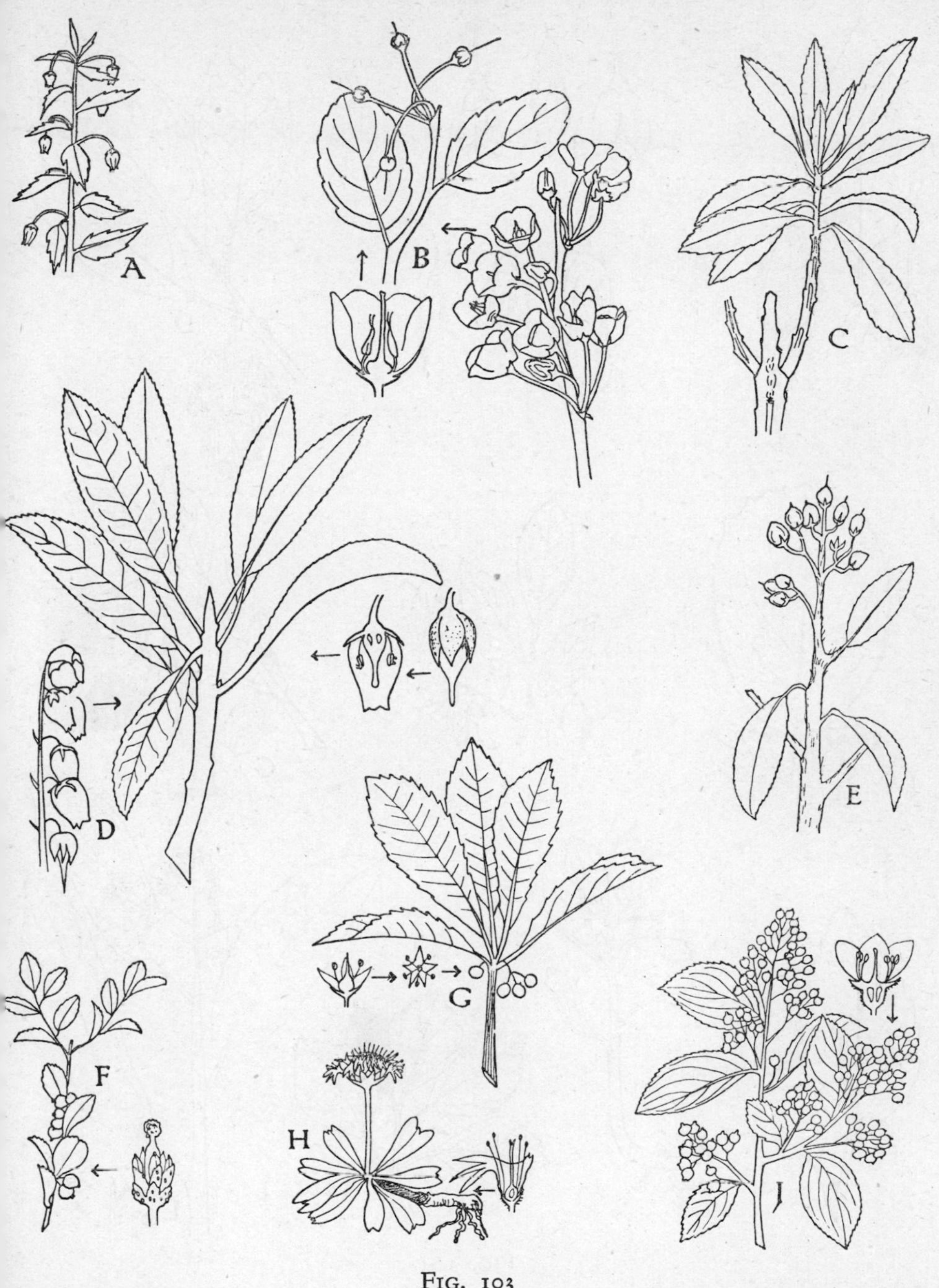

FIG. 103

A. Prickly Heath, *Pernettya mucronata* (264)
B. *Zenobia pulverulenta* (270)
C. *Pieris japonica* (265)
D. *P. formosa* (265)
E. *P. floribunda* (265)
F. *Myrsine africana* (272)
G. *Ardisia japonica* (271)
H. Globe Daisy, *Globularia cordifolia* (288)
J. *Symplocos paniculata* (273)

(J after Collett.)

FIG. 104

A. Snowdrop Tree, or Silver Bell Tree, *Halesia carolina* (272)
B. *H. diptera* (273)
C. *H. monticola* (273)
D. Epaulette Tree, *Pterostyrax hispida* (273)
E. *Styrax Obassia* (273)
F. American Storax, *S. americana* (273)
G. *S. japonica* (273)
H. Leaf of *Lomatia obliqua* (295)
J. Mountain Spurge, *Pachysandra terminalis* (299)
K. Alleghany Spurge, *P. procumbens* (299)
L. *Ehretia thyrsiflora* (283)

Genus not figured: *Sinoiackia* (273)

(Fruits of B and C after Sargent.)

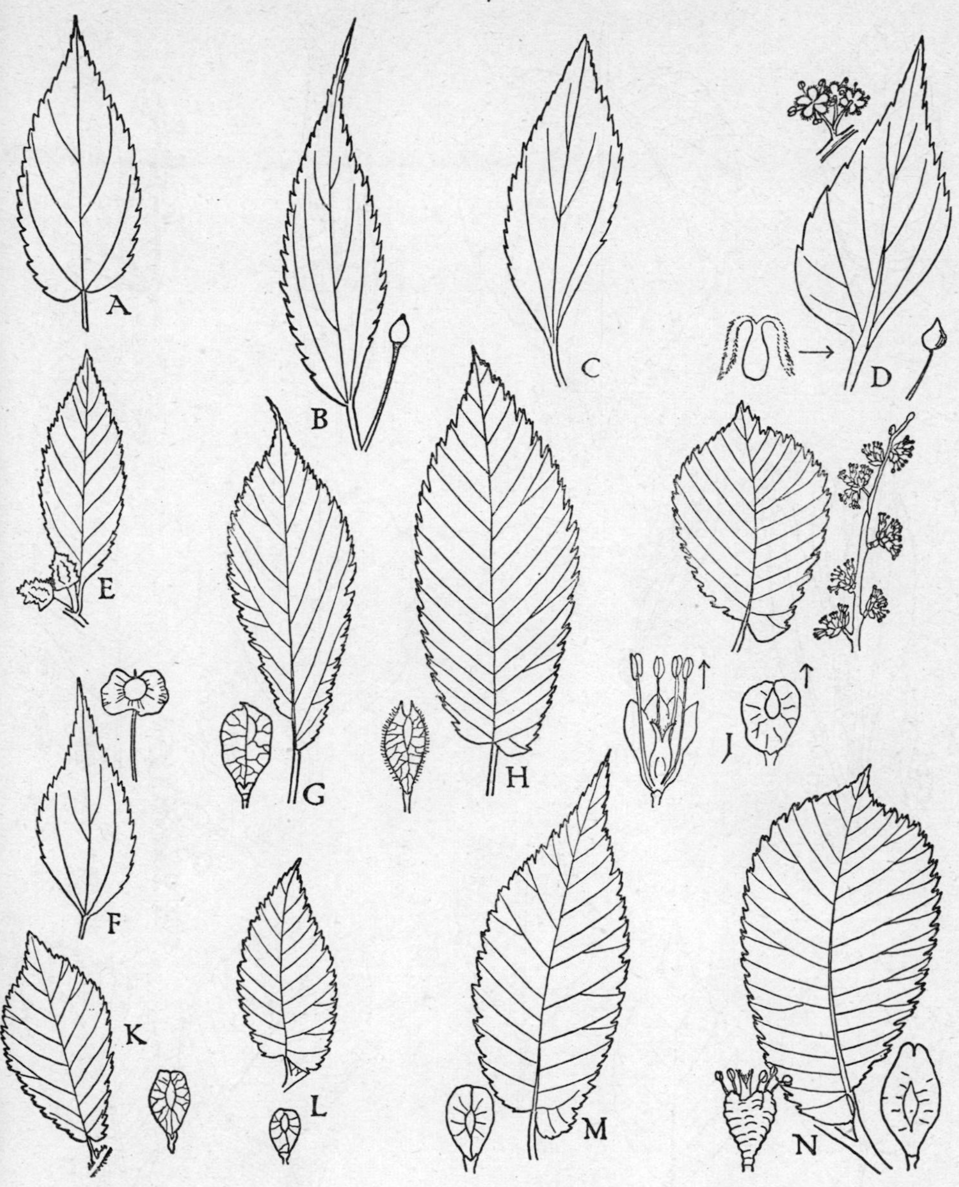

FIG. 105

A. *Aphananthe aspera* (300)
B–D. Nettle Trees:
- B. *Celtis australis* (300)
- C. *C. caucasica* (300)
- D. Sugarberry, or Hackberry, *C. occidentalis* (300)

E. Water Elm, *Planera aquatica* (300)
F. *Pteroceltis Tatarinowii* (300)
G. Smooth-leaved or Feathered Elm, *Ulmus nitens* (301)
H. American or White Elm, *U. americana* (301)
J. Common English Elm, *U. procera* (302)
K. Cornish Elm, *U. stricta* (301)
L. East Anglian or Lock Elm, *U. minor* (302)
M. Huntingdon or Chichester Elm, *U. vegeta* (302)
N. Wych Elm, *U. glabra* (301)

(H after Sargent, G and K–M after Moss and Hunnybun.)

FIG. 106

A. *Zelkova carpinifolia* (302)

B. Common Mulberry, *Morus nigra* (303) (for flowers and fruits see Fig. 28 F)

C. *Debregeasia longifolia* (303)

D. Sweet Gale, or Bog Myrtle, *Myrica Gale* (305)

E. Californian Wax Myrtle, *M. californica* (305)

F. Wax Myrtle, *M. cerifera* (305)

G. Common Alder, *Alnus glutinosa* (306)

H. Italian Alder, *A. cordata* (306)

J. Himalayan Alder, *A. nitida* (307)

K. Grey Alder, *A. incana* (306)

L. Oregon Alder, *A. rubra* (307)

(L after Sargent.)

Fig. 107

A. Dwarf Birch, *Betula nana* (307)

B. Silver Birch, *B. verrucosa* (308)

C. White Birch, *B. pubescens* (308)

D. Yellow Birch, *B. lutea* (308)

E. River or Red Birch, *B. nigra* (308)

F. *B. Maximowicziana* (308)

G. Paper or Canoe Birch, *B. papyrifera* (308)

H. Himalayan Birch, *B. utilis* (308)

J. Common Hornbeam, *Carpinus Betulus* (309)

K. American Hornbeam, *C. caroliniana* (309)

L. Hop Hornbeam, *Ostrya virginiana* (310)

(A after Moss and Hunnybun, D, E, G, and fruits of K and L after Sargent, H after Brandis.)

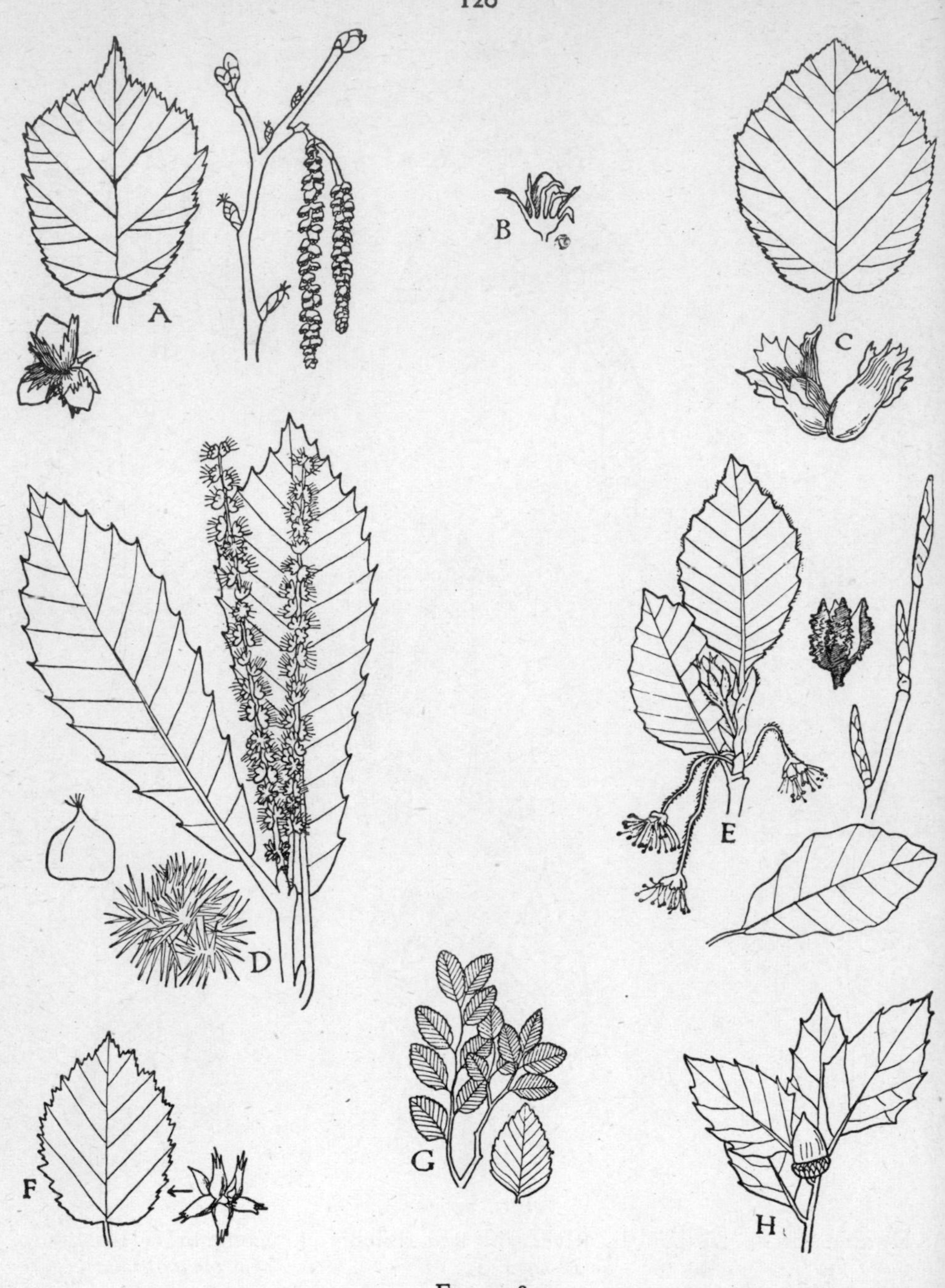

FIG. 108

A. Common Hazel, *Corylus Avellana* (309)

B. Fruit of Turkish Hazel, *C. Colurna* (309)

C. Filbert, *C. maxima* (309)

D. Sweet or Spanish Chestnut, *Castanea sativa* (310)

E. Common Beech, *Fagus sylvatica* (311)

F. *Ostryopsis Davidiana* (310)

G. *Nothofagus Dombeyi* (311)

H. Encena, or Live Oak, *Quercus argifolia* (312)

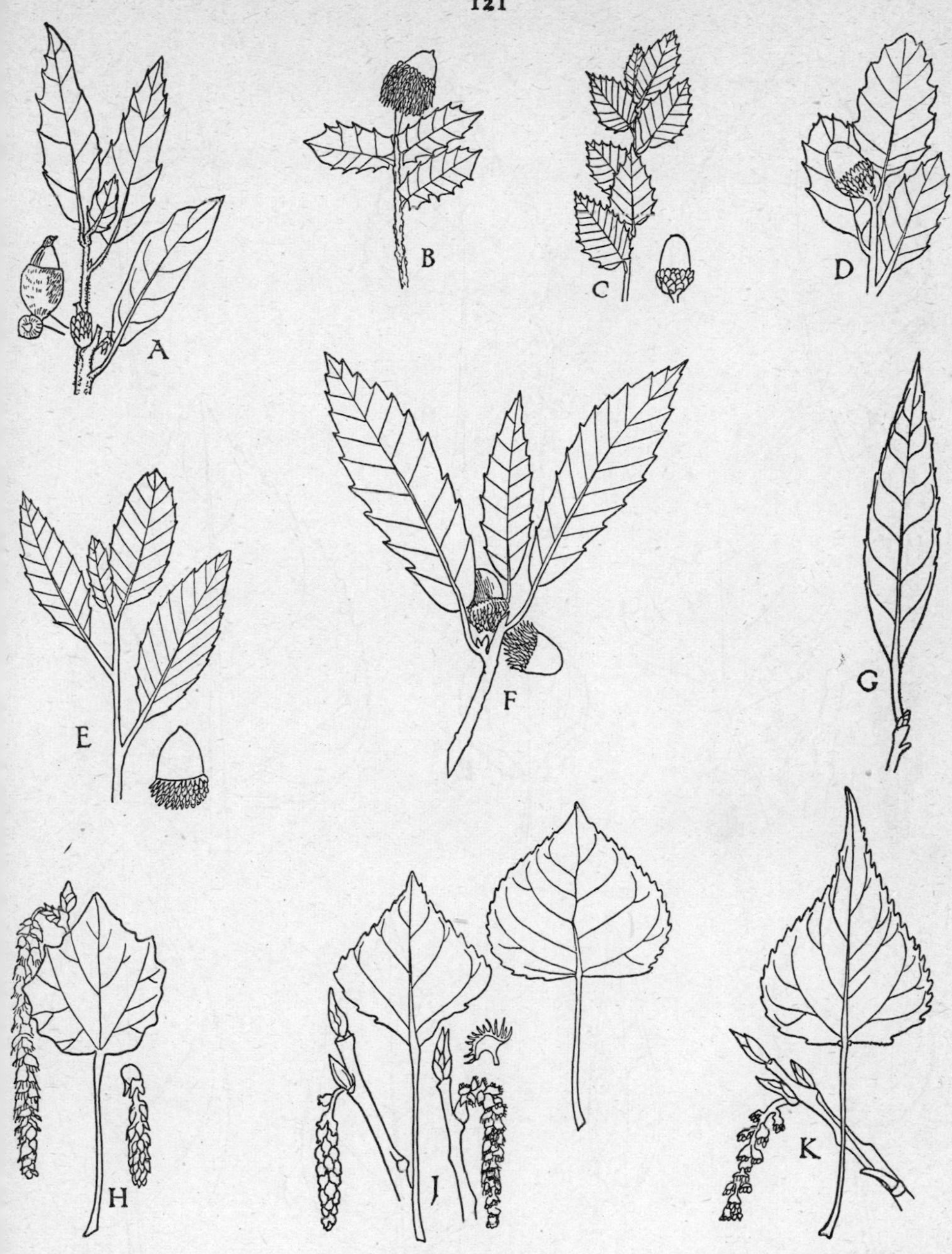

FIG. 109

A. Common Evergreen Oak, or Holm Oak, *Quercus Ilex* (312)

B. Kermes Oak, or Grain Tree, *Q. coccifera* (312)

C. Maul Oak, *Q. chrysolepis* (312)

D. Cork Oak, *Q. Suber* (312)

E. Tanbark Oak, *Q. densiflora* (311)

F. Chestnut-leaved Oak, *Q. castaneaefolia* (312)

G. Bamboo-leaved Oak, *Q. myrsinaefolia* (312)

H. Grey Poplar, *Populus canescens* (316)

J. Black Poplar, *P. nigra* (316)

K. Black Italian Poplar, *P. serotina* (316)

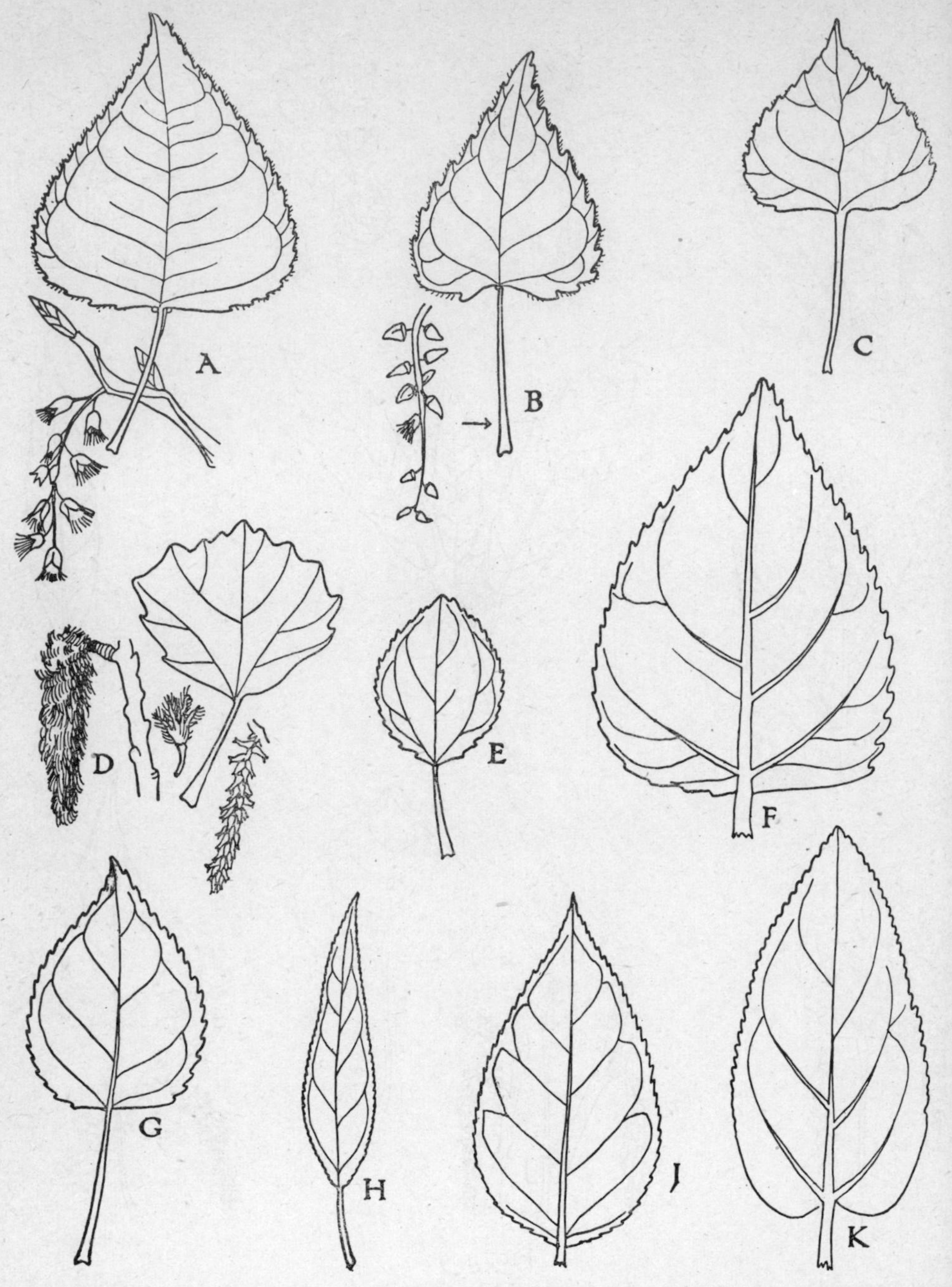

Fig. 110

A. Carolina Poplar, *Populus angulata* (316)
B. Canadian Black Poplar, or Necklace Poplar, *P. monilifera* (316)
C. *P. Eugenei* (316)
D. Aspen, *P. tremula* (317)
E. American Aspen, *P. tremuloides* (317)
F. *P. generosa* (316)
G. Balsam Poplar, *P. candicans* (317)
H. Willow-leaved Poplar, *P. angustifolia* (317)
J. Black Cottonwood, *P. trichocarpa* (317)
K. *P. szechuanica* (317)

FIG. 111

A. White Willow, *Salix alba* (318)
B. *S. Arbuscula* (318)
C. Round-eared Willow, *S. aurita* (318)
D. Goat Willow, or Sallow, *S. Caprea* (318)
E. Crack Willow, *S. fragilis* (319)
F. Whortle Willow, *S. myrsinites* (319)
G. Tea-leaved Willow, *S. phylicifolia* (319)
H. Grey Willow, *S. cinerea* (318)
J. Bay Willow, *S. pentandra* (319)
K. Almond-leaved Willow, *S. amygdalina* (319)
L. Weeping Willow, *S. babylonica* (319)
M. Pussy Willow, *S. discolor* (320)
N. Dark-leaved Sallow, *S. nigricans* (320)
O. *S. myrsinifolia* (318)
P. Violet Willow, *S. daphnoides* (320)

(B and O after Butcher and Strudwick, E and N after Moss and Hunnybun.)

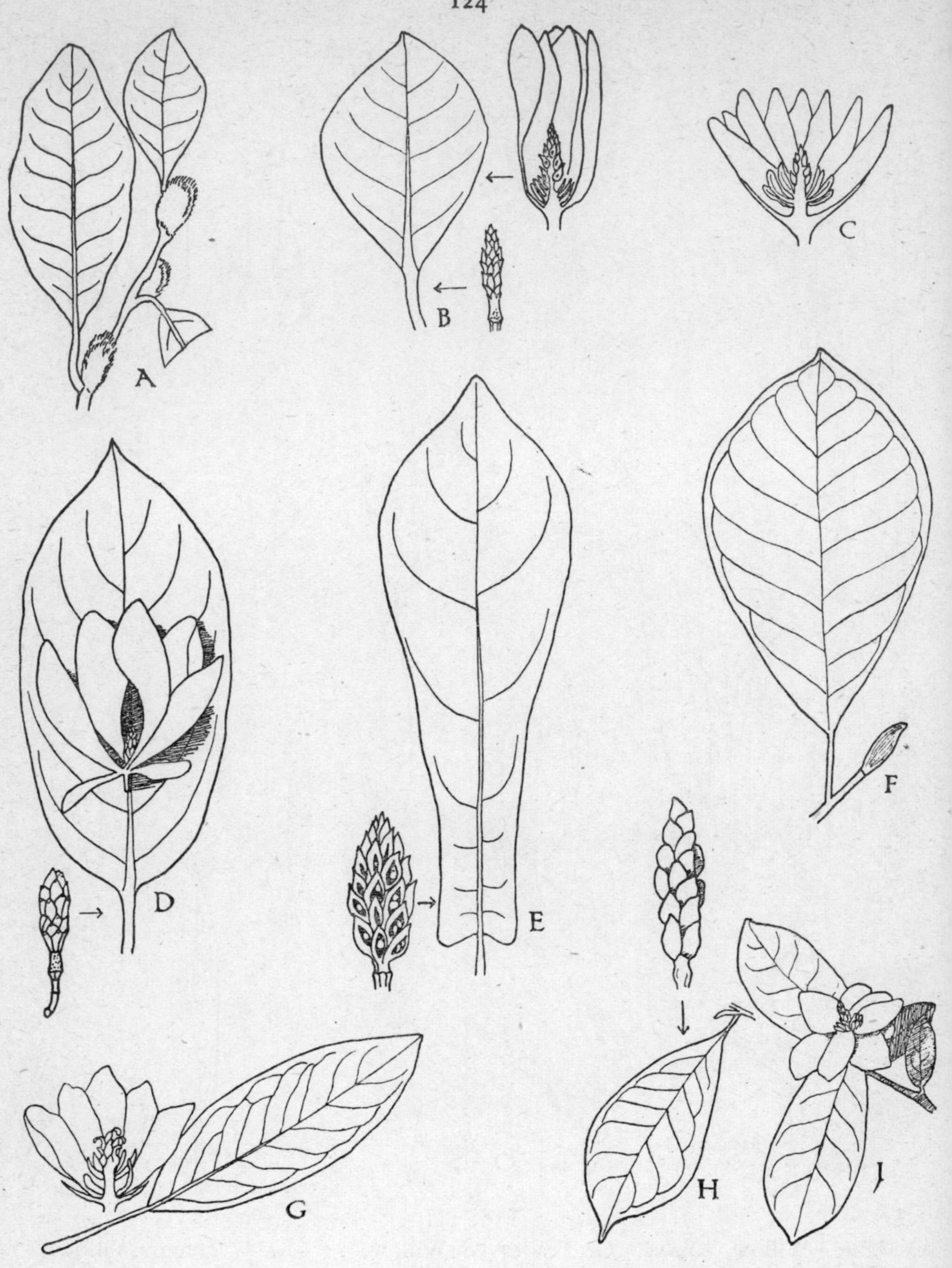

FIG. 112

A. Yulan, or Lily Tree, *Magnolia denudata* (146)
B. *M. Soulangiana* (146)
C. Flower of *M. stellata* (146)
D. Cucumber Tree, *M. acuminata* (147)
E. *M. Fraseri* (147)
F. *M. obovata* (147)
G. Laurel Magnolia, Swamp Bay, or Beaver Tree, *M. virginiana* (147)
H. *M. Kobus* (146)
J. *M. parviflora* (147)

(D and E after Sargent.)

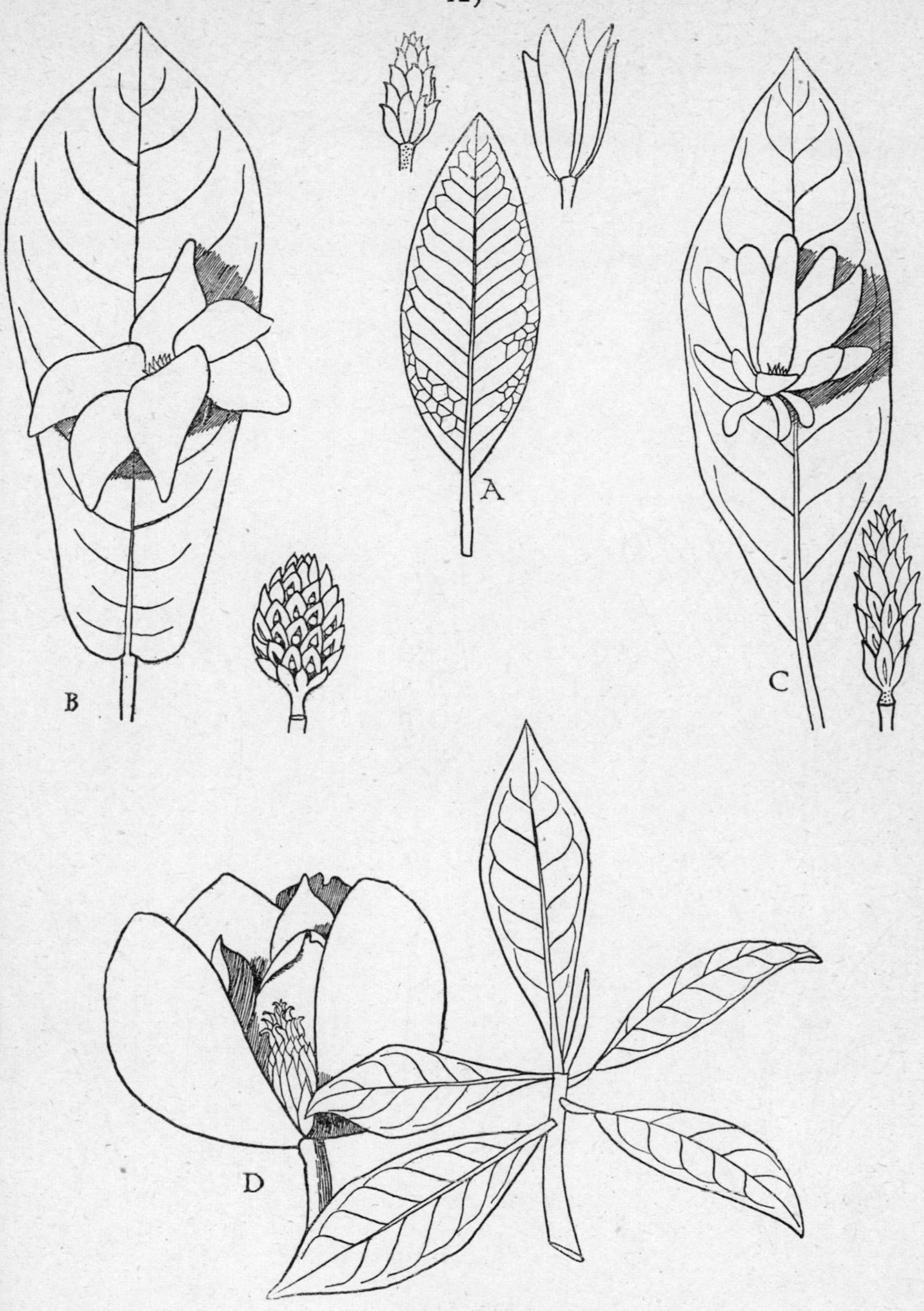

FIG. 113

A. *Manglietia insignis* (148)
B. Large-leaved Cucumber Tree, *Magnolia macrophylla* (146)
C. Umbrella Tree, *M. tripetala* (147)
D. Bull Bay, *M. grandiflora* (147)

(B and C after Sargent.)

FIG. 114

A. Banana Shrub, *Michelia fuscata* (148)
B. *M. compressa* (148)
C. Anise, *Illicium anisatum* (148)
D. *I. floridanum* (148)
E. *Drimys aromatica* (148)
F. Winter's Bark, *D. Winteri* (148)
G. Leaf of Californian Tree Poppy, *Dendromecon rigidum* (155)
H. *Cocculus laurifolius* (150)
J. Carolina Moonseed, *C. carolinus* (150)
K. Pawpaw, *Asimina triloba* (149)

(Fruit and flower of K after Sargent.)

FIG. 115

A. Gold Dust, or Golden Tuft, *Alyssum saxatile* (155)
B. Purple Apple Berry, *Billardiera longiflora* (158)
C. *Pittosporum Tobira* (159)
D. *P. crassifolium* (159)
E. Cress Rocket, *Vella Pseudocytisus* (155)
F. *Alyssum spinosum* (155)
G. Australian Bluebell Creeper, *Sollya heterophylla* (159)
Ga. Flower of ditto
H. *Hymenanthera crassifolia* (157)
J. Milkwort, *Polygala Chamaebuxus* (160)
K. *Podalyria sericea* (192)
L. *Pittosporum undulatum* (159)
M. *P. pauciflorum* (159)

FIG. 116

A. *Pittosporum eugenioides* (159)
B. *P. tenuifolium* (159)
C. *P. revolutum* (159)
D. Kangaroo Thorn, *Acacia armata* (194)
E. *Eurya ochnacea* (162)
F. *Orixa japonica* (167)
G. *Cleyera Fortunei* (162)
H. *Skimmia japonica* (168)
J. *S. Laureola* (168)

(J after Collett.)

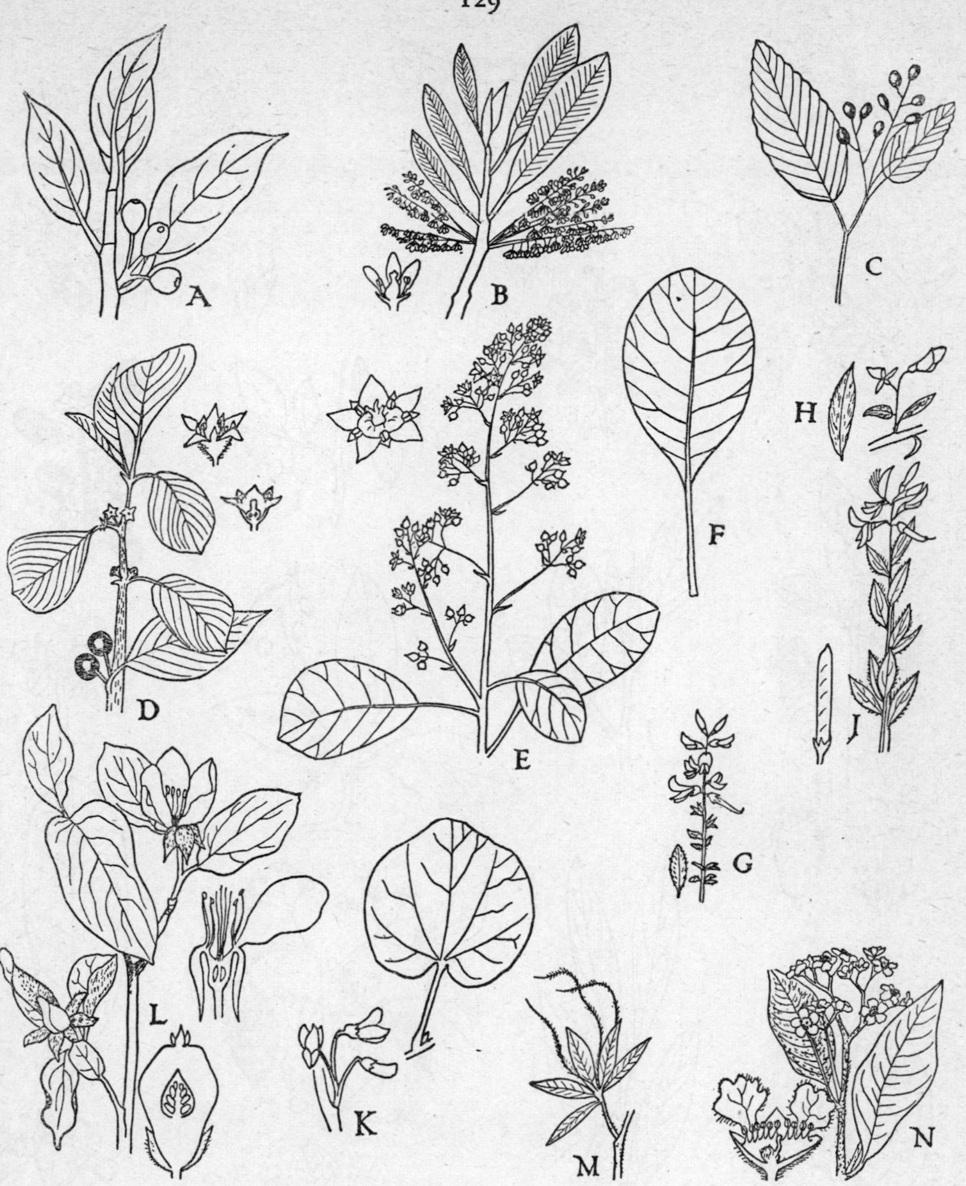

FIG. 117

A. Holly, *Ilex Aquifolium* (169)
B. Leatherwood, *Cyrilla racemiflora* (170)
C. Supple Jack, *Berchemia volubilis* (173)
D. Alder Buckthorn, *Rhamnus Frangula* (174)
E. Venetian Sumach, or Smoke Tree, *Rhus Cotinus* (183)
F. Chittam Wood, *R. cotinoides* (183)
G. Hairy Greenweed, *Genista pilosa* (187)
H. Madeira Broom, *G. virgata* (187)
J. Dyer's Greenweed, *G. tinctoria* (187)

(M after Sargent.)

K. Judas Tree, *Cercis Siliquastrum* (193)
L. Common Quince, *Cydonia oblonga* (214)
M. *Cercocarpus ledifolius* (198)
N. *Dichotomanthes tristaniaecarpa* (204)

Genera not figured: *Cliftonia* (170), *Cornus* (237)

FIG. 118

A. *Cotoneaster adpressa* (209)
B. *C. Franchetii* (210)
C. *C. horizontalis* (209)
D. *C. integerrima* (210)
E. *C. microphylla* (211)
F. *C. pannosa* (211)
G. *C. buxifolia* (211)
H. *C. Simonsii* (209)
J. *C. Harroviana* (210)
K. *C. serotina* (211)
L. *C. rotundifolia* (209)
M. *C. bullata* (210)
N. *C. Henryana* (210)
O. *C. multiflora* (210)
P. *C. frigida* (210)
Q. *C. nummularia* (210)

FIG. 119

A. *Exochorda Giraldii* (195)
B. Oso Berry, *Osmaronia (Nuttallia) cerasiformis* (204)
C. *Docynia Delavayi* (214)
D. Willow-leaved Pear, *Pyrus salicifolia* (218)
E. *Stranvaesia Davidiana* (220)
F. *Hakea saligna* (295)
G. *Disanthus cercidifolius* (230)
H. *Distylium racemosum* (230)
J. Adult shoot of Blue Gum, *Eucalyptus globulus* (232)
K. *E. coccifera* (232)

(J after Gräbner.)

FIG. 120

A. *Bupleurum fruticosum* (235)
B. Flowering shoot of Ivy, *Hedera Helix* (236)
C. *Corokia Cotoneaster* (238)
D. *C. macrocarpa* (238)
E. *C. buddleioides* (238)
F. *C. virgata* (238)
G. *Griselinia littoralis* (238)
H. Tupelo Tree, *Nyssa sylvatica* (239)
J. *Ozothamnus Antennaria* (252)
K. *Mutisia decurrens* (251)
L. *Olearia aviceniifolia* (255)
M. *O. Forsteri* (255)
N. *O. nummularifolia* (255)
O. *O. albida* (255)
P. *O. oleifolia* (255)
Q. *O. furfuracea* (255)
R. *O. Haastii* (255)

FIG. 121

A. *Pachystegia insignis* (255)
B. *Senecio elaeagnifolius* (252)
C. *S. compactus* (252)
D. *S. Greyii* (252)
E. *S. Huntii* (253)
F. *S. laxifolius* (253)
G. *S. Monroi* (253)
H. Cranberry, *Oxycoccus palustris* (256)
J. American Cranberry, *O. macrocarpus* (256)
K. Bog Whortleberry, or Bog Bilberry, *Vaccinium uliginosum* (257)
L. Hairy Huckleberry, *V. hirsutum* (257)
M. Swamp Blueberry, *V. corymbosum* (257)
N. Sour-top, or Velvet Leaf, *V. canadense* (257)

(H and K after Fitch and Smith.)

Fig. 122

A. Red Bearberry, *Arctostaphylos Uva-ursi* (259)
B. Manzanita, *A. Manzanita* (258)
C. Australian Beard Heath, *Leucopogon Fraseri* (271)
D. *Elliottia racemosa* (260)
E. Male-berry, *Lyonia ligustrina* (263)
F. *Pieris ovalifolia* (264)
G. Stagger Bush, *P. Mariana* (264)
H. Indian Azalea, *Rhododendron indicum* (265)
J. R. *luteum* (*Azalea pontica*) (265)
K. R. *japonicum* (*Azalea mollis*) (265)
L. R. *Anthopogon* (266)
M. Swamp Honeysuckle, R. *viscosum* (266)
N. Chinese Azalea, R. *molle* (265)
O. R. *Rhodora* (*Rhodora canadensis*) (266)
P. R. *occidentale* (265)
Q. Creeping Snowberry, *Chiogenes hispidula* (256)

(A after Berger and Schmidt, F after Collett.)

A B D E C G F H J K L

FIG. 123

A. *Rhododendron cinnabarinum* (266)
B. Alpenrose, or Rose des Alpes, *R. ferrugineum* (267)
C. R. *arboreum* (266)
D. R. *praecox* (267)
E. R. *moupinense* (267)
F. R. *campanulatum* (268)
G. R. *Nobleanum* (269)
H. R. *Falconeri* (268)
J. R. *fictolacteum* (268)
K. R. *obtusum* (269)
L. R. *Thomsonii* (270)

Fig. 124

A. *Rhododendron ciliatum* (269)
B. R. *croceum* (269)
C. R. *ponticum* (270)
D. *Menziesia pilosa* (264)
E. *Tripetaleia paniculata* (270)
F. *Cladothamnus pyrolaeflorus* (259)
G. Calico Bush, *Kalmia latifolia* (262)
H. *Rhodothamnus Chamaecistus* (270)
J. *Therorhodion camtschaticum* (270)
K. Date Plum, *Diospyros Lotus* (272)
L. Southern Buckthorn, *Bumelia lycioides* (272)
M. Shrubby Plumbago, *Ceratostigma Griffithii* (271)

Genus not figured: *Ledum* (263)

Fig. 125

A. *Buddleia alternifolia* (281)
B. Potato Tree, *Solanum crispum* (284)
C. *Streptosolen Jamesonii* (284)
D. *Convolvulus Cneorum* (283)
E. Chinese Box Thorn, or Cottage Tea Tree, *Lycium chinense* (284)
F. Woody Nightshade, or Bittersweet, *Solanum Dulcamara* (284)
G. Tree Purslane, *Atriplex Halimus* (292)
H. *Eurotia ceratoides* (292)
J. *Ercilla volubilis* (292)
K. *Cestrum elegans* (284)
L. Willow-leaved Jessamine, *C. Parqui* (284)
M. *Muehlenbeckia complexa* (293)
N. Goat Wheat, *Atraphaxis* (293)
O. *A. Muschketowi* (293)
P. *Brunnichia cirrhosa* (293)
Q. *Polygonum baldschuanicum* (293)

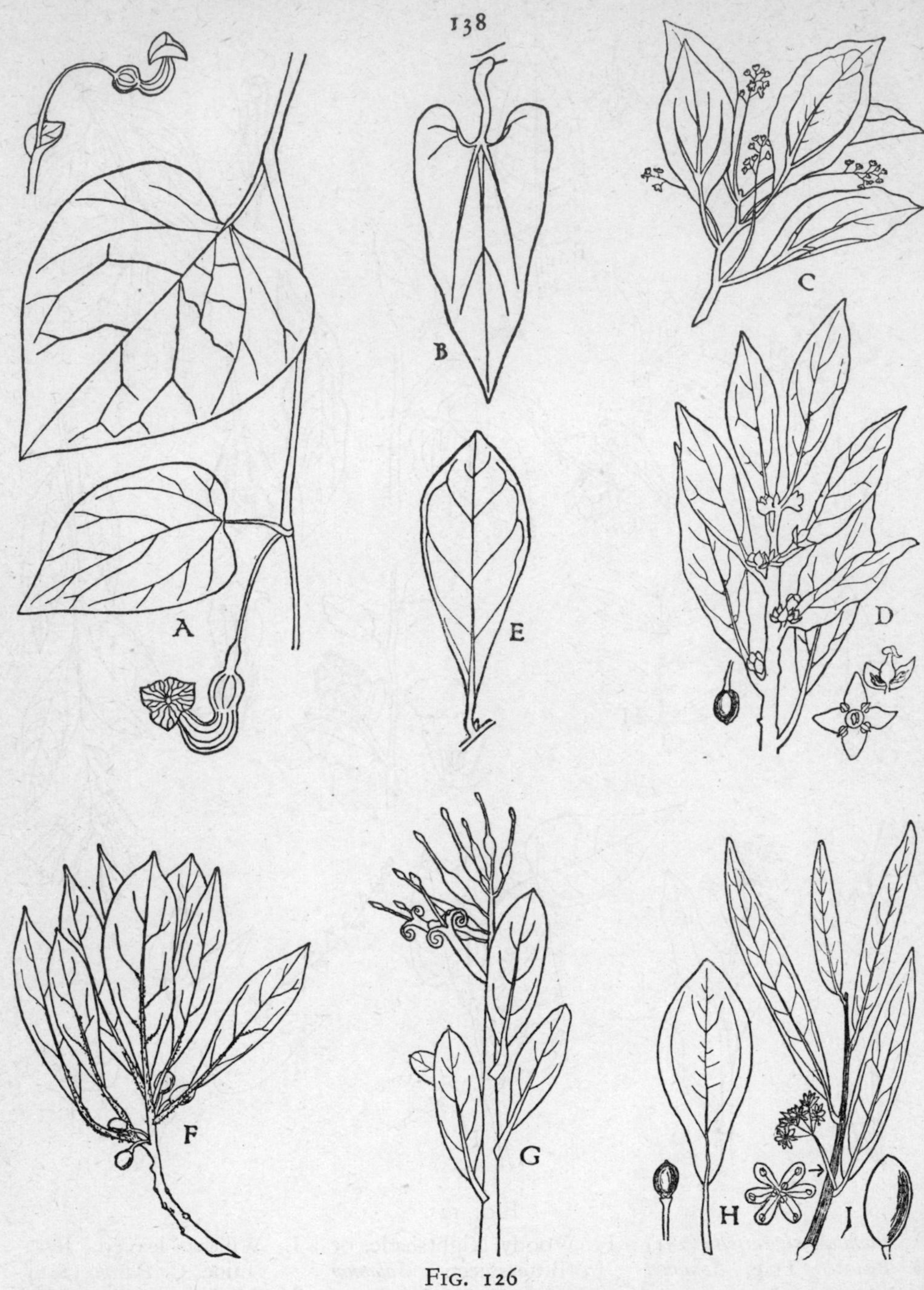

Fig. 126

A. Dutchman's Pipe, or Birthwort, *Aristolochia Sipho* (293)

B. *A. moupinense* (293)

C. Camphor Tree, *Cinnamomum Camphora* (294)

D. Sweet Bay, or Poet's Laurel, *Laurus nobilis* (294)

E. Spice Bush, *Lindera Benzoin* (294)

F. *Litsaea japonica* (294)

G. Fire Bush, *Embothrium coccineum* (295)

H. Ague Tree, *Sassafras officinale* (294) (see also Fig. 31 G)

J. Californian Laurel, or Spice Tree, *Umbellularia californica* (294)

(A from Kew Herbarium and after *Botanical Magazine*, C after Berger and Schmidt.)

Fig. 127

A. Spurge Laurel, *Daphne Laureola* (296)
B. *D. Blagayana* (296)
C. *D. pontica* (296)
D. Mezereon, *D. Mezereum* (296)
E. Garland Flower, *D. Cneorum* (296)
F. *D. collina* (296)
G. *D. odora* (296)
H. *D. petraea* (297)
J. Tasmanian Waratah, *Telopea truncata* (295)
K. *Edgeworthia papyrifera* (297)
L. Leatherwood, *Dirca palustris* (297)
M. Silkworm Thorn, *Cudrania tricuspidata* (302)
N. *Elaeagnus umbellata* (297)
O. Oleaster, *E. angustifolia* (297)
P. *E. glabra* (298)
Q. *E. pungens* (298)
R. Silver Berry, *E. argentea* (297)

(N after Collett.)

FIG. 128

A. *Sarcococca saligna* (299)
B. *S. ruscifolia* (299)
C. *S. humilis* (299)
D. *Andrachne colchica* (299)
E. *Securinega flueggeoides* (300)
F. Osage Orange, or Bow Wood, *Maclura pomifera* (303)
G. *Daphniphyllum macropodum* (300)
H. *Quercus acuta* (312)
J. *Q. edulis* (312)
K. Willow Oak, *Q. Phellos* (313)
L. Golden Chestnut, *Castanopsis chrysophylla* (310)
M. Corkwood, *Leitneria floridana* (304)
N. Mountain Beech, *Nothofagus cliffortioides* (311)
O. Woolly Willow, *Salix lanata* (318)
P. Creeping Willow, *S. repens* (319)
Q. Lapland Willow, *S. Lapponum* (318)
R. *S. reticulata* (320)

(Fruit of F after *Gardener's Chronicle*, of M after Sargent, O–R after Moss and Hunnybun.)

DESCRIPTIONS

LIST OF SYMBOLS, ABBREVIATIONS, ETC.

∞ Numerous or an indefinite number.

$+$ Shows separation into two or more layers or whorls (e.g. $P3+3$=perianth of two whorls, not differentiated into sepals and petals).

* Not hardy at Kew.

( ) Joined together (e.g. C (5)=a corolla of 5 united petals which cannot be pulled off without tearing; G (5)=a pistil of 5 united carpels).

A. Stamens (e.g. $A5=5$ stamens).

C. Corolla (e.g. $C5=$corolla with 5 petals).

D. Deciduous.

E. Evergreen.

Fl., Fls. Flower, Flowers.

fol. Foliolate (e.g. 3-fol.=trifoliolate, a leaf with 3 leaflets).

G. Pistil; $\underline{G}$, a pistil with superior ovary; $\bar{G}$, with inferior ovary; $\bar{\underline{G}}$, with either superior or inferior (e.g. $\underline{G}3$=a pistil made up of 3 separate carpels with ovaries in a position above that of the outer floral parts).

K. Calyx (e.g. $K5=$calyx with 5 sepals).

L., Ls. Leaf, Leaves.

Lanc. Lance-shaped.

Lflt., Lflts. Leaflet, Leaflets.

Oblanc. Inversely lance-shaped (i.e. with broader end outwards).

Obov. Inversely ovate : ovate (see below) with broader end outwards.

Ov. Ovate (oval or elliptical in general outline, disregarding teeth or lobes).

P. Perianth (e.g. $P3$=perianth of 3 parts, not differentiated into sepals and petals).

Var. Variety.

First numeral after name of species shows maximum height in feet. Second and subsequent numerals show dimension in inches.

A full description of these and other terms is given on pages 4–10.

CLASS I. DICOTYLEDONS

The embryo contains two leaves (cotyledons) which, on germination of the seed, usually push up to the light and appear as the first leaves. Bark, wood, and pith are clearly distinguished in the stem. The parts of the flower are usually in fours or fives, a multiple of four or five, or a large indefinite number.

SUB-CLASS I. POLYPETALAE

Petals and sepals both present as a rule (sometimes one or both absent); petals, when present, not united (can be pulled off one by one).

Family 1. **RANUNCULACEAE.** P4 or more, A ∞, $\underline{G}2-\infty$

The stamens always arise from a position below the carpels. Contains few woody plants. Anemone, Buttercup, Christmas Rose, Columbine, Delphinium, Love-in-a-mist, and Monkshood are well-known herbaceous plants.

CLEMATIS. Virgin's Bower. Climbers climbing by leaf-stalks. Ls. opposite, compound. Fls. without conspicuous petals, their place being taken by showy sepals. Fruit usually with long feathery styles.

(a) Fls. cup-shaped (sepals upright)

C. aethusifolia Turcz. 6. August–October. D. Ls. pinnate; lflts. ov., 2, deeply dissected. Fls. ½, yellow, nodding. Manchuria.

C. alpina Mill. (*Atragene alpina* L.). Alpine Clematis. 6. April. D. Ls. twice 3-fol.; lflts. ov., 2, toothed. Fls. 1½, violet-blue or white, with petal-like sterile stamens, slender-stalked, nodding. North Europe.

C. campaniflora Brot. Bell-flowered Clematis. 20. May–July. D. Ls. 2-pinnate; lflts. ov., lanc., 3, entire or lobed. Fls. 1, white, tinged with violet, long-stalked, nodding. Portugal.

C. cirrhosa L. 10. January–March. E. Ls. simple, ov., 1½, coarsely toothed or lobed. Fls. 1½, yellowish white, stalk with bracts. South Europe.

Similar is *C. balearica* Rich. (*C. calycina* Ait.) with 3-fol. leaves and greenish-yellow flowers.

C. crispa L. Frilled Clematis. 10. June. D. Ls. pinnate; lflts. ov., lanc., entire or lobed. Fls. 1, bluish purple, long-stalked, nodding, sepals with frilled edges. U.S.A.

C. heracleifolia DC. 3. September. D. Ls. 3-fol.; lflts. broadly ov., 6, coarsely toothed. Fls. 1, tubular, blue, in axillary clusters, sepals recurved at ends. China.

C. macropetala Ledeb. (*Atragene macropetala* Mey.). Like *C. alpina* but flowers up to 3 across; P4, spreading. North Asia.

C. Rehderiana Craib. 25. July. D. Ls. pinnate; lflts. ov., 3, coarsely toothed or lobed. Fls. ¾, yellow, nodding, fragrant, in axillary panicles. China.

C. tangutica Korsh. 10. June. D. Like *C. orientalis* but flowers larger and deeper yellow and leaflets with many teeth. China.

CLEMATIS—*continued*

C. texensis Buckl. (*C. coccinea* Engelm.). Scarlet Clematis. 6. June–August. D. Ls. pinnate or deeply lobed; lflt. often a tendril. Fls. 1, urn-shaped, red. U.S.A.

C. Viorna L. Leather Flower. 10. May–August. D. Ls. pinnate; lflts. ov., 3, entire or lobed. Fls. 1, urn-shaped, with thick reddish purple sepals recurved at ends, nodding. U.S.A.

(*b*) *Fls. saucer-shaped* (*sepals spreading*), *solitary or in clusters of five or less*

C. chrysocoma Franch. 15. August–September. D. Ls. and fl.-stalks covered with yellow down. Ls. 3-fol. Fls. 2, white tinged with pink. China.

C. Fargesii Franch. 15. July–September. D. Ls. 2-pinnate; lflts. ov., 2, coarsely toothed or lobed. Fls. 2, white, in 3-flowered clusters. China.

C. florida Thunb. 10. April–May. D. Ls. twice 3-fol.; lflts. ov., 2, entire or lobed, glossy dark green above, hairy below. Fls. 3, solitary, white, with green band on back of sepals, long-stalked, the stalk with two ov. bracts in the middle, P6 or more. Japan.

C. Jackmannii T. Moore. 10. August–September. D. Ls. pinnate; lflts. ov., rather large, entire or lobed. Fls. 5, purple, P usually 4. Hybrid. (Fig. 18 A.)

Numerous varieties in cultivation, with white, red, pink, and pale blue flowers.

C. lanuginosa Lindl. 6. July. D. Ls. 3-fol. or simple; lflts. 5, heart-shaped base, woolly below. Fls. 8, white to pale lilac. China.

There are cultivated varieties with single or double flowers of various colours.

C. montana Buch.-Ham. 20. April–May. D. Ls. 3-fol.; lflts. ov., 4, toothed, rather wrinkled. Fls. 2½, white. Himalaya. (Fig. 1 A.)

Var. *rosea* Rehd. (*C. Spooneri* var. *rosea* Vilm.). Fls. 3, pink.

Var. *rubens* Kuntze. Ls. dark brownish green on purple stems. Fls. 3, rosy red.

Var. *Wilsonii* Sprague. Fls. 3, white, on downy stalk.

C. orientalis L. 20. August–October. D. Young stems ribbed. Ls. pinnate or 2-pinnate, last division 3-fol.; lflts. ov., 2, coarsely toothed or lobed. Fls. 2, yellow, solitary, on slender stalk. Caucasus to Himalaya.

C. patens Morren. 12. May–June. D. Like *C. florida*, but no bracts on the fl.-stalk. Fls. white to blue. China and Japan.

C. venosa Schneid. Like *C. florida*, but flowers reddish purple. Hybrid.

C. Viticella L. 12. July–September. D. Stems slender, ribbed. Ls. pinnate or 2-pinnate; lflts. ov., 2, blunt-ended, entire or 3-lobed. Fls. 1½, purple, P4. Fruiting appendages short. Europe.

White-, blue-, and reddish-flowered varieties in cultivation.

(*c*) *Fls. saucer-shaped* (*sepals spreading*), *in many-flowered panicles*

C. apiifolia DC. 10. September–October. D. Ls. 3-fol. or twice 3-fol.; lflts. ov., 2, coarsely toothed or lobed. Fls. ½, white. Fruiting heads small. China and Japan.

CLEMATIS—*continued*

C. Armandi Franch. 10. March–April. E. Ls. 3-fol.; lflts. ov., 5, 3-nerved, leathery, hairless. Fls. 2½, white. China.

C. Flammula L. 10. August. D. Lflts. not toothed, 2-3-lobed or 3-fol., bright green on both sides. Fls. 1, white, scented. Europe.

Var. *rubro-marginata* Rehd. Fls. white, with reddish margin.

C. grata Wall. 12. September–October. D. Ls. pinnate, 5-fol.; lflts. ov., 2, hairy, coarsely toothed or lobed. Fls. ½, white. Himalaya.

C. paniculata Thunb. 30. September–October. D. Ls. 3-fol. or pinnate; lflts. ov., 3, entire, hairless. Fls. 1, white, fragrant. Japan.

C. virginiana L. Virgin's Bower. 20. August–September. D. Ls. 3-fol.; lflts. ov., 3, coarsely toothed. Fls. ½, dull white, unisexual, the sexes on different plants. U.S.A.

C. Vitalba L. Old Man's Beard, Traveller's Joy. 30. August. D. Ls. pinnate, 5-fol.; lflts. ov., 4, entire or with a few coarse teeth. Fls. ¾, greenish white or cream. Europe (including Britain). (Fig. 9 D.)

PAEONIA. Peony. Branchlets thick, rough and pithy, dying back more than half their length after flowering. Ls. twice 3-fol. or pinnate, 18. Fls. large and showy; K5, C5 or more, A∞, $\underline{G}$2–5. Fruit of two or more splitting pods on a fleshy base or disk. Most of the species are herbaceous, but the following two can be classed as shrubs.

P. lutea Franch. 5. May. D. Fls. 4, yellow. Carpels three, hairless. China.

P. suffruticosa Andr. (*P. Moutan* Sims). Moutan. 5. April–May. D. Fls. 12, white, pink, or red. Carpels downy. China. (Fig. 18 B.)

ZANTHORRHIZA APIIFOLIA L'Hérit. Yellow Root. 2. March. D. A creeping plant, with erect stems. Ls. pinnate or 2-pinnate, with a long hollowed main stalk; lflts. ov., 2, coarsely toothed or lobed. Fls. small, purple, in clusters of drooping panicles; K5, C small and gland-like, A5–10. Roots and stem bright yellow when cut. U.S.A. (Fig. 18 C.)

Family 2. CALYCANTHACEAE. P ∞, A5–30, $\underline{G}$ ∞

Aromatic woody plants. Ls. opposite, entire, without stipules. The stamens arise from a position on a level with the carpels, which are in consequence half inferior. Fruit cup-shaped, hollow, containing numerous seeds.

CALYCANTHUS. Fls. large, with numerous strap-shaped petals.

C. fertilis Walt. 10. May–June. D. Buds hidden by base of leaf-stalk. Ls. ov., 6, glaucous below. Fls. 1½, greenish purple to reddish purple. Fruit 2½, pear-shaped. South United States.

Var. *nanus* Schnelle. Dwarf form. Ls. 3, green below.

C. floridus L. Carolina Allspice. 10. May–June. D. Buds hidden. Ls. ov., 4, downy below. Fls. 3, dark wine-red, fragrant. Fruit 2½, pear-shaped. South United States.

C. Mohrii Small. 10. May–June. D. Fls. 2, purple. South United States.

C. occidentalis Hook. & Arn. Californian Allspice. 10. May–June. D. Buds visible. Ls. ov., 8. Fls. similar to *C. floridus*, but larger, and longer-stalked, and petals change to a more tawny shade near the tip. California. (Fig. 77 E.)

CHIMONANTHUS PRAECOX (L.) Link (CALYCANTHUS PRAECOX L., CHIMONANTHUS FRAGRANS Lindl. MERATIA PRAECOX Rehd. & Wils.). Winter Sweet. 10. November–March. D. Ls. lanc., 6, long-pointed, rough above. Fls. 1, transparent yellowish green, inner petals smaller and purplish, very fragrant, solitary on short stalk on old wood. Fruit 1½, a stalked gourd-like structure (Bean). China and Japan. (Fig. 77 B.)

Family 3. MAGNOLIACEAE. K3, C6–∞, A ∞, G ∞

All woody plants. Ovaries arranged spirally round a column.

LIRIODENDRON. Tulip Tree. Ls. alternate, lobed, with concave apex. Young ls. enclosed by stipules. Petals six. Fruit cone-like. The timber of *L. Tulipifera* is imported as canary whitewood.

L. chinense Sarg. Chinese Tulip Tree. 50. July. D. Branchlets grey. Ls. deeply lobed. Petals without orange band. China.

L. Tulipifera L. American Tulip Tree. 100. July. D. Branchlets brown. Ls. 8. Fls. 1½, resemble tulip, greenish white, with orange band near base of petal. U.S.A. (Fig. 36 D.)

Var. *aureo-maculatum* Rehd. Ls. blotched with yellow.

MAGNOLIA. Buds large, with a single outer scale. Young leaves enclosed by stipules. Ls. alternate, entire, large. Fls. large, solitary, ovary with not more than two ovules. Fruit cone-like. Southern whitewood is the timber of several American species.

(*a*) *Fls. appear before leaves*

M. Campbellii Hook. f. 100. February–April. D. Bark black. Ls. ov., 12, tapering to both ends, hairy below. Fls. 10, deep rose to crimson, fragrant. Fruit 6, seeds red. East Himalaya.

M. denudata Desr. (*M. conspicua* Salisb.). Yulan, Lily Tree. 30. April. D. Buds covered with shaggy hairs. Ls. ov., 6, blunt or short-pointed, downy below. Fls. 3, white, petals thick. Fruit 8, spindle-shaped. China. (Fig. 112 A.)

M. Kobus Thunb. 30. April–May. D. Usually shrubby. Twigs hairless; leaf-buds slightly hairy, flower-buds densely so. Ls. obov., 4, abruptly pointed, tapering to base, light green below. Fls. 4, creamy white, petals with faint purple line at base outside. Fruit 4, cylindrical. Japan. (Fig. 112 H.)

M. liliflora Desr. 12. April–May. D. Twigs hairless; buds downy. Ls. obov., 4, tapering base. Fls. 3, petals erect, white inside, rosy purple outside; sepals green, much shorter than petals. China.

M. Soulangiana Soul. 30. May. D. Ls. ov., 6. Fls. white or purple, sepals at least half as long as petals, which they resemble. Hybrid. (Fig. 112 B.)

Var. *Lennei* Van Houtte. Ls. 8, pale green. Fls. 4, petals white inside, rosy purple outside.

Var. *speciosa* Hort. Fls. striped purple outside. (Fig. 112 B.)

M. stellata Maxim. 15. March–April. D. Buds hairy. Ls. oblong, 3,

MAGNOLIA—*continued*
margins recurved. Fls. 3, white or pink, petals more numerous than those of any other magnolia. Japan. (Fig. 112 C.)

(*b*) *Fls. appear with or after leaves*

M. acuminata L. Cucumber Tree. 90. May–June. D. Buds hairy. Ls. ov., 10, pointed, base rounded, downy below. Fls. 3, dull greenish yellow, petals erect. Fruit 3, dark red. U.S.A. (Fig. 112 D.)
Var. *aureo-variegata* Hort. Ls. blotched with yellow.

M. Delavayi Franch. 30. June. E. Buds and young twigs downy. Ls. ov., 12, dull green above, greyish white below; stalk stout, up to 3 long. Fls. 8, white. Fruit 4, egg-shaped. China.

M. Fraseri Walt. 50. June–July. D. Buds hairless. Ls. obov., 20, round-ended, heart-shaped base, hairless; stalk slender, up to 3 long. Fls. 8, creamy white, fragrant. Fruit 4, egg-shaped or cylindrical, red. South United States. (Fig. 112 E.)

M. grandiflora L. Bull Bay. 80. July–September. E. Buds hairy. Ls. ov., 10, leathery, glossy, dark green above, felted with reddish brown below, clustered at end of branch. Fls. 10, round, creamy white; petals thick, concave. Fruit 4, egg-shaped, rusty-woolly. South United States. (Fig. 113 D.)

M. macrophylla Michx. Large-leaved Cucumber Tree. 50. July. D. Buds hairy. Ls. obov., 36, slightly heart-shaped at base, green above, white below. Fls. 12, cup-shaped, creamy white, fragrant, petals reflexed above middle, purplish at base, thick. Fruit 3, egg-shaped, rose-coloured, hairy. South United States. (Fig. 113 B.)

M. obovata Thunb. (*M. hypoleuca* Sieb. & Zucc.). 60. April–May. D. Twigs purplish, hairless. Buds hairless, Ls. obov., 16. Fls. 6, cup-shaped, fragrant, white with red centre. Fruit 8, cylindrical, red. Japan. (Fig. 112 F.)

M. parviflora Sieb. & Zucc. 30. May–June. D. Branchlets slender. Buds hairy. Ls. oblong, 6, apex contracted abruptly to short point. Fls. 2, white, carpels and stamens crimson. Fruit 2, egg-shaped, red, with red seeds. Japan. (Fig. 112 J.)

M. tripetala L. Umbrella Tree. 35. June. D. Buds and twigs hairless. Ls. ov., 24, pointed, downy beneath. Fls. 9, white, heavy-scented. Fruit 4, rose-coloured. U.S.A. (Fig. 113 C.)

M. virginiana L. (*M. glauca* L.). Sweet Bay, Swamp Bay, Beaver Tree, Laurel Magnolia. 70. June–August. D or ½ E. Twigs slender, hairless. Buds hairy. Ls. ov., oblong, or lanc., 4, leathery, bluish green above, greyish white beneath; stalk slender, ¾. Fls. 2½, round, white, fragrant. Fruit 2, egg-shaped, dark red. South United States. (Fig. 112 G.)

M. Watsonii Hook. f. 30. May–June. D. Like *M. parviflora*, but flowers are larger and have fewer carpels, and the fruit is longer and not so egg-shaped. Japan.

M. Wilsonii Rehd. 30. May–June. D. Buds and twigs downy. Ls. ov., 4, pointed, base rounded, silky below. Fls. 4, cup-shaped, white, fragrant, petals thin, carpels and stamens crimson. Fruit 2, cylindrical. W. China.

MANGLIETIA INSIGNIS Blume. 100. E. Ls. alternate, lanc., entire, with prominent polygonal venation (Brandis). Fls. 4, white or yellowish white tinged with pink, scented, K3, C9, ovary with six or more ovules. Fruit 3, narrowly egg-shaped. East Himalaya. (Fig. 113 A.)

MICHELIA. Differs from magnolia in the carpel-bearing centre of the flower being stalked. Leaf-stalk very short.

* **M. compressa** Sarg. 20. April–June. E. Ls. ov., lanc., 4, hairless, glaucous below. Fls. 2, white, fragrant. Japan. (Fig. 114 B.)
* **M. fuscata** Blume. Banana Shrub. 20. April–June. E. Young shoots hairy. Ls. ov., 4, tapering to both ends, blunt, becoming nearly hairless, stalk hairy. Fls. 1, yellowish green or purple, fragrant with 'pear-drop' scent. China. (Fig. 114 A.)

Family 4. WINTERACEAE. K3–6, C ∞, A ∞, G few

Aromatic shrubs with alternate, entire, and hairless leaves. Carpels in a single whorl.

DRIMYS. K3. Fruit berry-like.

* **D. aromatica** F. Muell. 15. May. E. Ls. oblanc., 3, crowded radially at end of shoot. Fls. ½, greenish white. Victoria and Tasmania. (Fig. 114 E.)
* **D. Winteri** Forst. Winter's Bark. 25. Summer. E. Ls. lanc., 10, bright pale green, usually crowded at end of shoot. Fls. 1½, ivory white; petals linear, spreading, pointed. South America. (Fig. 114 E.)

ILLICIUM. Ls. lanc., entire, leathery, hairless. Fls. 1, solitary or in pairs in the leaf-axils. Fruit 1, star-shaped.

* **I. anisatum** L. Anise. 12. March–May. E. Ls. 3. Fls. greenish yellow. China and Japan. (Fig. 114 C.)
* **I. floridanum** Ellis. Poison Bay. 8. March–May. E. Ls. 4. Fls. purple. South United States. (Fig. 114 D.)

Family 5. SCHIZANDRACEAE. K ∞, C ∞, A ∞, G ∞

Woody climbers. Ls. alternate, faintly toothed or entire. Fls. unisexual. Fruit a berry.

KADSURA JAPONICA Juss. 10. September. E. Ls. ov., lanc., 4, long-pointed, tapering base, dark green, hairless. Fls. ¾, white, cup-shaped, petals fleshy, solitary on slender stalk. Fruit a round head of red berries. China and Japan. (Fig. 78 D.)

SCHIZANDRA. Ls. aromatic, with transparent dots. Fruit an elongated spike of red berries hanging from a slender stalk.

S. chinensis Baill. (*S. japonica* Hance). 30. April–May. ½ E. Stems reddish brown, slightly angled, hairless, warted. Ls. ov., 4, tapering at base to a slender stalk, veins on lower surface appear dark green against a pale green background. Fls. ½, rose-coloured, fragrant, on slender stalks, in clusters. Fruit spike 6, persisting through winter. China and Japan. (Fig. 78 A.)

SCHIZANDRA—*continued*

S. glaucescens Diels. April–May. ½ E. Stem nearly cylindrical. Ls. glaucous below. China.

S. grandiflora Hook. f. April–May. ½ E. Like *S. chinensis*, but thicker. Fls. 1, white tinged with pink. Himalaya.

S. Henryi Clarke. April–May. ½ E. Stem triangular when young, each angle winged. Ls. ov., 4, leathery, glaucous below. Fls. ½, white, on stout stalks up to 2 long. Berries sticky. West China.

S. rubriflora Rehd. & Wils. 20. April–May. ½ E. Fls. deep crimson. West China.

Family 6. TROCHODENDRACEAE. P4 or 0, A4–∞, G few

Ls. alternate, without stipules. Fls. bisexual. Buds with several scales.

EUPTELEA. Ls. broadly ov., 4, sharp-pointed, broadly wedge-shaped base, toothed, long-stalked. Fls. small, with numerous red stamens, in axillary clusters. Fruit flat, ½, narrowly wedge-shaped, notched on one side.

E. Franchetii Van Tieghem. 40. March–April. D. Ls. finely and more or less evenly toothed. Fruit 1-3-seeded. China. (Fig. 78 E.)

E. polyandra Sieb. & Zucc. 40. March–April. D. Ls. coarsely and unevenly toothed. Japan. (Fig. 78 F.)

TETRACENTRON SINENSE Oliv. 100. Midwinter. D. Buds slender-pointed. Ls. alternate, ov., 3, palmately 5-7-nerved, heart-shaped base, finely round-toothed, slender-stalked. Fls. small, yellowish, in hanging spikes up to 6 long. Fruit ¼, dry, brown, 4-celled. China. (Fig. 78 C.)

TROCHODENDRON ARALIOIDES Sieb. & Zucc. 30. June. E. Ls. ov., lanc., 6, long-pointed, long-stalked, leathery, toothed, in whorls or grouped radially at end of whorled branches. Fls. rather like ivy, greenish yellow, in terminal upright racemes. Fruit ¾, brown. Japan. (Fig. 55 F.)

Family 7. CERCIDIPHYLLACEAE. P4, A ∞, G2–5

Buds with two outer scales. Ls. opposite or sub-opposite.

CERCIDIPHYLLUM JAPONICUM Sieb. & Zucc. Katsura Tree. 100. March. D. Forming several spirally twisted and furrowed trunks. Ls. opposite, ov. round, 2½, heart-shaped base, palmately nerved, round-toothed, slender-stalked. Fls. inconspicuous, unisexual, on separate trees. Fruit ½, a many-seeded pod. Japan. (Fig. 59 C.)

Var. *sinense* Rehd. & Wils. Colours better in autumn according to Messrs. Stewart & Son, Wimborne.

Family 8. ANONACEAE. K3, C6, A ∞, G ∞

Mostly woody plants of tropical regions (including the Custard apple, *Anona squamosa* L.) with alternate leaves and bisexual flowers.

ASIMINA TRILOBA Dunal. Pawpaw. 15. May–June. D. Ls. alternate, obov., 12, entire, pointed, hairless, short-stalked, with a disagreeable odour when crushed. Fls. 2, purple, solitary, nodding at the end of a short thick stalk. Fruit 5, bottle-shaped, in whorls, edible. South United States. (Fig. 114 K.)

Family 9. **MENISPERMACEAE.** K3+3, C3+3, A3+3 or more, G̲3 or more

Fls. unisexual, with sexes on different plants. Mostly climbers. Ls. alternate, palmately nerved, entire or lobed.

COCCULUS. Fls. small, in axillary or terminal spikes or panicles. Fruit a berry.

C. carolinus DC. (*Menispermum carolinum* L.). Carolina Moonseed. 12. June–July. D. Ls. round or triangular, 3½, rounded or heart-shaped base, sometimes lobed, hairless above, downy below. Berry red. South United States. (Fig. 114 J.)

C. laurifolius DC. 10. E. Ls. lanc., 8, 3-ribbed, dark glossy green. Himalaya. (Fig. 114 H.)

C. trilobus DC. (*Cebatha orbiculata* Kuntze). 12. August. D. Ls. ov., 4, heart-shaped or tapering base, sometimes lobed, downy on both sides. Berry bluish black. Corea and Japan.

MENISPERMUM. Ls. peltate. Seed crescent-shaped.

M. canadense L. Moonseed. 15. June. D. Ls. as broad as long, base straight or rounded, strongly veined, long-stalked; stalk attached just inside margin, which is sometimes divided into shallow angular lobes. Fls. numerous, inconspicuous, greenish yellow, in slender, long-stalked clusters. Berries like black currants, in long loose panicles. North America. (Fig. 31 B.)

M. dauricum DC. 15. June. D. Like above, but leaves more distinctly peltate. East Asia.

SINOMENIUM ACUTUM Rehd. & Wils. (MENISPERMUM ACUTUM Thunb., COCCULUS DIVERSIFOLIUS Franch.). Chinese Moonseed. 12. June. D. Ls. very variable in shape and size, ov., 6, heart-shaped or kidney-shaped, sometimes lobed, deep bright green, hairless, long-stalked. Fls. small, yellow, in slender panicles up to 12. Berry black, with blue bloom. China and Japan. (Fig. 30 D.)

Family 10. **LARDIZABALACEAE.** P3+3, A3+3, G̲3 or more

Mostly climbers. Ls. alternate, compound, long-stalked, without stipules. Fls. unisexual. Fruit fleshy.

AKEBIA. Climbers. Lflts. notched at apex. P3.

A. lobata Decne. (*A. trifoliata* Thunb.). 20. April. ½ E. Ls. 3-fol.; lflts. ov., 3, base rounded or straight, hairless, margin undulate; long-stalked. Female fls. 1, maroon red; male much smaller, purple. Fruit 2, sausage-shaped, pale purple, edible. Japan. (Fig. 2 J.)

A. quinata DC. 40. April. ½ E. Ls. digitate, 5-fol.; lflts. ov., 2, entire, rounded or tapering base, hairless. Female fls. 1½, dark chocolate purple; male ¼, purple; all slender-stalked in slender fragrant drooping sprays. Fruit 4, sausage-shaped, grey or purple, containing numerous seeds in white pulp. China and Japan. (Fig. 5 G.)

DECAISNEA. Buds large and pointed. Young shoots stout, hairless. Ls. pinnate, 36; lflts. ov., 6, pointed, entire, hairless, glaucous below. Fls. 1, yellowish green, in drooping panicles. Fruit 4, sausage-shaped.

D. Fargesii Franch. 10. June. D. Fruit bright blue. China. (Fig. 10 A.)

D. insignis Hook f. & Thoms. 10. June. D. Fruit yellow. Himalaya.

HOLBOELLIA. Climbers. Ls. 3-fol. or digitate; lflts. pointed.

H. coriacea Diels. 30. May. E. Ls. 3-fol.; lflts. ov., 3, entire, hairless, leathery, dark glossy green. Fls. 1, fragrant, in branched clusters in l.-axils; male greenish white, female purplish. Fruit 3, sausage-shaped, purple. China. (Fig. 1 K.)

H. latifolia Wall. (*Stauntonia latifolia* Wall.). 50. May. E. Ls. 3-9-fol.; lflts. ov., 7. Fls. and fruit as above. Himalaya.

LARDIZABALA BITERNATA Ruiz. & Pav. Climber. 30. May. E. Ls. 3-fol. or twice 3-fol.; lflts. ov., 4, with a few sharply pointed teeth. Male fls. $\frac{3}{4}$, purple, fleshy, in a drooping spike; female fls. 1, purple, fleshy, solitary on slender stalk. Chile. (Fig. 1 M.)

SARGENTODOXA CUNEATA Rehd. & Wils. (HOLBOELLIA CUNEATA Oliv.). Climber. May. D. Ls. 3-fol., long-stalked; lflts. unequal; terminal one ov., 5, tapering base, stalked; lateral ones slightly larger, very unequal at base, nearly stalkless; all palmately nerved, green below. Fls. $\frac{3}{4}$, in drooping racemes, sexes on different plants. Fruit $\frac{1}{4}$, a black 1-seeded berry. China. (Fig. 2 D.)

SINOFRANCHETIA SINENSIS Hemsl. Climber. 40. May. D. Ls. 3-fol. at end of long stalk; lateral lflts. ov., 6, entire, unequal-sided, nearly stalkless; terminal one stalked. Fls. small, dull white, in drooping racemes. Fruits grape-like, purple, borne alternately on a long hanging stalk. China. (Fig. 1 N.)

STAUNTONIA HEXAPHYLLA Decne. Climber. May. E. Ls. 3-7-fol., long-stalked; lflts. ov., 5, pointed, leathery, hairless, long-stalked. Fls. $\frac{3}{4}$, white tinged with violet, in few-flowered racemes. Fruit the size and shape of a walnut, purple, sweet and watery. China and Japan. (Fig. 5 A.)

Family 11. BERBERIDACEAE. P3+3, A3+3, $\underline{G}$1

Woody or herbaceous plants with alternate or clustered leaves and watery juice. Fls. bisexual; stamens opposite the perianth segments; carpel one.

BERBERIS. Barberry. Spiny shrubs, with the spines usually in threes. Ls. in the spine axils. Fls. small, yellow, usually in nodding clusters or racemes, sometimes solitary. Fruit a berry.

(I) DECIDUOUS BARBERRIES. Ls. usually obov. Berry usually red

(*a*) *Fls. in racemes*

B. aetnensis Presl. 2. May. Branchlets erect, grooved. Ls. obov., $\frac{3}{4}$, bristle-toothed. Fls. in short racemes. Sicily. (Fig. 79 A.)

B. aristata DC. 10. June–July. Branches shining reddish brown, slightly drooping. Ls. obov., 3, leathery, entire or with a few large teeth, green below. Fls. in long hanging sprays. Berry spindle-shaped. Himalaya. (Fig. 79 C.)

B. brachypoda Maxim. 8. May. Branches angled, downy grey. Ls. obov., 3, strongly veined below, green and downy on both sides. Fls. in racemes up to 2 long. China. (Fig. 79 D.)

B. canadensis Mill. American Barberry. 8. May. Like *B. vulgaris* (see below), but young branches brown. East North America.

B. chitria Lindl. 10. June. $\frac{1}{2}$ E. Ls. obov., 3, sparsely toothed or entire, green on both sides. Fls. $\frac{1}{2}$, pale yellow, in drooping panicles. Berry $\frac{1}{2}$, oblong, dark red or purple. Himalaya. (Fig. 80 K.)

BERBERIS—*continued*

B. dasystachya Maxim. 12. April–May. Spines few, single. Ls. ov., 1½, bristle-toothed, blunt-ended, long-stalked. Fls. ¼, in racemes 2½ long. Berry ¼, coral-red. China.

B. Dielsiana Fedde. 10. May. Ls. oblanc., 1, entire or with a few spiny teeth, glaucous below. Fls. in long racemes. Berry ½, egg-shaped. China.

B. Francisci-Ferdinandi Schneid. 10. May. Spines mostly simple. Ls. ov., 2½, spiny-toothed, green and glossy on both sides. Fls. in long drooping racemes. Berry ½, egg-shaped. China.

B. heteropoda Schrenk. 5. June. Branchlets cylindrical, shining brown. Ls. ov., 1½, finely toothed, bluish green. Fls. ½, orange-yellow, fragrant. Berry black. Turkestan.

B. polyantha Hemsl. 12. August. Ls. obov., 1, blunt-ended, spine-toothed, dull green above, glaucous below, net-veined on both sides. Fls. in long much-branched panicles. Berry oblong, salmon-red. China. (Fig. 79 H.)

B. Sieboldii Miq. 3. May. Ls. narrow, obov., 2½, thin, margins crowded with fine bristles. Fls. in short clusters of two to three on a long stalk. The leaves turn scarlet in autumn. West China. (Fig. 79 J.)

B. Vernae Schneid. 10. April. Branches grooved, spines single near the top. Ls. oblanc., 1¾, with a few bristle-like teeth. Fls. in dense sprays up to 1½. Berry round, transparent, salmon-red. West China. (Fig. 79 N.)

B. vulgaris L. Common Barberry. 10. May. Branches strongly grooved, yellowish when young, grey in second year. Ls. obov., 1½, tapering to a stalk, dull green, finely toothed. Fls. in drooping racemes up to 3 long. Berry ½, egg-shaped. Europe (including Britain). (Fig. 79 M.)

Var. *atropurpurea* Regel. Ls. purple.

B. yunnanensis Franch. See under (*b*).

(*b*) *Fls. solitary or in clusters*

B. aggregata Schneid. 6. July. Branchlets angled. Ls. obov., 1, spine-toothed, net-veined. Fls. in dense short clusters. Style persistent on berry. Himalaya. (Fig. 79 B.)

Var. *Prattii* Schneid. Ls. 1½, often entire. Berry coral-scarlet.

B. concinna Hook. f. 3. June. Branches furrowed. Ls. obov., 1, glossy green above, white below, spine-toothed. Fls. ½, round, solitary. Berry ¾, oblong. Himalaya. (Fig. 79 E.)

B. diaphana Maxim. 6. May. Branches stout, grooved, yellowish. Ls. obov., 1½, blunt-ended, toothed or entire, glaucous and net-veined below. Fls. in two or threes on a common stalk. Berry egg-shaped, with slight bloom. China. (Fig. 79 G.)

B. dictophylla Franch. 6. May. Branches covered with white bloom when young. Ls. obov., 1, spine-tipped, entire or with a few spiny teeth on the margin, bright green and net-veined above, chalky white below. Fls. solitary or in pairs. Berry egg-shaped. China. (Fig. 79 F.)

B. sibirica Pall. 1. May. Branchlets angled. Ls. ov., ½, spine-toothed, bright green, net-veined below. Fls. ¼, yellow, solitary or in pairs. Berry egg-shaped, red. Siberia.

B. Sieboldii Miq. See under (*a*).

BERBERIS—*continued*

B. Thunbergii DC. 8. April. Much branched; branches strongly grooved, yellowish or purplish red; spines usually single. Ls. obov., 1, very unequal in size, entire, bright green, turning red in autumn. Fls. inconspicuous, reddish outside, solitary or in small clusters. Berry egg-shaped, glossy. Japan. (Fig. 79 K.)

Var. *minor* Rehd. Dwarf form with small leaves.

Var. *pluriflora* Koehne. Low spreading shrub turning brilliant scarlet in autumn.

B. Wilsonae Hemsl. 4. May. Branches thin, reddish brown, with short internodes. Ls. oblanc., ¾, entire, glaucous below. Berry round, style persistent. West China. (Fig. 79 L.)

Var. *Stapfiana* Schneid. Berry egg-shaped.

Var. *subcaulialata* Schneid. Ls. obov., sometimes with one or a few teeth near apex, whitish below, turning brilliant red in autumn. Berries bright red, produced in abundance.

B. yunnanensis Franch. 6. May. Like *B. diaphana*, but branches reddish and flowers usually in racemes. China. (Fig. 79 O.)

(II) EVERGREEN BARBERRIES. Ls. often lanc.
Berry blue or black

(*a*) *Ls. entire*

B. buxifolia Poir. 10. April. Ls. obov., ½. Fls. solitary or in pairs, golden yellow. Berry egg-shaped, dark purple. Chile.

B. empetrifolia Lam. 1½. May. Ls. linear, ½, spine-tipped, margins recurved. Fls. golden yellow, solitary or in pairs. Berry black. Chile.

B. linearifolia Philippi. 6. April. Ls. linear, 1, spine-tipped, dark glossy green above, glaucous below, margins recurved. Fls. ¾, golden yellow, in small clusters. Berry ½, egg-shaped, black. Chile.

B. Lycium Royle. 8. June. Branches grey or white, rigid. Ls. oblanc., 2½, entire, stiff-pointed. Fls. in short racemes. Berry oblong, violet-blue. Himalaya. (Fig. 80 B.)

B. stenophylla Lindl. 12. April–May. Branches slender, cylindrical, downy. Ls. narrow lanc., 1, spine-pointed, margin recurved, dark green above, whitish below. Fls. golden yellow, in small clusters, produced in great profusion. Hybrid. (Fig. 80 J.)

(*b*) *Ls. toothed*

B. chitria Lindl. See under (I) (*a*).

B. Darwinii Hook. 12. April–May. Ls. 1½, holly-like, 3-spined at apex. Fls. golden yellow, produced in great abundance in drooping racemes up to 4 long. Berry egg-shaped, dark purple, with long style. Chile. (Fig. 80 A.)

B. Gagnepainii Schneid. 5. May–June. Ls. lanc., 5, dark green, toothed, wavy. Fls. ½, in small clusters. Berry ½, egg-shaped, bluish black, bloomy. China. (Fig. 80 C.)

B. hakeoides Schneid. 12. May. Stem-spines small. Ls. round, 1, spiny-toothed. Fls. in dense round clusters. Berry bluish black. Chile. (Fig. 80 F.)

BERBERIS—*continued*

B. Hookeri Lam. (*B. Wallichiana* Hort.). 5. April–May. Ls. lanc., 3, with a few spiny teeth, glossy dark green above, white below. Berry ½, conical, black-purple. Himalaya. (Fig. 80 D.)

B. insignis Hook. f. & Thoms. 6. May. Ls. lanc., 5, solitary or in threes, long-pointed, spiny-toothed or entire. Himalaya. (Fig. 80 E.)

B. Julianae Schneid. 6. June. Branchlets yellowish, slight-angled. Ls. lanc., 2, spine-toothed, dark green above, leathery. Fls. ½, in short clusters. West China.

B. pruinosa Franch. 8. June. Branchlets cylindrical, yellowish. Ls. obov., 2½, leathery, glossy above, often grey-white below, teeth slender and spiny. Fls. in short clusters. Berry covered with white bloom. China. (Fig. 80 C.)

B. replicata W. W. Sm. 4. March–May. Like *B. Gagnepainii*, but ls. smaller and margins recurved. Berry red, becoming black. China.

B. Sargentiana Lindl. 6. June. Branches cylindrical, reddish when young. Ls. lanc., oblong, 4, closely spine-toothed, leathery. China. (Fig. 80 H.)

B. Veitchii Schneid. (*B. acuminata* Veitch). 6. May. Stem-spines stout. Ls. narrow lanc., 5, spine-toothed. Fls. ¾, brownish yellow, in small clusters. Berry ½, oblong. China. (Fig. 80 M.)

B. verruculosa Hemsl. & Wils. 3. May. Branchlets cylindrical, thickly warted. Ls. ov., lanc., 1, with a few spiny teeth, margin recurved, glossy dark green above, glaucous below. Fls. ¾, golden yellow, solitary or in pairs. China. (Fig. 80 L.)

MAHONIA. Stem without spines. Ls. alternate, pinnate, usually spine-toothed. Fls. yellow, fragrant, in erect racemes. Fruit a bluish-black berry.

M. Aquifolium Nutt. (*Berberis Aquifolium* Pursh.). Oregon Grape. 3. February–April. E. Lflts. ov., 3, unequal at base, with small spiny teeth, leathery, dark green, glossy. North America. (Fig. 12 F.)

M. Fremontii Fedde. 12. May–June. E. Lflts. ov., 1½, pale bluish grey, very spiny. South United States.

M. japonica DC. (*Berberis japonica* R.Br.). 10. March–April. E. Thick unbranched stem bearing a few leaves at the top. Lflts. ov., 5, unequal at base, with a few large spiny teeth. Fls. lemon-yellow, very fragrant. Japan. (Fig. 12 G.)

M. nepalensis DC. (*Berberis nepalensis* Spreng.). 20. March–April. E. Bark soft, corky. Lflts. lanc., 4½, equal at base or nearly so, spine-toothed, leathery, glossy. Himalaya. (Fig. 12 E.)

M. nervosa Nutt. 1. May–June. E. A low shrub with long-persistent bud-scales and long-stalked leaves. Lflts. ov., 3, 3-5-nerved at base, leathery, glossy. North America.

M. pinnata Fedde. 12. March–April. E. Like *M. Aquifolium*, but taller and with duller foliage. California.

* NANDINA DOMESTICA Thunb. Heavenly Bamboo. 8. June–July. E. Stems erect; spineless, unbranched. Ls. opposite, 2-3-pinnate; lflts. linear, lanc., 4, entire, long-pointed, hairless, tinged with red when young, purplish in autumn. Fls. ½, white, with large yellow anthers, in a large erect panicle. Fruit ¼, a bright red or purplish 2-seeded berry with persistent style. China and Japan. (Fig. 22 A.)

Family 12. **PAPAVERACEAE.** K2–3, C4–6, A ∞, G̲ (2–∞)

Mostly herbaceous plants, including the poppies and greater celandine. Juice milky, yellow, white, or red. Fruit usually a many-seeded capsule, either splitting, or opening by pores. The most important economic member is the opium poppy, from which opium and morphia are obtained from the juice of the capsule.

DENDROMECON RIGIDUM Benth. Californian Tree Poppy, Shrubby Poppy. 10. Summer. D. Ls. alternate, lanc., 3, pointed, entire, thick, bluish green, net-veined, short-stalked. Fls. 3, yellow, solitary, fragrant, K2, C4. Seed-pod 4, linear, curved and grooved. California. (Fig. 114 G.)

ROMNEYA COULTERI Harvey. Matilija Poppy. 8. Summer. D. Stems herbaceous. Ls. alternate, 4, lobed, very glaucous, a few spiny bristles on midrib and stalk. Fls. 5, solitary or in pairs, five or six white satiny petals, sepals smooth, stamens yellow. Seed-pod densely covered with stiff yellowish bristles. California. (Fig. 36 E.)

Var. *trichocalyx* Eastw. Sepals bristly.

Family 13. **CRUCIFERAE.** K2+2, C4, A6, G̲ (2)

The chief characteristics are the cruciform corolla of four petals; the six stamens, four long and two short, and the superior 2-celled ovary having a single style and stigma. The family consists almost entirely of herbaceous plants, many of great value owing to their rich vitamin content. Examples are the common cabbage and its varieties kale, broccoli, Brussels sprouts, etc.; turnip, radish, swede, watercress, sea-kale, and mustard. Among ornamental plants are wallflower, stock, candytuft, honesty, and aubrietia. There are no trees.

ALYSSUM. Ls. alternate, downy with star-shaped hairs, usually silvery grey. Fruit egg-shaped, with one or two seeds in each cell.

A. argenteum Vitm. 1½. June–July. E. Young stems covered with silvery down. Ls. linear, oblanc., 1, silvery-downy below. Fls. yellow, in flattish branched clusters about 4 across. South Europe. (Fig. 50 N.)

A. saxatile L. Gold Dust, Golden Tuft. 1½. April–May. E. Ls. oblanc., 6, blunt-ended with small abrupt point, downy below. Fls. ¼, yellow, in rounded heads about 1 across. Europe. (Fig. 115 A.)

A. spinosum L. 1. April–May. E. Spiny, spines slender. Ls. narrow, oblong, oblanc., 2, entire, silvery-downy on both sides. Fls. white, fragrant, in terminal heads ¾ across. South Europe. (Fig. 115 F.)

IBERIS. Candytuft. Ls. green, hairless or nearly so, blunt-ended. Petals unequal. Fruit ov., winged, deeply notched at apex.

I. gibraltarica L. Gibraltar Candytuft. 1½. April–May. E. Ls. oblanc., 2, toothed near apex or entire. Fls. lilac-pink. South Spain, Morocco.

I. sempervirens L. Evergreen Candytuft. 1½. April–June. E. Ls. linear, 2. Fls. white. South Europe. (Fig. 52 B.)

VELLA. Ls. alternate, entire, bristly. Fls. yellow, in erect terminal racemes. Seed-pod ¼, egg-shaped, one or two seeds in each cell.

* **V. Pseudocytisus** L. Cress Rocket. 2. June–July. E. Ls. obov., ¾, covered with stiff bristly hairs (like a miniature cactus). Fls. 1. Pod beaked. Spain. (Fig. 115 E.)

* **V. spinosa** Boiss. 2. May. E. Spiny. Ls. linear, 1, fleshy. Fls. ¾, few. Spain. (Fig. 50 M.)

Family 14. **CAPPARIDACEAE.** K4–8, C4–8, A6–∞, G̲ (2)

Ls. alternate. Ovary usually stalked. Capers are the flower-buds of *Capparis spinosa*.

CAPPARIS SPINOSA L. Caper Bush. 3. June. D. Stem straggling. Ls. ov., 2, entire, short-stalked, with two reflexed spines at the base of each. Fls. 2, white, ovary on a stalk longer than the corolla. Fruit a berry. Mediterranean region.

Family 15. **CISTACEAE.** K3–5, C5, A ∞, G̲ (3) or (5–10)

Ls. opposite. Fls. showy; sepals three, often with two smaller ones. Fruit a capsule splitting lengthwise.

CISTUS. Rock Rose, Sweet Cistin. May–June. E. Leaf-stalks in contact at base. G̲ (5–10).

(a) Ls. 3-nerved, or 3-nerved at base

C. albidus L. 6. Young parts white-felted. Ls. ov., 2, blunt-ended, margins recurved, net-veined below. Fls. 2½, pale lilac with patch of yellow at base of each petal, K5. South-west Europe.

C. crispus L. 2. Stems clammy, shining. Ls. narrowly wedge-shaped, 1½, clammy, margins wavy. Fls. 1½, purplish red, K5, crowded in terminal heads. Mediterranean region.

C. cyprius Lam. 8. Ls. lanc., 3. Fls. 3, white with red blotch at base of petal, in long-stalked clusters. Cyprus.

C. florentinus Lam. 4. Not clammy. Ls. lanc., 1½, wavy. Fls. 2, white with yellow blotch. Hybrid.

* **C. ladaniferus** L. Gum Cistus. 5. Very clammy. Ls. linear, lanc., 4, covered with dirty white down. Fls. 4, white with purple blotch, K3, solitary. South-west Europe. (Fig. 68 H.)

Var. *albiflorus* Dunal. Petals yellow at base, not blotched with purple.

C. laurifolius L. Bush Rock Rose. 8. Ls. ov., lanc., 3, wavy, hairy, long-stalked. Fls. 3, white with yellow at base of petals, K3, in hairy erect clusters. South-west Europe. (Fig. 68 J.)

C. laxus Ait. 6. Ls. lanc., 3, dark green. Fls. 2, white, rose-like. South France.

C. Loretii Rouy & Fouc. 3. Clammy. Ls. linear, lanc., 2½, margins recurved, grey below. Fls. 2, white with crimson blotches. Hybrid.

C. lusitanicus Mill. 4. Ls. oblong, 2½, rough and sticky. Fls. 2½, white with crimson blotches, in terminal clusters. Hybrid.

C. monspeliensis L. 3. Clammy. Ls. lanc., 2, dark green and wrinkled above, greyish and hairy below, margins recurved. Fls. 1, white. Mediterranean region.

C. populifolius L. 6. Clammy. Ls. ov., 2½, long-pointed, heart-shaped base, long-stalked. Fls. 3, white with yellow stain.

C. purpureus Lam. 4. Clammy. Ls. lanc., 2, greyish green. Fls. 3, reddish purple with dark red blotches. Hybrid.

C. salvifolius L. 2. Ls. ov., 1½, greyish green, wrinkled above, hairy on both sides. Fls. 1½, white with yellow stain. Mediterranean region.

(b) Ls. not 3-nerved

C. corbariensis Pourr. 4. Clammy. Ls. ov., 2, hairy, margins wavy. Fls. 1½, white with yellow stain at base of each petal. South Europe. (Fig. 68 G.)

CISTUS—*continued*

C. villosus L. 4. Ls. ov., 2, grey down on both sides, wrinkled. Fls. 2½, purple or rose-coloured. Mediterranean region.

HELIANTHEMUM. Rock Rose, Sun Rose. May–June. E. G (3).

H. alpestre Dunal. Alpine Sun Rose. 1. Ls. ov., lanc., ¾, green on both sides, hairless or nearly so. Fls. ½, yellow. Alpine regions of Central Europe, Caucasus, and Asia Minor.

H. alyssoides Vent. 2. Ls. lanc., 1, grey with dense down. Fls. 1½, yellow. South-west Europe.

H. appeninum Lam. & DC. (*H. polifolium* Pers.). White Rock Rose. 1½. Ls. linear, 1, grey down on both sides. Fls. 1, white, K5 (three large, two small). Europe (including Britain). (Fig. 68 L.)

H. canum Baumg. Hoary Rock Rose. ½. Ls. lanc., 1, green and hairy above, white-felted below. Fls. ½, yellow. Europe (including Britain). (Fig. 68 K.)

H. formosum Dunal (*H. lasianthum* Pers., *Cistus formosus* Curt.). Sweet Cistin. 3. Ls. ov., 1, downy on both sides, 3-nerved. Fls. 1½, lemon-yellow with five purple patches in centre. Portugal.

H. nummularium L. (*H. Chamaecistus* Mill., *H. vulgare* Gaertn.). Common Rock Rose. 1. Ls. oblong, 1, green above, greyish below. Fls. 1, yellow, K5 (three large, two small). Europe (including Britain). (Fig. 68 M.)

White, red, and copper-coloured varieties in cultivation.

Family 16. **VIOLACEAE.** K5, C5, A5, G (3)

Ls. alternate, with stipules. Each stamen has a spur projecting above the anthers. The two following genera have no superficial resemblance to violets or pansies.

HYMENANTHERA. Fls. small, inconspicuous, brownish yellow, solitary or in crowded axillary clusters. Fruit a white berry.

* **H. chathamica** T. Kirk. 6. E. Ls. ov., lanc., 4, toothed, prominently veined on both sides, short-stalked. New Zealand. (Fig. 78 G.)

H. crassifolia Hook. f. 6. April. ½ E. Branches grey, stout, rigid, spreading. Ls. obov., 1, entire, rounded or notched at apex, hairless, often in clusters. New Zealand. (Fig. 115 H.)

* MELICYTUS RAMIFLORUS Forst. 30. June. D. Bark white. Branchlets pale green spotted with white, hairless. Ls. oblong, lanc., 6, tapered towards both ends, coarsely toothed, two pointed stipules at base of leaf-stalk. Fls. small, yellowish green, in clusters in joints of previous year's growth. Clusters of violet-blue berries. New Zealand. (Fig. 78 M.)

Family 17. **FLACOURTIACEAE.** K5, C5 or 0, A ∞, G (2)

Mostly tropical and subtropical trees and shrubs. Ls. alternate, with stipules; usually leathery. Fruit a berry or capsule.

AZARA. Ls. with very large stipules, one of which is usually enlarged to resemble a second leaf. Fls. small, without petals, but with conspicuous yellow stamens, crowded in small axillary branched clusters. Fruit a berry.

AZARA—*continued*

* **A. dentata** Ruiz & Pav. 12. July. E. Ls. ov., 2, toothed, bitter. Fls. fragrant. Chile.

* **A. Gilliesii** Hook. & Arn. 20. April–May. E. Ls. ov., 3, distantly toothed, glossy green, hairless. Chile. (Fig. 78 J.)

* **A. lanceolata** Hook. f. 20. April. Branchlets downy. Ls. lanc., 2, coarsely toothed, bright green, turning inky black on cut shoots (Bean). Fls. very numerous, fragrant. Chile.

A. microphylla Hook. f. 25. February–April. E. Ls. ov., 1, with a few teeth or entire, glossy, hairless, crowded. Fls. vanilla-scented. Berry red or orange. Chile. (Fig. 78 H.)

* BERBERIDOPSIS CORALLINA Hook. f. Strangle Bush, Coral Barberry. July–September. E. Climber. Ls. ov., 4, square-cut at base, coarsely spine-toothed, leathery, glaucous below. Fls. ½, round, crimson, drooping, long-stalked. Fruit ½, a berry. Chile. (Fig. 78 K.)

CARRIEREA CALYCINA Franch. 30. June. D. Young shoots and leaf-stalks reddish. Ls. ov., 5, 3-nerved and rounded or heart-shaped at base, distantly round-toothed, slender-stalked. Fls. 1, bluish white, cup-shaped, stalk with pair of yellowish bracts, in terminal panicles. Fruit 3, spindle-shaped, splitting into three; seeds winged. China. (Fig. 81 D.)

IDESIA POLYCARPA Maxim. 30. June. D. Ls. ov., 6, heart-shaped base, distantly toothed, dark green above, glaucous white below, long-stalked. Fls. ¼, yellowish green, without petals, in large terminal panicles. Bunches of red berries turning from green to dark brown or red. China and Japan. (Fig. 81 A.)

POLIOTHYRSIS SINENSIS Oliv. 40. July–August. D. Ls. ov., 6, long-pointed, toothed, hairless or nearly so, long-stalked. Fls. ¼, greenish white or yellow, in loose terminal panicles. Fruit ¾, an egg-shaped many-seeded capsule, seeds winged. China. (Fig. 78 L.)

At Abbotsbury there is a variety with wedge-shaped leaves that are thicker and coarser and 3-nerved at base.

XYLOSMA RACEMOSA Miq. Tung-Ching Tree. 80. August. E. Stem spiny. Ls. broadly ov., 3, rounded or broadly wedge-shaped base, unevenly toothed, short-stalked. Fls. small, yellow, fragrant, unisexual, in small axillary racemes. Fruit ¼, dark purple, style persistent. China. (Fig. 82 H.)

Family 18. **PITTOSPORACEAE.** K5, C5, A5, $\underline{G}$ (2–5)

Resinous trees or shrubs, some climbing. Ls. alternate, leathery, evergreen, usually entire, without stipules. Fruit a capsule or berry.

* BILLARDIERA LONGIFLORA Labill. Purple Apple Berry. Climber. 6. July. E. Stems slender, hairless. Ls. lanc., 1½, entire. Fls. ¾, greenish yellow, drooping, slender-stalked, solitary in leaf-axils. Fruit 1, oblong, dark blue. Tasmania. (Fig. 115 B.)

Var. *fructu-albo* Hort. Berries white.

* BURSARIA SPINOSA Cav. 15. August. E. Ls. obov., 1½, toothed at apex, stalkless. Fls. ¼, white, petals narrow, in terminal panicles. Fruit ¼, a flat reddish-brown capsule, produced in great abundance. Australia. (Fig. 81 B.)

PITTOSPORUM. Evergreen shrubs or small trees. Ls. rather fleshy, usually with a pretty green-and-white network of veins (best seen when the leaf is held

PITTOSPORUM—*continued*
up against the light), often grouped radially at the end of the branch. Fruit a round or egg-shaped capsule.

(*a*) *Fls. dark red or purple*

* **P. bicolor** Hook. f. 40. November–April. Ls. linear, 2½, entire, margins recurved. Fls. deep crimson. Tasmania. (Fig. 51 J.)

* **P. crassifolium** Banks & Soland. 15. May. Ls. ov., 4, entire, leathery, covered with pale brown or whitish down. Fls. 1, dark purple, petals strap-shaped. New Zealand. (Fig. 115 D.)

* **P. divaricatum** Cockayne. 12. May. Ls. linear, obov. or pinnately lobed, ¾. Fls. very small, deep maroon, almost black, solitary. New Zealand. (Fig. 36 M.)

* **P. patulum** Hook. f. 15. May. Ls. linear, 2, lobed on young plants. Fls. bell-shaped, dark crimson, in terminal clusters. New Zealand. (Fig. 51 H.)

* **P. Ralphii** T. Kirk. Like *P. crassifolium*, but with larger and more oblong ls. New Zealand.

* **P. tenuifolium** Banks & Soland. 30. Trunk slender; branchlets almost black. Ls. ov., 2½, entire, pale shining silvery green, with wavy margins. Fls. ¼, dark chocolate-purple, very fragrant. New Zealand. (Fig. 116 B.)

(*b*) *Fls. white, yellow, or greenish*

* **P. Dallii** Cheeseman. 18. June–July. Ls. lanc., 4½, toothed or entire, crowded radially at end of shoot. Fls. ½, white, crowded in terminal cluster. New Zealand. (Fig. 81 C.)

* **P. eugenioides** Cunn. 40. Ls. lanc., 5, margins often wavy. Fls. very small, greenish yellow, in dense terminal clusters. New Zealand. (Fig. 116 A.)

* **P. pauciflorum** Oliv. 6. May. Ls. oblanc., 5. Fls. ½, dull yellow, fragrant. China. (Fig. 115 M.)

* **P. revolutum** Ait. 12. May. Young shoots and leaves felted with pale brown wool. Ls. lanc., 4½, brown wool below. Fls. yellow, petals curved. Australia. (Fig. 116 C.)

* **P. Tobira** Ait. 20. May–July. Ls. obov., 4, blunt-ended, leathery, hairless, midrib white, strongly aromatic, grouped radially at end of shoot. Fls. 1, white or yellow, fragrant, in terminal clusters. China and Japan. (Fig. 115 C.)

* **P. undulatum** Vent. 40. May–July. Ls. ov., lanc., 6, entire, laurel-like, glossy green, margins often wavy, grouped radially at end of shoot. Fls. ¾, creamy white, in terminal clusters. Australia. (Fig. 115 L.)

* SOLLYA HETEROPHYLLA Lindl. Australian Bluebell Creeper. 6. April–May. E. Climber. Ls. alternate, ov., lanc., 2, entire, short-stalked. Fls. ¾, blue, in dropping branched clusters. Fruit 1, a sausage-shaped berry. West Australia. (Fig. 115 G.)

Family 19. **POLYGALACEAE.** K5, C3–5, A4+4, $\underline{G}$(2)

Fls. irregular, not unlike those of the pea family, but there are only eight stamens and the ovary is 2-celled, with one ovule in each cell.

POLYGALA CHAMAEBUXUS L. Milkwort. 1. April–May. E. Creeping plant. Ls. alternate, ov., 1, box-like, dull green, with small pointed tip. Fls. ½, pea-like, creamy white, end of keel bright yellow. Fruit a flat 2-seeded capsule. Alps of Central Europe. (Fig. 115 J.)

Var. *purpurea* Neilr. Fls. purple, with yellow centre.

Family 20. **FRANKENIACEAE.** K (4–7), C4–6, A6, G̲ (3)

This family contains only one genus of which the best known species is described below.

FRANKENIA LAEVIS L. Sea Heath. May. E. Low heath-like shrub seldom exceeding 3 inches in height. Ls. in whorls, ¼, thick, much recurved. Fls. small, pinkish white, solitary, petals spreading. Europe (including east coast of Britain). (Fig. 48 O.)

Family 21. **TAMARICACEAE.** K (4–5), C4–5, A4–10 or ∞, G̲ (4–5 or 2)

Ls. alternate, minute, scale-like, giving the slender branches the appearance of green plumes. Fruit a capsule with bearded seeds.

MYRICARIA GERMANICA Desv. (TAMARIX GERMANICA L.). 8. Summer. E. Branches erect, plume-like. Ls. greyish glaucous. Fls. very small, pink or pinkish white in dense terminal racemes, stamens united at base, beard of seed stalked. Europe.

TAMARIX. Tamarisk. Ls. green or hairy. Stamens free. Beard of seed not stalked.

(a) Fls. in spring on lateral or previous year's branchlets, 4-parted

T. tetrandra Pall. 15. May. D. Branchlets arching, almost black. Fls. very small, rose-coloured, A4, in straight cylindrical racemes. Mediterranean region. (Fig. 49 A.)

(b) Fls. in late summer in terminal racemes, 5-parted

T. anglica Webb. 10. August–October. E. Branchlets erect, reddish brown. Fls. pink, petals deciduous, A5. Europe (including Britain).

T. gallica L. 12. July–September. ½ E. Branchlets purplish. Fls. white tinged with pink, petals deciduous, A5. Mediterranean region.

T. hispida Willd. 4. August–September. D. Branchlets and leaves downy. Ls. very glaucous. Fls. bright pink. West Asia.

T. pentandra Pall. 15. July–August. D. Branchlets purple. Fls. rose-carmine, petals persistent. Mediterranean region.

Family 22. **HYPERICACEAE.** K4–5, C4–5, A ∞, G̲ (3–5)

Ls. opposite, entire, dotted with transparent glands, stalkless or nearly so. Fls. yellow, showy, the stamens in bundles. Fruit a capsule.

ASCYRUM HYPERICOIDES L. St. Andrew's Cross. 1. July–September. D. Stems 2-edged. Ls. narrow obov., 1. Fls. ¾, solitary or in threes, terminal; petals four, arranged in form of St. Andrew's Cross. U.S.A. (Fig. 68 E.)

HYPERICUM. St. John's Wort. Petals and sepals five; stamens in three to five bundles, styles three or five.

(*a*) *Fls. with five styles*

H. calycinum L. Rose of Sharon. 1½. June–September. E. Stems angled. Ls. ov., 4, glaucous below. Fls. 3. South-east Europe and Asia Minor. (Fig. 68 A.)

H. Hookerianum Wight & Arn. (*H. oblongifolium* Choisy). 5. August–September. E. Stems cylindrical. Ls. ov., lanc., 4, blue-green above, glaucous below. Fls. 2, cup-shaped. Himalaya.

H. Kalmianum L. 3. August–September. D. Stems 4-angled; branchlets 2-edged. Ls. lanc., 2, bluish green above, glaucous below. Fls. 1. East North America.

H. Moserianum André. 1. August–September. E. Stems arching, reddish. Ls. ov., 2. Fls. 2. Hybrid.

H. patulum Thunb. 3. August–September. E. Stems arching, purplish, 2-edged. Ls. ov., 2, the pairs often some distance apart, pointed. Fls. 2. India and China. (Fig. 68 B.)

(*b*) *Fls. with three styles*

H. Androsaemum L. Tutsan. 3. July–August. ½ E. Stems 2-edged. Ls. ov., 4, heart-shaped base, whitish below, slightly aromatic. Fls. ¾, pale yellow. Europe (including Britain). (Fig. 68 E.)

H. aureum Bartr. 3. August–September. D. Branchlets 2-edged. Ls. ov., 3, blue-green above, glaucous below. Fls. 2, terminal, sepals leaf-like. South United States.

* **H. Coris** L. 2. August–September. D. Stems cylindrical. Ls. linear, ¾, in whorls, margins recurved. Fls. ¾, in terminal panicles. South Europe. (Fig. 52 F.)

H. elatum Dryand. 5. July–August. ½ E. Stems slightly 2-edged. Ls. ov., 3, blunt-ended, often with heart-shaped base, aromatic when crushed. Fls. 1, sepals reflexed in fruit. Canary Islands. (Fig. 68 C.)

* **H. empetrifolium** Willd. 3. June–July. D. Like *H. Coris*, but sepals spreading in fruit. South Europe.

H. hircinum L. 3. August–September. ½ E. Stems 2-edged. Ls. ov., lanc., 2, with a goat-like smell when crushed. Fls. 1, sepals deciduous. South Europe.

Family 23. **TERNSTROEMIACEAE.** K5, 6 or 7, C5 or more, A 5–∞, G̲ (3–5) or 3–5

Trees and shrubs with alternate and generally leathery leaves. No stipules. Fls. with numerous stamens, except in *Stachyurus*. Ovary 3-5-celled or with 3–5 carpels. The family includes several genera with doubtful affinities; *Actinidia* and *Clematoclethra*, for instance, have been placed by Engler in *Dilleniaceae*. Tea is obtained from the leaves of *Camellia chinensis*, not hardy except in very mild localities. The related family *Dipterocarpaceae* produces many important tropical hardwoods, such as Borneo camphorwood, eng, gurjun, red lauan, seraya, and sal.

ACTINIDIA. Deciduous climbers with chambered pith. Fruit a berry.

A. arguta Sieb. & Zucc. 50. June. Stems hairless or nearly so. Ls. ov., 5, abruptly pointed, heart-shaped or rounded at base, the margins set with

ACTINIDIA—*continued*

fine bristly teeth, green and bristly on midrib below, long-stalked, the stalk often bristly. Fls. ¾, greenish white, in 3-flowered clusters in the leaf-axils. Fruit 1, an oblong greenish-yellow berry. Japan.

A. chinensis Planch. 25. June. Similar to the above, but stems densely hairy. Leaf-stalk rose-coloured. Fls. 1½, creamy white. Fruit 2, egg-shaped, hairy, edible. China and Japan. (Fig. 81 F.)

A. Kolomikta Maxim. Kolomikta Vine. 10. June. Stems hairless or nearly so. Ls. ov., 5, long-pointed, unevenly toothed, often with a white or pink blotch at apex of blade. Fls. 1, white, fragrant. China and Japan.

CAMELLIA (THEA). Ls. smooth, shiny, and somewhat leathery. Fls. large and showy, solitary or in few-flowered clusters in the leaf-axils. Fruit a woody capsule.

(*a*) *Sepals five*

* **C. chinensis** (L.) Kuntze (*C. Thea* Link, *Thea chinensis* Sims). Tea Plant. 20. May. E. Ls. ov., lanc., 6, blunt-ended, toothed, upper surface somewhat raised between the veins. Fls. 1½, white, petals rounded. India and China. (Fig. 82 A.)

C. cuspidata Veitch. 6. May. E. Young stems downy. Ls. ov., lanc., 3, long-pointed, vaguely toothed. Fls. 1½, white, solitary. West China. (Fig. 82 C.)

(*b*) *Sepals more than five*

C. japonica L. 40. April–May. E. Branchlets hairless. Ls. ov., 4, short-pointed, toothed. Fls. 3, red. Japan. (Fig. 81 G.)

Var. *Donckelaarii* Hort. Ls. lanc. Fls. red, double.

Numerous other varieties are in cultivation, with white or red fls.

* **C. Sasanqua** Thunb. 6. May. E. Branchlets downy. Ls. ov., 3, hairy on midrib above. Fls. 2, white. China. (Fig. 82 B.)

There are several garden varieties in cultivation, with white to deep rose, single or double flowers.

CLEMATOCLETHRA. Climbers. July. D. Buds conspicuous, with overlapping scales. Ls. alternate, ov., toothed (sometimes minutely), hairless except on midrib above and below. Fls. ½, white, in axillary branched clusters; A5. Fruit berry-like. Several species from China. (Fig. 81 E.)

* CLEYERA FORTUNEI Hook. f. 6. September. E. Branchlets hairless. Ls. lanc., 6, entire, tapering to both ends, hairless, margins yellow. Fls. ¾, pale yellow, in axillary pairs. China. (Fig. 116 G.)

EURYA. Fls. small, inconspicuous; sepals and petals five. Fruit a berry.

E. japonica Thunb. 3. E. Ls. ov., 3, dark glossy green, toothed, base of leaf-stalk continued down the stem as a prominent raised line on both sides. Fls. white, nodding, in few-flowered clusters in the leaf-axils, unisexual. Fruit a black berry. Japan. (Fig. 82 D.)

* **E. ochnacea** Szys. (*Cleyera ochnacea* DC.). Small tree. E. Ls. ov., 5, entire, leathery, glossy, longish point with rounded tip. Fls. white or yellow, fragrant, in small clusters in the leaf-axils. Fruit a red berry. Himalaya, China, and Japan. (Fig. 116 E.)

GORDONIA. Fls. large and showy, the parts of the flower in fives, stamens in groups of five, sepals very unequal; seed-pod with persistent axis.

GORDONIA—*continued*

* **G. Altamaha** Sarg. (*G. pubescens* L'Hérit., *Franklinia Altamaha* Marsh.). 20. September–October. D. Branchlets downy. Ls. obov., oblanc., 6, tapering gradually to a short stalk, toothed towards apex, dark glossy green above, pale and downy below. Fls. 3, white, solitary in leaf-axil on a very short stout stalk. Seed-pod round. South United States. (Fig. 82 E.)

* **G. axillaris** Szys. 20. November–May. E. Branchlets hairless, grey. Ls. oblanc., 7, thick and leathery, toothed towards end, hairless, dark glossy green. Fls. 6, creamy white, petals deeply notched, stamens yellow; solitary on a short stalk. China. (Fig. 82 G.)

* **G. Lasianthus** Ellis. Loblolly Bay. 70. July–August. E. Ls. obov., oblanc., 4, toothed, hairless. Fls. 2, white, long-stalked, solitary. Seed-pod egg-shaped, pointed. South United States. (Fig. 82 F.)

* HARTIA SINENSIS Dunn. 50. June. E. Ls. ov., 5, pointed, toothed, dark glossy green, conspicuously veined below, stalk broad and hairy. Fls. 1½, white, petals roundish, with jagged edges, solitary in leaf-axils. Fruit ¾, conical, woody. China. (Fig. 83 A.)

STACHYURUS. Fls. small, the parts in fours, in drooping spikes. Fruit berry-like.

S. chinensis Franch. 12. March–April. D. Branchlets greenish or dark brown. Ls. ov., 4, long-pointed, with a rounded or heart-shaped base. Fls. yellow, the spikes attaining their full length in autumn and persisting in bud throughout winter. Fruit ½, greenish yellow with reddish cheek. China. (Fig. 83 B.)

S. praecox Sieb. & Zucc. 12. March–April. D. Like above, but branchlets reddish, smooth, and shining. Japan.

STEWARTIA. Bark smooth and flaky; buds silky. K5, C5, A ∞, $\underline{G}$ (5). Fruit a woody capsule splitting into five.

S. Malachodendron L. (*S. virginica* Cav.). 15. July–August. D. Branchlets downy. Ls. ov., 4, toothed, tapering base, margins fringed with fine hairs, short-stalked. Fls. 3½, white, petals spreading, stamens purple; solitary in leaf-axils. Fruit ½, egg-shaped. South United States. (Fig. 83 D.)

S. pentagyne L'Hérit. 15. July–August. D. Branchlets hairless. Ls. ov., 4, rounded base, tinged with red, sparsely toothed, short-stalked. Fls. 2½, white, cup-shaped, stamens yellow; solitary in leaf-axils. Fruit ¾, egg-shaped, sharply 5-angled. South United States. (Fig. 83 E.)

S. Pseudo-camellia Maxim. 50. July–August. D. Branches upright; bark red, peeling off in large flakes; branchlets hairless, slender. Ls. ov., 3, thick, tapering base, sparsely toothed, bright green tinged with red above, pale green below. Fls. 2, waxy white, cup-shaped, stamens yellow, solitary in leaf-axils. Fruit egg-shaped, 5-angled. Japan. (Fig. 83 C.)

Family 24. **MALVACEAE.** K5 or (5), C5, A (∞), $\underline{G}$ (1–∞)

Ls. alternate, velvety with star-shaped hairs. Fls. usually showy, the stamens united into one bundle. Fruit a capsule dividing into separate carpels.

The most important economic member of the family is the cotton plant (*Gossypium*) from the seeds of which cotton and oilcake are obtained. Balsa wood is the timber of *Ochrona lagopus*, a native of tropical America. The seeds of *Eriodendron anfractuosum* give kapok.

ABUTILON. Ls. long-stalked, palmately nerved, heart-shaped base. Fls. solitary, drooping, sepals often brightly coloured.

* **A. megapotamicum** St. Hil. & Naud. Summer. Ls. lanc., 3, toothed. Fls. 1½, sepals red, petals yellow, stamens long and drooping (like a fuchsia). Brazil. (Fig. 83 H.)

* **A. vitifolium** Presl. 30. May–July. Stems white-felted. Ls. ov., 5, covered with velvety down, 3-5-lobed, the lobes pointed. Fls. 2, pale mauve, cup-shaped, stamens yellow. Chile. (Fig. 29 C.)

HIBISCUS SYRIACUS L. (ALTHAEA FRUTEX Hort.). Shrubby Althaea. 10. August. D. Ls. ov., 4, 3-lobed, coarsely toothed, with a tapering or rounded base, palmately nerved, slender-stalked. Fls. 4, trumpet-shaped, white, red, purple, blue, or striped, double or semi-double; solitary in leaf-axils. Seed-pod divided into five compartments. India and China. (Fig. 29 B.)

Var. *variegatus* Hort. Ls. variegated with white.

HOHERIA. Fls. 1, white, in axillary few-flowered clusters.

H. Lyalli Hook. f. (*Plagianthus Lyalli* Gray, *Gaya Lyalli* Baker). 30. July. D. Ls. ov., 4½, heart-shaped base, jaggedly toothed or slightly lobed, bright green above, pale or whitish below, long-stalked. Petals broad and overlapping. Fruit 1½, round. New Zealand. (Fig. 83 K.)

* **H. populnea** Cunn. New Zealand Ribbon Wood. 30. July. E. Ls. ov., 5, firm, edged with sharply pointed unequal teeth. Petals narrow, oblong. Seed-pod winged. New Zealand.

Var. *angustifolia* Hort. Ls. lanc., 2.

Var. *lanceolata* Hook. f. (*H. sexstylosa* Colenso). Ls. lanc., 4. (Fig. 83 G.)

LAVATERA ARBOREA L. Tree Mallow. 8. July–September. D. Ls. ov., 9, palmately nerved at base, lobed, covered with soft hairs, heart-shaped base. Fls. 1½, purple, each petal with a blotch of purple at the base. Europe. (Fig. 29 A.)

* PLAGIANTHUS BETULINUS Cunn. 40. April–May. D. Very twiggy when young. Ls. ov., 1½–3, toothed, often lobed, slender-stalked. Fls. small, greenish yellow, in terminal panicles. New Zealand. (Fig. 83 F.)

Family 25. **STERCULIACEAE.** K5, Co, A (5), G̱ (5)

Similar to *Malvaceae*, from which it differs in the structure of the anthers. Mostly tropical. Mansonia and obeche are valuable hardwoods imported from West Africa. Cocoa is obtained from the seeds of *Theobroma Cacao*, a native of tropical America.

FREMONTIA CALIFORNICA Torr. 30. May–July. D. Ls. alternate or in clusters, ov., 4, 3-7-lobed or almost entire, dark green above, speckled with star-shaped hairs when young, white- or brown-felted below. Fls. 2½, yellow, solitary on a short stalk. California. (Fig. 29 J.)

* STERCULIA ACERIFOLIA Cunn. (BRACHYCHITON ACERIFOLIUM F. Muell.). Flame Tree. 100. E. Ls. alternate, ov., 6, 3-7-lobed, hairless, long-stalked.

Fls. 1, red, in axillary racemes or panicles. Fruit a large dry pod. Australia. (Fig. 29 H.)

Family 26. **TILIACEAE.** K4–5 or (4–5), C4–5, A ∞, G̲ (2–5)

Like the two preceding families, but the flowers are usually much smaller, with the stamens free or in bundles. Several species yield important timbers such as basswood and thitka (Burma mahogany). Bast is obtained from the inner bark of *Tilia*, which has long tough fibres, and jute for gunny bags from species of *Corchorus* in India.

ARISTOTELIA. Ls. mostly opposite or sub-opposite, sometimes alternate, ov., 5, pointed, toothed. Fls. very small, in axillary branched clusters or panicles, unisexual and the sexes on different plants. Fruit ¼, a purplish-black berry.

* **A. Macqui** L'Hérit. 10. June. E. Ls. finely toothed, dark glossy green, hairless. Fls. greenish white. New Zealand. (Fig. 59 B.)

* **A. racemosa** Hook. f. 25. May. D. Ls. thin, coarsely and unevenly toothed, green and scurfy above, tinged with bronze below. Fls. rose-coloured. New Zealand. (Fig. 59 A.)

* ELAEOCARPUS CYANEUS Sims. 50. Summer. E. Ls. alternate, ov., 2, pointed, distantly toothed, leathery, net-veined. Fls. ¼, white, in axillary racemes. Fruit ½, a blue berry. Australia. (Fig. 83 J.)

GREWIA PARVIFLORA Bunge. 6. August. D. Ls. alternate, in two opposite rows, ov., 4, pointed, 3-nerved at base, unequally toothed, rough above. Fls. ½, creamy yellow, in stalked clusters opposite a leaf. Fruit ¼, a red berry. North China.

TILIA. Lime. Linden. Basswood. Ls. alternate, usually in two opposite rows, roundish, ov., toothed, heart-shaped or straight base, long-stalked. Fls. small, yellowish or whitish, crowded into a small head, the stalk of which grows from a large strap-shaped bract. Fruit ¼, dry, round or egg-shaped, 1-3-seeded. The first seedling leaves are palmately lobed. The flowers are sweet-scented and attractive to bees.

(*a*) *Ls. green below*

T. cordata Mill. (*T. microphylla* Vent., *T. parvifolia* Ehrh.). Small-leaved Lime. 80. June–July. D. Ls. nearly circular, 2, abruptly pointed, sharply and finely toothed, hairless except for brown tufts in vein-axils below, heart-shaped base. Europe and North Asia. (Fig. 84 B.)

T. euchlora Koch (*T. dasystyla* Kirchn.). 80. July. D. Branchlets hairless, red. Ls. broad, ov., 6, glossy above, with pale axil-tufts below, unequally heart-shaped at base, coarsely bristle-toothed. Caucasus.

T. glabra Vent. (*T. americana* L.). American Lime. 120. July. D. Branchlets green, hairless. Ls. broadly ov., 7, teeth large and long-pointed, axil tufts below except at base. East North America.

T. platyphyllos Scop. Large-leaved Lime. 100. June–July. D. Branchlets hairy. Ls. roundish ov., 5, abruptly pointed, hairy, sharply toothed, unequally heart-shaped base, no axil tufts. Europe. (Fig. 84 A.)

Var. *asplenifolia* Kirchn. (*T. laciniata* Hort.). A smaller tree. Ls. deeply and unevenly lobed, with a tapering or rounded base. (Fig. 29 D.)

TILIA—*continued*

Var. *corallina* Hartw. Twigs red.

Var. *pyramidalis* Kirchn. Narrow form.

Var. *vitifolia* Simonkai. Ls. slightly 3-lobed, less hairy.

T. vulgaris Hayne (*T. europaea* L.). Common Lime. 100. June–July. D. Twigs hairless. Ls. nearly circular, 4, abruptly pointed, with a heart-shaped or straight base, sharply and finely toothed, hairless except for pale tufts in vein-axils below. Hybrid of the above two. (Fig. 84 C.)

(*b*) *Ls. white below*

T. petiolaris DC. (*T. tomentosa* var. *pendula* Hort.). Weeping Lime. Branches drooping; young twigs densely hairy. Ls. roundish ov., 4, evenly and sharply toothed, slightly hairy above. East Europe. (Sport of *T. tomentosa*.)

T. tomentosa Moench (*T. argentea* Desf.). White Lime. 100. July. D. Like above, but branches erect. East Europe.

TRICUSPIDARIA. Ls. alternate, sometimes opposite, leathery, distantly toothed, short-stalked. Fls. bell- or urn-shaped, drooping from long stalks, solitary in leaf-axils. Fruit 1, a capsule containing numerous large black seeds covered with a thin semi-transparent white coat.

T. dependens Ruiz & Pav. 30. May and again in September. E. Young shoots reddish. Ls. ov., 3, shallowly toothed, dark green and hairless above, much paler below, stalk reddish. Fls. $\frac{3}{4}$, white, bell-shaped; petals five, fleshy, 3-toothed at ends. Chile. (Fig. 84 F.)

T. lanceolata Miq. (*Crinodendron Hookerianum* Hort.). 20. May–June. E. Ls. lanc., 5, pointed, sharply and distinctly toothed, margins often recurved. Fls. $\frac{3}{4}$, crimson, urn-shaped. Chile. (Fig. 84 E.)

Family 27. **LINACEAE.** K4–5, C4–5, A4–5, $\underline{G}$ (5)

The flax family. Ls. entire. Fls. regular, usually 5-parted, the stamens as many as the petals and united at the base, styles three to five. Fruit a capsule surrounded by the persistent overlapping sepals. Flax is obtained from *Linum usitatissimum*; cocaine from the leaves of *Erythroxylon Coca*, a native of tropical South America.

LINUM ARBOREUM L. Tree Flax. 2. May–June. D. Ls. alternate, oblanc., 2, bluish white, with purple midrib, often crowded in rosette-like tufts. Fls. $1\frac{1}{2}$, yellow, in erect terminal panicles. Greece. (Fig. 51 F.)

Family 28. **RUTACEAE.** K4–5, C4–5, A8–10, $\underline{G}$ (4–5)

Ls. usually with a prominent midrib and transparent oil glands. Stamens twice as many as the petals. Fruit a capsule or soft. Of economic importance in yielding the citrus fruits (oranges, lemons, limes, grape-fruit, etc.). The imported timber known as Queensland Maple is obtained from species of *Flindersia*, and the golden-yellow East Indian Satinwood from *Chloroxylon Swietenia*. The related family *Zygophyllaceae* yields the very hard and heavy wood known as Lignum Vitae, the timber of *Guaiacum officinale*, a native of tropical America.

* ACRADENIA FRANKLINIAE Kipp. 12. May. E. Ls. opposite, 3-fol., short-stalked; lflts. lanc., 2½, round-toothed in outer half, hairless, dark green above, pale bright green below, dotted with oil glands. Fls. ½, white, in terminal branched clusters, petals five. Tasmania. (Fig. 1 D.)

* ADENANDRA UNIFLORA Willd. 2. April–May. E. Ls. alternate, linear, lanc., ¾, dark glossy green above, dotted with oil glands below, margins hairy. Fls. 1, white, in few-flowered terminal clusters, petals five. South Africa. (Fig. 50 Q.)

AEGLE SEPIARIA DC. (CITRUS TRIFOLIATA L.). Hardy Orange. 12. May–June. D. Stem with spines in leaf-axils. Ls. 3-fol.; lflts. lanc., 2, entire; leaf-stalk winged. Fls. 2, white, appearing in the axils of the spines before the leaves. Fruit 1½, like a small orange in colour and shape. China and Japan. (Fig. 3 A.)

CHOISYA TERNATA H. B. & K. Mexican Orange Blossom. 10. June–November. E. Ls. opposite, 3-fol., stalk grooved; lflts. obov., oblanc., 3, entire, hairless, stalkless or nearly so, aromatic when crushed. Fls. 1, white, fragrant, in terminal clusters. Mexico. (Fig. 1 E.)

* CORREA SPECIOSA Ait. 4. August–October. E. Branchlets and under side of leaves covered with brown scurf. Ls. opposite, roundish ov., 1, entire, gland-dotted, dark green above, tawny below. Fls. 1, yellowish white, K4, C4, A8, solitary at end of shoot. Australia. (Fig. 66 C.)

EVODIA. Small trees with smooth bark. Ls. opposite, pinnate; lflts. ov., 5, entire or with faint signs of teeth, pointed, stalkless or nearly so. Fls. very small, creamy white, fragrant, in terminal panicles. Seed-pod ¼, with short hooked beak.

E. Daniellii Hemsl. 30. August. D. Lflts. with long hairs on midrib below, stalkless. North China. (Fig. 7 A.)

E. hupehensis Dode. 30. August. D. Lflts. with short hairs on midrib below, or none; distinctly stalked. West China.

ORIXA JAPONICA Thunb. 10. April–May. D. Ls. alternate, ov., 4, entire or very faintly toothed, short-stalked, with a spicy odour when crushed. Fls. ¼, unisexual, greenish, K4, C4, sexes on different plants; male flowers in short racemes on previous year's wood, female solitary. Fruit ¾, brown, of four flattened 1-seeded carpels. Japan. (Fig. 116 F.)

PHELLODENDRON. Ls. opposite, pinnate, aromatic. Bud completely enclosed in base of leaf-stalk. Fruit a black berry.

P. amurense Rupr. Amur Cork Tree. 30. June. D. Bark corky. Lflts. ov., 4½, entire or very faintly toothed, long-pointed, margin fringed with hairs, dark green and glossy above, nearly hairless below. Fls. small, yellowish green, inconspicuous, in terminal panicles, sexes on different trees. Berry ½, smelling of turpentine when crushed. North China. (Fig. 7 D.)

P. japonicum Maxim. 20. June. D. Like the above, but bark thin and lflts. hairy below and not glossy. Japan.

PTELEA TRIFOLIATA L. Hop Tree. 15. June. D. Bark fawn-coloured. Ls. alternate, 3-fol.; lflts. ov., 4, faintly toothed, dark green and glossy above, pale and downy below, stalkless or nearly so. Fls. small, greenish white, in terminal branched clusters at the end of short side shoots. Fruit 1, winged (elm-like), 2-seeded. U.S.A. (Fig. 2 C.)

RUTA GRAVEOLENS L. Common Rue. 3. July–August. D. Ls. alternate, 4, 2-pinnately dissected, bluish green, hairless, aromatic. Fls. ¾, dull yellow, petals with fringed margins, in terminal branched clusters. Seed-pod 4-5-lobed, many-seeded. South Europe. (Fig. 36 F.)

SKIMMIA. Ls. alternate, entire, leathery, hairless, aromatic, grouped radially. Fls. small, in terminal panicles. Fruit a red berry.

S. Fortunei Mast. 2. April. E. Ls. lanc., 4, pointed, dark green above. Fls. ½, white. Berry dull crimson. China.

Var. *variegata* Rehd. Ls. with white margin.

S. japonica Thunb. 4. April. E. Ls. ov., 4, bright green above. Fls. ½, yellowish white, 4-parted, unisexual, the sexes on different plants. Berry bright red. Japan. (Fig. 116 H.)

S. Laureola Sieb. & Zucc. 3. April. E. Ls. lanc., 6, more prominently veined than in the above two, very aromatic. Fls. ½, yellow, 5-parted. Berry red. Himalaya. (Fig. 116 J.)

ZANTHOXYLUM. Prickly shrubs with a pair of spines below the stipules. Ls. alternate, pinnate; lflts. finely toothed. Fls. small, in axillary clusters on previous year's wood. Fruit ¼.

* **Z. alatum** Roxb. 12. June. D. Lflts. lanc., 4, the terminal one the largest, common stalk broadly winged. Fls. yellowish. Fruit red, warted, strongly aromatic, seeds black and shining. India. (Fig. 9 E.)

Z. americanum Mill. Toothache Tree, Prickly Ash. 10. April. D. Lflts. ov., 2½. Fls. yellowish green, appearing before the leaves. Fruit blackish. U.S.A. (Fig. 9 F.)

Z. piperitum DC. Japan Pepper. 12. June. D. Prickles slender. Lflts. ov., 1½, notched at apex, distinctly toothed. Fls. greenish. Fruit reddish black. China and Japan. (Fig. 9 G.)

Family 29. **SIMARUBACEAE.** K3–7 or (3–7), C3–7, A6–14, $\underline{G}$ (4–5)

Trees and shrubs with bitter bark. Ls. alternate. Fls. small, generally unisexual.

AILANTHUS. Tree of Heaven. Ls. pinnate, spreading palm-like from end of branch; lflts. lanc., with a few coarse teeth near the base. Fls. small, greenish, in large terminal panicles, sexes usually on different trees. Fruit 1½, oblong, dry, winged, reddish brown.

A. altissima Swingle (*A. glandulosa* Desf.). 70. July. D. Lflts. 4, hairless. China. (Fig. 10 H.)

A. Vilmoriniana Dode. 50. July. D. Lflts. 6, hairy, stalk often red and prickly. China.

* CNEORUM TRICOCCUM L. 2. Summer. E. Stems erect, forking. Ls. linear, lanc., 2, ending in a tiny abrupt point, greyish green, midrib raised on upper side, hairless. Fls. small, yellow, in few-flowered terminal or axillary clusters. Fruit ½, brownish red, 3-lobed, each lobe about the size of a pea. Mediterranean region. (Fig. 53 H.)

PICRASMA AILANTHOIDES Planch. 40. May–June. D. Branches reddish brown, with yellow spots. Ls. pinnate, spreading palm-like from end of branch. Lflts. ov., 5, finely toothed, hairless, glossy green above, unequal-sided at base; common leaf-stalk grooved. Fls. small, green, in axillary panicles. Fruit ½, berry-like, red, supported by the persistent sepals. China and Japan. (Fig. 9 J.)

Family 30. **MELIACEAE.** K (4–5) or 4–5, C4–5, A8–10, G (2–5)

Trees with hard, coloured wood, alternate compound leaves, and showy panicles of flowers. Stamens twice as many as the petals and united into a tube. Mahogany, sapele, African walnut, crabwood, cigar-box cedar, toon, guarea, and gedu nohor are some of the valuable hardwoods imported from the tropics.

CEDRELA SINENSIS Juss. 70. June. D. Bark scaly or shredding. Ls. pinnate, long-stalked; lflts. lanc., 5, entire or vaguely and distantly toothed, hairless between the veins, short-stalked. Fls. small, white, in large terminal panicles. Seed-pod 1, pear-shaped, seeds winged. China. (Fig. 10 B.)

* MELIA AZEDARACH L. Persian Lilac, Bead Tree, China Tree. 40. June. D. Bark furrowed. Ls. 2-pinnate; lflts. ov., 2, unevenly toothed or lobed, hairless, stalked. Fls. ¾, lilac, in large axillary panicles. Fruit ¾, a round yellow berry. India. (Fig. 21 E.)

Family 31. **OLACACEAE.** K4–6, C4–6, A8–12, G2–5

Tropical and subtropical trees and shrubs allied to the holly family, from which they differ in having bisexual flowers, with the stamens opposite the petals.

* VILLARESIA MUCRONATA Ruiz & Pav. 60. June. E. Branchlets ribbed and downy. Ls. alternate, ov., 3½, leathery, dark glossy green, heart-shaped base, hairless, spiny on young trees, stalk very short. Fls. small, yellowish white, K5, C5, in panicles of densely crowded clusters. Chile. (Fig. 84 G.)

Family 32. **AQUIFOLIACEAE.** K4, C4, A4, G (4)

Trees and shrubs with alternate and usually evergreen leathery leaves. Fls. small, generally unisexual. Fruit a berry.

ILEX. Holly. Mostly small evergreen trees with bright red berries in axillary clusters. In two species the berries are black, and in another the leaves are thin and deciduous.

(a) Ls. evergreen, leathery

I. Aquifolium L. Common Holly. 80. May. Trunk and branches green. Ls. ov., 3, glossy, hairless, spine-tipped and often with large spiny teeth and wavy margins. Fls. ½, greenish white, in few-flowered axillary clusters, often unisexual, the sexes usually on different plants. Berry ½, red, remaining on the tree throughout the winter. Europe (including Britain). (Figs. 85 A and 117 A.)

Var. *ferox* Ait. Hedgehog Holly. Spines shorter and more numerous.

There are other varieties in cultivation, some with variegated leaves.

I. cornuta Lindl. Horned Holly. 8. May. Ls. rectangular, 3, dark green and glossy above, 3-spined at apex, and spiny at base. Berry ¼, red. China.

I. crenata Thunb. 6. May–June. Ls. ov., 1, finely toothed, dark glossy green, hairless, crowded. Berry ¼, black. Japan.

I. dipyrena Walt. Himalayan Holly. 40. May. Branchlets angular. Ls. lanc., 5, entire or with short marginal spines, dull green above, very shortly stalked. Fls. ¼, white, in axillary clusters on old wood, unisexual. Berry ½, red. Himalaya. (Fig. 84 K.)

I. glabra Gray (*Prinos glaber* L.). Inkberry. 6. July. Branchlets angular.

ILEX—*continued*

Ls. obov., oblanc., 1½, toothed near apex, dark glossy green above, hairless. Fls. on young wood, female solitary. Berry black. East United States. (Fig. 84 H.)

* **I. insignis** Hook. f. 30. May. Branchlets stout, silver-grey, lustrous. Ls. lanc., 9, spiny or vaguely toothed, dull dark green above with prominent midrib, prominently veined below, stalk purplish. Berry red. East Himalaya. (Fig. 85 E.)

I. integra Thunb. 30. June. Branchlets angular. Ls. ov., 4, entire, blunt-ended, dark glossy green above, pale green below. Fls. clustered on old wood. Berry ½, red. Japan.

I. latifolia Thunb. Tarajo. 50. June. Branchlets very stout, angular, hairless. Ls. oblong, lanc., 8, shallowly toothed. Berries red, in dense clusters on old wood. Japan. (Fig. 85 C.)

I. opaca Ait. American Holly. 40. June. Like common holly, but the veins are conspicuous on the lower side of the leaf and the stalk is grooved. Berry red, solitary, on young wood. East United States.

I. Pernyi Franch. 30. May. Branches stiff and densely covered with leaves. Ls. ov., 2, dark glossy green, with a few spines on each side. Fls. pale yellow, in dense stalkless clusters on old wood. Berry red. China. (Fig. 85 B.)

(*b*) *Ls. deciduous, thin*

I. verticillata Gray (*Prinos canadensis* Hort.). Winter Berry, Black Alder. 10. June–July. Ls. ov., lanc., 3, shallowly and often double-toothed, downy below, prominently veined. Berry red. North America. (Fig. 84 J.)

NEMOPANTHUS MUCRONATA Trel. (ILEX CANADENSIS Michx.). Mountain Holly. 10. May. D. Branches slender, hairless. Ls. ov., 1½, bright green turning yellow, entire or slightly toothed, slender-stalked. Fls. small, whitish, with linear petals. Berry dull red. Canada. (Fig. 85 D.)

Family 33. **CYRILLACEAE.** K5, C5, A5+5, G̲ (2–5)

Trees and shrubs with alternate entire leaves and small bisexual flowers in racemes. Fruit a capsule.

CLIFTONIA MONOPHYLLA Sarg. Buckwheat Tree. 25. April. E. Ls. lanc., 2, tapering base, dark green above, hairless. Fls. small, white or pinkish, fragrant, in terminal racemes up to 2½ long. Fruit ¼, egg-shaped, 3-4-winged (like buckwheat). South-east United States.

CYRILLA RACEMIFLORA L. Leatherwood. 4. September. D. Ls. lanc., 4, much tapered at base, hairless, dark glossy green, lateral veins numerous and close together. Fls. very small, white, crowded in long axillary spikes forming a whorl at base of young wood. South United States. (Fig. 117 B.)

Family 34. **CELASTRACEAE.** K4–5 or (4–5), C4–5, A4–5, G̲ (2–5)

Trees, shrubs, or woody climbers with small greenish flowers in clusters or solitary. Seed usually attached to a fleshy appendage.

CELASTRUS. Climbers. Ls. alternate, ov., round-toothed. Fls. small,

CELASTRUS—*continued*
greenish yellow, in terminal or axillary clusters. Seed-pod 3-celled, yellow inside and containing red seeds.

C. angulatus Maxim. (*C. latifolius* Hemsl.). 20. June. D. Stems angular, corky in second year. Ls. 7, hairless. Fls. in terminal clusters. China.

C. articulatus Thunb. (*C. orbiculatus* Thunb.). 30. June. D. Stems cylindrical; a pair of spines at each bud when young. Ls. 4. Fls. in axillary clusters. Japan. (Fig. 85 F.)

C. scandens L. Staff Tree, Waxwork. 20. July. D. Stems cylindrical. Ls. 4. Fls. in terminal clusters. North America. (Fig. 85 G.)

* ELAEODENDRON CAPENSE Eckl. & Zeyh. 10. July–August. E. Ls. opposite or sub-opposite, ov., 2½, distantly toothed, hairless. Fls. small, green, 4-parted, in axillary branched clusters. Fruit ½, egg-shaped, yellow, fleshy and containing a hard nut. South Africa. (Fig. 59 F.)

EUONYMUS. Spindle Tree. Young branches usually 4-angled. Ls. opposite, minutely toothed. Fls. small, in axillary clusters. Fruit with four or five orange or red fleshy lobes, each holding one or two large orange- or red-coated seeds.

(*a*) *Ls. deciduous*

E. alatus Regel. Winged Spindle Tree. 6. May–June. Branchlets with corky wings. Ls. ov., 1½. Fruit of nearly separate lobes with orange-coated seeds. China and Japan.

E. americanus L. Strawberry Bush. 6. June. Ls. lanc., 3. Fruit 3-5-lobed, pink, covered with prickly warts, seeds red-coated. U.S.A.

E. atropurpureus Jacq. Burning Bush. 25. May–June. Ls. ov., 4, downy. Fls. purple, seven to fifteen on a stalk. Fruit 4-lobed, crimson, seeds scarlet-coated. U.S.A.

E. Bungeanus Maxim. 20. June. Ls. lanc., 3, long-pointed. Fruit 4-lobed, yellowish or pinkish white, seeds orange-coated. China.

Var. *semi-persistens* Schneid. Ls. ov., ½ E.

E. europaeus L. Common Spindle Tree. 25. May. Ls. ov., lanc., 3½. Fruit 4-lobed, red, seeds orange-coated. Europe (including Britain). (Fig. 60 G.)

E. latifolius Mill. 10. May. Ls. ov., 4, stalk grooved. Fruit 4-5-lobed, bright red, larger than the above, drooping on long slender stalk. Europe and Asia. (Fig. 60 F.)

E. nanus Bieb. 3. May–June. A low creeping shrub with alternate or whorled leaves. Ls. linear, 1. Fruit 4-lobed, pink, with orange-coated seeds. Caucasus.

E. obovatus Nutt. 1. May. A low creeping shrub. Ls. opposite, obov., 2, light green. Fruit 3-lobed, crimson, seeds scarlet-coated. North America.

E. planipes Koehne. 25. June. Ls. obov., 4, stalk not grooved. Fruit 5-lobed, red, seeds orange-coated. Japan.

E. verrucosus Scop. Warty Spindle Tree. 6. May. Branchlets densely warted. Ls. ov., 2. Fls. brownish. Fruit 4-lobed, yellowish red, seeds black and partly oranged-coated. Canada and U.S.A.

E. yedoensis Koehne. 20. June. Ls. obov., 5. Fruit deeply 4-lobed, crimson, seeds orange-coated. China.

(*b*) *Ls. evergreen*

E. echinatus Wall. Like *E. radicans* (see below), but fruit prickly. Himalaya.

EUONYMUS—*continued*

E. japonicus Thunb. 15. July–August. Branchlets bright green. Ls. ov., 3, leathery, glossy; round-toothed, each tooth tipped with a black gland; often rounded or notched at apex. Fruit pinkish. Japan. (Fig. 60 D.)

Var. *albo-marginatus* T. Moore. Ls. with thin white margin.
Var. *aureus* Hort. Ls. bright yellow in middle.
Var. *latifolius-variegatus* Hort. Ls. broad, with broad white margin.
Var. *ovatus-aureus* Hort. Ls. with broad yellow margin.

E. myrianthus Hemsl. 6. May. Branchlets green, slightly angled. Ls., lanc., 3, leathery. Fls. ½, greenish yellow, in crowded and attractive clusters. China.

E. pendulus Wall. (*E. fimbriatus* Wall.). 20. June. Ls. lanc., 5, leathery, glossy, pointed, sharply toothed, hairless. Fruit 4-lobed. Himalaya. (Fig. 60 E.)

E. radicans Sieb. (*E. Fortunei* Turcz.). Trailing and rooting, or climbing with aerial roots. 25. June. Branchlets nearly cylindrical, warted. Ls. ov., 1½, dull green above, with pale broad veins. Fruit pinkish. Japan. (Fig. 60 H.)

Var. *foliis variegatus* Hort. Ls. with broad white or pink margin.
Var. *Silver Queen* Hort. Ls. variegated with white.

E. tingens Wall. 20. June. Ls. ov., lanc., 3, leathery, dark green and wrinkled above. Fruit 3-5-angled, seeds orange-coated. Himalaya.

* MAYTENUS CHILENSIS Decne. 25. E. Branchlets long and slender. Ls. alternate, ov., lanc., 2, pointed, leathery, finely toothed, short-stalked. Fls. small, yellowish green, 5-parted, in axillary clusters. Seed-pod 2-celled, containing four red seeds. Chile. (Fig. 86 A.)

PACHYSTIMA. Low evergreen shrubs. Branchlets 4-angled, warted. Ls. opposite, ov., lanc., 1, toothed at outer end or entire, hairless, margins often recurved. Fls. very small, reddish, in axillary clusters. Seed-pod ¼, leathery, whitish, 2-celled.

P. Canbyi Gray. 1½. April–May. Ls. linear, lanc. North Carolina, Virginia.

P. Myrsinites Rafin. 1½. May–August. Ls. broader. West North America. (Fig. 56 N.)

TRIPTERYGIUM REGELII Sprague & Takeda (T. WILFORDII Regel). 6. July–August. D. Ls. alternate, roundish ov., 6, round-toothed, slender-pointed, light green, hairless, stalk ½ to 1. Fls. small, yellowish white, in large terminal panicles. Fruit 3-winged, 1-seeded. China and Japan. (Fig. 86 B.)

Family 35. **RHAMNACEAE.** K4–5, C4–5 or 0, A4–5, G̲ (2–3)

Ls. with stipules or stipular spines. Fls. small; the stamens opposite the petals, which are often less conspicuous than the sepals.

BERCHEMIA. Climbers. Ls. alternate, ov., entire, with numerous parallel veins. Fls. small, greenish white, in terminal panicles. Fruit a sausage-shaped black berry.

B. flavescens Brongn. 10. June–July. D. Branchlets slender, with dark

BERCHEMIA—*continued*

outstanding hairs (Bean). Ls. 6, broadly tapering or rounded at base, smooth metallic green above, with 9–16 pairs of parallel veins. East Himalaya.

B. racemosa Sieb. & Zucc. 15. July September. D. Ls. 2½, somewhat glaucous beneath, with 6–8 pairs of parallel veins. Fruit egg-shaped. Japan.

B. volubilis DC. (*B. scandens* Koch). Supple Jack. 15. June. D. Ls. 3, rounded at base, with 9–12 pairs of parallel veins. South United States. (Fig. 117 C.)

CEANOTHUS. Mountain Sweet. Fls. small, 5-parted (buds star-shaped), in small clusters forming spikes or panicles; sepals curved inwards, the petals spreading outwards from between them. Seed-pod round or top-shaped, 3-lobed at end.

(a) Ls. 3-nerved, alternate

C. americanus L. New Jersey Tea. 3. June–August. D. Ls. ov., 3, bright green, downy below. Fls. white, in terminal panicles. East United States. (Fig. 86 C.)

* **C. aureus** Desf. 6. July–September. D. Ls. ov., 2, white-felted below. Fls. blue. Mexico.

* **C. Delilianus** Spach. 6. July–September. D. Like *C. americanus*, but flowers blue. Hybrid. (Fig. 86 G.)

Var. *Gloire de Plantières* Hort. Fls. deep blue.
Var. *Gloire de Versailles* Hort. Fls. bright blue.
Var. *Léon Simon* Hort. Fls. dark blue.
Var. *Victor Jouin* Hort. Fls. pale blue.

C. pallidus Lindl. 3. July–September. D. Like *C. Delilianus*, but leaves nearly hairless. Fls. pale blue or pink. Hybrid.

C. thyrsiflorus Esch. Californian Lilac. 30. June–August. E. Branchlets angular. Ls. ov., 2, glossy above, pale green below. Fls. pale blue (sometimes white), in lateral racemes. California. (Fig. 86 D.)

* **C. Veitchianus** Hook. 12. June–August. E. Like *C. thyrsiflorus*, but leaves smaller and 3-nerved at base only. California (hybrid). (Fig. 86 F.)

(b) Ls. pinnately nerved

* **C. dentatus** Torr. & Gray. 6. May. E. Ls. alternate, ov., 1. Fls. bright blue. California. (Fig. 86 E.)

Var. *floribundus* Trel. (*C. floribundus* Hook.). More floriferous.

* **C. papillosus** Torr. & Gray. 12. May. E. Ls. alternate, oblong, lanc., 2, conspicuously warted, margins recurved. Fls. blue. California.

C. prostratus Benth. ½. May. E. Ls. opposite, 1, spiny and leathery. Fls. blue. California.

* **C. rigidus** Nutt. 12. April–May. E. Ls. opposite, obov., ½, coarsely toothed, white below or white between veins, much crowded on stiff branches. Fls. deep purplish blue. California. (Fig. 56 M.)

COLLETIA. Stems green, furnished with opposite spines. Ls. very small or absent. Fls. small, white, or in few-flowered clusters below spines. Fruit a dry pod.

COLLETIA—*continued*

C. armata Miers. 10. September. Spines straight, cylindrical. Chile. (Fig. 37 G.)

C. cruciata Hook. 10. September. Spines triangular, flattened. Chile. (Fig. 37 H.)

C. infausta N. E. Br. 10. May. Spines cylindrical, slightly curved. Chile.

DISCARIA. Stems with opposite spines. Ls. opposite or in clusters, 1 or less. Fls. small, greenish white, crowded in axillary clusters. Seed-pod 3-lobed.

D. serratifolia Benth. & Hook. f. 14. May. D. Branches long, slender, and drooping. Spine ¾. Ls. toothed. Chile. (Fig. 54 F.)

* **D. Toumatou** Raoul. Wild Irishman. May. D. Spine 1½. Ls. entire. New Zealand. (Fig. 54 E.)

HOVENIA DULCIS Thunb. Japanese Raisin Tree. 30. June–August. D. Ls. alternate, broadly ov., 6, 3-nerved at base, coarsely toothed, unequal-sided at base, hairless, long-stalked. Fls. ¼, greenish, in branched clusters. Fruit ¼, fleshy, edible. India, China, and Japan. (Fig. 86 H.)

PALIURUS SPINA-CHRISTI Mill. (P. ACULEATUS Lam., P. AUSTRALIS Gaertn.). Christ's Thorn. 20. July. D. Ls. alternate, ov., 1½, 3-nerved at base, minutely toothed or entire, slender-stalked, in two opposite rows; two unequal thorns at the base of each leaf. Fls. small, greenish white, in axillary clusters on new wood. Fruit dry, winged. South Europe. (Fig. 87 F.)

* POMADERRIS ELLIPTICA Labill. 8. May. E. Branchlets and under side of leaves covered with grey or tawny wool. Ls. alternate, ov., 3, entire, prominently veined below. Fls. ¼, yellow, in terminal panicles. Fruit a small capsule. New Zealand. (Fig. 86 J.)

RHAMNUS. Branches often with thorns. Ls. usually alternate. Fls. small, greenish yellow or white, in axillary clusters or racemes. Fruit a black berry. Many of the species yield purgatives and dyes.

(*a*) *Ls. with numerous parallel veins*

R. crenata Sieb. & Zucc. 10. June. D. Young shoots with rusty down. Ls. alternate, ov., lanc., 4, minutely toothed, with 7–12 pairs parallel veins. Japan. (Fig. 87 D.)

R. Frangula L. (*Frangula Alnus* Mill.). Alder Buckthorn. Berry-bearing Alder. 18. June. D. Young branchlets spotted. Ls. alternate, ov. or obov., 3, entire, with 8–9 pairs parallel veins. Europe (including Britain). (Fig. 117 D.)

Var. *aspleniifolia* Dipp. Ls. linear, margins wavy.

R. imeretina Booth. 10. June. D. Twigs stout. Ls. ov., oblong, 10, minutely toothed, dark green above, downy below, with 15–30 pairs parallel veins. West Caucasus. (Fig. 87 E.)

R. Purshiana DC. Cascara Sagrada. 50. May–June. D. Young shoots very downy. Ls. ov., oblong, 5, minutely toothed, with 10–15 pairs parallel veins. California. (Fig. 87 C.)

(*b*) *Ls. without numerous parallel veins, often 3-nerved at base*

R. Alaternus L. 12. March–April. E. Ls. alternate, ov., 2, tapered at both ends, toothed, dark glossy green. South-west Europe. (Fig. 87 A.)

RHAMNUS—*continued*

Var. *angustifolia* Willd. Ls. lanc. (Fig. 87 B.)

Var. *variegata* Bean. Ls. with white margin.

R. cathartica L. Common Buckthorn. 20. May–June. D. Twigs hairless, often ending in a spine. Ls. opposite or sub-opposite, ov., 2½, toothed, slender-stalked. Fls. unisexual, the sexes on different trees. Europe (including Britain). (Fig. 54 J.)

ZIZYPHUS JUJUBA Mill. (Z. SATIVA Gaertn.). Jujube. 30. June. D. Like *Paliurus*, but the fruit is an edible berry. South-east Europe to India. (Fig. 87 G.)

Family 36. AMPELIDACEAE. K (4–5), C4–5, A4–5, G̲ (2)

Woody climbers, the most important being the grape vine, which also yields sultanas, raisins, and currants (the dried fruit of varieties). Fls. small, the stamens being opposite the petals. Fruit a berry.

VITIS. Vine. Climbing by tendrils or suckers. Ls. alternate, digitate or pinnate, or palmately lobed or veined, coarsely toothed, pointed. Fls. in branched clusters or panicles which are usually opposite a leaf. Some authorities split this genus into five, referring to *Vitis* only those species in which the petals cohere at the tip and are cast off as a whole. Of the remainder only two are of general interest: *Ampelopsis*, climbing by tendrils, and *Parthenocissus*, adhering by suckers. Since, however, there has been much confusion, both by botanists and gardeners, it has been thought better to lump them all under *Vitis*.

(a) Tendrils with adhesive disks

V. Henryana Hemsl. (*Parthenocissus Henryana* Diels). July. D. Stems angled. Ls. 3-fol. or digitate; lflts. ov., 2½, velvety, variegated with silver and pink along the veins. China.

V. inconstans Miq. (*Ampelopsis Veitchii* Hort., *Parthenocissus tricuspidata* Planch.). 60. June–July. D. Tendrils very short, with large disks. Ls. very variable in shape and size, 3-lobed or 3-fol. China and Japan. (Fig. 30 F.)

V. quinquefolia Lam. (*Ampelopsis hederacea* DC., *Parthenocissus quinquefolia* Planch.). True Virginia Creeper. 100. July–August. D. Tendrils long and slender. Ls. digitate (5-fol.), lflts. ov., 4. East North America. (Fig. 4 D.)

V. semicordata Wall. (*Parthenocissus himalayana* Planch.). D. Ls. 3-fol.; lflts. ov., 5, the lateral ones unequally heart-shaped at base. Himalaya.

V. Thomsonii Laws. (*Parthenocissus Thomsonii* Planch.). Young stems and leaves purple. Tendrils long and slender. Ls. digitate. Himalaya.

(b) Tendrils without adhesive disks

V. arborea L. (*Ampelopsis arborea* Koehne). Pepper Vine. 30. August. D. Stems hairless. Ls. 2-pinnate; lflts. ov., coarsely toothed. South United States.

V. Coignetiae Planch. (*V. Kaempferi* Koch). 100. June–July. D. Young stems ribbed, woolly. Ls. ov., 12, vaguely 3-5-lobed, brown-felted below. Japan. (Fig. 30 E.)

V. Davidii Foëx. (*V. armata* Diels). June–July. D. Stems and leaf-stalks prickly. Ls. heart-shaped, 10, dark green above, glaucous below. China.

VITIS—*continued*

V. heterophylla Thunb. (*Ampelopsis brevipaniculata* Dipp.). July–August. D. Stems hairless and leaf-stalks reddish. Ls. very variable in shape and size, ov., often 3-5-lobed, heart-shaped base, glossy below. Berry porcelain-blue, with black dots (Bean). China and Japan.

Var. *variegata* Hort. Ls. tinged with pink and white.

V. Labrusca L. Fox Grape. June. D. Tendril opposite each leaf or flower cluster. Ls. ov., 6, 3-lobed towards the top, thick, strongly veined, white- or tawny-felted below. New England to Georgia.

V. megalophylla Veitch (*Ampelopsis megalophylla* Diels). 30. August. D. Stems hairless. Ls. 2-pinnate; lflts. ov., 4, coarsely toothed, the veins ending in teeth, stalked. West China. (Fig. 22 B.)

V. Romanetii Du Caill. May–June. D. Young stems woolly and bristly, purplish. Ls. roundish ov., 8, vaguely 3-lobed, bristle-toothed, dark green above, grey-woolly below, stalk woolly and bristly. Fls. in a large panicle. Fruit ½, black. China.

V. Thunbergii Sieb. & Zucc. July–August. D. Stems angled, covered with tawny wool. Ls. deeply 3-5-lobed, 5, green above, rusty below. Japan.

V. vinifera L. Grape Vine. June. D. Bark peeling. Ls. roundish ov., 6, 3-5-lobed, the spaces between the lobes rounded, the lobes coarsely toothed and usually overlapping, often hairy or cobwebby below, the stalk more than half as long as blade. Caucasus. (Fig. 31 A.)

Var. *laciniosa* L. (*apiifolia* Loud.). Parsley-leaved Vine. Ls. deeply 3-5-cleft, with deeply cut subdivisions.

Var. *purpurea* Bean. Teinturier Grape. Ls. purple.

V. vitacea Bean (*Parthenocissus vitacea* Hitch.). Common June–July. D. Like *V. quinquefolia*, but without adhesive disks. East North America.

V. vulpina L. Riverbank Grape. June. D. Stems hairless. Ls. ov., 6, 3-lobed, bright green above. Stamens long and fragrant. North America.

Family 37. **SAPINDACEAE.** K4–5 or (4–5), C4–5, A4–10, G̲ (3)

Trees and shrubs with compound leaves. Fls. in racemes or panicles. The delicious litchi is the fruit of *Nephelium Litchi*, a native of China, but cultivated in India. *Aesculus* is now usually placed in a separate family: *Hippocastanaceae.*

AESCULUS. Horse Chestnut. Ls. opposite, digitate. Fls. showy, in upright panicles. Fruit 3-parted, with one or more very large seeds (chestnuts). The wood is white and soft, easily worked, but not durable.

(*a*) *L.-buds resinous*

A. carnea Hayne. Red Horse Chestnut. 80. May. D. Lflts. obov., 6, coarsely double-toothed, green below, short-stalked. Fls. flesh-coloured to deep red. Fruit with a few small prickles. Hybrid.

A. Hippocastanum L. Common Horse Chestnut. 100. May. D. Lflts. obov., oblanc., 9, coarsely double-toothed, green below, stalkless. Fls. white tinged with yellow or red. Fruit very prickly. Europe. (Fig. 4 A.)

Var. *flore pleno* Hort. Fls. double.

Var. *rosea* Hort. Fls. pink.

AESCULUS—*continued*

A. indica Colebr. Indian Horse Chestnut. 100. June–July. D. Bark twisted, peeling off in long strips. Lflts. lanc., 9, finely single-toothed, stalked. Fls. white tinged with yellow or red. Fruit rough, not prickly. West Himalaya. (Fig. 4 B.)

A. turbinata Blume. Japanese Horse Chestnut. 100. May. D. Lflts. obov., oblanc., 16, evenly round-toothed, stalkless. Fls. white. Fruit pear-shaped, warty. Japan.

A. Wilsonii Rehd. 80. June–July. D. Lflts. oblanc., 7, finely toothed, greyish below, short-stalked. Fls. white, in long cylindrical panicles. Fruit smooth. China.

(*b*) *L.-buds not resinous*

A. discolor Pursh. 30. May–June. D. Lflts. obov., 6, finely toothed, dark glossy green above, whitish below. Fls. red and yellow. Fruit smooth. South United States.

Var. *flavescens* Sarg. Fls. yellow.
Var. *molle* Sarg. Fls. brick red.

A. glabra Willd. Ohio Buckeye. 30. May–June. D. Lflts. obov., 5, finely toothed. Fls. greenish yellow. Fruit prickly. U.S.A.

A. neglecta Lindl. 75. May–June. D. Like *A. octandra* (see below), but flowers red or tinged with red. North Carolina.

A. octandra Marsh. (*A. flava* Ait.). Sweet Buckeye. 90. May–June. D. Bark smooth, with horizontal scars. Lflts. ov., 7, finely single-toothed, downy below. Fls. yellow. Fruit smooth. East United States.

Var. *sanguinea* Hort. Fls. scarlet.
Var. *rosea* Hort. Fls. deep rose.
Var. *purpurea* Hort. Fls. purple and red.

A. parviflora Walt. (*Pavia macrostachya* Loisel.). Shrubby Pavia. 12. August. D. Lflts. obov., 8, finely round-toothed, greyish white below. Fls. white, with red stamens. Fruit smooth. South-east United States. (Fig. 4 C.)

A. Pavia L. (*Pavia atropurpurea* Spach). Red Buckeye. 12. June. D. Bark smooth. Lflts. oblanc., 5, sharply and often double-toothed, green below. Fls. red. Fruit smooth. South United States.

KOELREUTERIA PANICULATA Laxm. Pride of India. 60. July–August. D. Ls. alternate, pinnate or 2-pinnate; lflts. ov., 3, unevenly toothed, often lobed. Fls. ½, yellow, in large terminal panicles. Fruit 2, inflated, with papery walls, containing three black seeds. China. (Fig. 19 A.)

SAPINDUS DRUMMONDII Hook. & Arn. Soapberry, Wild China Tree. 30. May–June. D. Bark reddish brown, scaly. Ls. alternate, pinnate, without a terminal lflt.; lflts. lanc., 2½, entire, pointed, unequal-sided, downy below. Fls. ¼, yellowish white, in loose downy panicles up to 9 long. Fruit ½, a semi-transparent berry at first yellow and then black. South United States. (Fig. 11 J.)

* UNGNADIA SPECIOSA Endl. Mexican Buckeye. 30. April–May. D. Ls. alternate, pinnate; lflts. ov., lanc., 4, toothed, dark glossy green above, light green below. Fls. 1, rose-coloured, in lateral stalked clusters. Fruit 2, pear-shaped. South-west United States. (Fig. 17 C.)

XANTHOCERAS SORBIFOLIA Bunge. 20. May. D. Branchlets pithy. Ls.

alternate, pinnate, leaf-stalk channelled; lflts. ov., lanc., 2, deeply and sharply toothed, stalkless. Fls. 1, white, K5, C5, A8, petals with thin yellow or red blotch at base; in erect panicles. Fruit 2, a top-shaped, thick-walled capsule; seeds ½, dark brown. China. (Fig. 12 A.)

Family 38. ACERACEAE. K4–5, C4–5 or 0, A8, G (2)

Trees and shrubs with opposite leaves and 2-winged fruits. Fls. small, bisexual or unisexual, in racemes or clusters, which often fall to the ground after fertilization. Maple syrup is obtained from the sap of *Acer saccharum*, but the tree does not do well in Britain. *A. griseum* and *A. pennsylvanicum* are remarkable for their bark. Sycamore yields a smooth white wood suitable for furniture, utensils, brush backs, and textile rollers. Imported rock maple is the timber of *A. saccharum*.

ACER. Maple. Ls. opposite, long-stalked, usually palmately lobed. Fls. small, yellow or greenish, usually 5-parted, in branched clusters or panicles, insect-pollinated. Wings of fruit long and narrow.

(*a*) *Ls. usually 3-lobed*

A. capillipes Maxim. 30. June. D. Like *A. pennsylvanicum* (see below), but leaves without reddish hairs when young. Japan.

A. crataegifolium Sieb. & Zucc. Hawthorn Maple. 25. April. D. Twigs green striped with white lines. Ls. variously shaped, 3, 2-5-lobed, unevenly toothed, bluish green, hairless. Fl.-panicles erect. Wings of fruit wide-spreading. China and Japan. (Fig. 23 E.)

Var. *Veitchii* Nichols. Ls. marbled with rose and white.

A. Ginnala Maxim. 20. June. D. Branches slender, arching. Ls. 3, middle lobe much longer than side ones, round-toothed, hairless. Wings of fruit nearly parallel. China and Japan. (Fig. 25 A.)

A. glabrum Torr. Rock Maple. 25. April. D. Ls. 5, often obscurely 5-lobed, dark glossy green above, pale or glaucous below, stalks thin and red. Wings of fruit nearly parallel. West North America.

A. Hersii Rehd. 30. May. D. Twigs olive green, striped with white lines. Ls. 3, faintly 3-lobed. North China.

A. monspessulanum L. Montpelier Maple. 25. May. D. Ls. 2, usually broader than long, base heart-shaped, lobes entire or nearly so. Fls. greenish yellow, in drooping clusters. Wings of fruit spreading at wide angle. South Europe and West Asia. (Fig. 23 G.)

A. nigrum Michx. Black Maple. 100. April. D. Bark dark and deeply furrowed. Ls. 4, sometimes faintly 5-lobed, lobes entire or obscurely toothed. Wings of fruit spreading horizontally. U.S.A.

A. orientale L. (*A. creticum* L.). Cretan Maple. 15. April. ½ E. Ls. 1½, often not lobed, entire or faintly toothed, hairless, leathery. Fls. in erect clusters. Wings of fruit parallel. (Fig. 24 E.)

A. pennsylvanicum L. Moose Wood, Snake-bark Maple. 30. May. D. Twigs green, striped with white lines. Ls. ov., 3, lobed near apex, double-toothed, heart-shaped base, with reddish hairs below when young. Fls. yellow, in drooping panicles. Wings of fruit spreading at wide angle. East United States. (Fig. 24 B.)

ACER—*continued*

A. rubrum L. See (*b*) below.

A. rufinerve Sieb. & Zucc. 30. May–June. D. Bark smooth, dark green, with long pale vertical stripes. Twigs bluish white. Ls. ov., 5, sometimes vaguely 3-lobed, finely and unevenly toothed, with reddish hairs on the veins below when young. Fl.-panicles erect. China and Japan. (Fig. 23 F.)

A. spicatum Lam. Mountain Maple. 25. June. D. Ls. 5, coarsely and unevenly toothed, yellowish green above, downy below. Wings of fruit at acute angle. U.S.A.

A. tataricum L. Tartarian Maple. 30. May. D. Ls. ov., 4, unevenly double-toothed. Fls. greenish white, in a long upright panicle. Fruit red, wings nearly parallel. East Europe.

(*b*) *Ls. usually with 5 or more lobes*

A. argutum Maxim. 25. April. D. Ls. 3, lobes long-pointed, sharply toothed, pale green. Wings of fruit horizontal. Japan.

A. barbinerve Maxim. Like the preceding species, but leaves coarsely double-toothed and wings of fruit not horizontal. Japan.

A. caesium Wall. 100. April–May. D. Ls. 8, coarsely blunt-toothed, pale and glaucous below, bright red when young. Wings of fruit at acute angle. Himalaya.

A. campestre L. Common or Field Maple. 35. May. D. Bark rough, twigs often corky. Ls. 3, lobes rounded, each with a few round teeth or entire, stalk with milky juice; turning orange or red in autumn. Fls. greenish, in upright clusters, petals often absent. Wings of fruit spreading horizontally. Europe (including Britain). (Fig. 23 D.)

Var. *postelense* Lauche. Ls. golden yellow.
Var. *pulverulentum* Kirchn. Ls. speckled with white.
Var. *Schwerinii* Hesse. Ls. purple.
Var. *variegatum* Nichols. Ls. edged with white.

A. cappadocicum Gleditsch (*A. laetum* Mey.). Cappadocian Maple. 60. May–June. D. Ls. 5, 5-7-lobed, lobes not toothed. Fls. pale yellow. Wings of fruit spreading at wide angle. Caucasus. (Fig. 25 C.)

Var. *colchicum rubrum* Hort. Twigs reddish. Ls. red when young, green with red margin when older.

A. caudatum Wall. 80. March–April. D. Ls. 5, lobes long-pointed, sharply toothed, the two outer ones smaller or absent. Wings of fruit at acute angle. Himalaya.

A. circinatum Pursh. Vine Maple. 30. April–May. D. Bark smooth, red. Ls. almost circular, 5, 7-9-lobed, unevenly toothed. Fls. $\frac{1}{2}$, in small branched clusters, sepals purple, petals white. Wings of fruit spreading horizontally. California. (Fig. 24 C.)

A. crataegifolium Sieb. & Zucc. See (*a*) above.

A. diabolicum Koch. Horned Maple. 30. April. D. Ls. 6, coarsely toothed, downy when young. Wings of fruit nearly parallel, nuts bristly. Japan.

A. glabrum Torr. See (*a*) above.

ACER—*continued*

A. grandidentatum Nutt. 40. April. D. Like *A. campestre*, but bark smoother and sepals united. South United States.

A. japonicum Thunb. 30. May. D. Ls. roundish, 5, 7-11-lobed, double-toothed. Fls. purple, in long-stalked nodding clusters. Wings of fruit nearly horizontal. Japan. (Fig. 25 D.)

A. Lobelii Tenore. 60. May. D. Like *A. platanoides* (see below), but leaves smaller (4) and lobes usually entire. South Italy.

A. macrophyllum Pursh. Oregon Maple. 100. April–May. D. Ls. 12, cut more than half-way to base, stalk milky. Oregon and California. (Fig. 24 A.)

A. Miyabei Maxim. 40. May. D. Twigs corky. Ls. 6, deeply heart-shaped base, coarsely blunt-toothed, downy below. Wings of fruit horizontal, nuts velvety. Japan.

A. nigrum Michx. See (*a*) above.

A. Opalus Mill. Italian Maple. 30. March. D. Ls. 4, lobes roundish, undulating, dark green above, slightly downy or glaucous below. Wings of fruit at acute angle. Italy.

A. palmatum Thunb. Japanese Maple. 25. May. D. Ls. 4, deeply 5-9-lobed; lobes lanc., double-toothed, long-pointed. Fls. purple. Wings of fruit spreading and curved inward forming a broad arch (Bean). Japan. (Fig. 25 B.)

Var. *atropurpureum* Nichols. Ls. purple.

Var. *dissectum* Koch. Ls. digitate. See (*c*) below.

A. pictum Thunb. 80. April. D. Like *A. cappadocicum*, but twigs yellowish grey the second year and leaves more deeply lobed. Himalaya to Japan.

A. platanoides L. Norway Maple. 70. April–May. D. Ls. 7, 5-lobed, lobes coarsely and remotely toothed, spaces between teeth rounded, green below, hairless except for tufts in vein-axils below, stalk with milky juice. Fls. yellow, in erect clusters. Fruit drooping, wings nearly horizontal. Europe. (Fig. 23 B.)

Var. *aureo-marginatum* Hort. Ls. with yellow margin, sometimes blotched with yellow.

Var. *laciniatum* Ait. Eagle's Claw Maple. Ls. with tapering base, lobes curved downwards.

Var. *Reitenbachii* Nichols. Ls. reddish when young and dark red in autumn.

Var. *Schwedleri* Koch. Ls. bright red when young.

A. Pseudoplatanus L. Sycamore. 100. April–May. D. Ls. 6, 5-lobed, coarsely double-toothed, grey below, stalk not milky. Fls. yellowish green, in drooping panicles. Wings of fruit at acute or right angle. Europe (including Britain) and West Asia. (Fig. 23 A.)

A. rubrum L. Red Maple. 100. March–April. D. Ls. 4, 3-5-lobed, unevenly toothed, dark glossy green above, white below. Fls. red. Narrow angle between wings of fruit. U.S.A. (Fig. 23 C.)

Var. *sanguineum* Lav. Ls. downy, richer red in autumn. Fls. brilliant red.

A. saccharinum L. (*A. dasycarpum* Ehrh., *A. eriocarpum* Michx.). Silver

ACER—*continued*

Maple. 120. April. D. Bark smooth and silver-grey. Ls. 4, deeply 5-lobed, double-toothed, bright green above, white below. Fls. greenish, without petals, ovary downy. Wings of fruit sickle-shaped. East North America. (Fig. 24 D.)

A. **saccharum** Marsh. Sugar Maple. 100. May. D. Bark rough, grey. Ls. 4, 5-lobed, lobes with a few coarse teeth, light green or glaucous below. Fls. greenish yellow, bell-shaped. Wide angle between wings of fruit. East North America. (Fig. 23 H.)

A. **truncatum** Bunge. 25. May. D. Ls. 3, 5-lobed, lobes entire and spreading at wide angle. Wings of fruit make a right angle. North China.

(*c*) *Ls. compound*

A. **cissifolium** C. Koch. 30. April–May. D. Ls. 3-fol.; lflts. ov., 3, stalked, coarsely and unevenly toothed, pale green below. Wings of fruit at acute angle. Japan.

A. **glabrum** Torr. See (*a*) above.

A. **griseum** Pax. 40. May–June. D. Bark smooth, shining, copper-coloured, flaking. Ls. 3-fol.; lflts. ov., lanc., 2½, with a few large blunt teeth, blue-grey below. Wings of fruit at acute or right angle. Cochin China. (Fig. 1 B.)

A. **Henryi** Pax. 30. April. D. Ls. 3-fol.; lflts. ov., 4, stalked, with a few large blunt teeth, green below. Wings of fruit nearly parallel. China.

A. **Negundo** L. Box Elder. 70. March. D. Ls. 3-fol. or pinnate; lflts. ov., lanc., 4, coarsely and unevenly toothed. Fls. yellowish green, in drooping panicles appearing before the leaves. Wings of fruit at acute angle and often curved inwards. U.S.A. (Fig. 1 C.)

Var. *aureum* Hort. Ls. yellow.
Var. *variegatum* Carr. Ls. with white margin.

A. **nikoense** Maxim. Nikko Maple. 40. May. D. Ls. 3-fol.; lflts. ov., 4½, distantly toothed. Wings of fruit curved inwards. Japan.

A. **palmatum** var. *dissectum* Koch. Japanese Maple. 25. May. D. Ls. digitate; lflts. lanc., 4, double-toothed, long-pointed, often pinnately lobed. Japan. (Fig. 5 B.)

Var. *ornatum* Nichols. Ls. deep red.
Var. *roseo-marginatum* Hort. Ls. rosy at edge.

(*d*) *Ls. unlobed*

A. **carpinifolium** Sieb. & Zucc. Hornbeam Maple. 30. May. D. Ls. ov., oblong, 4, long-pointed, double-toothed. Wings of fruit wide-angled. Japan.

A. **Davidii** Franch. 40. May. D. Twigs green, striped with white lines. Ls. ov., 6, dark green, unevenly toothed. Fls. yellow, in drooping racemes. Wings of fruit horizontal. China.

A. **Hersii** Rehd. See (*a*) above.

A. **nikoense** Maxim. See (*c*) above.

A. **oblongum** Wall. 30. April–May. ½ E. Ls. oblong, 5, entire except on young trees, leathery, 3-nerved, glaucous below. Wings of fruit spreading at wide angle. Himalaya.

ACER—*continued*

A. laevigatum (Wall.) is similar, but the leaves are green and with shorter stalks. Himalaya.

A. tataricum L. Tatarian Maple. 25. May. D. Ls. ov., 4, unevenly toothed. Wings of fruit nearly parallel. East Europe and West Asia.

DIPTERONIA SINENSIS Oliv. 25. May. D. Ls. opposite, pinnate; lflts. lanc., 4, sharply and unevenly toothed, long-pointed. Fls. small, greenish white, in erect panicles. Wing of fruit nearly circular, elm-like. China. (Fig. 7 B.)

Family 39. STAPHYLEACEAE. K5, C5, A5, G (2–3)

Trees and shrubs with compound stipulate leaves, small flowers in panicles, and capsular or berried fruits.

* EUSCAPHIS JAPONICA Dipp. (E. STAPHYLEOIDES Sieb. & Zucc.). 12. May–June. D. Twigs stout, pithy. Ls. opposite, pinnate; lflts. ov., 3, finely toothed, stalked. Fls. small, yellowish white, in terminal panicles. Fruit ½, reddish, of three boat-shaped spreading bracts (Bean). Japan. (Fig. 7 C.)

STAPHYLEA. Bladder Nut. Small deciduous trees. Ls. opposite, 3-fol. or pinnate; lflts. ov., lanc., finely toothed. Fls. small, white, in terminal panicles. Fruit bladder-like, 2-3-lobed.

S. Bumalda Sieb. & Zucc. 6. May. Ls. 3-fol.; lflts. ov., 2½, middle one short-stalked. Fruit 1. Japan.

S. colchica Stev. 10. May. Ls. pinnate; lflts. ov., 3, glossy below. Fruit 4. Caucasus. (Fig. 7 E.)

Var. *Coulombieri* André. Larger and more vigorous; fls. smaller.

S. emodii Wall. 10. May. Bark with conspicuous raised white longitudinal stripes. Ls. 3-fol.; lflts. ov., 6. Fls. in long drooping panicles. Fruit 3. West Himalaya.

S. holocarpa Hemsl. 20. May. Ls. 3-fol.; lflts. ov., 2½, middle one long-stalked. Fls. white or pinkish, in drooping panicles. China.

Var. *rosea* Rehd. & Wils. Fls. large, pink.

S. pinnata Blume. 15. May. Ls. pinnate; lflts. ov., 4, sharply toothed. Fls. in terminal drooping panicles. South Europe.

S. trifolia L. American Bladder Nut. 15. May. Ls. 3-fol.; lflts. ov., 4, downy below, middle one long-stalked. Fls. dingy white, bell-shaped, in short drooping panicles. Fruit 3-lobed. North America.

TAPISCIA SINENSIS Oliv. 30. July. D. Ls. alternate, pinnate; lflts. ov., 4, pointed, rounded or heart-shaped base, sharply toothed, glaucous below, hairless, short-stalked. Fls. small, yellowish, fragrant, in axillary panicles or spikes. Fruit ¼, a black berry. China. (Fig. 17 D.)

TURPINIA NEPALENSIS Bedd. (T. POMIFERA DC.). 50. January–June. D. Ls. opposite, pinnate; lflts. ov., 6, leathery, sharply toothed. Fls. very small, in terminal and axillary panicles. Fruit 2, fleshy, green, yellow, or purplish. Himalaya. (Fig. 7 F.)

Family 40. SABIACEAE. K (3–5), C4–5, A5, G (2)

Trees and shrubs with alternate leaves without stipules. Fls. generally in panicles; the stamens opposite the petals.

MELIOSMA. Buds without scales. Fls. small, yellowish white, in large erminal panicles. Fruit ½, a purplish-black berry.

M. cuneifolia Franch. 20. July. D. Ls. simple, obov., 6, tapering base, toothed, with numerous straight veins. Fls. in erect panicles. China. (Fig. 84 D.)

M. Veitchiorum Hemsl. 40. May. D. Branchlets stout, erect. Ls. pinnate, stalk red and warted at lower end; lflts. ov., 7, deeply veined, teeth few or none, hairless except on midrib below. Fls. in drooping panicles. China. (Fig. 10 D.)

Family 41. **ANACARDIACEAE.** K (3 or more), C3–7 or 0, A5–14, G1

Trees and shrubs with alternate leaves without stipules. Fls. in spreading or pike-like panicles; the stamens alternating with the petals. The bark of many pecies contains an aromatic resin. Mastic is obtained from the bark of *Pistacia Lentiscus*, and lacquer-like varnishes from species of *Rhus*. The mango is the ruit of *Mangifera indica*.

PISTACIA. Ls. pinnate; lflts. entire. Fls. small, without petals, unisexual, in ateral panicles, the sexes on different trees. Fruit ¼, red to black.

P. chinensis Bunge. Chinese Pistacia. 80. April. D. Lflts. an even number, ov., lanc., 3½, spicy-scented. China. (Fig. 11 H.)

* **P. Lentiscus** L. Mastic Tree. 20. April. E. Branchlets warted. Lflts. an even number, lanc., 1½, with short abrupt point. Mediterranean region. (Fig. 12 D.)

P. Terebinthus L. Chian Turpentine Tree. 30. June. D. Lflts. an odd number, ov., 2, dark glossy green, hairless, resin-scented. South Europe. (Fig. 9 H.)

RHUS. Sumach. Fls. small, yellow or greenish, 5-parted, in terminal or xillary panicles. Fruit a berry.

(*a*) *Ls. simple*

R. cotinoides Nutt. (*Cotinus americanus* Nutt.). Chittam Wood. 15. June. D. Ls. obov., 5, entire, tapering gradually to base, long-stalked. Fls. greenish yellow, in thin panicles or racemes. Fruiting panicles inconspicuous. South United States. (Fig. 117 F.)

R. Cotinus L. (*Cotinus coggyria* Scop.). Venetian Sumach, Smoke Tree. 12. June–July. D. Ls. ov., 3, entire, rounded or notched at apex, tapering abruptly to base, strong smelling. Fls. in broad flesh-coloured to smoky grey panicles. Fruiting panicles conspicuous with long, spreading purplish hairs. South Europe. (R. *Cotinus* of the Himalayas is downy on the under side of the leaves.) (Fig. 117 E.)

Var. *atropurpurea* Hort. Ls., branchlets, and fls. purple.

Var. *pendula* Dipp. Branches drooping.

(*b*) *Ls. compound*

R. canadensis Marsh. (R. *aromatica* Ait.). Fragrant Sumach. 3. March–April. D. Ls. 3-fol.; lflts. ov., 2½, coarsely toothed, aromatic. Fruit round, red, hairy. North America. (Fig. 2 F.)

R. copallina L. Shining Sumach. 30. July–August. D. Ls. pinnate; lflts. ov., lanc., 4, entire or with a few teeth near apex, glossy above,

RHUS—*continued*

downy below, common stalk winged. Fls. greenish, in dense termina panicles. Fruit crimson, hairy. East United States. (Fig. 10 G.)

R. glabra L. Smooth Sumach. 12. August. D. Branchlets hairless glaucous. Ls. pinnate; lflts. lanc., 4, toothed, hairless, glaucous below Fls. greenish, in dense terminal panicles. Fruiting panicles erect, red hairy, and sticky. U.S.A.

Var. *laciniata* Carr. Lflts. 2-pinnate, or 2-pinnately lobed.

R. javanica L. 20. August. D. Branchlets yellowish, hairless. Ls. pinnate lflts. ov., 4, coarsely toothed, brownish and hairy below. Fls. creamy white, in erect terminal panicles. China and Japan.

R. Potanini Maxim. 25. May–June. D. Branchlets hairless. Ls. pinnate lflts. ov., lanc., 4, entire (or coarsely toothed in young plants,) hairless or nearly so. Fls. whitish, in terminal panicles. Fruiting panicles drooping, dark red, hairy. China.

R. punjabensis Stev. 30. June–July. D. Like R. *Potanini*, but branchlets downy. Himalaya to China.

R. Toxicodendron L. Poison Ivy. 9. June–July. D. Rambler, or climbing by aerial roots. Ls. 3-fol.; lflts. ov., 4, entire or with a few coarse teeth. Fruit a white berry. North America and Japan. (Fig. 3 D.)

R. typhina L. Staghorn Sumach. 25. July. D. Branchlets velvety-hairy Ls. pinnate; lflts. lanc., 5, toothed, long-pointed. Fls. greenish, in dense hairy panicles. Fruiting panicles red, hairy. East United States (Fig. 10 F.)

Var. *laciniata* Cow. Lflts. pinnately lobed. (Fig. 22 C.)

R. verniciflua Stokes (R. *vernicifera* DC.). Lacquer Tree, Varnish Tree 60. July. D. Ls. pinnate; lflts. broadly ov., 6, entire, velvety downy below. Fls. yellowish white, in loose axillary panicles. Fruit a yellowish berry. China and Japan. (Fig. 10 E.)

R. vernix L. Poison Sumach. 20. June–July. D. Branchlets hairless Ls. pinnate; lflts. ov., oblong, 4, entire, hairless. Fls. greenish yellow Fruit yellowish. East United States.

SCHINUS DEPENDENS Ortega. 15. May. E. Branchlets stiff, spine-tipped Ls. obov., 1, blunt-ended, tapering to a very short stalk, entire or toothed Fls. very small, C4, A8, in small axillary branched clusters. Fruit a purple berry Chile. (Fig. 87 H.)

Family 42. **CORIARIACEAE.** K5, C5, A5+5, G5

Contains only one genus, *Coriaria*.

CORIARIA. Branchlets 4-angled. Ls. opposite, ov., 3-5-nerved, entire, in two opposite rows. Fls. small, greenish, in racemes; petals enlarge and become fleshy, enclosing the black fruit.

(*a*) *Fls. in terminal racemes*

C. terminalis Hemsl. 3. June. D. Semi-herbaceous. Ls. ov., 3, 5-9 nerved, abruptly pointed. Himalaya. (Fig. 76 B.)

(*b*) *Fls. in lateral racemes*

C. japonica Gray. 3. September. D. Stems semi-herbaceous, pithy

CORIARIA—*continued*

renewed annually from the base. Ls. 4, 3-nerved, long-pointed, hairless. Japan.

C. myrtifolia L. Redoul. 6. Summer. D. Branches erect. Ls. 2½, 3-nerved, hairless. Mediterranean region.

C. nepalensis Wall. 8. April–May. D. Bark rough, reddish brown. Branches spreading. Ls. 4, 3-7-nerved, heart-shaped base. Himalaya.

C. sinica Maxim. 15. D. Branchlets warted. Ls. 3, 3-nerved, short-pointed. China.

Family 43. **LEGUMINOSAE.** K4–5 or (4–5), C5, A4–∞, $\underline{G}1$

Ls. alternate, stipulate, usually compound. Fruit a dry pod, often elongated, and usually splitting along both edges revealing a single row of seeds. Members of this family have the power to make their own nitrogen by tubercles on the root. A very large family of great economic importance, giving peas, beans, lentils, gram, the soya-bean, vetches, clover, sainfoin, lucerne (alfalfa), liquorice, senna, and indigo and other dyes. Among garden plants are sweet peas and lupins.

Sub-family. **PAPILIONACEAE.** K5 or (5), C5, A10 or (10) or (9)+1, $\underline{G}1$

The flowers usually resemble those of the sweet pea, having standard, wings, and keel (Fig. 14 B). The tree members of the sub-family give hard and heavy timber, usually coloured. Among them are Australian black bean, the wood of which is dark brown streaked or mottled with black, padauk (red), Indian rosewood (dark purplish brown), locust (yellowish green), and laburnum (yellow sapwood and dark brown heart).

(I) Stamens All United

ADENOCARPUS DECORTICANS Boiss. 10. May–June. D. Branches long, horizontal. Ls. 3-fol., crowded, slender-stalked; lflts. linear, ¾, entire, hairy, margins usually rolled inward, stalkless. Fls. yellow, in short erect racemes on upper side of branch. Pod 2×¼, glandular, sticky. Spain. (Fig. 3 E.)

AMORPHA. Ls. pinnate; lflts. small, entire. Fls. purple, with orange stamens; in dense terminal spikes. Pod short, 1-seeded, not splitting.

A. canescens Nutt. Lead Plant. 4. July. D. Entirely covered with grey down. Stems erect, unbranched. Lflts. ov., ½, hairy, stalkless, the lowest pair close to the main stem. Fls. ¼. Pod less than ¼. U.S.A.

A. fruticosa L. False Indigo. 15. July–August. D. Lflts. ov., 2, ending in bristle-like tip, a short thread-like stipule at the base of each leaflet, the lowest pair some distance from the main stem. Pod more than ¼, very warty. South United States. (Fig. 13 F.)

ANTHYLLIS. Branchlets crooked. Ls. hairy. Fls. yellow.

A. Barba-Jovis L. Jupiter's Beard, Silver Bush. 12. May–June. D. Stems and leaves covered with silky hairs. Ls. pinnate; lflts. lanc., 1, entire, white-edged. Fls. small, in rounded heads. Mediterranean region. (Fig. 14 E.)

A. Hermanniae L. 2. June. D. Branchlets end in a thin spine. Ls. simple or 3-fol.; lflts. linear, obov., 1, entire, blunt-ended, base tapering. Fls. ¼, in few-flowered axillary clusters. Pod ½, oblong, hairless. South Europe. (Fig. 50 O.)

CYTISUS. Broom. Stems usually long, green, and ribbed. Ls. usually 3-fol; lflts. entire. Pod flattened, seed with appendage.

(*a*) *Ls. simple*

C. Beanii Nichols. 1½. May. D. Ls. linear, ½, hairy. Fls. deep golden yellow. Hybrid raised at Kew.

C. praecox Wheeler. Warminster Broom. 10. April–May. D. Like *C. albus* (see below), but with denser and heavier masses of branches, bending over with their own weight. Ls. silky. Fls. sulphur-yellow, produced in remarkable abundance (Bean). Hybrid. (Fig. 37 O.)

(*b*) *Ls. 3-fol.*

C. albus Link. White Spanish Broom. 10. May. D. Stems very slender, in broom-like masses. Lflts. linear, ½, silky (ls. simple at top). Fls. ¾, white. Pod 1, hairy. Spain and Portugal. (Fig. 37 F.)

C. Battandieri Mairet. 15. June. D. Lflts. ov., 3, covered with silky hairs. Fls. ½, yellow, fragrant, in upright terminal racemes. Pod 2×¼. North Africa. (Fig. 2 H.)

C. Dallimorei Rolfe. 9. May. D. Ls. downy. Fls. ½, pink to crimson. Hybrid raised at Kew.

C. nigricans L. 5. June–July. D. Stems erect, cylindrical, downy. Lflts. obov., 1, pointed. Fls. ½, yellow, slender-stalked, in terminal spikes. Pod 1½ or less, hairy. Europe. (Fig. 3 F.)

C. Porlock Hort. Porlock Broom. 6. May–June. E. Stems leafy, erect, angled, downy. Lflts. obov., ¾, hairy on midrib below. Fls. ½, yellow, fragrant, short-stalked, borne profusely towards end of side shoots. Hybrid offered by Messrs. Scott & Co., Merriott, and said to be hardy and fast-growing.

C. purpureus Scop. Purple Broom. 1½. May–June. D. Prostrate, with ascending hairless branchlets. Ls. long-stalked; lflts. ov., obov., 1. Fls. ¾, purple. Pod 1½, hairless. East Europe.

C. scoparius Link (*Sarothamnus scoparius* Koch.). Common Broom. 6. May. D. Branches erect, green, angular. Lflts. lanc., ½, slightly hairy. Fls. 1, bright yellow. Pod 2, hairy on margins. Europe (including Britain). (Fig. 37 N.)

Var. *Andreanus* Dipp. Fls. yellow, with chocolate wings.
Var. *fulgens* Hort. Fls. yellow, with red wings.
Var. *sulphureus* Hort. Fls. pale yellow. Smaller and more compact.

ERINACEA PUNGENS Boiss. Hedgehog Broom. 1. April–May. D. Branches erect, green, stiff, and spiny-pointed. Ls. few, simple, linear, ½, entire. Fls. ¾, purplish blue, in few-flowered clusters just below apex of branchlet. Pod ¾, oblong, hairy, splitting. East Pyrenees and North-west Africa. (Fig. 37 A.)

GENISTA. Stems green. Ls. usually simple. Fls. yellow, in terminal racemes or clusters. Pod linear-oblong; seed without appendage.

(*a*) *Ls. opposite, 3-fol.*

G. horrida DC. 1. July. D. Stems rigid, spiny, silver-grey. Fls. ¼. South France and Spain. (Fig. 37 E.)

G. radiata Scop. 3. June. D. Lflts. ½, linear. Fls. in small heads. Central and South Europe. (Fig. 37 Q.)

GENISTA—*continued*

(*b*) *Ls. alternate, simple*

G. aetnensis DC. Etna Broom. 20. July. Branches long, dark green, with very few leaves. Ls. linear, ½. Fls. scattered singly. Pod ½, ending in a sharp curved point. Sicily. (Fig. 37 T.)

G. anglica L. Needle Furze, Petty Whin. 2. June. D. Spiny. Ls. lanc., ov., ½. Europe (including Britain). (Fig. 37 C.)

G. anxantica Tenore. Neapolitan Broom. 1. June. D. Ls. ov., 1, hairless. Pod hairless. South Italy.

G. cinerea DC. 10. April–July. Ls. few, lanc., ¼, downy. Pod ¾, silky. South Europe.

G. hispanica L. Spanish Gorse. 1½. May–June. Clusters of branching spines. Ls. few, lanc., ½. Fls. in small heads. South-west Europe. (Fig. 37 D.)

G. pilosa L. Hairy Greenweed. 1½. June. D. Ls. obov., ½, blunt-ended, hairy, in clusters on older shoots. South-west Europe (including Britain). (Fig. 117 G.)

G. saggitalis L. 1. May–June. Prostrate. Stems broadly 2-winged, hairy. Ls. few, ov., ¾. Europe.

G. tinctoria L. Dyer's Greenweed. 2. June–July. D. Semi-prostrate. Ls. linear, lanc., 1, margins fringed with hairs. Fls. ¾, in erect racemes. Europe (including Britain). (Fig. 117 J.)

G. virgata Link. Madeira Broom. 12. June. D. Stems grooved. Ls. lanc., ½, grey-green, silky below. Fls. ½. Madeira. (Fig. 117 H.)

HALIMODENDRON ARGENTEUM Fisch. (H. HALODENDRON Voss). Salt Tree. 6. June–July. D. Ls. pinnate, with four lflts., silver-grey, the common stalk ending in a stiff spine; lflts. oblanc., 1½, entire, stalkless. Fls. ½, purple or lilac. Pod 1, inflated. Siberia. (Fig. 13 K.)

LABURNUM. Ls. 3-fol., long-stalked; lflts. ov., entire, very shortly stalked. Fls. usually yellow, in drooping terminal panicles. Pod linear.

L. Adamii Kirchn. Purple Laburnum. 25. May. D. Branchlets and ls. hairless or nearly so. Lflts. 2½. Fls. purple. Graft hybrid.

L. alpinum J. S. Presl. Scotch Laburnum. 20. June. D. Lflts. 4, slightly hairy. Fls. ¾, golden yellow, in panicles up to 15 long. Pod 3, flattish, keel winged. Europe.

Var. *pendulum* Kirchn. Weeping form.

L. anagyroides Med. Common Laburnum, Golden Chain, Golden Rain. 25. May. D. Lflts. 3, downy below. Fls. ¾, golden yellow, in panicles up to 10 long. Pod 3, keel not winged. Europe. (Fig. 3 C.)

Var. *aureum* Rehd. Ls. yellow.

Var. *pendulum* Rehd. Weeping form.

Var. *quercifolium* Schneid. Lflts. lobed.

Var. *Watereri* Dipp. (*L. Parksii* Hort.). A cross with *L. alpinum*. Panicles longer and keel of pod slightly winged.

LUPINUS ARBOREUS Sims. Tree Lupin. 9. May–September. D. Ls. digitate, long-stalked; lflts. oblanc., 1½, silky below, stalkless. Fls. sulphur-yellow, in erect terminal spikes. Pod 3, long and narrow, spirally twisted, hairy, 8-12-seeded. California. (Fig. 5 K.)

ONONIS. Restharrow. Branchlets crooked. Ls. 3-fol., the stipules clasping the stalk; lflts. toothed, stalkless. Pod swollen.

O. aragonensis Asso. 2. June. D. Young shoots pale grey. Lflts. roundish ov., ½, green. Fls. ½, yellow, in pairs on a crooked terminal spike. Pod ½, hairy. Pyrenees.

O. fruticosa L. 3. May–June. D. Lflts. oblanc., 1, wrinkled. Fls. ¾, pale rose, three on a stalk. Pod 1, bristly. Europe. (Fig. 3 C.)

O. Natrix L. 1½. May–July. D. Lflts. oblanc., 1, hairy. Fls. 1, yellow striped with purple, in dense leafy racemes. Mediterranean region.

O. spinosa L. 1. July–October. D. Spiny. Lflts. oblanc., ¾, hairy. Fls. ½, pink, solitary in the l.-axils. Europe (including Britain).

PETTERIA RAMENTACEA Presl. (CYTISUS FRAGRANS Weld.). Dalmatian Laburnum. 8. May–June. D. Ls. 3-fol., slender-stalked; lflts. ov., 2, entire, very shortly stalked, blunt-ended, hairless. Fls. ¾, yellow, in short erect dense racemes. Pod linear-oblong, 2, flat, pointed, dark brown, splitting. East Europe. (Fig. 3 H.)

SPARTIUM JUNCEUM L. Yellow Spanish Broom. 12. June–September. Stems erect, green, rush-like, cylindrical, nearly leafless. Ls. linear, 1, bluish green. Fls. 1, yellow, fragrant, in loose terminal racemes. Pod 3, linear, hairy. South Europe. (Fig. 37 M.)

ULEX. Gorse, Furze, Whin. Branchlets green, furrowed, and very spiny. Ls. small, simple, usually reduced to scales. Fls. yellow, ¾, solitary. Pod ½, scarcely longer than the calyx.

U. europaeus L. 6. January–June. E. Calyx very hairy, the bracts at base conspicuous. Europe (including Britain). (Fig. 37 F.)

U. minor Roth. 1. July–December. E. Calyx hairless or nearly so, the bracts at base minute. Europe (including Britain). *U. Gallii* (Planch.) is similar but larger.

(II) NINE STAMENS UNITED, ONE FREE

ASTRAGALUS TRAGACANTHA L. Goat's Thorn. 1. May–June. D. Ls. pinnate, crowded, the common stalk becoming a long stiff spine; lflts. ov., ¼, entire, silky. Fls. ¾, white or pale purplish red. Pod ½, cylindrical, divided by a longitudinal partition. Asia Minor. (Fig. 14 H.)

CALOPHACA WOLGARICA Fisch. 3. June–July. D. Branchlets reddish brown, hairy. Ls. pinnate; lflts. roundish ov., ½, entire, with a minute point at the tip, downy below. Fls. 1, yellow, in hairy racemes. Pod cylindrical, 1, hairy. South Russia. (Fig. 13 D.)

CARAGANA. Ls. pinnate, without a terminal leaflet, or digitate, the common stalk usually spine-tipped and persistent; lflts. entire.

(*a*) *Ls. with four leaflets*

C. Chamlagu Lam. 3. May–June. D. Ls. pinnate; lflts. obov., 1½, hairless. Fls. 1, reddish yellow, solitary. Pod 1½, slender, hairless. China and Japan. (Fig. 13 E.)

C. frutescens DC. 10. May–June. D. Ls. digitate; lflts. obov., 1, notched at apex. Fls. 1, bright yellow. Pod cylindrical, 1½, hairless. South Russia to Japan. (Fig. 5 F.)

(*b*) *Lflts. more than four*

C. arborescens Lam. Pea Tree. 20. May–June. D. Common leaf-stalk

CARAGANA—*continued*

deciduous, grooved, with or without a pair of stipular spines at the base. Lflts. ov., 1, hairless or nearly so. Fls. ½, yellow, solitary or in few-flowered clusters. Pod 2, slender-stalked. Siberia. (Fig. 13 J.)

C. jubata Poir. 2. April–May. D. Hairy and very spiny. Common leaf-stalk persistent, spine-tipped. Lflts. oblong, ½, hairy. Fls. 1, white, solitary. Pod 1. Siberia.

C. microphylla Lam. 10. May–June. D. Common l.-stalk deciduous, spine-tipped. Lflts. ov., ¼, rounded or notched at apex. Fls. ¾, yellow, solitary. Pod 1. Siberia.

C. spinosa DC. (*C. ferox* Lam.). 6. June–July. D. Branches long, undivided, spiny. Ls. sometimes digitate; lflts. ov., ¾. Fls. 1, yellow. Pod ¾, hairless. Siberia.

CARMICHAELIA. Lilac Broom. Stems erect, green, flattened, leafless except when young. Fls. small, lilac, in axillary racemes. Pod ½, beaked, the central part falling out and leaving an empty frame.

* **C. australis** R. Br. Makaka. 12. July. Young stems ⅛ wide, hairless. New Zealand. (Fig. 37 R.)

C. flagelliformis Colenso. 5. July. Stems grooved. New Zealand.

* **C. odorata** Colenso. 10. July. Young stems very slender, ⅛, downy. New Zealand.

* CHORDOSPARTIUM STEVENSONII Cheeseman. 25. May–July. E. Branchlets green, slender, drooping, leafless or nearly so. Fls. ¼, purple, in small clusters or racemes. Pod very small, 1-seeded. New Zealand.

CLIANTHUS. Glory Pea, Parrot's Bill. Climbers. 10. June. E. Ls. pinnate; lflts. oblong, 1, entire, blunt-ended, tapering base, downy below, stalkless or nearly so. Fls. 3, in drooping axillary racemes; standard and keel much larger than the wings. Pod 3×½.

* **C. Dampieri** Cunn. Stems hairy. Fls. red, with black boss. New Zealand.

* **C. puniceus** Banks & Soland. Stems hairless or nearly so. Fls. red. New Zealand. (Fig. 14 J.)

COLUTEA. Bladder Senna. 12. June–July. D. Branches with fibrous or flaky bark. Ls. pinnate; lflts. obov., 1, entire, inversely heart-shaped. Fls. ¾, yellow or yellowish red, in racemes. Pod 3, inflated, with papery walls.

C. arborescens L. Fls. yellow. Mediterranean region. (Fig. 14 G.)

C. media Willd. Fls. brownish red or coppery. Hybrid.

NOTOSPARTIUM CARMICHAELIAE Hook. f. Pink Broom. 10. July. D. Branches arching, slender, rush-like, slightly flattened, grooved. Ls. few or absent, simple, roundish ov., ¼, only seen on young plants. Fls. ¼, purplish pink, in downy axillary racemes. Pod ¾, slender, 3-8-jointed. New Zealand. (Fig. 37 S.)

* PSORALEA GLANDULOSA L. 6. July–August. E. Ls. alternate, 3-fol.; lflts. ov., lanc., 3, gland-dotted, stalked. Fls. ½, blue and white, in long axillary racemes. South America. (Fig. 2 K.)

* PUERARIA THUNBERGIANA Benth. (P. HIRSUTA Schneid.). Kudzu Vine. Tall climber. July–August. E. Ls. 3-fol., long-stalked; lflts. ov., 6, entire or lobed,

the terminal one the largest, hairy on margins, stipulate. Fls. $\frac{3}{4}$, violet, in dense erect terminal racemes up to 9 long. Pod $3 \times \frac{1}{2}$, hairy. The root is fleshy and tuberous. China and Japan.

CORONILLA. Scorpion Senna, Crown Vetch. 8. May–October. D. Branchlets green, corrugated. Ls. pinnate; lflts. obov., $\frac{3}{4}$, entire, greyish green, often with a prominent red midrib below, hairless or nearly so. Fls. $\frac{3}{4}$, yellow, sometimes blotched with red, in small long-stalked axillary clusters; each petal with a long claw. Pod 2, linear, jointed.

C. Emurus L. Lflts. green or grey. Europe. (Fig. 14 F.)

* **C. glauca** L. Lflts. bluish white, glaucous. South-east Europe. (Fig. 13 L.)

DESMODIUM TILIAEFOLIUM Don. 4. September. D. Ls. 3-fol.; lflts. broadly ov., 4, entire, stipulate, the terminal one long-stalked. Fls. $\frac{1}{2}$, red or pink, in large terminal panicles. Pod, 2, 6-9-jointed. Himalaya. (Fig. 3 J.)

DORYCNIUM. 2. June–September. D. Ls. digitate, 5-fol., stalkless; lflts. $\frac{1}{2}$, entire.

D. hirsutum Ser. Stem and ls. very hairy. Fls. $\frac{3}{4}$, white, in rounded heads. Pod $\frac{1}{4}$, egg-shaped, 4-seeded. Mediterranean region. (Fig. 5 C.)

D. suffruticosum Vill. Stem and ls. slightly hairy. Fls. $\frac{1}{4}$, pinkish white, in rounded heads. Pod $\frac{1}{4}$, round, 1-seeded. South Europe.

* ERYTHRINA CRISTA-GALLI L. Coral Tree. 8. May–July. D. Stem and leaf-stalks prickly. Ls. 3-fol.; lflts. ov., 4, entire, somewhat glaucous below. Fls. 2, scarlet, the standard petal much the largest, in dense terminal racemes. South America. (Fig. 2 G.)

* HARDENBERGIA COMPTONIANA Benth. (KENNEDYA COMPTONIANA Link). Climber. E. Ls. alternate, digitate; lflts. lanc., 3, entire, with a rounded or straight base. Fls. $\frac{1}{2}$, blue, white, or pinkish, with a yellowish or greenish spot on the standard, in axillary racemes. Pod cylindrical, $1\frac{1}{2}$, leathery. Australia. (Fig. 5 E.)

HEDYSARUM MULTIJUGUM Maxim. French Honeysuckle. 3. June–July. D. Young branchlets erect, zigzag. Ls. pinnate; lflts. ov., $\frac{1}{2}$, entire, numerous, hairy, the lowest pair close to the main stem. Fls. $\frac{3}{4}$, rosy purple, in long upright racemes. Pod flat, separating into circular 1-seeded segments. Mongolia. (Fig. 14 M.)

INDIGOFERA GERARDIANA Wall. 8. July–September. D. Branches downy, slightly ribbed. Ls. pinnate, stalk grooved; lflts. ov., $\frac{1}{2}$, hairy, apex with short bristle. Fls. $\frac{1}{2}$, rosy purple, in axillary racemes. Pod linear, $1\frac{1}{2}$, cylindrical. Himalaya. (Fig. 14 A.)

LESPEDEZA FORMOSA Koehne (L. SIEBOLDII Miq.). Bush Clover. 8. September. D. Ls. 3-fol.; lflts. elliptical, lanc., $2\frac{1}{2}$, entire, without stipules, apex rounded (with minute tip), terminal lflt. long-stalked. Fls. $\frac{1}{2}$, rosy purple, in axillary racemes. Pod not jointed, or 1-jointed. China and Japan. (Fig. 3 L.) (CAMPYLOTROPIS is similar except that the flower-stalks are jointed.)

MEDICAGO ARBOREA L. Moon Trefoil. 8. April–September. D. Stems very leafy, little branched, covered with grey down. Ls. 3-fol., stalk hairy; lflts. wedge-shaped, $\frac{3}{4}$, toothed or entire, the middle one stalked, silky below. Fls. $\frac{1}{2}$, yellow, crowded at the end of the shoot in axillary racemes. Pod $\frac{1}{2}$, curled. South Europe. (Fig. 3 K.)

ROBINIA. Buds small, hidden by the base of the leaf-stalk, no terminal bud. Branches usually with stipular spines in pairs. Ls. pinnate; lflts. ov., entire. Fls. in drooping racemes. Pod oblong or linear, splitting into two.

R. hispida L. Rose Acacia. 12. June. D. Branchlets bristly, usually without spines. Lflts. 2, with minute point at end, hairless or nearly so. Fls. 1, deep rose. Pod 3, bristly. South United States.

R. Kelseyi Cow. 12. June. D. Branchlets hairless, with slender prickles. Lflts. lanc., 1½, pointed, hairless. Fls. 1, bright rose. Pod 2, reddish, bristly. East United States. (Fig. 14 B.)

R. Pseudacacia L. Locust Tree, Black Locust, Acacia. 80. June. D. Bark with deep interlacing fissures. Branches tortuous. Lflts. 2, rounded or notched at apex; downy at first, then smooth. Fls. ¾, white. Pod 3, not bristly. East United States. (Fig. 13 G.)

Var. *aurea* Kirchn. Ls. yellow.
Var. *Decaisneana* Carr. Fls. pink.
Var. *fastigiata* Lem. Branches all upright like a Lombardy poplar.
Var. *inermis* DC. A small mop-headed tree, without spines.

WISTARIA. Woody climbers. 25. May–June. D. Ls. pinnate; lflts. ov., lanc., 3, entire, pointed, on short foot-stalks, margins often wavy. Fls. ¾, lilac or white, in long vertically hanging racemes. Pod 6, elongated, flattened, with persistent style.

W. floribunda DC. Ls. with 13–19 lflts. Racemes lilac, up to 10 long. Japan.

Var. *alba* Rehd. & Wils. Fls. white.
Var. *macrobotrys* Rehd. & Wils. (*multijuga* Hook. f.). Racemes up to 36 long.

W. sinensis Sweet. Ls. with 9–13 lflts. Racemes lilac, up to 12 long. China. (Fig. 13 A.)

Var. *alba* Lindl. Fls. white.

W. venusta Rehd. & Wils. Lflts. downy. Racemes white, up to 6 long.

(III) Stamens All Free

* Anagyris foetida L. 12. May–June. D. Ls. 3-fol.; lflts. ov., lanc., 2½, entire, greyish green, downy below. Fls. 1, yellow, in short racemes on previous year's wood. Pod 5×¾, curved, pointed at both ends. Mediterranean region. (Fig. 1 L.)

* Calpurnia lasiogyne Mey. (C. aurea Benth.). 20. D. Branches slender, downy. Ls. alternate, pinnate, stalk channelled; lflts. ov., 2, rounded or notched at end. Fls. 1, yellow, in axillary racemes. Pod 2×½, thin, 5-6-seeded. South Africa.

CLADRASTIS. Yellow Wood. Buds completely enclosed in the swollen base of the leaf-stalk. Ls. pinnate; lflts. alternate, ov., 4, entire, pointed, the terminal one the largest. Fls. white or pinkish, in terminal panicles. Pod flattened, narrow-oblong, 3-6-seeded.

C. platycarpa Makino (*Platyosprion platycarpum* Maxim.). 60. July. D. Ls. with 7–15 lflts.; lflts. narrowly ov., lanc., 4, with stipules. Fls. ½.

CLADRASTIS—*continued*

white, with a yellow spot at the base of the standard, in erect panicles. Pod 3, winged. Japan.

C. sinensis Hemsl. 70. July. D. Ls. with 9–13 lflts.; lflts. lanc., 5, downy. Fls. ½, pinkish white, panicles erect. Pod 3, hairless. West China.

C. tinctoria Rafin. (*C. lutea* C. Koch, *Virgilia lutea* Michx.). 40. July. D. Ls. with 7–9 lflts.; lflts. broadly ov., 5, hairless. Fls. 1, white, fragrant, in drooping panicles. Pod 4. East United States. (Fig. 13 B.)

C. Wilsonii Takeda. 50. July. D. Ls. with 9–15 lflts.; lflts. narrowly ov., 3, downy. Fls. 1, white, fragrant, in lax panicles. Pod 2, downy. West China.

MAACKIA AMURENSIS Rupr. (CLADRASTIS AMURENSIS Benth.). 40. July. D. Bark peeling. Ls. pinnate; lflts. opposite, ov., 3, blunt-ended, hairless. Fls. ½, white, in dense erect racemes. Pod 3×½, flat, the seam slightly winged. North China. (Fig. 13 C.)

PIPTANTHUS NEPALENSIS D. Don. Evergreen Laburnum. 10. May–July. E. Ls. 3-fol., long-stalked; lflts. lanc., 4, entire, pointed, glaucous below, stalkless. Fls. 1, yellow, in stiff erect terminal racemes. Pod 5×¾. Himalaya. (Fig. 3 B.)

* PODALYRIA SERICEA R. Br. 3. November–February. E. Ls. alternate, ov. or obov., 2, tapering base, covered on both sides with silky silvery hairs. Fls. ¾, rosy purple, solitary in the leaf-axils. South Africa. (Fig. 115 K.)

SOPHORA. Branchlets jointed. Ls. pinnate. Fls. in racemes or panicles. Pod cylindrical, constricted between the seeds like a string of beads, style persistent.

S. japonica L. Pagoda Tree. 80. September. D. Lflts. ov., lanc., 2, pointed, rounded base, dark green and glossy above, grey below. Fls. ½, creamy white, in terminal panicles. Pod 3, hairless. China. (Fig. 14 C.)

S. tetraptera Ait. (*Edwardsia grandiflora* Salisb.). 40. May. E. Young branchlets zigzagged, covered with tawny down. Lflts. ov., ½, entire, often very numerous. Fls. 1½, yellow. Pod 8, 4-winged. New Zealand. (Fig. 10 C.)

Var. *microphylla* Hook. f. (*Edwardsia microphylla* Salisb.). Lflts. smaller and more numerous.

S. viciifolia Hance. 8. June. D. Branches spiny, downy. Lflts. ov., ½, entire, silky on both sides, the common leaf-stalk channelled. Fls. ¾, blue and white. Pod 2½, 1-4-seeded, long-beaked. China. (Fig. 14 D.)

Sub-family. **CAESALPINIACEAE.** K5 or (5), C5, A10, G1

Fls. irregular, but not or only slightly resembling those of the sweet pea. Senna is obtained from the leaves of various tropical species of *Cassia*. The tamarind tree of the east is a member of this sub-family. The imported timber purpleheart is obtained from species of *Peltogyne* from Central America.

* BAUHINIA DENSIFLORA Franch. 10. June. D. Ls. simple, ov., 2½, divided to one-third of their depth into kidney-shaped halves, downy below. Fls. ½, white, in short downy racemes. West China. (Fig. 27 A.)

Various species of *Bauhinia*, having the same characteristic leaf are familiar gigantic climbers in eastern jungles.

CAESALPINIA JAPONICA Sieb. & Zucc. 8. June–July. D. Branches rambling and prickly. Ls. 2-pinnate; lflts. ov., $\frac{3}{4}$, entire, downy below. Fls. $1\frac{1}{4}$, yellow, in large terminal racemes; petals spreading, nearly equal; stamens red. Pod 3×1, ov., lanc., flat, 6-9-seeded. Japan. (Fig. 20 F.)

CASSIA. Ls. pinnate, without a terminal lflt.; lflts. lanc., entire. Fls. $\frac{1}{2}$, yellow, in terminal or axillary racemes, petals spreading. Pod 4. (*Cassia Fistula* L., the Indian Laburnum, with its hanging chains of yellow flowers and long black cylindrical pods, is a common sight in India and Burma.)

* **C. corymbosa** Lam. (*C. floribunda* Hort.). 10. June–September. D. Ls. with 6 lflts. Fls. in branched clusters. South America.

C. marylandica L. Wild Senna. 3. June–September. D. Ls. with 10–20 lflts., which are about $2\frac{1}{2}$ long ending in a bristle. Petals yellow, stamens purple. Pod linear, flat. U.S.A. (Fig. 13 H.)

CERCIS. Ls. laternate, simple, broadly ov. or circular, 4, heart-shaped base, hairless, the chief veins palmately arranged. Fls. $\frac{3}{4}$, pink or purplish, in clusters on the old wood and appearing before the leaves. Pod $5\times\frac{1}{2}$, flat, red.

C. canadensis L. Redbud. 30. May. D. L. with a short spine at the tip. Fls. rosy pink. North America.

C. Siliquastrum L. Judas Tree. 20. May. D. L. rounded or notched at the tip. Fls. purplish red. Mediterranean region. (Fig. 117 K.)

GLEDITSCHIA. Locust. Trunks and branches usually armed with stout and often branched spines. Ls. pinnate or 2-pinnate. Fls. small, green, in racemes, petals spreading. Pod large, flattened.

G. aquatica Marsh. Water Locust. 60. June. D. Trunk with branched spines. Lflts. ov., 1, toothed. Pod 2, thin, diamond-shaped, 1-2-seeded. South United States. (Fig. 19 C.)

G. caspica Desf. Caspian Locust. 40. July. D. Very spiny. Lflts. ov., 2, toothed. Pod 8, curved. North Persia.

G. japonica Miq. (*G. horrida* Makino). Japanese Locust. 70. June–July. D. Spines slightly flattened, up to 4 long, often branched. Lflts. ov., $1\frac{1}{2}$, entire or sparsely toothed. Pod 12, curved, twisted, the seeds near the middle. Japan.

G. triacanthos L. Honey Locust. 140. July. D. Trunk with bunches of large spines. Lflts. ov., lanc., $1\frac{1}{2}$, toothed. Pod 18 long, sickle-shaped. East United States. (Fig. 19 B.)

Var. *inermis* Pursh. Without spines or nearly so, and of more slender growth.

GYMNOCLADUS CANADENSIS Lam. (G. DIOICA Koch). Kentucky Coffee Tree. 100. July. D. Ls. 2-pinnate; lflts. ov., 3, entire, the lowest pairs not divided; the common stalk is left on the branches after the lflts. fall. Fls. $\frac{1}{2}$, greenish white, in terminal panicles, unisexual. Pod oblong, 9, thick and brown; seeds large and circular. North America. (Fig. 19 E.)

Sub-family. MIMOSEAE. K4–5, C4–5, A (4–∞), $\underline{G}1$

Fls. regular. Ls. 2-pinnate or replaced by leaf-like branches. Tropical hardwoods imported into this country include Australian blackwood, kokko (dark brown) from India and Burma, and pynkado (dark reddish brown) from Burma.

* ALBIZZIA JULIBRISSIN Durazz. Pink Siris. 40. July–August. D. Ls. 2-pinnate; lflts. oblong, ½, the midrib on one side. Fls. small, in round heads or axillary spikes, conspicuous by means of the numerous pink stamens, K5, C5. Pod strap-shaped, 6. Orient. (Fig. 18 D.)

ACACIA. Ls. alternate, 2-pinnate, usually with minute lflts., or absent and replaced by flattened leaf-like branches. Fls. small, yellow, in ball-like or brush-like clusters. Often called mimosa, but the genus *Mimosa* has not more than ten stamens. *Mimosa pudica* L. is the Sensitive Plant, the leaves of which fold up when the plant is touched.

(*a*) *Ls. 2-pinnate*

* **A. Baileyana** F. Muell. Bailey's Mimosa. 30. March–April. E. Branchlets hairless. Ls. arranged more or less radially round the stem; lflts. minute, linear, bluish grey. Fls. in round heads in axillary racemes on the old wood. Australia. (Fig. 20 D.)

* **A. dealbata** Link. Mimosa, Silver Wattle. 100. March–April and July–September. E. Young branchlets downy. Lflts. minute, linear. Fls. fragrant, in round heads in axillary panicles. Pod 3×½, blue-white, flat. Australia. (Fig. 20 C.)

(*b*) *L.-like branches simple*

* **A. armata** R. Br. Kangaroo Thorn. 10. April–May. E. Young branchlets bristly. False ls. linear or oblong, 1, point curved, closely set on the twigs. Fls. in round heads. Pod 2×¼, silky. Australia. (Fig. 116 D.)

* **A. juniperina** Willd. 30. August–September. E. False ls. linear, awl-shaped, ½, prickly pointed, alternate. Fls. in round heads. Australia. (Fig. 52 P.)

* **A. longifolia** Willd. Golden Wattle. 30. April–May. E. Young branchlets hairless. False ls. oblong, lanc., 6, tapered at base, dark green. Fls. in slender cylindrical spikes. Pod 4×¼. Australia.

* **A. melanoxylon** R. Br. Blackwood. 80. April–May. E. Young branchlets downy. Ls. present in young trees, 2-pinnate; lflts. ¼. False ls. lanc., curved, tapered at both ends, 3-5-nerved. Fls. in round heads. Pods 4×½, flat, curved. Australia.

* **A. neriifolia** Cunn. (*A. retinodes* Schlecht). 25. August–September. E. False ls. linear, lanc., 3, 1-nerved. Fls. in round heads in short racemes. Pod 4×½, straight. Australia. (Fig. 52 G.)

* **A. verticillata** Willd. Prickly Mimosa. 30. April–May. E. Young branchlets downy. False ls. linear, awl-shaped, ½, prickly pointed, in whorls. Fls. in spikes like bottle brushes 1 long. Pod 2, slender, curved. Australia. (Fig. 52 D.)

Family 44. **ROSACEAE.** K4–5, C4–5 or 0, A5–∞, $\underline{G}$1–∞ or (1–∞)

Ls. usually stipulate. The axis of the flower is often enlarged into a flattish or hollow structure on the rim of which the stamens are borne. The family is important chiefly for its flowers and fruit, which include plums, cherries, peaches, apricots, almonds, apples, pears, pedlars, quinces, strawberries, raspberries, and blackberries. *Potentilla* and *Geum* are favourite garden flowers, while meadowsweet is a herbaceous species of *Spiraea*. Attar or Otto of Roses is an oil distilled in India and Persia from rose petals.

(I) OVARY SUPERIOR; fruit dry, usually splitting
(SPIRAEA SECTION)

EUCRYPHIA. Brush Bush. Ls. opposite. Fls. 2, white, solitary or in pairs, K4–5, C4–5, A∞, G̲ (5–12). Fruit a woody pear-shaped capsule.

* **E. cordifolia** Cav. 20. July–August. E. Ls. ov., 3, heart-shaped base, dull green, toothed, margins wavy, downy below. Fls. 5-petalled. Chile. (Fig. 59 E.)

E. glutinosa Focke (*E. pinnatifolia* Gay). 25. July–August. E. Ls. pinnate; lflts. ov., 1½, evenly toothed, dark glossy green, stalkless. Fls. 4-petalled. Chile. (Fig. 9 B.)

E. nymansayensis Bausch. August. E. Ls. simple or 3-fol., regularly toothed, leathery, dark glossy green above, pale green and downy below. Fls. 2½, white, 4-petalled. Hybrid.

EXOCHORDA. Ls. alternate or in clusters, ov., 3, entire or toothed near apex, thin, without stipules. Fls. 1½, white, 5-petalled, the petals narrowed at the base into a claw. Fruit ½, bony, 5-angled.

E. Giraldii Hesse. 20. May–June. D. Ls. ov., entire, with a broadly wedge-shaped base and pink stalk. Petals gradually narrowed. China.

E. Korolkowii Lav. (*E. Albertii* Regel). 15. May–June. D. Branches erect; twigs hairless. Ls. obov., with a narrowly wedge-shaped base, toothed at apex, hairless. Stamens in five groups of five each. Turkestan. (Fig. 89 H.)

E. macrantha Lem. 10. April–May. D. Hybrid with more abundant flowers.

E. racemosa Rehd. (*E. grandiflora* Lindl.). Pearl Bush. 10. May–June. D. Ls. ov., lanc., entire, or toothed towards apex, stamens in three groups of five each. China. (Fig. 119 A.)

* LYONOTHAMNUS FLORIBUNDUS var. ASPLENIFOLIUS Brandegee. 50. E. Ls. opposite, pinnate; lflts. 4, deeply lobed, dark green and smooth above, paler and downy below. Fls. ¼, white, in terminal branched clusters, K5, C5, A15. Fruit woody. Islands off California.

NEILLIA. Nine Bark. Branches slender, arching or spreading. Ls. alternate, ov., 3-nerved at base, double-toothed, often lobed. Fls. ½, white or pinkish, tubular, in terminal panicles, K5, C5, A20–40. Fruit of four or five shining pointed pods.

N. capitata Greene (*Physocarpus capitatus* Kuntze). 10. June. D. Ls. broadly ov., 4, 3-lobed, downy below. California.

N. opulifolia Benth. & Hook. f. (*Physocarpus opulifolius* Maxim.). 10. May. D. Ls. ov., 3, sometimes 3-lobed. Fls. white, tinged with pink, in hemispherical panicles. North America. (Fig. 28 A.)

SPIRAEA. Ls. alternate, usually toothed and with veins extending to the margin, without stipules. Fls. small, white, pink, or red, in many-flowered clusters or panicles, K5, C5, A∞, G̲5. Fruit a dry splitting capsule.

(*a*) *Ls. simple, fls. red or pink*

S. bella Sims. 3. June. D. Branches slender, spreading, angled. Ls.

SPIRAEA—*continued*

ov., 2, sharply toothed from beyond the middle, somewhat glaucous beneath, nearly hairless. Fls. pink, unisexual, in small branched clusters. Himalaya. (Fig. 95 M.)

S. Douglasii Hook. 6. July–August. D. Stems reddish-felted when young. Ls. lanc., 4, coarsely toothed towards the end, dark green above, grey-felted below. Fls. purplish rose, in large erect terminal panicles; stamens pink. North-west America. (Fig. 95 D.)

S. japonica L. f. 5. July–August. D. Stems erect, shining brown. Ls. lanc., 4, coarsely toothed, dark green above, glaucous beneath. Fls. red, in large flat terminal panicles. China and Japan. (Fig. 95 J.)

Var. *Bumalda* Hort. Dwarf.

Var. *Bumalda Anthony Waterer* Hort. Fls. brilliant carmine.

S. Menziesii Hook. 5. July–August. D. Stems erect, brown, suckering freely; buds hairy. Ls. ov., lanc., 3, toothed in outer half, grey-green and downy below. Fls. rose-coloured, in large erect panicles. West North America. (Fig. 95 E.)

Var. *triumphans* Hort. Ls. toothed nearly to base.

S. salicifolia L. Bridewort. 6. June–July. D. Stems erect, hairless, suckering freely. Ls. lanc., 3, sharply toothed, green on both sides. Fls. pale pink, crowded in erect terminal racemes. Europe (including Britain) to Japan. (Fig. 95 H.)

S. tomentosa L. Steeplebush, Hardhack. 5. August–September. D. Stems erect, suckering freely, brown-felted when young. Ls. ov., 3, coarsely toothed almost to base, dark green above, tawny-felted below. Fls. red, in erect branching panicles. U.S.A. (Fig. 95 F.)

(*b*) *Ls. simple, fls. white or cream*

S. arguta Zabel. 8. April. D. Stems slender, downy and leafy. Ls. oblanc., obov., 1, entire or with a few teeth near apex, veins prominent below. Fls. white, in small clusters forming long arching sprays of bloom. Hybrid. (Fig. 95 A.)

S. bracteata Zabel (*S. nipponica* Maxim.). 6. June. D. Branches angled. Ls. obov., 1, toothed near apex, dark green above, blue-green below. Fls. white, in many-flowered clusters. Japan.

S. canescens D. Don (*S. flagelliformis* Hort.). 15. June. D. Stems erect, but arching or drooping at the top, ribbed. Ls. ov., 1, rounded and toothed at apex, grey and downy below. Fls. white or cream, in branched clusters forming long arching sprays of bloom. Himalaya. (Fig. 95 B.)

S. crenata L. 5. May. D. Ls. ov., 1, toothed at apex or entire, 3-nerved. Fls. white, in small rounded clusters. South-east Europe. (Fig. 95 C.)

S. discolor Pursh (*S. ariaefolia* Sm., *Holodiscus discolor* Maxim.). 12. June–July. D. Stems erect, but arching or drooping at the top, ribbed. Ls. ov., 3, lobed, the lobes toothed, grey-felted below. Fls. creamy white, in large drooping panicles. Fruit non-splitting. North-west America. (Fig. 36 H.)

S. laevigata L. (*Sibiraea laevigata* Maxim.). 6. May. D. Branches stout, erect, reddish brown. Ls. ov., 3, entire, tapering base, bluish green, hairless. Fls. white, in terminal panicles. Siberia.

SPIRAEA—*continued*

S. media F. Schmidt (*S. confusa* Regel & Kern.). 6. April–May. D. Stems cylindrical, hairless. Ls. ov., 2, toothed near apex or entire. Fls. white, in erect racemes. Europe. (Fig. 95 L.)

S. prunifolia Sieb. & Zucc., var. *flore pleno* Hort. 6. April–May. D. Stems arching. Ls. ov., 1½, finely and evenly toothed, downy below. Fls. double, white, in small clusters produced in profusion. China and Japan. (Fig. 95 K.)

S. Thunbergii Sieb. & Zucc. 5. March–April. D. Stems slender, angled, downy. Ls. linear, lanc., 1, teeth incurved, green on both sides. Fls. white, in small clusters on leafless twigs. China and Japan. (Fig. 52 K.)

S. Van Houttei Zabel. 6. May–June. D. Stems brown, arching, hairless. Ls. obov., 1, often lobed, coarsely toothed in outer half, dark green above, glaucous below. Fls. white, in small clusters in great profusion. Hybrid. (Fig. 95 N.) (*S. cantoniensis* Lour. is similar, but the leaves are narrower and longer.) China.

S. Veitchii Hemsl. 12. June–July. D. Stems arching, reddish brown. Ls. usually in two opposite rows, ov., lanc., 1½, entire, blunt-ended (with minute point), somewhat glaucous below. Fls. white, in branched clusters. China. (Fig. 95 G.)

S. Wilsonii Duthie. 6. June–July. D. Like *S. Veitchii*, but the upper side of the leaf is downy. China.

(*c*) *Ls. pinnate; lflts. lanc., 4, long-pointed, stalkless. Fls. ivory-white, in large branching terminal panicles*

S. Aitchisonii Hemsl. (*Sorbaria angustifolia* Hemsl.). 10. July–August. D. Young stems red. Lflts. evenly toothed, green and hairless on both sides. Afghanistan.

S. arborea Bean (*Sorbaria arborea* Schneid.). 20. July–August. D. Lflts. oblong, lanc., double-toothed, with star-shaped hairs beneath. West China. (Fig. 12 K.)

S. Lindleyana Wall. (*Sorbaria Lindleyana* Maxim.). 20. July–August. D. Lflts. double-toothed, with simple hairs beneath. Himalaya. (Fig. 12 J.)

S. sorbifolia L. (*Sorbaria sorbifolia* R. Br.). 6. July–August. D. Stems erect, suckering freely. Lflts. double-toothed. Flowering panicles stiff and erect. Himalaya to Japan.

STEPHANANDRA. Ls. alternate, 3-lobed, sharply toothed, long-pointed, the veins in grooves. Fls. small, greenish or yellowish white, in terminal panicles up to 4 long, K5, C5, A10–20, G1. Fruit of one or two dry pods.

S. incisa Zabel (*S. flexuosa* Sieb. & Zucc.). 8. June. D. Ls. deeply lobed. Fls. with ten stamens. China and Japan.

S. Tanakae Franch. 6. June. D. Ls. slightly lobed. Fls. with fifteen to twenty stamens. Japan. (Fig. 28 B.)

(II) OVARY SUPERIOR (apparently, though not really, inferior in Roses); fruit fleshy or berry-like, with more than one seed; or, if dry, does not split

(ROSE SECTION)

CERCOCARPUS. Mountain Mahogany. Ls. alternate, often in clusters.

CERCOCARPUS—*continued*

Fls. small, without petals, in axillary clusters; ovary 1-celled, enclosed in the calyx tube. Fruit 1-seeded, with long feathery appendage.

C. intricatus S. Wats. 6. June. E. Stiff and intricately branched. Ls. linear or narrowly lanc., 1, entire, margins recurved, grey-felted below. West North America. (Fig. 52 C.)

C. ledifolius Nutt. 30. June. E. Ls. lanc., 1, entire, glossy above, downy below, margins recurved. West North America. (Fig. 117 M.)

C. montanus Rafin. (*C. parvifolius* Nutt.). 15. June. E. Ls. ov., 1½, toothed in outer half, with four to six pairs of parallel veins. West North America. (Fig. 87 K.)

CHAMAEBATIA FOLIOLOSA Benth. Tarweed. 3. July. ½ E. Ls. alternate, ov., 2½, 3-pinnately dissected, hairy. Fls. 1, white, in terminal branched clusters, C5. California. (Fig. 19 D.)

* COWANIA STANSBURIANA Torr. (C. MEXICANA Don). 6. July–September. E. Ls. alternate or in clusters, ov., ½, 3-5-lobed, dark green above, white-felted below, margins recurved. Fls. ¾, yellow or white, at the end of short twigs, K5, C5, A∞, G̲1–12. Fruit with silky tails. South-west United States. (Fig. 34 C.)

DRYAS OCTOPETALA L. Mountain Avens. ¼. July–August. E. Prostrate rock plant. Ls. alternate, ov., 1, heart-shaped base, blunt-ended, with a few large teeth or lobes, white below, slender-stalked. Fls. 1, white, solitary on an erect and very slender stalk, K8, C8. Fruit of numerous seed vessels each with a long silky tail. North Europe (including Britain), North America. (Fig. 87 J.)

FALLUGIA PARADOXA Endl. 5. June–August. D. Branchlets slender, greyish white. Ls. wedge-shaped, ¾, cut into narrow oblong lobes running into the leaf-stalk, downy all over, margins recurved. Fls. 1½, white, solitary or in few-flowered racemes, K5, C5, A∞, G̲∞. Fruit with feathery tails. California. (Fig. 34 B.)

KERRIA JAPONICA DC. (CORCHORUS JAPONICUS Thunb.). Jew's Mallow. 6. April–May. D. Branchlets slender, zigzagged, with a l. at each angle. Ls. alternate, ov., 4, long-pointed, sharply double-toothed, heart-shaped base, hairless above, hairy below. Fls. 1½, yellow, solitary, slender-stalked, K5, C5, A∞, G̲5–8. Fruit of five to eight dry, brownish-black seed vessels. China. (Fig. 89 G.)

Var. *pleniflora* Witte. Fls. double. (Fig. 89 G.)

Var. *variegata* T. Moore. Ls. with white edge.

MARGYRICARPUS SETOSUS Ruiz & Pav. Pearl Fruit. 1. Summer. E. Prostrate. Branches yellow, partly covered by the sheathing bases of the leaf-stalks. Ls. alternate, pinnate; lflts. linear, ¼ or more, green, margins recurved. Fls. small, solitary, inconspicuous, without petals. Fruit a small white berry. Chile. (Fig. 49 D.) (*M. alatus* (Gill.) is very similar, but with winged fruits.) (Fig. 49 E.)

NEVIUSA ALABAMENSIS Gray. Snow-in-Summer. 6. June–July. D. Ls. alternate, ov., 3, pointed, double-toothed, hairless or nearly so. Fls. 1, without petals, but with four to five white-toothed and conspicuous sepals; stamens white, numerous and conspicuous. Alabama. (Fig. 93 E.)

POTENTILLA FRUTICOSA L. Shrubby Cinquefoil. 4. May–September. D. Bark shreddy. Ls. pinnate, 5-fol.; lflts. lanc., 1, pointed, entire. Fls. 1, yellow, solitary, 5-petalled, short-stalked. Northern Hemisphere. (Fig. 14 K.)

Purshia tridentata DC. 10. May. D. Ls. alternate or in clusters, obov., 1, 3-lobed at apex, whitish and hairy below, with a tapering base. Fls. ½, yellowish, K5, C5, A25, G1 or 2, solitary. Fruit ¼, spindle-shaped, projecting beyond the persistent calyx. West North America. (Fig. 29 E.)

Rhodotypos kerrioides Sieb. & Zucc. White Kerria. 6. June–July. D. Branches erect, hairless. Ls. opposite, ov., 4, long-pointed, deeply and unevenly toothed, prominently parallel-veined, dark green above, hairy below. Fls. 2, white, solitary, K4, C4, A∞, G4. Fruit of four hard black berries, each containing one seed. China and Japan. (Fig. 61 F.)

ROSA. Rose. Shrubs or woody climbers, usually with thorns or prickles. Ls. alternate, pinnate; the stipules expanded into two pointed wings. K5, C5, A∞, G1–∞. The ovaries are enclosed in a fleshy urn-shaped receptacle which becomes the fruit (hip). In many cultivated varieties some or all of the stamens are converted into extra petals. It is impossible in a book of this size to list all the ornamental species, far less all the varieties, which are constantly being added to.

(*a*) *Styles projecting conspicuously beyond mouth of receptacle*

R. arvensis Huds. Trailing Wild Rose. June. Stems long and very slender. Lflts. ov., 2, simply toothed, glaucous below. Fls. 1½, white, often solitary, the styles united into a column almost as long as the stamens. Fruit egg-shaped, dark red. Europe (including Britain). (Fig. 16 B.)

R. chinensis Jacq. (*R. indica* Lindl.). China or Monthly Rose. June–November. Stems green, with short flattened hooked prickles. Lflts. ov., 3, glossy green above, glaucous below, hairless. Fls. 2, pink, semi-double, in clusters; styles free. Fruit ¾, pear-shaped, scarlet. China. (Fig. 15 A.)

Var. *fragrans* Rehd. Tea-scented (source of Tea Roses, Gloire de Dijon, Maréchal Niel, etc.).

R. foetida Herrm. (*R. lutea* Mill.). See under (*b*) (ii).

R. moschata Mill. Musk Rose. June–July. Lflts. ov., lanc., 3, simply and evenly toothed. Fls. 1½, pale yellow to white, in large branched clusters, styles united into a column almost as long as the stamens. Fruit ¼, pear-shaped, red. South Europe to India. (Fig. 16 A.)

R. multiflora Thunb. (*R. polyantha* Sieb. & Zucc.). June–July. Very vigorous rambler. Stems hairless, with small recurved prickles. Stipules deeply and pinnately dissected. Lflts. ov., 1½, downy. Fls. 1, white, pink, or red, in branching panicles, styles united into a column almost as long as the stamens. Fruit ½, egg-shaped, red, calyx deciduous. China and Japan. (Fig. 15 G.)

(Source of American Pillar, Crimson Rambler, etc.)

R. Noisettiana Red. Noisette Rose. June. Branches arching; prickles reddish. Lflts. oblong, lanc., 2, glossy, hairless. Fls. 2, white, pink, or red, styles free; in large terminal panicles. Hybrid.

(Source of William Allen Richardson.)

R. setigera Michx. Prairie Rose. June–August. Ls. mostly 3-fol.; lflts. ov., 3. Fls. 2, pink fading to white, in few-flowered clusters. Fruit ¼, round. North America.

R. stylosa Desv. June–July. Stems erect or arched. Lflts. ov., 2, hairy

ROSA—*continued*

below. Fls. 2, white or pink, styles forming a conical head shorter than the stamens. Fruit egg-shaped. Europe (including Britain).

R. Wichuriana Crép. July–August. Barren stems unbranched. Lflts. ov., 1, coarsely toothed, glossy green on both sides. Fls. 2, white, in panicles, styles united into a column almost as long as the stamens. Fruit ¼, round, calyx deciduous. Japan.

Var. *rubra* Hort. Fls. red.

(Source of Alberic Barbier, Dorothy Perkins, Lady Gay, etc.)

(*b*) *Styles projecting slightly or not at all beyond mouth of receptacle*

(i) FRUIT WITH HAIRS OR BRISTLES

R. bracteata Wendl. Macartney Rose. July–August. Stems thick, downy and bristly, with pairs of hooked prickles. Lflts. obov., 2, rounded at end, glossy dark green above. Stipules joined to leaf-stalk near base only. Fls. 3, white, surrounded by several downy and deeply dissected bracts. Fruit 1½, round, orange-red, woolly. China. (Fig. 15 E.)

R. centifolia L. Cabbage Rose. June–July. Stems very prickly. Lflts. ov., 2½, usually five in number, heart-shaped base, firm, downy below, the common stalk not prickly. Fls. pink or red, fragrant, very double, nodding, in clusters, the stalks with numerous gland-tipped hairs or bristles. Fruit round or egg-shaped. Origin unknown.

Var. *muscosa* Ser. Moss Rose. Fls. pink, very fragrant, the stalk and calyx covered with a moss-like growth of glandular hairs.

Var. *parvifolia* Rehd. Burgundian Rose. Lflts. 1½. Fls. bright red, fragrant, stalk very bristly.

Var. *pomponia* Lindl. Pompon Rose. Dwarf. Lflts. 1. Fls. 1½, red.

R. damascena Mill. Damask Rose. 6. June–July. Ls. usually 5-fol.; lflts. ov., 2, evenly toothed, pale green and downy below. Fls. pinkish to red, double, in large clusters, very fragrant. Fruit 1, pear-shaped, red, bristly. East Europe.

Var. *trigintipetala* Dieck. Fls. semi-double, red. Used for attar in the East.

Var. *variegata* Thory. York and Lancaster Rose. Petals striped.

R. Davidii Crép. June–July. Prickles few and straight. Lflts. ov., 1½, evenly toothed, slightly glaucous and downy below. Fls. 2, pink, in branched clusters, styles projecting. Fruit ¾, scarlet. China.

R. Eglanteria Mill. (*R. rubiginosa* L.). Sweet Briar, Eglantine. Lflts. ov., 1, double-toothed, fragrant. Fls. 1½, pale pink, solitary or in small clusters. Fruit ¾, egg-shaped, orange-scarlet. Europe (including Britain). (Fig. 15 F.)

(Source of Penzance Briars.)

R. gallica L. French Rose. June–July. A bush 3–4 feet high, with creeping roots and erect stems (Bean). Lflts. ov., 2, rounded or heart-shaped base, glandular on margins. Fls. 2, dark red, solitary or in twos or threes, stiff-stalked, sepals pinnately lobed. Fruit ½, round or pear-shaped, dark dull red, calyx deciduous. South Europe.

(Source of Hybrid Perpetual Roses.)

ROSA—*continued*

R. involuta Sm. Sabine's Rose. June. Prickles straight, unequal. Lflts. ov., 1, downy below. Fls. 2, pink, solitary on a short bristly stalk. Fruit round, red. Europe (including Britain). (Fig. 16 J.)

R. laevigata Michx. Cherokee Rose. May–July. Tall climber. Ls. mostly 3-fol.; lflts. ov., 2, glossy above, net-veined below. Fls. 3, white, fragrant, solitary. Fruit 1½, pear-shaped, bristly. China.

R. micrantha Sm. Small-flowered Briar. June. Prickles equal, hooked. Lflts. broadly ov., 1, double-toothed, with glandular hairs below. Fls. 1, pink or white. Fruit egg-shaped. Europe (including Britain). (Fig. 16 G.)

R. Moyesii Hemsl. & Wils. June–July. Stems erect. Lflts. ov., roundish, 1½. Fls. 2, dark red, solitary or in pairs. Fruit 1½, bottle-shaped, orange-red, with scattered glandular hairs, calyx persistent. China. (Fig. 15 D.)

R. sericea Lindl. May–June. Large spreading bush; branches arching and very leafy. Pair of curved prickles at base of leaf-stalk. Lflts. obov., ¾, rounded at end, toothed in outer half, silky hairs below. Fls. 1½, creamy white, with four petals. Fruit ½, red, pear-shaped, calyx persistent. India and China. (Fig. 16 K.)

R. sertata Rolfe. June. Prickles straight, slender. Branchlets glaucous. Lflts. ov., ¾, hairless, slightly glaucous below. Fls. 2, rosy purple, solitary or in two or threes, sepals entire. Fruit ¾, egg-shaped, deep red. China.

R. setipoda Hemsl. & Wils. June. Prickles straight, broad. Lflts. ov., 2, dark green above, glaucous below. Fls. 2, pinkish purple, in branched clusters, the stalk and receptacle covered with gland-tipped bristles, sepals long and narrow, with toothed leaf-like tips. Fruit 1, deep red, nodding. China.

R. villosa L. Downy Rose. June–July. Dense shrub. Lflts. ov., 2, greyish green, hairy, double-toothed. Fls. 1½, pink, solitary or in clusters of two or three, stalks bristly. Fruit 1, bristly. Europe (including Britain). (Fig. 16 C.)

R. virginiana Mill. (*R. lucida* Ehrh.). June–July. Dense mass of erect stems up to 3 feet. Lflts. ov., 2, glossy, hairless. Fls. 2, pink, solitary or in small clusters; sepals 1, long-pointed. Fruit ½, red, orange-shaped. East United States. (*R. carolina* (L.) is very similar, but remains in flower up to September and the leaves are usually 5-fol.)

Var. *alba* Hort. Fls. white.

(ii) FRUIT PERFECTLY SMOOTH

R. Banksiae R. Br. Banksian Rose. June–August. Climber. Few or no prickles. Lflts. ov., oblong, 1½, evenly toothed, hairless or nearly so. Fls. 1, white or yellow, on slender smooth stalks in clusters. Fruit round, red, small. China.

R. canina L. Dog Rose. June–July. Prickles of about equal size. Lflts. ov., 1½, evenly toothed, hairless. Fls. 1½, white or pinkish, in clusters, fragrant, sepals pinnately lobed. Fruit ¾, red, egg-shaped or roundish. Europe (including Britain). (Fig. 15 B.)

ROSA—*continued*

R. Ecae Aitch. April–May. Like R. *Hugonis* (see below), but leaflets glandular and aromatic. China.

R. foetida Herrm. (R. *lutea* Mill.). Austrian Briar. June. Stems slender, with straight prickles. Lflts. obov., ov., 1½, coarsely and unevenly toothed, dark green above, downy below. Fls. 2½, orange or orange-red, solitary or in small clusters, unpleasantly scented. Fruit round, red. West Asia. (Fig. 16 H.)

R. gallica L. See under (i).

R. hibernica Sm. Irish Rose. May–June. Stems erect, branches arching. Lflts. ov., 1, downy below. Fls. 1½, pink, solitary or in threes, smooth-stalked, sepals with expanded tips. Fruit ½, round, red, calyx persistent. Ireland. (Fig. 16 E.)

R. Hugonis Hemsl. April. Stems red, slender, arching, thorns straight and flattened. Lflts. ov., ¾, finely toothed. Fls. 2, solitary, yellow. Fruit ½, round, blackish red, calyx persistent. China. (Fig. 15 H.) (R. *cantabrigiensis* (Hort.), with fls. a little deeper yellow, is a cross between this and R. *sericea*.)

R. omeiensis Rolfe. Mount Omi Rose. May–June. Stems erect; prickles wide, flattened. Lflts. ov., 1, hairless or nearly so. Fls. 1½, white. Fruit ½, pear-shaped, bright red on a thick yellow stalk. China.

R. pendulina L. (R. *alpina* L.). May–June. Stems slender; prickles few or none. Lflts. ov., 2, double-toothed, downy below. Fls. 1½, purplish pink, solitary or in few-flowered clusters. Fruit 1, oblong, bright red, nodding. Europe.

R. rubrifolia Vill. (R. *ferruginea* Déségl.). June–July. Stem and leaves purple. Fls. 1½, deep red, in small clusters. Fruit ½, round, red. Mountains of Central Europe.

R. rugosa Thunb. Ramanas Rose. June–July. Stems stout, very prickly. Lflts. ov., 1½, toothed at outer end, wrinkled above, downy below. Fls. 3½, purplish rose, very fragrant, solitary or in small clusters, sepals long and hairy. Fruit 1, bright red, with long persistent calyx. The leaves turn golden yellow in autumn. Japan. (Fig. 15 C.)

Var. *alba* Ware. Fls. white.

Var. *plena* Regel. Fls. double.

R. sericea Lindl. See under (i).

R. spinosissima L. Scotch or Burnet Rose. Dwarf bush though often up to 4 feet high, with creeping roots and erect short-branched thorny and bristly stems. Ls. closely set on branches; lflts. roundish ov., ½, deep green, hairless. Fls. 2, white or pink, solitary. Fruit ½, round, dark brown or black, calyx persistent. Europe (including Britain) and Siberia. (Fig. 16 F.)

Var. *lutea* Bean. Fls. yellow.

R. Willmottiae Hemsl. 10. June–July. Prickles straight, in pairs. Lflts. roundish ov., ½, hairless. Fls. 1, rose, solitary. Calyx deciduous. China.

R. xanthina Lindl. 10. June–July. Stems not bristly. Ls. round, ½. Fls. 1½, yellow, solitary. China.

RUBUS. Brambles. Stem usually prickly or bristly, often long and trailing Ls. alternate, usually lobed or compound, stipules linear. Fls. white or pink

RUBUS—*continued*
generally in terminal racemes or panicles, K5, C5, A ∞, $\underline{G}$ ∞. Fruit a compound berry consisting of a small rounded mass of 1-seeded fleshy carpels.

(*a*) *Ls. simple*

R. deliciosus Torr. Rocky Mountain Bramble. May–June. D. Stem without prickles. Ls. ov., 2½, 3-5-lobed, downy below. Fls. 2, white. Fruit ½, dry, dark purple. Rocky Mountains. (Fig. 26 J.)

R. flagelliflorus Focke. June. E. Prickles very small. Ls. ov., 6, heart-shaped base, slightly lobed, finely toothed, velvety green above, white- or yellow-felted below. Fls. ½, white, sepals red inside and conspicuous when reflexed. Fruit ½, black. China. (Fig. 26 K.)

R. odoratus L. Purple-flowering Raspberry. June–August. D. Stems pale brown, with peeling bark. Ls. ov., 12, 5-lobed, hairy on both sides, velvety. Fls. 2½, bright pink or purple, in many-flowered racemes. Fruit ¾, flat, red. North America.

R. parviflorus L. (*R. nutkanus* Moc.). Salmon Berry. June. D. Ls. ov., 8, 3-5-lobed, hairy on both sides. Fls. 2, white, in few-flowered branched clusters. Fruit ¾, red. North America. (Fig. 31 D.)

(*b*) *Stems with thick white waxy coating*

R. biflorus Buch.-Ham. July. D. Ls. 3-5-fol.; lflts. ov., 4, white-felted below. Fls. white. Fruit yellow. Himalaya.

R. Giraldianus Focke. June. D. Ls. pinnate, 7-9-fol.; lflts. ov., 2, white-felted below. Fls. purple. Fruit black. China.

R. lasiostylus Focke. June. D. Ls. 3-5-fol.; lflts. ov., 4, white-felted below. Fls. red. Fruit red. China.

R. thibetanus Franch. June. D. Ls. pinnate, 7-13-fol., lflts. ov., 2, white- or grey-felted below, the terminal one pinnately lobed. Fls. purple. Fruit black. China and Tibet.

(*c*) *Ls. compound; stems without thick white waxy coating*

R. australis Forst. Lawyer Vine. June. E. Stems slender, zigzagged. Ls. 3-fol. or consisting merely of three slender leaf-stalks without lflts.; lflts. vary in size from ¼ to 5. Fls. white, pink, or yellow, in panicles; fragrant, unisexual. Fruit ¼, reddish orange. New Zealand. (Fig. 2 B.)

R. caesius L. Dewberry. June–July. D. Ls. 3-fol.; lflts. green below. Fls. white or pink, in few-flowered racemes. Fruit of a few large black carpels. Europe (including Britain). (Fig. 2 E.)

Var. *turkestanicus* Regel. Fruit with more numerous carpels.

R. fruticosus L. Common Bramble, Blackberry. July–September. D. Ls. 3-5-fol.; lflts. green below. Fls. white or pink, in few-flowered racemes. Fruit black. Europe (including Britain). (Fig. 6 A.)

Has been divided into a very large number of species and varieties, for which Babington's *Manual of British Botany* and the Rev. W. Moyle Rogers's *Handbook of the British Rubi* may be consulted.

R. Idaeus L. Raspberry. May–June. D. Stems erect, numerous, suckering freely; with very small prickles. Ls. pinnate; lflts. white below. Fls.

RUBUS—*continued*

small, white or pinkish. Fruit red and juicy. Europe (including Britain), West Asia. (Fig. 12 H.)

Var. *albus* Fern. Fruit yellow.

R. laciniatus Willd. Cut-leaved Bramble. June–August. D. Stems angled. Ls. digitate, 5-fol.; lflts. pinnately lobed or dissected, downy below. Fls. 1, pinkish white, in large terminal clusters. Fruit ½, black, sweet. Origin unknown. (Fig. 20 E.)

R. loganobaccus Bailey. Loganberry. May–June. D. Stems long, rambling, and prickly. Ls. pinnate, 5-fol.; lflts. ov., 4, downy or white-felted below. Fls. large, white or pinkish. Fruit 1, conical, purple. Hybrid.

R. phoenicolasius Maxim. Wineberry. July. D. Stem and leaf-stalks densely covered with reddish bristles. Ls. 3-fol.; lflts. white-felted below, the terminal one much the largest. Fls. pink, sepals much longer than petals. Fruit ¾, conical, bright red. China and Japan.

R. procerus P. J. Muell. Himalaya Berry. July–August. D. Very vigorous. Stems stout, grooved, with scattered reflexed prickles. Ls. 5-fol.; lflts. broadly ov., white-felted below. Fls. 1, white, in white-felted panicles; stamens large. Fruit ¾, black. Europe.

R. spectabilis Pursh. April. D. Ls. 3-fol.; lflts. ov., 4, hairless or nearly so. Fls. 1, purplish red, fragrant, solitary or a few together on the old wood. Fruit large, egg-shaped, orange-yellow. West North America.

R. ulmifolius Schott (*R. rusticanus* Merc.). July. D. Stems arching, grooved, plum-coloured, rooting freely at the tips. Ls. 3-5-fol.; white-felted below. Fls. rosy red, in conspicuous cylindrical racemes or panicles. Fruit small, black. Europe (including Britain).

Var. *bellidiflorus* Voss. Fls. double.

Var. *inermis* Focke. Stems without prickles.

Var. *variegatus* Rehd. Veins of leaf yellow.

(III) Ovary Superior; fruit fleshy, 1-seeded

(Plum and Cherry Section)

Dichotomanthes tristaniaecarpa Kurz. 20. June. E. Young branchlets covered with white wool. Ls. alternate, ov., 4, entire, pointed, tapering base, dark green above, silkly-hairy below, stalk very short. Fls. ¼, white, in terminal branched clusters, C5, A15–20; the sepals enlarge and become fleshy, entirely enclosing the fruit. (Fig. 117 N.)

Osmaronia cerasiformis Greene (Nuttallia cerasiformis Torr. & Gray). Oso Berry. 8. March. D. Numerous stems springing erect from ground. Ls. alternate, oblong, lanc., 3½, entire, thin, downy and greyish below. Fls. ¼, white, in short stiff drooping racemes, often unisexual, with the sexes on different bushes. Fruit ¾, plum-like, purple. California. (Fig. 119 B.)

PRINSEPIA. Stem with axillary spines and chambered pith. Ls. alternate or in clusters. Fls. in small axillary clusters or racemes, K5, C5, A10, $\underline{G}1$. Fruit a berry.

P. sinensis Oliv. 6. May. D. Ls. lanc., 3, entire or faintly toothed,

PRINSEPIA—*continued*

the margins fringed with hairs. Fls. ½, yellow. Berry ¾, red, juicy. Manchuria.

P. uniflora Batal. 6. April. D. Ls. linear, lanc., 2, minutely toothed or entire, hairless. Fls. ¾, white. Berry ½, round, red or purple, juicy. China. (Fig. 52 L.)

P. utilis Royle. 12. March–April. D. Spines up to 2 long. Ls. ov., lanc., 4, toothed, hairless. Fls. ¼, white, fragrant, in short racemes. Berry ½, cylindrical, purple. Himalaya. (Fig. 93 D.)

PRUNUS. Winter buds with numerous scales. Ls. alternate or in clusters, simple, toothed, stipulate; leaf-scars broad. Fls. white, pink, or red, K5, C5, A ∞, G̲1. Fruit fleshy, containing one hard stone.

(*a*) *Fls. in elongated racemes 2 inches or more in length*
(LAUREL SECTION)

P. Laurocerasus L. Cherry Laurel. 20. April. E. Ls. oblong, lanc., 6, leathery, dark glossy green, finely and distantly toothed, tapering base, hairless, margins slightly recurved. Fls. ¼, white, in short erect racemes on leafless stalks. Fruit ¼, egg-shaped, black. East Europe, Orient. (Fig. 90 A.)

Var. *magnoliaefolia* Bean. Ls. up to 12×4.

P. lusitanica L. Portugal Laurel. 20. June. E. Branchlets hairless. Ls. oblong, ov., 5, rounded base, dark glossy green above, finely toothed, margins wavy, stalk usually red. Fls. ½, white, in long erect racemes on leafless stalks. Fruit ¼, egg-shaped, dark purple. Spain and Portugal.

Var. *myrtifolia* Mouillef. Compacter and with smaller leaves.
Var. *variegata* Nichols. Ls. edged with white.

P. Padus L. Bird Cherry. 50. May. D. Ls. ov., 5, shining green above, rounded or broadly tapering base, finely toothed, leaf-stalk with glands. Fls. ½, white, in long drooping racemes with leafy stalks. Fruit ¼, round, black, calyx deciduous. Europe (including Britain), Asia. (Fig. 90 C.)

Var. *aucubaefolia* Jaeg. Ls. spotted yellow.
Var. *plena* Bailey. Fls. semi-double.
Var. *Watereri* Bean. Larger flowers in racemes up to 8 long.

P. serotina Ehrh. Rum Cherry. 100. May. D. Twigs hairless. Ls. ov., lanc., 5, glossy above, teeth minute and incurved, often hairy along midrib below. Fls. ½, white, in cylindrical racemes up to 6 long. Fruit ¼, black, calyx persistent. U.S.A. (Fig. 90 E.)

(*b*) *Fls. in clusters, or short racemes 2 inches or less in length*

(i) Fruit without groove or furrow (CHERRY SECTION).

P. angustifolia Marsh. Mountain Cherry, Chickasaw Plum. 10. March–April. D. Twigs thin, zigzagged, reddish. Ls. lanc., 1½, finely and sharply toothed, glossy above, strongly keeled. Fls. ½, white, short-

PRUNUS—*continued*

stalked, in few-flowered clusters; sepals upright or spreading, hairless. Fruit ½, round, red or yellow. North America. (Fig. 91 E.)

P. avium L. (*Cerasus avium* Moench). Gean, Mazzard, Wild Cherry. 60. May. D. Ls. oblong, ov., 6, unevenly toothed, slender-pointed, hairy on midrib and veins below, stalk with red glands. Fls. 1, white, in drooping clusters. Fruit ¾, round, blackish red, sweet. Europe (including Britain). (Fig. 91 A.)

Var. *plena* Schneid. Double-flowered Gean.

P. Cerasus L. (*Cerasus vulgaris* Mill.). Wild Dwarf, Dwarf Cherry. 20. May. D. Twigs hairless. Ls. ov., 3, short-pointed, firm, finely and often doubly toothed, hairless. Fls. 1, white, long-stalked, in erect or semi-erect clusters. Fruit round, blackish red, sour. Europe (including Britain). (Fig. 91 C.)

Var. *plena* L. Fls. double.

Var. *salicifolia* Jaeg. Ls. long and narrow.

P. Conradinae Koehne. 25. February–March. D. Twigs hairless. Ls. ov., oblong, 4, abruptly long-pointed, rounded base, sharply and doubly toothed, 10–12 pairs veins. Fls. 1, white or pinkish. Fruit ½, red, egg-shaped. China. (Fig. 92 J.)

P. glandulosa Thunb. (*P. japonica* Hort., *P. sinensis* Pers.). 5. May. D. Three buds in each leaf-axil. Ls. ov., lanc., 2½, long-pointed, finely toothed, hairless or nearly so. Fls. ½, white or pink, short-stalked, in small clusters. Fruit ½, red. China and Japan.

Var. *plena* Dipp. Fls. double, pink. (Fig. 92 B.)

P. incana Stev. Willow Cherry. 6. May. D. Ls. lanc., 2, finely and sharply toothed, dark green above, whitish and hairy below, nearly stalkless. Fls. ½, rose-coloured. Fruit ½, round, red. Europe. (Fig. 91 F.)

P. Lannesiana Wils. 30. April–May. D. Twigs pale grey, hairless. Ls. ov., lanc., 5, long-pointed, sharply double-toothed, hairless. Fls. 1, pink or white, fragrant, in branched clusters or short racemes. Fruit egg-shaped, black. Japan. (Fig. 91 G.)

Var. *albida* Wils. Fls. white.

Var. *amanogawa* Hort. Fls. pale pink.

Var. *amanogawa erecta* Hort. Branches erect; fls. tinged with pink.

P. Mahaleb L. (*Cerasus Mahaleb* Mill.). St. Lucie Cherry. 40. May–June. D. Twigs downy. Ls. broadly ov. or circular, 2½, abruptly pointed, finely toothed, rounded base. Fls. ½, white, in elongated racemes up to 2 long. Fruit ¼, egg-shaped, black. Europe. (Fig. 91 D.)

P. pennsylvanica L. f. (*Cerasus borealis* Michx.). Wild Red Cherry. 40. April–May. D. Twigs hairless, slender, reddish. Ls. ov., lanc., 4, long-pointed, finely and sharply toothed, hairless. Fls. ½, white, in clusters or short racemes. Fruit ¼, round, red. North America. (Fig. 90 D.)

P. pumila L. Sand Cherry. 8. May. D. Young twigs hairless. Ls. oblanc., 2, hairless, finely and sharply toothed, dull green above, greyish white below. Fls. ¼, white, in clusters of two or four. Fruit ¼, round, purple-black, glossy. U.S.A.

PRUNUS—*continued*

P. serrulata Lindl. (*Cerasus serrulata* Don). Japanese Cherry. 20. April–May. D. A small tree with wide-spreading, almost horizontal branches and smooth dark chestnut-brown bark. Twigs hairless. Ls. ov., lanc., 6, abruptly long-pointed, sharply toothed, somewhat glaucous below, stalk with glands. Fls. 2, white or tinged with pink, in short racemes. Fruit ¼, black. China and Japan. (Fig. 91 B.)

Var. *alboplena* Schneid. Fls. double, white.
Var. *fugenzo* Wils. (*James Veitch* Hort.). Fls. double, deep pink.
Var. *hizakura* Koehne. Fls. double, pale pink.
Var. *rosea* Wils. Weeping habit. Fls. small, pink, very double.
Var. *sachalinensis* Makino (*P. Sargentii* Rehd.). Fls. single, pink.
Var. *sekiyama* Wils. Fls. double, rose-red, very large, late.

P. subhirtella Miq. 30. April. D. Young twigs downy. Ls. ov., 3, sharply, unevenly and often double-toothed, hairy on veins below. Fls. ¾, pink, in short-stalked clusters. Fruit black. Japan. (Fig. 92 A.)

Var. *autumnalis* Makino. Fls. single, nearly white, in bloom from October to Christmas.
Var. *pendula* Tanaka (*P. pendula* Maxim.). Rosebud Cherry, Weeping Cherry. Twigs drooping, hairy.

P. tomentosa Thunb. 10. March–April. D. Shrub with hairy twigs and crowded hairy ls. Ls. obov., 2, unevenly toothed, wrinkled above, densely hairy below. Fls. ¾, solitary or in pairs, numerous. Fruit ½, scarlet. China and Japan.

(ii) Fruit with groove or furrow (Plum Section).

P. Armeniaca L. Apricot. 30. April. D. Bark reddish; twigs brown. Ls. rolled in bud, broadly ov. or circular, 4, pointed, round-toothed. Fls. 1, white or pinkish, solitary, short-stalked. Fruit 1¼, round, yellow tinged with red. North China. (Fig. 92 K.)

P. blireana André. 30. March. D. Twigs slender, hairless. Ls. rolled in bud, ov., 3, round-toothed, coppery purple. Fls. 1, pink, double, solitary or two or threes. Hybrid.

P. cerasifera Ehrh. Cherry Plum, Myrobolan. 30. March. D. Twigs slender, sometimes spiny, hairless. Ls. rolled in bud, ov., 3, round-toothed, hairless or nearly so. Fls. 1, white, solitary or in twos or threes. Fruit 1, red. Caucasus. (Fig. 92 E.)

Var. *Pissardii* Carr. Ls. purple. Fls. pink. Fruit purple.

P. communis Fritsch (*P. Amygdalus* Stokes, *Amygdalus communis* L.). Almond. 30. March. D. Twigs hairless; three buds in each leaf-axil. Ls. folded in bud, lanc., 5, toothed, hairless, stalk with glands. Fls. 2, pink or white, solitary or in pairs, appearing before the leaves. Fruit 2, egg-shaped, compressed, covered with velvety down. South Europe. (Fig. 92 D.)

P. Davidiana Franch. 30. March. D. Like *P. communis*, but sepals hairless and fruit 1, round, yellowish. China. (Fig. 92 F.)

P. domestica L. (*P. communis* Huds.). Plum. 20. April. D. Ls. rolled in bud, ov., 3, evenly round-toothed, downy below. Fls. 1, white, short-stalked, solitary or in pairs. Fruit 1½, egg-shaped, black, with

PRUNUS—*continued*

blue bloom. Origin uncertain (occasionally found wild in Britain). (Fig. 93 B.)

P. insititia L. Bullace. 20. April. D. Branches somewhat spiny; young twigs downy. Ls. ov., 3, coarsely toothed, net veined. Fls. 1, white. Fruit 1½, round, often white or yellow (Bean). Europe, Orient. (Fig. 92 G.)

Damson, Mirabella, and Greengage are crosses between this and *P. domestica*.

P. Mume Sieb. & Zucc. Japanese Apricot. 20. March–April. D. Bark grey; twigs green. Ls. ov., 4, long-pointed, sharply toothed. Fls. ¾, pink, solitary or in pairs, short-stalked. Fruit 1¼, round, yellow, sour. Japan.

P. nana Stokes (*Amygdalus nana* L.). Dwarf Russian Almond. 3. April. D. Twigs hairless; three buds in each leaf-axil. Ls. rolled in bud, lanc., 3½, sharply toothed, hairless. Fls. ½, rosy red, stalkless. Fruit 1, dry, covered with velvety down, egg-shaped, compressed. South Russia. (Fig. 92 C.)

P. Persica Stokes (*Amygdalus Persica* L.). Peach. 20. April. D. Twigs hairless; three buds in each leaf-axil; buds downy. Ls. rolled in bud, lanc., 6, long-pointed, finely toothed, hairless. Fls. 1½, pink, short-stalked, solitary. Fruit 3, velvety, yellow with red. China. (Fig. 92 H.)

There are white, crimson, single- and double-flowered varieties in cultivation.

P. spinosa L. Sloe, Blackthorn. 15. April. D. Twigs black, spiny. Ls. ov., lanc., 1½, sharply toothed. Fls. ½, white, solitary or in pairs, sometimes appearing before the leaves. Fruit ½, round, blue to black, erect. Europe (including Britain). North Asia. (Fig. 93 A.)

Var. *plena* West. Fls. double.

P. triloba Lindl. (*Amygdalus Lindleyi* Carr.). 15. March–April. D. Three buds in each leaf-axil. Ls. broadly ov., long-pointed, often 3-lobed at apex, coarsely and doubly toothed, slightly hairy below. Fls. 1, pinkish white, solitary or in pairs. Fruit ½, red, round, hairy. China. (Fig. 93 C.)

(IV) Ovary Inferior; fruit fleshy, with more than one seed

(Apple and Pear Section)

AMELANCHIER. Buds long and narrow. Ls. alternate, ov., toothed, rounded or heart-shaped base. Fls. 1, white, in terminal racemes. Fruit a 4-10-seeded berry.

A. canadensis Medic. June Berry, Service Berry. 30. April. D. Branches slender, the lower ones drooping. Ls. 3, evenly and sharply toothed, firm, very downy below when young, nearly hairless when older. Racemes many-flowered, nodding. Berry ¼, purplish black when ripe. North America. (Fig. 87 M.)

Var. *Botryapium* Hort. Fls. finer and larger.

A. laevis Wieg. 30. April. D. Branches spreading. Ls. ov., 2, short-pointed, sharply and evenly toothed, hairless, purplish when young.

AMELANCHIER—*continued*

Racemes slender, nodding. Berry ½, purplish black, sweet. East North America.

A. ovalis Medic. (*A. rotundifolia* Dum.-Cours., *A. vulgaris* Moench.). Snowy Mespilus. 20. May. D. Ls. 2, rounder than the above two, unevenly toothed or entire. Fls. larger. Europe. (Fig. 87 L.)

ARONIA. Chokeberry. Ls. alternate, finely and evenly toothed, tapering base, glands along midrib on upper side, rolled in bud. Fls. ½, in small branched clusters.

A. arbutifolia Medic. (*Pyrus arbutifolia* L. f.). Red Chokeberry. 10. May. D. Ls. ov., 3½, dark dull green above, grey-felted below, short-stalked. Fls. white or pinkish. Fruit ¼, red. East North America. (Fig. 93 F.)

A. floribunda Spach. Purple Chokeberry. 10. May. D. Like the above, but fruit dark purple. East North America.

A. melanocarpa Nutt. (*Pyrus melanocarpa* Willd.). Black Chokeberry. 5. May. D. Ls. obov., 3½, dark glossy green above, nearly hairless below. Fls. white. Fruit ½, round, glossy black. East North America. (Fig. 93 G.)

COTONEASTER. Branchlets usually spreading and hairy. Ls. alternate or in clusters, entire, stiff, usually with hairs, short-stalked. Fls. small, white or pinkish, solitary or in branched clusters at the end of short side-shoots. Fruit a red or black 2-5-seeded berry.

(a) Fls. with upright petals

(i) LS. GREEN BELOW

C. acuminata Lindl. 12. June. D. Ls. ov., 2½, dull green above, pale green and downy below. Fls. pinkish, in few-flowered branched clusters. Berry ½, bright red. Himalaya.

C. adpressa Bois. 1. June. D. Ls. ov., ¾, dull green above, with wavy margins. Berry red, 2-seeded. West China. (Fig. 118 A.)

C. divaricata Rehd. & Wils. 6. June. D. Ls. ov., ¾, glossy dark green above, pale green below. Fls. pink. Berry egg-shaped, red, 2-seeded. China.

C. foveolata Rehd. & Wils. 6. June. D. Ls. ov., 2, veins in grooves above and prominent below. Fls. pinkish. Berry black. China.

C. horizontalis Decne. 3. June. D. Branches low, spreading, horizontal, covered with thick brown wool; branchlets in two opposite rows. Ls. roundish ov., ½, glossy above, nearly hairless below. Fls. pinkish. Berry red, 3-seeded. Himalaya. (Fig. 118 C.)

C. moupinensis Franch. 15. June. D. Like *C. bullata* (see below), but leaves smaller and green below and berry black. China.

C. nitens Rehd. & Wils. 6. June. D. Like *C. divaricata*, but berry purplish black. China.

C. rotundifolia Wall. 8. June. ½ E. Stiff upright branches, with the twigs often in two opposite rows. Ls. roundish ov., ½, in two opposite rows. Fls. solitary. Berry red. Himalaya. (Fig. 118 L.)

C. Simonsii Baker. 12. June. ½ E. Branches rigid, both erect and spreading. Ls. ov., 1, dark green above, downy below. Fls. white. Berry scarlet. Himalaya. (Fig. 118 H.)

COTONEASTER—*continued*

(ii) LS. GREY, WHITE, OR YELLOWISH BELOW

C. bullata Bois. 12. June. D. Branches few, long and arching. Ls. ov., 3, bright green above and swollen between veins, grey down on lower side. Fls. pinkish. Berry red, 4-5-seeded. West China, Tibet. (Fig. 118 M.)

C. Dielsiana Pritz. 6. June. D. Like *C. Franchetii* (see below), but berries scarlet and branches more spreading and drooping. China.

C. Franchetii Bois. 10. June. E. Ls. ov., 1, veins in deep grooves, white-felted below. Fls. pinkish, with hairy sepals. Berry orange-red, 3-seeded. China. (Fig. 118 B.)

C. integerrima Medic. 7. May. D. Ls. roundish ov., 1½, glossy above, grey-felted below. Berry red, 2-seeded. Mountains of Europe. (Fig. 118 D.)

C. tomentosa Lindl. 12. June. D. Like the foregoing, but leaves larger and sepals hairy. Mountains of Europe.

C. Zabelii Schneid. 6. May. D. Ls. ov., ¾, dull dark green above, grey or yellowish below. Fls. pinkish, nodding. Berry bright red, 2-seeded. China.

(*b*) *Fls. with spreading petals*

(i) HABIT ERECT

C. bacillaris Wall. 40. May–June. D. Like *C. frigida* (see below), but berry purplish brown. Himalaya.

C. frigida Wall. 40. June. D. Twigs becoming hairless. Ls. ov., lanc., 5, often rounded at end, dull green and hairless above, paler and at first woolly below. Fls. white, in flattish downy clusters. Berry red, 2-seeded. Himalaya. (Fig. 118 P.)

C. Harroviana Wils. 6. June. E. Branchlets turn almost black on the side exposed to the sun. Ls. ov., obov., 2½, dark green above, pale yellowish wool below. Berry red. China. (Fig. 118 J.)

C. Henryana Rehd. & Wils. 12. June. E. Branchlets purple, drooping. Ls. lanc., 4, pointed, veins in grooves, grey down beneath becoming tawny. Fls. white, with purple stamens. Berry dark red. China (Fig. 118 N.)

C. hupehensis Rehd. & Wils. 8. June. D. Very like *C. nummularia* (see below), but leaves mostly rounded at base, pointed, white-felted below and not so broad. China.

C. Lindleyi Stend. 10. June. E. Ls. roundish ov., 2½, rounded base, dark green above, grey-felted below. Fls. white, sepals grey-felted. Berry black. Himalaya.

C. multiflora Bunge. 12. May. D. Branches slender, arching or drooping, purplish. Ls. ov. to roundish, 2, blunt-ended, becoming hairless below. Berry red. China. (Fig. 118 O.)

C. nummularia Fisch. & Mey. (*C. racemiflora* Koch). 8. June. D. Branchlets slender, spreading, covered with grey down when young. Ls. obov., oblong, 1, rounded at end, dark green and hairless above, grey-felted below. Fls. white, with yellow stamens. Berry large, bright red, 2-seeded. Europe, Asia. (Fig. 118 Q.)

COTONEASTER—*continued*

C. pannosa Franch. 19. June–July. E. Branches slender, arching, white-felted when young. Ls. ov., 1, dull green above, white-felted below. Fls. white, with purple stamens, in dense many-flowered branched clusters. Berry dull red, 2-seeded. China. (Fig. 118 F.)

C. salicifolia Franch. 12. June. E. Branches spreading, woolly when young. Ls. lanc., 2½, sharp-pointed, glossy and wrinkled above, greyish white below, with 5–12 pairs prominent veins. Fls. small, white, with red stamens, in many-flowered branched clusters. Berry red, 2-3-seeded. West China.

Var. *floccosa* Rehd. & Wils. Silky-white floss on and under side of leaves.

C. serotina Hutch. 10. July–August. E. Young shoots covered with white or tawny down. Ls. ov., 3, pointed, tapering base, dark green above. Fls. small, white, with pinkish or reddish brown stamens, in many-flowered branched clusters. Berry bright red, egg-shaped, 2-seeded. West China. (Fig. 118 K.)

(ii) HABIT PROSTRATE OR TRAILING

C. buxifolia Wall. 2. June. E. Ls. ov., obov., ½, dull green above, tawny down underneath. Berry ¼, pear-shaped, red. Nilgiri Hills, South India. (Fig. 118 G.)

C. Dammeri Schneid. Prostrate. May–June. E. Branches long, trailing and rooting. Ls. ov., 2, glossy dark green above, pale green below, hairless. Fls. ½, white, with purple stamens. Berry ½, bright red, 5-seeded. China.

C. microphylla Wall. 3. June. E. Branches rigid, spreading, very leafy. Ls. ov., ½, glossy dark green above, grey and downy below. Fls. white, with purple stamens. Berry red. Himalaya. (Fig. 118 E.)

CRATAEGOMESPILUS. A cross between hawthorn and medlar, resembling the latter (see *Mespilus*), except that the fruits are smaller and the flower has less than thirty stamens.

C. Dardari Jouin. Bronvaux Medlar. 25. May–June. D. Branches more spiny than *Mespilus*. Fls. ½, white, in branched clusters. Fruit ½, 1-3-seeded. Graft hybrid.

Var. *Asnieresii* Rehd. More like hawthorn, with lobed leaves.

C. grandiflora Bean (*Mespilus Smithii* DC.). 25. May–June. D. Ls. ov., 3, pointed, unevenly toothed, downy below. Fls. 1, solitary or in few-flowered clusters. Fruit ½, downy. Natural hybrid. (Fig. 88 B.)

CRATAEGUS. Stem with spines. Ls. alternate, toothed or lobed, slender-stalked. Fls. white, pink, or red, in branched clusters, K5, C5, A5–25, $\bar{G}$ (1–5). Fruit a berry.

(*a*) *Veins of leaves extending to points of lobes or teeth, but not to the angles between*

(i) LEAF-STALKS LONG AND SLENDER

C. coccinoides Ashe. 20. May. D. Ls. ov., 2½, lobed, rounded or straight base, the stalk glandular only at the top. Fls. ¾, white. Berry ¾, dark crimson, glossy. U.S.A.

CRATAEGUS—*continued*

C. Ellwangeriana Sarg. 20. May. D. Ls. ov., 3, coarsely toothed, lobed, with a broadly wedge-shaped or rounded base. Fls. 1, white, stamens pink, in many-flowered downy clusters. Berry 1, bright crimson, shiny. East North America.

C. mollis Scheale. Red Haw. 40. May. D. Like *C. rotundifolia* (see below), but the leaves are larger (up to 4) and the lobes more numerous, longer pointed, and more deeply lobed. Fls. with red centre, sepals with gland-tipped teeth. Berry $\frac{3}{4}$, red, pear-shaped, downy. East United States. (Fig. 35 G.)

C. nitida Sarg. 30. May–June. D. Ls. ov., 2, coarsely toothed and often slightly lobed, dark glossy green above, paler below, hairless, the stalk without glands. Berry $\frac{1}{4}$, dull red, with yellow mealy flesh. U.S.A.

C. pedicellata Sarg. 20. May. D. Like *C. Ellwangeriana*, but flower-clusters hairless or nearly so. East North America.

C. Phaenopyrum Medic. (*C. cordata* Ait.). Washington Thorn. 30. July. D. Ls. broadly ov., $2\frac{1}{2}$, heart-shaped base, sharply toothed. Fls. $\frac{1}{2}$, white, sepals hairless, A20. Berry $\frac{1}{4}$, scarlet. North America. (Fig. 35 K.)

C. rotundifolia Moench (*C. coccinea* L.). Scarlet Haw. 20. May. D. Ls. ov., 3, generally with wedge-shaped base, finely toothed, shallowly lobed in outer half. Fls. $\frac{3}{4}$, white, sepals hairy, A10. Berry $\frac{1}{2}$, red, round, drooping. East United States. (Fig. 35 E.)

(ii) LEAF-STALKS SHORT

C. aestivalis Torr. & Gray. May Haw, Apple Haw. 30. March–April D. Spines stout. Ls. ov., 1, glossy above, rusty below. Fls. $\frac{1}{2}$ white, in few-flowered branched clusters. Berry $\frac{1}{2}$, bright red, juicy apple-scented. South-east United States.

C. aprica Beadle. 15. May. D. Spines thin and straight, about 1 long Ls. ov., 1, toothed in outer half, teeth glandular. Fls. $\frac{3}{4}$, in glandular clusters of two to five. Berry $\frac{1}{2}$, orange-red. South-east United States.

C. Crus-galli L. Cockspur Thorn. 30. June. D. Branches rigid spreading. Ls. obov., 3, wedge-shaped base, sharply toothed in outer half, hairless, stiff and somewhat leathery. Fls. $\frac{3}{4}$, white, A10. Berry $\frac{1}{2}$, deep red. North America. (Fig. 88 A.)

Var. *pyracanthifolia* Ait. Flat-topped habit.

C. Douglasii Lindl. 30. May. D. Twigs hairless. Ls. ov., 2, sharply toothed and slightly lobed, dark glossy green above, hairless below Fls. $\frac{1}{2}$, in hairless branched clusters. Berry $\frac{1}{2}$, black and shiny. West North America.

C. flava Ait. Like *C. aprica*, but berry brown. South-east United States

C. Lavallei Hérincq. 20. May. D. Spines stout, 2 long. Ls. ov., 4 wedge-shaped base, toothed in outer half, glossy above, downy below Berry $\frac{1}{2}$, red. Hybrid.

C. macracantha Lodd. 12. May–June. D. Spines long and slender Ls. ov., 3, dark glossy green above, double-toothed. Fls. $\frac{3}{4}$, white with ten yellow stamens, sepals covered with glandular hairs. Berry $\frac{1}{2}$ shining red. East United States.

CRATAEGUS—*continued*

C. persistens Sarg. 12. May. D. Like *C. Lavallei*, but the leaves are hairless below. Hybrid.

C. prunifolia Pers. 20. June. D. Like *C. Crus-galli*, but with glossy reddish-brown twigs and glossy dark green leaves with reddish stalks. Origin unknown.

C. punctata Jacq. 40. May–June. D. Spines short and stout, or absent. Ls. obov., 4, round-ended, coarsely and unevenly toothed in outer half, narrowly wedge-shaped base, downy below. Fls. ¾, white, A20. Berry ¾, red, pear-shaped, dotted. East North America. (Fig. 35 A.)

(*b*) *Veins of leaves extending to angles between lobes or teeth*

C. apiifolia Michx. Parsley-leaved Thorn. 15. April–May. D. Ls. broadly ov. or kidney-shaped, 1½, 5-7-lobed, base of blade often continued into stalk. Fls. ¾, white. Berry ½, scarlet, egg-shaped. South United States. (Fig. 35 D.)

C. Azarolus L. (*C. Aronia* Lindl.). Azarole. 30. June. D. Spines few. Ls. obov., 3, wedge-shaped base, 3-5-lobed often to midrib, bright green above, downy below. Fls. ½, white, A20. Berry 1, yellow or orange-red, tasting like an apple, 1-2-seeded. Orient. (Fig. 35 J.)

C. monogyna Jacq. Common Hawthorn, Quick. 35. May–June. D. Ls. ov., 2, lobed nearly to midrib. Fls. ½, white, A10, 1-styled. Berry ½, egg-shaped, red, 1-seeded. Europe (including Britain). (Fig. 35 B.)

Var. *praecox* Hort. Glastonbury Thorn. Flowers in winter as well as in summer.

C. nigra Waldst. & Kit. Hungarian Thorn. 20. May. D. Spines short and stout or absent. Ls. ov., 3, wedge-shaped base, 7-11-lobed, downy on both sides. Fls. ¾, white or pinkish, in many-flowered branched clusters. Berry ½, glossy black. East Europe. (Fig. 35 F.)

C. orientalis Pall. 25. June. D. Like *C. Azarolus*, but the leaves are duller above, with hairs on both sides, and 5-9-lobed. Orient.

C. Oxyacantha L. May. 15. May–June. D. Like *C. monogyna*, but less spiny and the lobes of the leaves are usually shallower. Fls. 2-3-styled. Berry 2-3-seeded. Europe (including Britain), North Africa, West Asia. (Fig. 35 C.)

Var. *coccinea* Hort. Fls. red.

Var. *coccinea plena* Hort. 'Paul's Double Scarlet.' Fls. double, red.

C. pinnatifida Bunge. 15. May–June. D. Twigs hairless, spines stout or none. Ls. ov., 3, pinnately lobed, glossy dark green above, pale green below, stipules large and toothed. Fls. ¾, in hairy branched clusters, A20. Berry ¾, red, 1-2-seeded. North-east Asia.

C. tanacetifolia Pers. Tansy-leaved Thorn. 35. June. D. Spines few or none. Ls. 2, deeply cut into narrow oblong lobes, hairy on both sides. Fls. 1, white, fragrant, in rounded clusters. Berry 1, yellow or reddish, 5-seeded, apple-scented. West Asia. (Fig. 35 H.)

CYDONIA. Quince. Ls. alternate or in clusters, simple, stipules usually large. Fls. solitary or in small clusters, K5, C5, A ∞, $\bar{G}$ (5). Fruit large, fleshy, many seeded.

CYDONIA—*continued*

(*a*) *Styles free, ls. entire*

C. oblonga Mill. (*C. vulgaris* Pers.). Common Quince. 20. May. D. Bark peeling on older trees; young twigs covered with grey wool. Ls. ov., 3, downy below. Fls. 2, pink or white, solitary. Fruit golden yellow, about the size and shape of a pear. West Asia. (Fig. 117 L.)

Var. *lusitanica* Schneid. Fruit ribbed.

Var. *maliformis* Schneid. Serbian Quince. Fruit apple-shaped.

(*b*) *Styles joined at base, ls. usually toothed*

C. cathayensis Hemsl. (*Chaenomeles lagenaria* var. *cathayensis* Rehd.). 10. March–April. D. Ls. lanc., 4, sharply toothed at outer end, downy and reddish below. Fls. 1½, white. Fruit round, 6, yellowish green, stalkless. China. (Fig. 88 E.)

C. japonica Lindl. (*C. Maulei* T. Moore). Dwarf Quince. 3. April–May. D. Branchlets very downy when young. Ls. ov., obov., 2, hairless. Fls. 1½, orange-red or scarlet, in clusters on previous year's wood. Fruit 1½, yellow stained with red. Japan. (Fig. 88 C.)

Var. *alba* Hort. Fls. white.

C. lagenaria Loisel. (*Chaenomeles lagenaria* Koidz., *Pyrus japonica* Sims). Japonica, Japanese Quince. 10. January–May. D. Ls. ov., 3½, evenly toothed, dark glossy green above, hairless. Fls. 1½, red, on old wood. Fruit round, 2½, greenish yellow speckled with small dots. China and Japan. (Fig. 88 D.)

Var. *alba* Hort. Fls. white tinged with rose.

Var. *sulphurea* Hort. Fls. yellowish white.

Var. *versicolor* Hort. Fls. rose and salmon.

C. sinensis Thouin (*Chaenomeles sinensis* Koehne). Chinese Quince. 20. May. D. Spineless. Ls. ov., 3, finely toothed. Fls. 1, pale pink. Fruit oblong, 6, dark yellow, woody. China. (Fig. 88 F.)

DOCYNIA DELAVAYI Schneid. (ERIOLOBUS DELAVAYI Schneid.). 30. April–May. E. Ls. alternate, ov., lanc., 3, glossy green above, white-felted below, entire. Fls. 1, white, in clusters. Fruit 1, egg- or pear-shaped. China. (Fig. 119 C.)

* ERIOBOTRYA JAPONICA Lindl. Loquat. 30. Autumn. E. Branchlets thick, woolly. Ls. alternate, ov., lanc., 12, crowded at end of shoot, coarsely and evenly toothed, wrinkled above, woolly brown below, prominently parallel-veined. Fls. ¾, yellowish white, in stiff terminal panicles, stalk and sepals covered with brown wool, C5, A20, $\bar{G}$ (3–5). Fruit 1½, yellow, oblong or pear-shaped, agreeably flavoured. China and Japan. (Fig. 88 K.)

MALUS. Apple. L.-buds with few scales. Ls. simple, alternate, with the lateral veins curved at the ends except when the leaf is lobed; leaf-scars narrow. Fls. white, pink, or red, solitary or in small and usually unbranched clusters, styles united in lower half. Fruit indented at junction with stalk, flesh mealy.

(*a*) *Ls. rolled in bud*

M. baccata Borkh. (*Pyrus baccata* L.). Siberian Crab Apple. 40. May. D. Ls. ov., 3½, evenly toothed, slender-stalked. Fls. 1½, white, slender

MALUS—*continued*

stalked, styles five. Fruit $\frac{1}{2}$, red or yellow. Himalaya to Japan. (Fig. 94 D.)

Numerous varieties and hybrids are in cultivation.

M. Elcyi Hcssc (*Pyrus Eleyi* Bcan). 30. May. D. Ls. ov., 4, sharp-toothed, purple when young, later a rich green with purple veins and stalk. Fls. 1, wine-red. Fruit 1, egg-shaped, deep purplish red, on a slender stalk, calyx persistent. Hybrid. (Fig. 94 C.)

M. Halliana Koehne. 15. May. D. Twigs hairless, purple. Ls. ov., 3, finely and somewhat distantly blunt-toothed, hairy on midrib above, otherwise hairless. Fls. 1$\frac{1}{2}$, bright rose-pink, calyx lobes broadly ov. and shorter than the tube, slender-stalked, styles four or five. Fruit $\frac{1}{4}$, pear-shaped, purplish red, calyx deciduous. West China. (Fig. 94 G.)

M. Lemoinei Lem. April–May. D. Like *M. Eleyi*, but flowers larger. Hybrid.

M. micromalus Makino (*Pyrus kaido* Mouillef.). 20. May. D. Ls. narrowly ov., 3, sharply toothed, firm, base tapering, glossy above, slender-stalked. Fls. 1$\frac{1}{2}$, pink. Fruit $\frac{1}{2}$, red. Japan.

M. prunifolia Borkh. (*Pyrus prunifolia* Willd.). 20. May. D. Ls. ov., 3, sharply toothed, rounded or broadly wedge-shaped base, slender-stalked. Fls. 1, white. Fruit $\frac{3}{4}$, yellow or red, with persistent calyx. North-east Asia.

M. pumila Mill. (*M. communis* DC., *Pyrus Malus* L.). Wild Crab Apple (origin of most cultivated apples by selection and grafting). 30. May. D. Twigs woolly when young. Ls. ov., 4, round-toothed, downy below, stalk stout and downy. Fls. 1, white, tinged with pink, especially when seen in bud, styles five or more. Fruit round, 1 or more, green to yellow and red, dented at both ends. Europe (including Britain). (Fig. 94 B.)

Var. *aldenhamensis* Rehd. (*M. aldenhamensis* Gibbs). Young leaves purple. Fls. 1, red, semi-double. Fruit round, purplish red, calyx persistent.

Var. *Dartmouth Crab* or *Hyslop Crab*. Fls. 1$\frac{1}{2}$, white. Fruit 1$\frac{1}{2}$, egg-shaped, reddish purple, plum-like.

Var. *John Downie*. Fruit 1$\frac{1}{2}$, egg-shaped, orange and scarlet, produced in abundance.

Var. *Niedzwetzkyana* Schneid. Young bark reddish purple. Leaf-stalk and midrib red. Fls. $\frac{3}{4}$, red. Fruit 2, round or conical, deep red.

M. purpurea Rehd. 30. April–May. D. Ls. ov., 3, blunt-toothed, slender-stalked, purple when unfolding, afterwards glossy green, with purple veins and stalk. Fls. 1, rosy crimson, with spreading oblong petals. Fruit $\frac{1}{2}$, round, light purple, calyx often deciduous. Hybrid. (Fig. 94 F.)

M. spectabilis Borkh. (*Pyrus spectabilis* Ait.). Chinese Crab Apple. 30. April–May. D. Ls. ov. or roundish, 3$\frac{1}{2}$, toothed, short-pointed, glossy green above. Fls. 2, pink, on long downy stalks in clusters borne in great profusion, styles three or four. Fruit $\frac{3}{4}$, roundish, yellow. China and Japan.

Var. *albi-plena* Schelle. Fls. double, white.

Var. *Riversii* Nash. Fls. double, pink.

MALUS—*continued*

M. theifera Rehd. (*Pyrus theifera* Bailey). 30. May. D. Ls. ov., 4, sharply toothed, firm. Fls. 1½, white or pinkish, fragrant, styles three. Fruit ½, round, greenish yellow, with red cheek. China to Assam. (Fig. 94 H.)

(b) Ls. folded in bud

(i) STYLES USUALLY LESS THAN FIVE

M. floribunda Sieb. (*Pyrus floribunda* Kirchn.). Japanese Crab Apple. 30. April. D. Ls. ov., 3, sharp-toothed, slender-stalked. Fls. ¾, pink, produced in great abundance, styles four. Fruit ¾, round, yellow or red, calyx deciduous. Japan. (Fig. 94 K.)

Var. *Arnoldiana* Sarg. Ls. and fls. larger.

Var. ***atrosanguinea*** Hort. Fls. deeper pink.

M. Sargentii Rehd. (*Pyrus Sargentii* Bean). 6. April–May. D. Branches often with spines. Ls. ov., 3, sharply toothed, sometimes 3-lobed. Fls. 1, white, without any pink tinge when fully open, base of petals abruptly rounded, styles four. Fruit ½, round, dark red. Japan. (Fig. 94 J.)

M. Scheideckeri Zabel (*Pyrus Scheideckeri* Spaeth). 30. May. D. Ls. ov., 4, coarsely toothed, sometimes lobed. Fls. 1½, pink, semi-double, on long downy stalks in clusters, styles four. Fruit ½, round, yellow. Hybrid.

M. Sieboldii Rehd. (*Pyrus Toringo* Sieb.). 15. May. D. Branches spreading, arching, or drooping. Ls. ov., 2½, unevenly toothed, often deeply 3-lobed, dull green above, downy on both sides. Fls. ½, pink or red, on slender thread-like stalks in small clusters, styles three or four. Fruit ¼, round, red or brownish yellow, calyx deciduous. Japan. (Fig. 94 L.)

M. Zumi Rehd. (*Pyrus Zumi* Matsumara). Like *M. Sieboldii*, but leaves not lobed. Japan.

(ii) STYLES FIVE OR MORE

M. coronaria Mill. (*Pyrus coronaria* L.). American Crab Apple. 30. May–June. D. Ls. ov., 4½, often 3-lobed, deeply and unevenly toothed, stalk slender and downy. Fls. 1½, pinkish, fragrant. Fruit 1, orange-shaped, yellowish green. East North America. (Fig. 94 E.)

Var. *ionensis* Schneid. (*M. ionensis* Britt.). Prairie States Crab Apple. Ls. thicker, woolly below.

M. florentina Schneid. (*Pyrus crataegifolia* Savi, *P. florentina* Targ.). Hawthorn-leaved Crab Apple. 30. June. D. Ls. ov., 2½, lobed, rounded or heart-shaped base; stalk slender, reddish. Fls. ¾, white, on slender pink stalks. Fruit ½, yellowish red. North Italy. (Fig. 36 J.)

M. glaucescens Rehd. (*Pyrus glaucescens* Bailey). 10. May. D. Round-headed, branches often spiny. Ls. broadly ov., 2½, double-toothed, shortly lobed, dark green above, glaucous below. Fls. 1, on hairless stalks. Fruit 1, oranged-shaped, yellow and waxy, fragrant. North America.

MALUS—*continued*

M. Prattii Schneid. (*Pyrus Prattii* Hemsl.). 30. May. D. Ls. ov., 6, rounded base, finely double-toothed, with six to ten pairs of veins. Fls. ¾, white, in many-flowered clusters. Fruit ½, round, red or yellow, dotted. China.

M. toringoides Hughes (*M. transitoria* Schneid., *Pyrus toringoides* Osborn). 25. May. D. Ls. ov., lanc., 3, unevenly toothed, deeply lobed. Fls. 1, white, in branched clusters. Fruit ½, round or pear-shaped, red and yellow. West China. (Fig. 31 C.)

M. Tschonoskii Schneid. (*Pyrus Tschonoskii* Maxim.). 40. May. D. Ls. ov., 5, unevenly toothed, base rounded, grey-felted below. Fls. 1, white or pinkish, in clusters. Fruit 1, round, yellowish green flushed with purple, calyx persistent. Ls. have brilliant autumn tints. Japan.

M. yunnanensis Schneid. 30. May. D. Like *M. Prattii*, but the ls. are more downy on the under surface and often shallowly lobed, turning brilliant colours in autumn. China.

MESPILUS GERMANICA L. Medlar. 15. June. D. Stem with a few spines; twigs very hairy. Ls. alternate, ov., lanc., 5, minutely toothed or entire, hairy on both sides, stalk very short. Fls. 1, white or pink, solitary on a very short woolly stalk. Fruit 1½, hairy, 5-celled, open at the top and surrounded by the persistent hairy calyx. Europe. (Fig. 88 L.)

OSTEOMELES SCHWERINAE Schneid. 8. June. D. Branches long and slender, covered with silky hairs. Ls. alternate, pinnate; lflts. ov., ½, hairy; common l.-stalk grooved and slightly winged. Fls. ½, white, in terminal open flattish panicles. Fruit a black berry. West China. (Fig. 14 L.)

O. anthyllidifolia (Lindl.) is similar, but evergreen.

PERAPHYLLUM RAMOSISSIMUM Nutt. 6. May. D. Ls. alternate or in clusters, oblanc., 2, entire or with a few teeth, stalkless or nearly so. Fls. ¾, white, with pink centre, K5, C5, A20, in few-flowered terminal branched clusters. Fruit a yellow berry with reddish cheek. Oregon to Colorado.

PHOTINIA. Ls. alternate, finely toothed, usually crowded at end of branch. Fls. white, in short branched clusters or panicles, K5, C5, A10–20. Fruit red, haw-like.

(*a*) *Ls. leathery, evergreen*

* **P. arbutifolia** Lindl. (*Heteromeles arbutifolia* Roem.). Toyou, Tollon. 30. June. Ls. oblong, lanc., 4, tapering base, hairless, teeth gland-tipped, stalk thick and downy. Fls. ¼, stamens ten. California. (Fig. 89 E.)

P. Davidsoniae Rehd. & Wils. 45. June. Young shoots reddish. Ls. ov., lanc., 6, tapering base, stalk ½ long. Fls. ½, stamens twenty. China. (Fig. 89 F.)

P. serrulata Lindl. Chinese Hawthorn. 40. April–May. Twigs stout, hairless. Ls. lanc., 8, rounded base, stalk 1½ long. Fls. ½, stamens twenty. China. (Fig. 89 C.)

(*b*) *Ls. thin, deciduous*

P. subumbellata Rehd. & Wils. 10. May–June. Ls. ov., 2, long-pointed, with a rounded or broadly wedge-shaped base, hairless. Fls. ½, in short flattish clusters without hairs, stamens twenty. China.

P. villosa DC. (*Pourthiaea arguta* Lav.). 15. May. D. Ls. ov., lanc.,

PHOTINIA—*continued*

3½, tapering base, long-pointed, hairy below, 5–7 pairs prominent veins, short-stalked. Fls. ½, stamens twenty, stalk warted, panicles downy. China and Japan. (Fig. 89 D.)

PYRACANTHA. Firethorn. Branches spiny. Ls. alternate or in clusters. Fls. small, white, in branched clusters. Fruit a 5-seeded berry.

P. angustifolia Schneid. (*Cotoneaster angustifolia* Franch.). 12. June. E. Branches rigid, spreading, downy. Ls. lanc., linear, 2, minutely toothed or entire, dark green above, grey-felted below. Fls. ¼. Berry ¼, orange-yellow. China. (Fig. 52 E.)

P. coccinea Roem. 15. June. E. Ls. ov., lanc., 2½, blunt-toothed, hairless below. Fls. ¼, with hairy stalks. Berry ¼, orange-shaped, coral-red. South Europe. (Fig. 88 H.)

Var. *Lalandii* Dipp. More upright and vigorous. Ls. wider. Berries brighter.

P. crenulata Roem. Nepalese White Thorn. 15. June. E. Ls. lanc., 1½, toothed towards apex, hairless. Fls. ¼, with hairless stalks. Berry round, yellow to orange-red. Himalaya.

Var. *Gibbsii* Hort. (*P. Gibbsii* Jacks., *P. yunnanensis* Chitt.). Ls. obov., 3, blunt-ended, round-toothed. Fls. larger. Berry red. China. (Fig. 88 J.)

Var. *Rogersiana* Jacks. (*P. Rogersiana* Chitt.). Ls. narrowly oblanc., 2. Hardier and more showy than parent. (Fig. 88 G.)

PYRUS. Pear. Ls. simple, alternate, with lateral veins curved at ends; leaf-scars narrow. Fls. white, in small unbranched clusters, styles free to base. Fruit not indented at junction with stalk, flesh gritty.

P. amygdaliformis Vill. (*P. nivalis* Lindl., *P. parviflora* Desf.). 20. April. D. Twigs spiny, shining brown. Ls. ov., obov., 2, faintly toothed or entire, glossy above, somewhat glaucous below, rather thick. Fls. 1. Fruit ¾, yellowish brown, on a stout stalk. South Europe.

P. betulifolia Bunge. Birch-leaved Pear. 30. April. D. Branches spreading and slightly drooping; twigs not spiny, woolly when young. Ls. ov., 2½, sharply and coarsely toothed (like a birch leaf), bright glossy green above, hairy below at first, stalk woolly. Fls. ¾. Fruit ½, brown, dotted. North China.

P. Calleryana Decne. 30. April. D. Twigs hairless. Ls. ov., 2, round-toothed, hairless. Fls. 1, styles usually two. Fruit ½, round, brown and dotted, slender-stalked. China.

P. communis L. Wild Pear (origin of cultivated pears). 40. April. D. Branchlets with short stiff spurs, sometimes spiny. Ls. ov., 4, short-pointed, round-toothed. Fls. 1, in small branched clusters. Europe (including Britain), Asia. (Fig. 94 A.)

Var. *cordata* Hook. f. Ls. 1½. Fls. in racemes. Fruit round, brown, with white spots.

P. nivalis Jacq. Snow Pear. 50. April. D. Ls. obov., 2½, entire. Fls. 1, in a white-felted cluster. Fruit 1½, yellowish green, long-stalked. East Europe.

P. Pashia Buch.-Ham. 35. April–May. D. Often spiny. Ls. ov., 4, rounded base, round-toothed, long-stalked. Fls. ¾, pink at first, in

PYRUS—*continued*

rounded branched clusters. Fruit 1, round, rough, brown and spotted. Himalaya.

Var. *kumaoni* Stapf. Ls. and fl.-stalk hairless.

P. salicifolia Pall. Willow-leaved Pear. 25. April. D. Ls. lanc., 3½, entire, silvery grey, short-stalked. Fls. ¾, in small rounded branched clusters. Fruit ½. Levant. (Fig. 119 D.)

Var. *pendula* Jacq. Branches drooping.

P. serotina Rehd. Sand Pear. 30. April. D. Ls. oblong, 3½, rounded or heart-shaped base, teeth incurved. Fls. 1, styles five. Fruit 1, round, brown and dotted. China.

RAPHIOLEPIS. Ls. alternate, roundish ov., 3, thick and leathery, distantly toothed in outer half, crowded radially at end of shoots. Fls. ¾, in erect terminal panicles or racemes, K5, C5, A15–20, $\bar{G}$ (2–3). Fruit ½, bluish black.

* **R. Delacourii** André. 10. June. E. Fls. pink. Hybrid.

R. umbellata Makino (*R. japonica* Sieb. & Zucc.). 10. June. E. Fls. white. Japan. (Fig. 89 A.)

SORBUS. Buds large, with overlapping scales. Ls. alternate, simple with straight veins, or compound with curved veins. Fls. small, white, in large flattish branched clusters. Fruit small and berry-like.

(*a*) *Ls. simple*

S. alnifolia Koch. 50. May. D. Ls. ov., 3, pointed, unequally toothed, rounded base. Fruit ¼, round, red and yellow, calyx deciduous. China and Japan.

S. Aria Crantz (*Pyrus Aria* Ehrh., *Aria nivea* Host). White Beam. 45. May. D. Twigs shining dark brown, warted; winter buds green, elongated. Ls. ov., 4, double-toothed, bright green above, white-felted below. Fruit ½, red, spotted, calyx persistent. North Temperate Zone (including Britain). (Fig. 93 H.)

Var. *lutescens* Hort. Ls. yellowish.

Eight distinct varieties or hybrids have been discovered in various parts of Britain and promoted to species. (See *Further Illustrations of British Plants* by Butcher and Strudwick.)

S. hybrida L. (*Pyrus pinnatifida* Ehrh.). Bastard Service Tree. 40. May. D. Twigs dark shining brown at end of season. Ls. ov., 3, pinnately lobed, toothed, grey down beneath. Fruit ½, egg-shaped, red. Europe. (Fig. 36 L.)

S. intermedia (Pers.) is similar and perhaps merely a variety. The leaves are less deeply lobed.

S. japonica Hedl. 50. May. D. Young twigs woolly. Ls. ov., 3, double-toothed, shallowly lobed, white-felted below. Fls. in dense white-felted clusters. Fruit ¼, egg-shaped, orange-red, calyx deciduous. Japan.

S. Torminalis Crantz (*Pyrus Torminalis* DC.). Wild Service. 70. May. D. Winter buds green, round. Ls. ov., 5, with three to four pointed lobes on each side, double-toothed, slender-stalked. Fruit ½, egg-shaped, brownish. Europe (including Britain). (Fig. 36 K.)

SORBUS—*continued*

(*b*) *Ls. pinnate*

S. americana Marsh. American Mountain Ash. 30. May–June. D. Winter buds sticky, hairless or nearly so. Otherwise like Common Mountain Ash (see below). East North America.

Var. *decora* Sarg. Showier, with larger berries.

S. Aucuparia L. (*Pyrus Aucuparia* Gaertn.). Mountain Ash, Rowan. 60. May. D. Winter buds dark brown, hairy. Lflts. lanc., 2, sharply toothed. Fruit ¼, bright red. North Hemisphere (including Britain). (Fig. 11 A.)

S. commixta Hedl. 20. June. D. Like *S. americana*, but leaves smaller and flowers in looser clusters. Japan.

S. discolor Hedl. (*S. pekinensis* Koehne). 30. May. D. Twigs purple, hairless. Ls. with persistent stipules; lflts. 2, sharply toothed in outer half, glaucous below. Fruit ¼, white. China.

S. domestica L. (*Pyrus Sorbus* Gaertn.). Service Tree. 150. May–June. D. Winter buds hairless, sticky and shining. Lflts. oblong, lanc., 2½, often rounded at end, toothed in outer half. Fls. ½, in panicles. Fruit 1, pear-shaped, green or brown tinged with red. Europe. (Fig. 11 B.)

S. tianshanica Rupr. (*Pyrus tianshanica* Regel). 15. June. D. Twigs hairless, glossy red-brown. Lflts. 1½, glossy dark green above, green below. Fruit bright red. Turkestan.

S. Vilmorinii Schneid. 15. May. D. Twigs and buds with rusty down. Lflts. numerous, oblong, 1, toothed in outer half. Fruit ¼, pale rosy red. China.

STRANVAESIA. Ls. alternate, lanc., 3½, leathery, hairless or nearly so, finely toothed or entire. Fls. ½, white, in terminal many-flowered branched clusters. Fruit a red berry.

S. Davidiana Decne. 20. June. E. Ls. entire, stalk red and hairy. China. (Fig. 119 E.)

Var. *salicifolia* Rehd. (*S. salicifolia* Hutch.). Ls. narrow-lanc.

Var. *undulata* Rehd. (*S. undulata* Decne.). L.-margins wavy; berry orange.

S. Nussia Decne. (*S. glaucescens* Lindl.). 20. July. E. Ls. finely toothed. Fruit ¼, pear-shaped. Himalaya. (Fig. 89 B.)

Family 45. **SAXIFRAGACEAE.** K4–6, C4–6, A4–∞, $\underline{G}$ (2–5)

A rather diverse family with very variable characters. The leaves generally have no stipules and the flowers are of regular shape. As in the *Rosaceae* the axis of the flower is usually swollen and partly or wholly encloses the pistil. The ovary contains numerous ovules; the fruit, therefore, is never 1-seeded, except in the tropical genus *Polyosma*.

* ANOPTERUS GLANDULOSUS Labill. Tasmanian Laurel. 40. May. E. Twigs stout and hairless. Ls. alternate, oblanc., 5, tapering gradually to the base, leathery, coarsely toothed, the teeth gland-tipped, dark glossy green, hairless, short-stalked, crowded at the end of the shoot. Fls. ½, white, cup-shaped, in terminal racemes, K6, C6, A6, $\underline{G}$1. Fruit ½, slender, erect, splitting into recurved halves. Tasmania. (Fig. 60 L.)

* CARPENTERIA CALIFORNICA Torr. Californian Mock Orange. 8. June–July. E. Twigs pithy, pale and downy. Ls. opposite, lanc., tapering at both ends, entire, bright green above, grey-felted below, very shortly stalked. Fls. 2, white, in terminal clusters, stamens yellow, K (5), C5–6, A ∞, G̲ (5). Fruit conical, leathery, splitting into five to seven parts. California. (Fig. 73 E.)

* CARPODETUS SERRATUS Forst. 30. May–June. E. Branches spreading, often flattened; twigs downy. Ls. alternate, ov., 1, sharply and somewhat distantly toothed, with two to four pairs of lateral veins, bright green and with scattered hairs above, pale and downy below, base rounded, slender-stalked. Fls. very small, white, in small axillary branched clusters. Fruit ¼, round, black and shining. New Zealand. (Fig. 96 P.)

DECUMARIA BARBARA L. Climber to 30. June. D. Aerial roots. Buds hairy. Ls. opposite, ov., 5, vaguely toothed in outer half or entire, hairless, slender-stalked. Fls. ¼, white, in erect terminal branched clusters, K7–10, C7–10, A ∞, Ḡ (5–10). Fruit ½, urn-shaped, the lower part striped with white. South United States. (Fig. 61 M.)

DEUTZIA. Stems brown, peeling; buds hairless. Ls. opposite, toothed, thin, scurfy with minute star-shaped hairs on both surfaces, withering rapidly. Fls. white or pink, K5, C5, A5+5, G̲ (3–5), the filaments of the stamens usually winged and often toothed. Fruit dry, splitting into three to five parts.

(*a*) *Ls. grey or white below*

D. discolor Hemsl. 6. June. D. Ls. ov., oblong, 4, finely toothed, dull green above, grey below. Fls. ¾, white or pinkish, in branched clusters. China. (Fig. 61 G.)

Var. *major* Veitch. Sprays of fl.-clusters on long arching stems.

D. grandiflora Bunge. 6. June. D. Ls. ov., 1, rough above, unevenly toothed. Fls. 1½, white, wings of stamens with large recurved teeth; solitary or in twos or threes. China.

D. hypoglauca Rehd. 6. June. D. Ls. hairless, glaucous below. Fls. ¾, white, in rounded clusters. China.

D. longifolia Franch. 6. June. D. Ls. lanc., 5, long-pointed, finely toothed, greyish green above, greyish white below, prominently veined. Fls. 1, pink or purplish, in branched clusters, wings of inner stamens deeply 2-lobed at top. China. (Fig. 61 J.)

D. magnifica Rehd. 10. June. D. Ls. ov., 6, sharply toothed, rough above. Fls. white, double, in panicles up to 2½. Hybrid.

D. Schneideriana Rehd. 6. May. D. Ls. ov., oblong, 2½, finely toothed. Fls. 1, white, in broad panicles. China.

D. setchuenensis Franch. 6. May–June. D. Ls. ov., lanc., 4, dull green and rough above, grey and downy below, base rounded, finely toothed. Fls. ½, white, in branched clusters, wings of longer stamens ending in two prominent teeth. China. (Fig. 61 L.)

D. Vilmorinae Lem. 8. June. D. Ls. oblong, lanc., 5, slender-pointed, sharply toothed, dark dull green above, grey-felted below. Fls. 1, white, in broad panicles, petals with upturned edges, wings of stamens broad in the middle. China.

D. Wilsonii Duthie. Like *D. discolor*, but leaves broader and hairy below. China.

DEUTZIA—*continued*

(*b*) *Ls. green below*

D. corymbosa R. Br. 9. June–July. D. Ls. ov., 5, long-pointed, finely toothed. Fls. ½, white, crowded in broad panicles, wings of stamens toothed. Himalaya.

D. gracilis Sieb. & Zucc. 4. May–June. D. Ls. lanc., 3, coarsely and unevenly toothed, deep green. Fls. ¾, white, in erect racemes. Japan. (Fig. 61 K.)

Var. *rosea* Hort. Fls. pinkish purple.

D. kalmiaeflora Lem. 3. May–June. D. Ls. ov., lanc., 2, finely toothed. Fls. ¾, white, flushed carmine, in rather loose branched clusters. Hybrid.

D. parviflora Bunge. 6. June. D. Ls. ov., 1, unevenly toothed. Fls. ½, white, in many-flowered branched clusters, staminal filaments without teeth. China.

D. purpurascens Rehd. 6. June. D. Ls. ov., lanc., 1½, unevenly toothed, rough above. Fls. ¾, purplish outside, in branched clusters, outer filaments with large teeth extending beyond the anthers. China.

D. scabra Thunb. (*D. crenata* Sieb. & Zucc.). 10. June–July. D. Ls. ov., lanc., 4, finely toothed, the teeth standing upwards or inwards. Fls. ½, white or pinkish, in erect panicles, petals erect. China and Japan. (Fig. 61 H.)

Var. *candidissima* Rehd. 'Pride of Rochester.' Fls. pure white.

Var. *plena* Rehd. Fls. 1, double.

Var. *Watereri* Rehd. Fls. 1, single, petals pink outside.

D. Sieboldiana Maxim. 6. June. D. Ls. ov., 2, wrinkled and rough above, bristly on veins below. Fls. ¼, white, produced in abundance in terminal and axillary clusters; filaments bottle-shaped, not toothed. Japan.

ESCALLONIA. Chilean Gum Box. Ls. alternate, finely toothed, gland-dotted, usually clammy, stalkless or nearly so. Fls. small, white, pink, or red, in panicles or racemes, K (5), C5, A5, $\bar{G}$ (2–3). Fruit dry, top-shaped, surmounted by the persistent style.

(*a*) *Fls. white*

(i) Fls. tubular

E. exoniensis Hort. 20. July–October. E. Branches ribbed, downy. Ls. obov., 1, double-toothed, glossy, hairless except on midrib below. Fls. in small terminal panicles. Hybrid. (Fig. 96 A.)

* **E. illinita** Presl. 10. August. E. Stem with stalked glands. Ls. obov., 2, very shortly stalked. Fls. in terminal panicles, possessing faint smell of pigsty. Chile. (Fig. 96 K.)

E. Iveyi Veitch. 10. August–October. E. Young stems angular. Ls. ov., 2½, rounded at apex, very glossy. Fls. ½, in terminal panicles, petals recurved. Hybrid. (Fig. 96 L.)

* **E. pterocladon** Hook. 8. July–August. E. Stems angled, downy. Ls. oblanc., 1, hairless except on midrib above. Fls. ¼, in slender racemes, fragrant. South America. (Fig. 96 O.)

* **E. revoluta** Pers. 20. June–August. E. Stems and ls. grey-felted. Ls.

ESCALLONIA—*continued*

ov., 2, unevenly toothed. Fls. ½, in short racemes or panicles. Chile. (Fig. 96 J.)

(ii) Fls. not tubular

* **E. floribunda** H. B. K. 10. July–August. E. Stems clammy. Ls. lanc., 3, often notched at apex, minutely toothed or entire, very shortly stalked. Fls. ½, in large terminal panicles up to 9 long. South America.

* **E. montevidensis** DC. 10. September. E. Ls. lanc., 3, often notched at apex, minutely toothed or entire, very shortly stalked. Fls. 1, in rounded trusses, style long and conspicuous. South America. (Fig. 96 G.)

* **E. pulverulenta** Pers. 12. July–September. E. Stems downy, very clammy. Ls. oblanc., 4, very clammy, hairy on both sides. Fls. densely crowded in cylindrical racemes up to 9 long. Chile. (Fig. 96 N.)

E. virgata Pers. (*E. Philippiana* Mast.). 8. June–August. D. Stems brown, very leafy, often arching. Ls. oblanc., ½, toothed at outer end, hairless. Fls. ½, in leafy racemes up to 1½ long. Chile. (Fig. 96 B.)

* **E. viscosa** Forbes. 10. June–August. E. Branchlets drooping, stems clammy. Ls. obov., 3. Fls. in open drooping panicles, with strong smell of pigsty. Chile. (Fig. 96 M.)

(*b*) *Fls. red or pink*

E. edinensis Hort. 10. June–August. ½ E. Stems often arching. Ls. obov., 1½, toothed at outer end, hairless. Fls. ½, pink, in racemes. Hybrid. (Fig. 96 C.)

E. Ingrami Hort. 10. June–September. E. Stems downy and clammy. Ls. ov., 2, double-toothed, hairless. Fls. ¼, tubular, red, in small terminal panicles. Chile. (Fig. 96 E.)

E. langleyensis Veitch. 8. June–September. ½ E. Stems long, slender and arching, with stalked glands. Ls. obov., 1, hairless. Fls. ½, red, funnel-shaped, in short few-flowered racemes. Hybrid. (Fig. 96 D.)

E. macrantha Hook. & Arn. 10. June–September. E. Stems clammy and downy. Ls. broadly ov., 3, double-toothed, hairless. Fls. ½, red or pink, tubular, in terminal racemes up to 4 long. Chile. (Fig. 96 F.)

Var. *C. F. Ball* Hort. Much hardier, fls. larger.

E. rubra Pers. 15. July–August. E. Stems reddish, clammy and downy. Ls. obov., lanc., 1½, double-toothed at outer end. Fls. ½, red, tubular, in loose terminal panicles. Chile. (Fig. 96 H.)

FENDLERA RUPICOLA Gray. 6. May–June. D. Stems ribbed. Ls. opposite, ov., ¾, entire, 3-ribbed, hairy, stalkless or nearly so. Fls. 1½, white or tinged with pink outside, K4, C4, A8, $\underline{G}$ (4). Fruit dry, ½, light brown. South-west United States. (Fig. 67 B.)

HYDRANGEA. Bark peeling; branchlets bright brown, pithy. Ls. opposite, toothed, prominently veined. Fls. usually in flattish or rounded terminal branched clusters, the outer flowers usually sterile and much larger than those in the centre. Fruit dry, 2-5-celled, splitting at the top.

(*a*) *Fls. in pyramidal panicles*

H. paniculata Sieb. 15. August–September. D. Ls. often in threes, ov.,

HYDRANGEA—*continued*

6, toothed, with scattered hairs. Outer fls. white changing to purple-pink, inner fls. yellowish white. Japan. (Fig. 55 B.)

H. quercifolia Bartr. Grey Beard. 3. July. D. Young stems woolly. Ls. ov. or circular, 4, 5-7-lobed, minutely toothed, downy below. Outer fls. 1½, white changing to purple. South United States. (Fig. 34 K.)

(*b*) *Fls. in flattish or rounded branched clusters*

(i) Ovary partly superior

H. Bretschneideri Dipp. 10. July. D. Ls. ov., 3, long-pointed, evenly toothed. Fl.-clusters flattish; outer fls. white changing to pink, inner fls. dull white. China. (Fig. 58 F.)

H. Davidii Franch. 6. July. D. Young stems slender and downy. Ls. lanc., 6, tapered at both ends; apex long, slender and curved; coarsely toothed. Outer fls. white, inner pale blue; clusters stalkless. China. (Fig. 58 B.)

H. heteromalla D. Don (*H. vestita* Wall.). 10. June–July. D. Young branchlets covered with thick down. Ls. ov., 8, coarsely toothed, dark green above, white below, stalk red. Fls. white. Himalaya.

H. macrophylla DC. (*H. opuloides* Koch, *H. hortensis* Sm.). 15. July–September. D. Branchlets stout, hairless. Ls. ov., obov., 6, coarsely toothed, bright green and glossy above, thick. Fls. blue or pink. China. (Fig. 58 A.)

Most garden hydrangeas—in which the flowers are all sterile—are derived from this.

Var. *mandschurica* Wils. Stems dark purple. Fls. mostly sterile, rose-coloured.

Var. *Mariesii* Wils. Outer fls. mauve-pink, inner pinkish white.

H. serrata DC. 8. July–September. D. Branchlets rather slender. Ls. ov., lanc., 3, finely or coarsely toothed. Fls. blue or white. China and Japan.

Var. *acuminata* Wils. Ls. 6, long-pointed.

Var. *rosalba* Wils. Fls. pink or white.

H. xanthoneura Diels. 15. July–August. D. Branchlets stout, bright brown and spotted. Ls. ov., 6, bright green, with yellow veins, hairless, short-pointed. Fls. white, in convex clusters. China.

(ii) Ovary wholly inferior

H. arborescens L. var. *grandiflora* Rehd. 4. July–August. D. Ls. ov. or circular, 6, short-pointed, coarsely toothed, hairless except on veins or in vein-axils. Fl.-clusters flattish; all fls. sterile, large, white. East United States.

H. aspera D. Don. 8. July. D. Branchlets covered with stiff straight hairs. Ls. oblong, lanc., 8, coarsely toothed, dark green above, white below, densely hairy. Outer fls. pink, inner blue. Himalaya.

H. involucrata Sieb. & Zucc. 1½. August–September. D. Stem and ls. downy. Ls. ov., rough above, teeth bristle-like. Outer fls. white or blue-white, inner blue. Japan. (Fig. 58 G.)

H. petiolaris Sieb. & Zucc. Climbing by aerial roots. July–August. D.

HYDRANGEA—*continued*

Ls. ov., 3, sharply and evenly toothed, nearly hairless, long-stalked. Fls. white. Japan. (Fig. 58 C.)

H. altissima (Wall.), from the Himalayas, is similar, with smaller cream-coloured flowers. In both species the petals fall off in a cap.

H. radiata Walt. 5. July–August. D. Ls. ov., 6, dark green above, white-felted below. Fls. white. South-east United States.

H. Sargentiana Rehd. 6. July–August. D. Stems very bristly. Ls. ov., 10, net-veined, bristly. Outer fls. pinkish white, inner rosy lilac. China. (Fig. 58 E.)

H. strigosa Rehd. 8. July. D. Like *H. aspera*, but ls. finely toothed and grey below. Outer fls. white or pale purple. China.

H. villosa Rehd. 9. July–August. D. Stems angular, hairy. Ls. lanc., dull green and bristly above, grey and downy below. Outer fls. blue or white, with four toothed petals (bracts); inner fls. white. China. (Fig. 58 D.)

ITEA. Branchlets with chambered pith. Ls. alternate, toothed, short-stalked. Fls. small, in long narrow spikes, K (5), C5, A5, $\bar{G}$ (2). Fruit $\frac{1}{4}$, dry, 2-grooved.

I. ilicifolia Oliv. 18. August. E. Ls. broadly ov., 4, spiny-toothed, glossy above, hairless except for axil tufts below. Fls. greenish white, in drooping spikes up to 12 long. China. (Fig. 97 A.)

I. virginica L. 5. July. D. Ls. narrowly ov., lanc., 3, finely toothed, downy below. Fls. creamy white, fragrant, in erect spikes up to 6 long. East United States. (Fig. 97 B.)

JAMESIA AMERICANA Torr. & Gray. 7. May. D. Stems bright brown, stout, pithy; bark peeling. Ls. opposite, ov., 2, coarsely and evenly toothed, very hairy. Fls. $\frac{1}{2}$, white, in erect terminal panicles, K5, C4, A10, $\underline{G}$1. Rocky Mountains. (Fig. 61 E.)

PHILADELPHUS. Mock Orange, Syringa. Stems with solid white pith. Ls. opposite, distantly toothed, 3-5-nerved or with the chief veins arising near the base, short-stalked. Fls. usually white, in terminal racemes or branched clusters at end of side shoots, K4, C4, A ∞, $\bar{G}$ (3–5). Fruit dry, 4-celled, with numerous seeds.

(*a*) *Fls. in panicles, racemes or clusters of five or more*

(i) Calyx hairless outside

P. coronarius L. 12. June. D. Ls. ov., lanc., 4, nearly hairless. Fls. 1, white, heavy-scented, in terminal 5-9-flowered racemes. Asia. (Fig. 61 A.)

Var. *flore pleno* Hort. Fls. double.
Var. *foliis aureis* Hort. Ls. yellow.
Var. *variegatus* West. Ls. with white border.

P. Delavayi L. Henry. 10. June. D. Ls. ov., 3, rounded or heart-shaped base, white-felted below. Fls. 1, white, fragrant, in 7-11-flowered racemes, calyx purple, hairless. China. (Fig. 61 C.)

P. Falconeri Sarg. 8. June–July. D. Twigs bright brown, with flaking bark. Ls. ov., lanc., 2, long-pointed, tapering base, minutely toothed

PHILADELPHUS—*continued*

or entire. Fls. 1, white, numerous, fragrant, the petals oblong and pointed, style longer than stamens. Hybrid.

P. Lemoinei Koehne. 6. June. D. Ls. ov., 2½, coarsely toothed, hairy. Fls. 1, white, fragrant, in 5-9-flowered racemes at end of leafy shoots. Hybrid.

Var. *Virginal* Hort. Fls. double.

P. Lewisii Pursh. 12. July. D. Branchlets greyish brown, drooping, not flaking. Ls. ov., lanc., 4, coarsely toothed or entire, with scattered hairs below. Fls. 1½, white, scentless, in 5-9-flowered racemes. West United States. (Fig. 61 B.)

P. nepalensis Koehne. 6. June. D. Like *P. Falconeri*, but petals ov., pointed, and styles shorter than the stamens. Himalaya.

P. pekinensis Rupr. 6. June. D. Branchlets hairless, bright brown or purplish. Ls. ov., 2½, wedge-shaped base, 3-nerved, hairless, stalks purplish. Fls. 1, creamy white, in 5-7-flowered racemes, style as long as stamens. North China.

P. purpurascens Rehd. 12. June. D. Like *P. Delavayi*, but young shoots downy and ls. smaller. Fls. very fragrant. China.

P. Satsumanus Miq. 6. June. D. Ls. ov., 3, coarsely toothed, hairless. Fls. ¾, white, in 5-7-flowered racemes. Japan.

P. Zeyheri Schrad. 6. June. D. Branches spreading and arching. Ls. ov., 2, long-pointed. Fls. 1½, cup-shaped. Hybrid.

(ii) Calyx downy outside

P. incanus Koehne. 10. July–August. D. Branches erect. Ls. ov., 3, grey and downy below. Fls. 1, white, scentless, in 5-7-flowered racemes. China.

P. insignis Carr. 12. June–July. D. Twigs greyish brown. Ls. ov., 2, rounded or broadly wedge-shaped base, hairless above, downy below. Fls. 1, numerous, in leafy panicles. Hybrid.

P. Magdalenae Koehne. 12. June. D. Branches spreading. Ls. ov., 1½, long-pointed, broadly wedge-shaped or rounded base, toothed, hairy on both sides. Fls. 1, in 7-11-flowered racemes. West China.

P. pubescens Loisel. 10. June. D. Twigs light grey, not flaking. Ls. ov., 3, pointed, rounded or broadly wedge-shaped base, dark green above, grey and downy below. Fls. 1½, in 5-9-flowered racemes. South United States.

P. sericanthus Koehne. 12. June. D. Twigs brown, flaking. Ls. ov., oblong, 3, dark green above, pale and hairless below. Fls. 1, scentless, in 5-9-flowered racemes. China.

P. subcanus Koehne. 10. June. D. Like *P. incanus*, but style hairy at base and the leaves with coarse stiff hairs below. China.

(*b*) *Fls. solitary or in threes*

P. bicolor Hort. 6. June. D. Ls. ov., 1, 3-nerved. Fls. solitary, terminal. Hybrid.

P. grandiflorus Willd. 15. June–July. D. Ls. ov., lanc., 5, slender-pointed, sharply toothed, bristly along chief veins. Fls. 2, white, scentless. South United States.

PHILADELPHUS—*continued*

P. inodorus L. 10. June. D. Branches arching. Ls. ov., 2½, rounded base, entire or very distantly toothed, glossy and hairless above. Fls. 1½, cup-shaped. South United States.

P. microphyllus Gray. 4. June. D. Branches slender, rigid, downy. Ls. ov., lanc., ¾, entire, bright green above, grey and hairy below. Fls. 1, white, very fragrant. Colorado and Arizona. (Fig. 67 A.)

P. purpureo-maculatus Lem. 6. June. D. Branchlets reddish brown, hairy. Ls. ov. or nearly circular, 1½, with one to three teeth on either side, hairy. Fls. 1½, white, with a purple blotch at the base of each petal, fragrant. Hybrid. (Fig. 61 D.)

P. speciosissimus Hort. 6. May–June. D. Ls. ov., 3, hairy on veins below. Fls. 1, pure white, in clusters of two to five. Hybrid.

P. splendens Rehd. 12. June. D. Ls. ov., 3. Fls. 1½, in terminal groups of three. Hybrid.

PILEOSTEGIA VIBURNOIDES Hook f. & Thoms. 20. September–October. E. Prostrate or climbing. Ls. opposite, lanc., 6, pointed, tapering base, strongly veined and keeled, minutely pitted below. Fls. ¼, white, with conspicuous white stamens; densely crowded in terminal panicles up to 6 long. Fruit small, dry, top-shaped. India (Khasi Hills). (Fig. 76 C.)

RIBES. Currants and Gooseberries. Ls. alternate or in clusters, palmately lobed, toothed. Fls. small, K (5), C5, A5, $\bar{G}$1. Sepals often petal-like, giving the appearance of gamosepalous flowers. Fruit a juicy berry.

(*a*) *Stems spiny* (*Gooseberry Section*)

R. Grossularia L. Common Gooseberry. 3. April. D. Stems and spines stout. Ls. ov., 2. Fls. greenish, solitary or in small clusters. Berry red, yellow, or green, bristly. Europe (including Britain), North Africa. (Fig. 26 D.)

R. lacustre Poir. 3. April–May. D. Stems and spines thin, weak. Ls. 1½. Fls. greenish or purplish, in long drooping racemes. Berry purplish black, bristly. North America.

R. leptanthum Gray. 4. April. D. Stems and spines slender. Ls. broadly ov. or kidney-shaped, ¾, deeply lobed, slender-stalked (stalk as long as blade). Fls. white tinged with pink, solitary or in small clusters. Berry dark red, or black. Colorado, New Mexico.

R. Lobbii Gray. 6. April–May. D. Ls. roundish, 2. Fls. with purple recurved sepals and white petals. Berry oblong, reddish brown. California.

R. Menziesii Pursh. 6. April. D. Stems bristly. Ls. roundish ov., 2. Fls. with reddish purple sepals and white or pinkish petals; solitary or in pairs. Berry round, bristly. West North America.

R. niveum Lindl. 8. May. D. Stems reddish brown. Ls. 1½, thin. Fls. white, solitary or in small clusters. Berry black, smooth. West North America.

R. pinetorum Greene. 6. April–May. D. Ls. 1, heart-shaped, thin. Fls. orange-red, solitary or in pairs. Berry purple, prickly. New Mexico.

R. Roezlii Regel. 4. May. D. Ls. ¾, thin. Fls. purple, solitary or in pairs or threes. Berry purple, bristly. California.

RIBES—*continued*

R. speciosum Pursh. (R. *fuchsioides* Moc. & Sesse.). Fuchsia-flowered Gooseberry. 9. April. D. Young stems with gland-tipped bristles. Ls. 1, straight or tapering base, slender-stalked. Fls. red, in drooping clusters; stamens four, long and drooping. Berry red, bristly. California. (Fig. 26 E.)

(*b*) *Stem without spines* (*Currant Section*)

(i) Fls. yellow

R. americanum Mill. (R. *missouriense* Hort.?). American Black Currant. 3. April. D. Ls. 3, heart-shaped base, gland-dotted below, odorous. Fls. yellowish white, funnel-shaped, in nodding racemes. Fruit black. North America.

R. aureum Pursh. Buffalo Currant, Golden Currant. 8. April. D. Ls. 2, with straight or tapering base, hairless or nearly so. Fls. tubular, bright yellow, fragrant in drooping racemes. Fruit purplish black. West North America. (Fig. 26 G.)

The true Buffalo Currant appears to be the very similar R. *odoratum* (Wendl.).

R. fasciculatum Sieb. & Zucc. 5. April. D. Ls. 2, stalk with feathered bristles near base. Fls. yellow, fragrant, unisexual, solitary or in small erect clusters. Fruit red. Japan.

R. Gayanum Steud. 4. June. E. Stems hairy. Ls. round, 1½, the lobes rounded. Fls. yellow, bell-shaped, fragrant, unisexual, in erect racemes. Fruit round, purplish black, hairy. Chile.

R. Gordonianum Lem. 6. April. D. Like R. *aureum*, but flowers tinged with red outside. Hybrid.

R. rubrum L. See (ii) below.

(ii) Fls. not yellow

R. alpinum L. Alpine Currant. 9. April. D. Twigs shining. Ls. 1, narrowly 3-lobed, with scattered hairs. Fls. greenish white, unisexual, in erect racemes. Fruit red, not edible. North Hemisphere (including Britain).

R. cereum Dougl. 3. April. D. Ls. 1, round or kidney-shaped. Fls. white or greenish, in few-flowered drooping racemes. Berry small, bright red. West North America.

R. glutinosum Benth. 12. March–April. D. Whole plant sticky and downy. Ls. 2, round or kidney-shaped. Fls. red, in racemes. Fruit oblong, black. West North America.

R. moupinense Franch. 12. April. D. Ls. large (up to 6), with three pointed lobes. Fls. red, or greenish red, stalkless, in drooping racemes up to 6 long. Fruit black and shining. China.

R. nigrum L. Black Currant. 6. April. D. Ls. 4, gland-dotted below, odorous. Fls. dull white, bell-shaped, in nodding racemes on the young wood. Fruit black. North Europe (including Britain). (Fig. 26 F.)

Var. *dissectum* (Nichols.) and *laciniatum* (Kuntze) are cut-leaved forms.

R. rubrum L. (R. *sativum* Syme). Red Currant. 3. April. D. Ls. 3,

RIBES—*continued*

heart-shaped base, downy below. Fls. greenish yellow, saucer-shaped, in drooping racemes on the old wood. Fruit red or white. North Europe (including Britain). (Fig. 26 F.)

R. sanguineum Pursh. Flowering Currant. 8. March–April. D. Branchlets pink. Ls. 4, heart-shaped base, whitish below. Fls. rosy red, in drooping or ascending racemes. Fruit covered with blue bloom. California. (Fig. 26 H.)

Var. *albidum* Paxt. Fls. white.
Var. *atrorubens* Hort. Fls. deep red, small.
Var. *Brocklebankii* Bean. Ls. yellow.
Var. *splendens* Barbier. Fls. blood red.

R. triste Pall. Swamp Red Currant. 1. April. D. Creeping rooting. Ls. 3, roundish ov., heart-shaped base, coarsely toothed, light green above, with conspicuous veins. Fls. purple, saucer-shaped. Fruit red, smooth. North America, North Asia.

R. viburnifolium Gray. 8. April. E. Ls. ov., 1½, blunt-ended, not lobed, glossy above, coarsely toothed, resin-dotted below, odorous when rubbed, shortly stalked. Fls. pink, in short erect racemes. California. (Fig. 97 C.)

SCHIZOPHRAGMA. Climbing by aerial roots. Ls. opposite, ov., toothed, long-stalked. Fls. yellowish white, similar to those of Hydrangea, but the outer flowers have one large bract only.

S. hydrangeoides Sieb. & Zucc. 40. July. D. Young stems reddish, hairless. Ls. broadly ov., 4, coarsely and evenly toothed, deep green above, silky hairs below. China and Japan. (Fig. 58 H.)

S. integrifolia Oliv. 30. July. D. Ls. 6, minutely and distantly toothed. China.

* WEINMANNIA TRICHOSPERMA Cav. 40. May. E. Ls. opposite, pinnate; lflts. ¾, toothed; triangular wing on each side of common stalk between each pair of lflts. Fls. small, white, fragrant, in short racemes (resembling mignonette). Chile. (Fig. 8 D.)

Family 46. **HAMAMELIDACEAE.** K (4–5), C4–5 or 0, A4–5, G̲ (2)

Trees or shrubs with alternate, simple, stipulate leaves. Fls. small, in heads or racemes. Fruit a 2-celled woody capsule.

CORYLOPSIS. Ls. ov., 4, with prominent parallel veins reaching to margin, which is finely and distantly toothed; straight or slightly heart-shaped base, slender-stalked. Fls. yellowish, in drooping catkins, K (5), C5, A5.

C. Gotoana Makino. 12. March–April. D. Twigs and hairless. Fls. pale yellow, in drooping catkins about 1 long. Japan.

C. pauciflora Sieb. & Zucc. 4. March–April. D. Twigs and ls. hairless or nearly so. Fls. in 2-3-flowered catkins, primrose yellow. Japan.

C. spicata Sieb. & Zucc. 6. March–April. D. Twigs and ls. downy. L.-stalk woolly. Fls. bright yellow, fragrant, in 7-10-flowered catkins up to 1½ long. Japan. (Fig. 97 E.)

C. Willmottiae Rehd. & Wils. 12. March–April. D. Twigs brown, spotted, hairless. Ls. glaucous below, with hairs on midrib and veins. Catkins up to 3 long. China. (Fig. 97 D.)

Disanthus cercidifolius Maxim. 10. October. D. Twigs spotted, hairless. Ls. roundish ov., 4, palmately veined, entire, hairless, long-stalked. Fls. ½, star-shaped, dark purple, in pairs set back at the end of a short stalk, 5-parted. Japan. (Fig. 119 G.)

Distylium racemosum Sieb. & Zucc. 25. March–April. E. Ls. ov., 3, leathery, entire, pointed, glossy, hairless. Fls. reddish purple, stalks covered with rusty scurf; in small erect racemes. Fruit erect, hairy, 2-horned. Japan. (Fig. 119 H.)

Fortunearia sinensis Rehd. & Wils. 25. May. D. Twigs and leaf-stalks densely covered with star-shaped hairs. Ls. obov., 6, rounded or straight base, abruptly pointed, margins undulating and minutely toothed, short-stalked. Fls. small and inconspicuous, K (5), C5, A5, in catkin-like terminal racemes developing in autumn. Fruit ½, a brown capsule containing two glossy dark brown seeds. China.

FOTHERGILLA. Ls. obov., broadly ov., margins toothed at outer end or wavy. Fls. crowded in erect brush-like heads, without petals, but with long, conspicuous stamens.

F. Gardenii Murr. (*F. alnifolia* L. f.). 3. April–May. D. Ls. 2, coarsely toothed at outer end, heart-shaped base, glaucous and downy below. Fl.-heads up to 1½ long. South-east United States. (Fig. 97 F.)

F. major Lodd. 8. May. D. Ls. 4, with a few undulating teeth or entire, glaucous and downy below. Fl.-heads up to 2 long. South United States. (Fig. 97 G.)

F. monticola Ashe. 6. May. D. Ls. 4, green and nearly hairless below, remotely toothed. Fl.-heads up to 2 long. Virginia and Carolina.

HAMAMELIS. Witch Hazel. Ls. ov., obov., unequal-sided at base, distantly toothed, prominently straight-veined, with star-shaped hairs on both sides, short-stalked. Fls. yellow, in small axillary clusters, petals strap-shaped, K (4,) C4, A4.

H. japonica Sieb. & Zucc. 12. February. D. Ls. 3½, base slightly heart-shaped; downy below at first, becoming nearly hairless and green. Petals ¾, golden yellow, very crumpled. Japan. (Fig. 97 J.)

Var. *arborea* Bean. 15. Ls. larger and firmer. Fls. deeper yellow, sepals purple inside.

Var. *Zuccariniana* Hort. Ls. dark green above, with tawny down on the midrib underneath. Fls. pale yellow.

H. mollis Oliv. 12. January. D. Branchlets zigzagged. Ls. 5, with a deeply heart-shaped base, grey- or tawny-felted below. Petals ½, yellow and red. China. (Fig. 97 H.)

H. vernalis Sarg. 6. January–March. D. Ls. 4, straight or tapering base, green below. Petals ½, yellow and red. U.S.A. (Fig. 97 K.)

H. virginiana L. 20. September–November. D. Branchlets crooked. Ls. 5, unevenly and coarsely round-toothed, with a slightly heart-shaped base. Petals ¾, bright yellow. East North America. (Fig. 97 L.)

Liquidambar styraciflua L. Sweet Gum, American Red Gum. 100. May. D. Young branchlets corky. Ls. alternate, ov., 6, palmately 5-7-lobed, toothed, long-stalked, turning brilliant colours in autumn. Fls. small, unisexual, without petals or sepals, in small terminal heads. The tree gives a beautiful wood often known as satin walnut. East United States. (Fig. 27 C.)

L. formosana (Hance) is a Chinese tree with 3-lobed ls.

* LOROPETALUM CHINENSE Oliv. 6. February–March. E. Branchlets zigzagged, wiry, covered with brown down. Ls. ov., 2, unequal-sided at base, minutely toothed, hairy. Fls. ¾, white, petals strap-shaped, K (4), C4, A4, $\bar{G}$ (2). China. (Fig. 97 M.)

PARROTIA PERSICA C. A. Mey. Iron Tree. 40. January–March. D. Bark flaking (like a plane). Ls. ov., 5, with vague undulating teeth at outer end, midrib usually not in centre of blade, star-shaped hairs on both sides, short-stalked, often in two rows, turning brilliant colours in autumn. Fls. small, in small axillary clusters; no petals, stamens bright red and enclosed by rough black bracts. Persia. (Fig. 98 B.)

PARROTIOPSIS JACQUEMONTIANA Rehd. (PARROTIA JACQUEMONTIANA Decne.). 20. May–June. D. Ls. alternate, ov. or nearly circular, 3, blunt-ended, toothed, star-shaped hairs below, short-stalked, resembling the common alder. Fls. greenish yellow, in small heads surrounded by four large whitish bracts up to 2 across. Fruit ½, a capsule covered by woolly star-shaped hairs. West Himalaya. (Fig. 97 N.)

SINOWILSONIA HENRYI Hemsl. 20. May. D. Ls. alternate, broadly ov., 6, pointed, heart-shaped or straight base, toothed, star-shaped hairs below. Fls. small, greenish yellow, in drooping racemes. Fruit ½, a bristly capsule. West China. (Fig. 98 A.)

SYCOPSIS SENENSIS Oliv. 20. January–March. E. Ls. ov., 4, with a few teeth or entire, leathery, glossy above, net-veined below. Fls. small, in small axillary clusters, stamens bright yellow or reddish enclosed by brown bracts. China. (Fig. 98 D.)

Family 47. **EUCOMMIACEAE.** K0, C0, A10, $\underline{G}$ (2)

EUCOMMIA ULMOIDES Oliv. Chinese Gutta-percha Tree. 50. April. D. Twigs with chambered pith. Ls. alternate, ov., lanc., 8, toothed, long-pointed, strands of rubber appearing when the leaf is torn across. Fls. inconspicuous, unisexual, the sexes on different trees. Fruit 1½, flat, winged, 1-seeded. China. (Fig. 98 D.)

Family 48. **MYRTACEAE.** K4–5 or (4–5), C4–5, A ∞, $\bar{G}$1–∞

Aromatic evergreen trees or shrubs with usually opposite leathery leaves and small fls. with numerous and often showy stamens. Jarrah, karri, Victorian oak, and tallow wood are all excellent timbers derived from Australian species of *Eucalyptus*. Australian brush box is the timber of *Tristania conferta*. Cloves are the flower-buds of *Eugenia aromatica*, a native of the Moluccas. Guava jelly is made from the berries of *Psidium Guajava* from tropical America. The berries of myrtilla (*Myrtus Ugni*) are pleasant to eat. Myrtle flowers yield *eau d'ange*. Brazil-nuts are the seeds of *Bertholletia excelsa*. *Combretaceae* is a nearly related family producing Indian silver greywood (*Terminalia bialata*) and Indian laurel (*T. tomentosa*).

* CALLISTEMON. Bottle-brush Tree. Summer. E. Ls. opposite or sub-opposite, ov., lanc., entire, pitted with oil glands. Fls. with showy red or yellow stamens in cylindrical brush-like spikes (see also MELALEUCA); the axis of the spike grows on beyond the fls. and continues to produce ls. (Willis). Fruit a dry capsule. Australia. (Fig. 74 C.)

EUCALYPTUS. Gum Trees. Bark smooth, peeling. Ls. opposite, ov. on young trees; alternate, linear or lanc. and drooping on older ones; bluish grey, hairless. Fls. small, pale yellow, in small axillary heads or clusters, stamens numerous and conspicuous. Fruit a dry capsule enclosed in the calyx.

E. coccifera Hook. f. 70. October–November. E. Twigs warted. Ls. on young trees abruptly pointed. Fl.-clusters 5-7-flowered. Tasmania. (Fig. 119 K.)

E. cordata Labill. 70. October–November. E. Twigs warted. Ls. on young trees warted, base heart-shaped, overlapping. Clusters 3-flowered. Tasmania. (Fig. 74 F.)

* **E. globulus** Labill. Blue Gum. 300. October–November. E. Twigs 4-angled. Ls. highly aromatic. Australia. (Fig. 119 J.)

E. Gunnii Hook. f. Cider Gum. 80. October–November. E. Ls. on young trees rounded or notched at outer end. Clusters 2-3-flowered, calyx tube funnel-shaped. Tasmania, South Australia. (Fig. 74 E.)

* **E. urnigera** Hook. f. 80. October–November. E. Ls. on young trees rounded or notched at outer end where there is also a minute point. Clusters 2-3-flowered, calyx tube urn-shaped. Tasmania.

E. vernicosa Hook. f. Dwarf Gum. 20. October–November. E. Twigs 4-angled, slightly warted. Ls. on young trees abruptly pointed, with a marginal vein, scented when crushed; shortly stalked, stalk wrinkled. Tasmania.

EUGENIA. Ls. opposite, ov., entire, gland-dotted. Fls. white, usually 4-parted, ovary 2-celled, in few-flowered branched clusters or racemes. Fruit a berry, 1-2-seeded, the embryo straight.

* **E. apiculata** DC. (*Myrtus Luma* Gray). 25. September. E. Twigs covered with reddish down. Ls. 1, abruptly pointed, tapering base, dark dull green above, with a well-defined marginal vein. Fls. ½. Berry black. Chile. (Fig. 74 H.)

* **E. myrtifolia** Sims. 25. September. E. Twigs 4-angled. Ls. ov., lanc., 3, short-stalked. Fls. ½, usually in threes. Orient. (Fig. 74 G.)

* FEIJOA SELLOWIANA Berg. 25. July. E. Young twigs white-felted. Ls. opposite, ov., 3, blunt-ended, entire, white-felted below. Fls. 1, 4-parted, solitary, long-stalked, stamens red, ovary 4-celled. Fruit 2, an egg-shaped berry. South America. (Fig. 74 B.)

LEPTOSPERMUM. South Sea Myrtle, New Zealand Tea Plant. Branchlets slender, twiggy, hairy, dotted with oil glands. Ls. alternate, ½, entire. Fls. ½, 5-parted, solitary. Fruit round and woody, about the size of a pea, many-seeded.

* **L. pubescens** Lam. 12. May. E. Ls. ov., obov., silky below. Fls. white. Australia, Tasmania.

* **L. scoparium** Forst. 12. May. E. Ls. linear. Fls. white. Australia, New Zealand. (Fig. 51 C.)

Var. *Nichollsii* Hort. Fls. red.

* MELALEUCA. Bottle-brush Tree. Like CALLISTEMON, but the stamens are in bundles opposite the petals. Australia.

* METROSIDEROS. Southern Rata. Summer. E. Like CALLISTEMON and MELALEUCA, except that the flowers are not in cylindrical brushes but in small terminal clusters. New Zealand. (Fig. 74 D.)

MYRTUS. Ls. usually opposite (sometimes opposite and alternate on the same plant), ov., lanc., entire, short-stalked. Fls. white, 4-5-parted, ovary 2-3-celled, solitary in the leaf-axils. Fruit a berry, embryo curved.

M. bullata Soland. 25. E. Ls. 1, the upper surface raised between the veins. Fls. ¾. Berry blackish red. New Zealand.

M. communis L. Myrtle. 12. August – September. E. Branchlets downy. Ls. ov., lanc., 2, pointed, hairless, dark glossy green above, fragrant when crushed, dotted with oil glands. Berry purplish black. Mediterranean region. (Fig. 74 A.)

Var. *tarentina* Mill. Tarentum Myrtle. Ls. ¾, often alternate. Berry white.

* **M. nummularia** Poir. ½. E. Prostrate. Young stems reddish, slender, hairy. Ls. ½, margins recurved. Fls. ½, short-stalked. Berry pink. South America. (Fig. 74 K.)

* **M obcordata** Hook. f. 15. E. Ls. ½, inversely heart-shaped, notched at apex. Fls. ¼, dull white, slender-stalked. Berry dark red or violet. New Zealand. (Fig. 74 L.)

* **M. Ugni** Mol. (*Eugenia Ugni* Hook.). Myrtilla. 12. September. E. Ls. 2, margins recurved. Fls. ½, sepals reflexed. Berry black. Chile. (Fig. 74 J.)

Family 49. **LYTHRACEAE.** K (8–12), C4–8, A8–16, G̲ (2–6)

Ls. generally opposite, though often alternate on young shoots, sometimes whorled. Petals crumpled in bud, stamens attached to the calyx tube. Fruit a woody capsule, dry or containing a fleshy pulp. Jarul and pyinma are the timbers of species of *Lagerstroemia* from India and Burma.

* LAGERSTROEMIA INDICA L. Crape Myrtle. 20. July–September. D. Twigs 4-angled, hairless. Ls. opposite on the lower and alternate on the upper part of the shoot, ov., 3, entire, fringed with fine hairs or nearly hairless. Fls. 2, bright pink, in terminal panicles, the petals long-clawed and much curled. Fruit a dry capsule. India and China. (Fig. 73 F.)

NESAEA SALICIFOLIA H. B. K. (HEIMIA SALICIFOLIA Link & Otto). 6. July–September. D. Stems erect, leafy, much branched, hairless. Ls. opposite on the lower and alternate on the upper part of the stem, linear, 2, entire, hairless. Fls. ½, yellow, solitary in the leaf-axils. Tropical America. (Fig. 50 G.)

Var. *grandiflora* Lindl. Fls. 1.

* PUNICA GRANATUM L. Pomegranate. 25. July–September. D. Ls. mostly opposite or sub-opposite, oblong, lanc., 3, entire, blunt-ended, very shortly stalked. Fls. 1½, red, solitary or in pairs at the end of short side shoots. Fruit 3, round, deep yellow or reddish brown, with a thick rind inside which are numerous seeds embedded in reddish yellow pulp. Persia, India. (Fig. 73 G.)

Var. *albescens* DC. Fls. white.

Var. *flavescens* Sweet. Fls. yellow.

Var. *nana* Pers. Dwarf Pomegranate. Low shrub with smaller flowers and narrower leaves.

Var. *plena* Voss. Fls. double.

Family 50. ONAGRACEAE. K (2–4), C4, A4–8, Ḡ (4)

Mostly herbaceous, e.g. *Willow-herb*, *Evening Primrose*, *Clarkia*, *Godetia*, *Gaura*, *Eucharidium*, etc. Fls. usually 4-parted, with four to eight stamens and an inferior ovary.

FUCHSIA. Ls. ov., toothed. Fls. drooping, with four spreading coloured sepals, four petals directed downwards, and eight long hanging stamens. Fruit a juicy 4-sided berry.

* **F. cordifolia** Benth. 6. May–June. D. Branchlets hairy. Ls. opposite or in threes, ov., 3, heart-shaped base, hairy, long-stalked. Fls. 2, tubular, drooping, calyx tube red, petals green. Central America. (Fig. 55 E.)

F. excorticata L. f. 40. June–October. D. Bark light brown, peeling; twigs hairless. Ls. alternate, ov., 4, pointed, minutely and distantly toothed or entire, dark green above, whitish below. Fls. 1, reddish purple. New Zealand. (Fig. 98 F.)

* **F. gracilis** Lindl. 6. June–October. D. Ls. opposite or threes, narrow ov., 2, tapering base, slender-stalked. Fls. 1, sepals red, linear-lanc.; petals ov., purple; on long and very thin stalks. Mexico. (Fig. 55 D.)

F. macrostemma Ruiz & Pav. (*F. magellanica* Lam.). 12. June–October. D. Ls. opposite or in threes, ov., 2, distantly toothed, bright green, with a few hairs on midrib and margins. Fls. 1, sepals red, petals purple. South America. (Fig. 55 C.)

F. Riccartonii (Bailey), the common hardy fuchsia, is probably a variety. According to Rehder it is distinguished by the purplish tinge of the oblong-ov. leaves and the short calyx tube, with shorter and broader lobes.

F. microphylla H. B. K. 1. June–October. D. Ls. $\frac{3}{4}$. Fls. 1, sepals deep pink, petals rosy purple. Mexico.

F. procumbens R. Cunn. $\frac{1}{2}$. June–October. D. Ls. nearly circular, $\frac{3}{4}$, heart-shaped base. Fls. $\frac{1}{2}$, erect; sepals yellow, recurved, the tube purplish green; petals none. Berry $\frac{3}{4}$, egg-shaped, pink. New Zealand.

* ZAUSCHNERIA CALIFORNICA Presl. Californian Fuchsia. 1$\frac{1}{2}$. August–September. D. Ls. alternate or opposite, ov., lanc., 2, distantly toothed or entire, pale green, hairy on both sides, stalkless. Fls. 1, scarlet, drooping, solitary in the leaf-axils. Fruit a 4-angled capsule containing many tufted seeds. California. (Fig. 98 E.)

Family 51. PASSIFLORACEAE. K (4–5), C4–5, A5, G̲1

* PASSIFLORA COERULEA L. Passion Flower. June–September. $\frac{1}{2}$ E. Climbing by tendrils; stems hairless. Ls. alternate, 7, 5-7-lobed, the lobes oblong, with rounded ends, hairless. Fls. 4, sepals and petals blue, corona purple, fragrant, on long slender stalks from the leaf-axils of growing shoots. Fruit 1$\frac{1}{2}$, egg-shaped, orange-coloured, containing numerous seeds embedded in pulp. Brazil. (Fig. 29 K.)

Var. *Constance Elliott* Hort. Fls. large, ivory-white.

P. racemosa (Brot.) has red fls. Granadillas are the edible fruits of several tropical species.

Family 52. **UMBELLIFERAE.** K5, C5, A5, Ḡ (2)

Mostly herbs with alternate leaves and numerous small flowers in umbels. Ovary inferior, 2-celled, with two styles. The fruit when ripe separates into two carpels attached to a common axis and often bearing oil ducts on their surface. Well-known representatives are carrot, parsnip, hemlock, celery, angelica, fennel, and coriander.

* Bupleurum fruticosum L. 8. July. ½ E. Ls. alternate, oblong, lanc., 3, entire, bluish green, firm, rounded at end, with a minute point. Fls. small, greenish yellow, in terminal umbels. Fruit of two round 5-ribbed carpels joined by a Y-shaped stalk. Mediterranean region. (Fig. 120 A.)

Family 53. **ARALIACEAE.** K5, C5, A5, Ḡ (5)

Trees, shrubs, or woody climbers with alternate leaves and small flowers in umbels. Differs from the *Umbelliferae* chiefly in the fruit, which is a berry.

ACANTHOPANAX. Ls. palmately lobed, 3-fol. or digitate. Stems usually prickly. Berry black.

(a) Ls. simple, 5-7-lobed

A. ricinifolius Seem. (*Aralia ricinifolia* Hort., *Kalopanax ricinifolius* Miq.). 90. July. D. Stems prickly. Ls. up to 14. China and Japan. (Fig. 31 E.)

(b) Ls. 3-5-fol. (Eleutherococcus Harms)

A. Giraldii Harms. 9. July. D. Stems dark green, bristly. Lflts. lanc., 2, double-toothed, long-pointed. China.

A. Henryi Harms. 10. June–July. D. Stems bristly and spiny. Lflts. ov., obov., 3, finely and evenly toothed, rough above. China.

A. lasiogyne Harms. 20. July. D. Branches grey, arching, wide-spreading. Ls. 3-fol., long-stalked; lflts. ov., 2, toothed or entire, very shortly stalked. Fls. white. China. (Fig. 2 A.)

A. leucorrhizus Harms. 8. July. D. Hairless. Stems yellowish green, with few prickles or none. Lflts. lanc., 4, double-toothed, long-pointed. Fls. greenish. China.

A. senticosus Harms. 6. July. D. Stems yellowish green, without spines but bristly. Lflts. ov., 5, finely toothed. Fls. purplish yellow. China.

A. sessiflorus Seem. 10. July–August. D. Stems stout, grey, very pithy, few or no prickles. Lflts. ov., 5, the middle one the largest, unevenly toothed. Fls. brown-purple, in tight umbels; stamens yellow, protruding. China.

A. setchuenensis Harms. 10. July. D. Stems yellow, hairless; prickles few or none, straight. Ls. 3-fol.; lflts. ov., 5, finely toothed or entire, glaucous below. China.

A. Simonii Schneid. 5. July. D. Stems green, the spines pointing downwards. Ls. 5-fol.; lflts. lanc., 6, toothed, hairy. China and Japan. (Fig. 5 L.)

A. spinosus Hort. (*A. pentaphyllus* March.). 10. June. D. Ls. 5-fol.; lflts. obov., 1½, thin, with a few hairs. Fls. greenish white, styles two. Japan.

Var. *variegatus* Hort. Ls. edged with white.

ARALIA. Stout upright prickly stems. Ls. pinnate or 2-3-pinnate, large and spreading. Fls. small, whitish, the umbels in large panicles. Berry black.

A. chinensis L. Chinese Angelica Tree. 30. August–September. D. Lflts. stalkless or nearly so, veins straight and ending in teeth. China. (Fig. 21 B.)

Var. *albo-marginata* Bean. Lflts. edged with white.

Var. *aureo-marginata* Bean. Lflts. edged with yellow.

Var. *mandschurica* Rehd. (*A. elata* Seem., *Dimorphanthus mandschuricus* Maxim.). Japanese Angelica Tree. Lflts. deeply toothed, often lobed, downy on midrib and veins below. (Fig. 21 C.)

A. spinosa L. Hercules Club, Devil's Walking Stick. 50. August. D. Lflts. distinctly stalked, veins curve before reaching margin. South United States. (Fig. 21 A.)

* DENDROPANAX JAPONICUS Seem. 12. August. E. Branchlets hairless. Ls. ov., 8, often 3-lobed, dark glossy green, leathery, hairless, long-stalked. Fruit ½, ribbed. Assam, China, and Japan. (Fig. 31 F.)

ECHINOPANAX HORRIDUS Decne. & Planch. (FATSIA HORRIDA Benth. & Hook.). Devil's Club. 12. June. D. Very prickly. Ls. alternate, ov., 9, 5-7-lobed, the lobes sharply toothed, prickly on both sides. Berry ¼, scarlet. North-west America, North-east Asia.

FATSIA JAPONICA Decne. 15. October. E. Stem thick, without spines. Ls. alternate, 16, palmately 7-9-lobed. Fls. white, in large branching panicles. Berry black. Japan. (Fig. 27 D.)

Var. *variegata* Hort. Ls. with white blotches near end of lobes.

HEDERA HELIX L. Ivy. October. E. Climbing by aerial roots. Ls. alternate, ov., 4, thick and leathery, 3-5-lobed on sterile shoots, unlobed on flowering shoots, hairless, long-stalked. Fls. greenish yellow, in small clusters. Berry black. Europe (including Britain), Asia. (Figs. 29 G. and 120 B.)

Var. *hibernica* Kirchn. Irish Ivy. Ls. up to 6, thinner and of lighter colour.

Var. *japonica* Tobl. Ls. on sterile shoots 3-lobed, 2.

Numerous other varieties in cultivation, many with variegated leaves.

PANAX ARBOREUS Forst. 25. E. Stems hairless, without spines or prickles. Ls. digitate, 3-7-fol.; lflts. ov., 3, coarsely and bluntly toothed, stalked. Fls. greenish brown. Berry black. New Zealand. (Fig. 5 J.)

PSEUDOPANAX FEROX T. Kirk. 20. D. Ls. in young plants alternate, linear, 18, deflexed, leathery, tapering base, coarsely and unevenly toothed; teeth large, hooked and almost spiny; stalk short and stout. Ls. in older plants linear, obov., 6, entire or vaguely toothed at outer end. Berry ½, broadly oblong. New Zealand.

Family 54. **CORNACEAE.** K4–10, C4–10, A4–20, $\bar{G}$ (1–2)

An anomalous family containing several genera of doubtful affinity, the only common characters being an inferior ovary with one drooping ovule in each cell, and a berry-like fruit. *Garrya*, however, has a 1-celled ovary containing two drooping ovules, with male and female flowers in separate catkins; Engler has placed it in a separate family between *Salicaceae* and *Myricaceae*, but the suspended ovules and epigynous disk, i.e. a lateral prolongation of the receptacle, point to a closer affinity with the families grouped by Bentham and Hooker in the *Umbellales*.

ALANGIUM. Ls. alternate, 8, palmately lobed, the lobes entire; downy, long-stalked. Fls. 1, white; petals linear, forming a tube; in small branched axillary clusters. Fruit $\frac{1}{4}$, egg-shaped, thin-walled.

- **A. chinense** Rehd. (*Marlea begonifolia* Roxb.). 20. March–June. D. L.-stalk 1 long. Stamens as many as the petals. India and China. (Fig. 29 F.)
- **A. platanifolium** Harms. 6. June–July. D. Leaf-stalks up to 3 long. Stamens twenty or more. China.

AUCUBA JAPONICA Thunb. Spotted Laurel. 10. April. E. Twigs green and stout. Ls. opposite, ov., lanc., 8, leathery, glossy green on both sides, hairless, coarsely toothed in outer half, spotted with yellow in female plants. Fls. $\frac{1}{4}$, in terminal panicles, unisexual, the sexes on different bushes; petals four, purplish. Fruit a red berry. Japan. (Fig. 60 B.)

CORNUS. Cornel, Dogwood. Ls. entire, pointed, the lateral veins evenly spaced and converging towards apex in a somewhat concentric arrangement, the smaller veins barely visible. Fls. 4-parted, in terminal branched clusters or heads.

(*a*) *Fls. arising from large bracts*

- * **C. capitata** Wall. (*Benthamia fragifera* Lindl.). Bentham's Cornel. 40. June–July. D. Ls. opposite, ov., lanc., 5, leathery, tapered at both ends, greyish green and downy. Fls. 4-6-bracted; the bracts obov., 2, sulphur-yellow. Fruit 1, crimson, fleshy. North India and China. (Fig. 75 G.)
- **C. florida** L. (*Benthamia florida* Spach). Flowering Dogwood. 20. May. D. Ls. opposite, ov., 6, dark green above, pale and downy below. Fls. 4-bracted; the bracts obov., 2, notched at apex, white. East United States. (Fig. 75 C.)
- **C. Kousa** Buerg. (*Benthamia japonica* Sieb. & Zucc.). 20. May. D. Ls. opposite, margins wavy. Fls. 4-bracted; the bracts lanc., 1½, long-pointed, creamy white. Berry pink. Japan. (Fig. 75 D.)
- **C. Mas** L. Cornel, Cornelian Cherry. 25. February. D. Ls. opposite, ov., 2½, long-pointed, 3–5 pairs veins. Fls. yellow, appearing before the ls., 4-bracted; bracts small, yellowish, boat-shaped. Berry red. Europe. (Fig. 75 B.)
- **C. Nuttallii** Audub. 50. May. D. Ls. opposite, ov., obov., 5, 5–6 pairs veins. Fls. 4-8-bracted; bracts 3, pointed, pinkish white. Berry red or orange. West North America. (Fig. 75 E.)

(*b*) *Fls. without bracts*

- **C. alba** L. 10. June. D. Twigs bright red or dark red in autumn. Ls. opposite, ov., 4, dark green above, glaucous white below, six pairs veins. Fls. yellowish white. Berry whitish or tinted with blue. North Asia. (Fig. 75 F.)

  Many variegated forms in cultivation, e.g. var. *sibirica* (Dodd) and *Spaethii* (Wittm.).
- **C. alternifolia** L. f. 25. June. D. Branches irregularly whorled, green, hairless. Ls. alternate, ov., 4, slender-stalked, 5–6 pairs veins, crowded at end of branch. Fls. white. Berry blue-black, bloomy. North America.
- **C. controversa** Hemsl. 60. June–July. D. Like the above, but the leaves have 6–9 pairs veins. Himalaya to Japan.
- **C. macrophylla** Wall. 50. July–August. D. Ls. opposite, ov., 7, dark

CORNUS—*continued*

green above, glaucous below, long-pointed, 6–8 pairs veins. Fls. yellowish white, in terminal panicles. Berry bluish black. Himalaya to Japan.

C. paucinervis Hance. 8. July–August. ½ E. Twigs 4-angled, reddish brown. Ls. opposite, lanc., 4, tapering base, dark green above, hairs on both sides, 2–4 pairs veins. Fls. yellowish white. Berry black. China.

C. sanguinea L. Common Dogwood. 12. June. D. Ls. opposite, ov., 3, with scattered hairs on both sides, 3–4 pairs veins. Fls. dull white. Berry black. Europe (including Britain). (Fig. 75 A.)

C. stolonifera Michx. Red-Osier Dogwood. 3. May–June. D. Stems prostrate and suckering; branchlets dark red. Ls. opposite, ov., 4, dark green above, glaucous below; 5 pairs veins. Fls. and berries white. North America.

COROKIA. Ls. alternate or in clusters, entire or lobed, white-felted below. Fls. ½, yellow, star-shaped, 5-parted. Fruit ¼, a red or orange-coloured berry.

* **C. buddleioides** Cunn. 8. May. E. Twigs slender, white-felted. Ls. lanc., 5, long-pointed, bright green above, short-stalked. Fls. in panicles up to 2 long. Berry blackish red. New Zealand. (Fig. 120 E.)

* **C. Cotoneaster** Raoul. 8. May. E. Twigs wiry and interlaced, white-felted when young, afterwards dark brown. Ls. ov., ¾, dark green above. Fls. solitary or in small clusters in the leaf-axils. Berry red. New Zealand. (Fig. 120 C.)

* **C. macrocarpa** T. Kirk. 20. June–July. E. Twigs stiffer and stouter than in the other species. Ls. lanc., 4, blunt-ended. Fls. in axillary racemes up to 1½ long. Berry red. New Zealand. (Fig. 120 D.)

* **C. virgata** Turrill. 15. May. E. Twigs slightly zigzagged, not interlaced. Ls. obov., oblanc., 1½. Fls. solitary in the leaf-axils. Berry orange-yellow. New Zealand. (Fig. 120 F.)

DAVIDIA. Bract Tree, Chinese Dove Tree. Ls. alternate or in clusters, ov., 6, heart-shaped base, bright green, slender-pointed, evenly and coarsely toothed, parallel-veined, long-stalked. Fls. small, in long-stalked rounded heads, each head enclosed by two large creamy-white bracts of unequal size. Fruit 1½, pear-shaped, green, with purplish bloom, 1-seeded.

D. involucrata Baill. 50. May. D. Ls. grey-felted below. China.

D. Vilmoriniana Dode. 50. May. D. Ls. hairless below. West China. (Fig. 98 J.)

GARRYA ELLIPTICA Dougl. 15. February. E. Ls. opposite, ov., 3, entire, margins wavy, dark green above, downy below, apex ending in a short abrupt tip. Fls. small, unisexual, enclosed in silvery grey cup-shaped bracts on long drooping catkins which hang on the plant through winter, the sexes on different plants. Fruit juicy, 2-seeded. California. (Fig. 76 A.)

GRISELINIA LITTORALIS Raoul. 25. May–June. E. Ls. alternate, ov., 3, entire, leathery, glossy, yellowish green, hairless, blunt-ended, often unequal-sided at base. Fls. small, unisexual, yellowish green, in small axillary racemes or panicles. Fruit ¼, oblong, green. New Zealand. (Fig. 120 G.)

HELWINGIA JAPONICA Dietr. (H. RUSCIFLORA Willd.). 4. May. D. Ls. alternate, ov., 3, tapering at both ends, finely toothed, hairless. Fls. very small, unisexual, situated in the middle of the leaf, the sexes on different plants. Fruit ¼, round. Japan. (Fig. 98 G.)

NYSSA SYLVATICA Marsh. Tupelo Tree. 100. June. D. Branches slender, spreading or drooping. Ls. alternate, ov., 6, entire, hairless or nearly so, tapering base, stalk slender and reddish, turning blood-red in autumn. Fls. minute, unisexual. Fruit a blue-black berry, ½, 1-seeded. East North America. (Fig. 120 H.)

The timber, also known as Black Gum, is imported in small quantities. *N. aquatica* (L.) has larger leaves and solitary female flowers.

SUB-CLASS II. GAMOPETALAE

Petals and sepals both present as a rule (sometimes one or both absent); petals, when present, are joined together (cannot be pulled off one by one); stamens usually inserted on the corolla; calyx usually persistent in fruit.

Family 55. **CAPRIFOLIACEAE.** K (5), C (5), A4–5, $\bar{G}$ (2–5)

Mostly trees or shrubs with opposite leaves usually without stipules. Fls. usually scented, with overlapping petals and a single style, the inflorescence being usually *cymose* (see footnote on page 5) when the flowers are not solitary or in pairs or whorls.

ABELIA. Stems usually slender and arching. Ls. opposite or in threes, short-stalked. Fls. white or pink, tubular or funnel-shaped, solitary or in small clusters in the terminal leaf-axils; sepals persistent, stamens four. Fruit dry, 1-celled, topped by the persistent sepals.

(a) Sepals two

A. Engleriana Rehd. 4. June–July. D. Ls. ov., lanc., 1, tapered at both ends, entire, hairy. Fls. ½, pink, funnel-shaped, in pairs at the end of short side twigs. China. (Fig. 71 A.)

A. Schumannii Rehd. 8. August–September. D. Ls. ov., 1, blunt-ended, with few or no teeth, margins hairy. Fls. 1, pink, solitary in the leaf-axils. China. (Fig. 62 A.)

A. uniflora R. Br. 6. June–July. D. Ls. ov., 2, long-pointed, toothed, downy on midrib below. Fls. 1, white or pinkish, with orange markings in throat, solitary or in pairs in the leaf-axils. China.

(b) Sepals two to five

A. grandiflora Rehd. 6. July–October. D. Ls. ov., 2, dark green and glossy above, paler below with white hairs at base of midrib, toothed. Fls. ¾, white or pinkish, funnel-shaped, throat hairy, solitary or in small axillary or terminal clusters. Hybrid. (Fig. 62 B.)

A. umbellata Rehd. 12. May–June. D. Ls. oblong, ov., 3, coarsely toothed, downy on midrib below. Fls. ½; sepals four, oblanc. China.

(c) Sepals five

A. chinensis R. Br. 4. July–August. D. Stems reddish, downy. Ls.

ABELIA—*continued*

ov., 1½, toothed, white hairs at base of midrib below. Fls. ½, white, fragrant, the stamens protruding. China. (Fig. 62 C.)

* **A. floribunda** Decne. 4. June. E. Stems reddish, downy. Ls. ov., 1½, toothed, firm, glossy on both sides, hairless except on margins. Fls. 1½, pink, tubular, drooping. Mexico.

* **A. spathulata** Sieb. & Zucc. 4. May. D. Ls. ov., lanc., 2, unevenly toothed, hairy, margins red when young. Fls. 1, funnel-shaped, white, with yellow in throat, in pairs at the end of short side shoots. Japan.

A. triflora R. Br. 12. June. D. Stems erect, bark corrugated. Ls. ov., lanc., 3, mostly entire, but lowest ones toothed or lobed. Fls. ½, white, with pinkish tinge, in erect clusters at the end of short twigs; sepals linear, feathery. Himalaya. (Fig. 71 B.)

DIERVILLA (WEIGELA). Stems with solid pith. Ls. opposite, ov., lanc., long-pointed, evenly toothed, very shortly stalked. Fls. red, white, pink, or yellow, funnel-shaped, 5-parted, usually in axillary clusters. Fruit dry, splitting into two.

(*a*) *Fls. yellow*

D. Lonicera Mill. 3. July. D. Stems cylindrical. Ls. 3, rounded or broadly wedge-shaped base, stalked. Fls. ½. North America.

D. Middendorffiana Carr. 3. April–May. D. Twigs with two rows of hairs. Ls. 2½, bright green. Fls. 1, calyx 2-lipped. North Asia.

D. sessilifolia Buckl. 3. July. D. Stems 4-angled. Ls. 7, heart-shaped or rounded base, stalkless. Fls. ½, crowded in terminal clusters. U.S.A.

(*b*) *Fls. deep red*

D. floribunda Sieb. & Zucc. 8. May–June. D. Stems slender, hairy. Ls. 4, tapering base, hairy. Fls. 1, stalkless; sepals linear. Japan. (Fig. 59 H.)

Various garden forms, e.g. *Eva Rathke*, *Lavallei*, *Lowei*, etc.

(*c*) *Fls. pink or white*

D. coraeensis DC. (*D. grandiflora* Sieb. & Zucc.). 10. May–June. D. Stems hairless. Ls. 5, stalk bristly. Fls. 1, pink, changing to carmine, stalked; sepals linear. Japan.

D. florida Sieb. & Zucc. (*Weigela amabilis* Hort.). 7. May–June. D. Stems arching, hairy. Ls. 4, hairy on midrib below. Fls. 1, deep pink outside, white inside; sepals lanc. China.

Var. *candida* Voss. Fls. white.
Var. *variegata* Hort. Ls. edged with yellow.

D. japonica DC. 8. June. D. Ls. densely downy below. Fls. pink, changing to carmine, stalked; sepals linear. Japan.

Var. *hortensis* Rehd. Fls. white. Ls. white-felted below.
Var. *Looymansii aurea* Hort. Ls. yellow.

D. praecox Lem. 6. April–May. D. Ls. 3. Fls. 1, pink, with yellow in throat, nodding, sepals lanc. Corea.

DIPELTA. Ls. opposite, short-stalked, entire or vaguely toothed. Fls. pink, with yellow in throat; stalk hairy, with four unequal bracts, the two larger

DIPELTA—*continued*
ones hiding the ovary and becoming wings to the fruit; solitary or in few-flowered clusters, K (5), C (5), A4.

D. floribunda Maxim. 15. May. D. Bark peeling. Ls. ov., lanc., 4, entire, long-pointed, downy on both sides and at margins, rounded or tapering base. Fls. 1, funnel-shaped. China. (Fig. 61 Q.)

D. ventricosa Hemsl. 15. May. D. Ls. often with a few teeth. Fls. bell- or pitcher-shaped. China. (Fig. 61 P.)

KOLKWITZIA AMABILIS Graebn. Wilson's Beauty Bush. 7. May. D. Stems bristly or rough. Ls. opposite, ov., 2, distantly toothed, deeply veined, hairy; stalk short and bristly. Fls. ½, pink, with yellow in throat, funnel-shaped, in pairs in small terminal branched clusters, K (5), C (5), A4. Fruit ¼, egg-shaped, bristly; sepals persistent. Hupeh province of China. (Fig. 59 D.)

LEYCESTERIA. Flowering Nutmeg. Stems hollow, thin-walled. Ls. opposite, ov., 6, long-pointed, vaguely toothed or entire, short-stalked. Fls. ¾, funnel-shaped, stalkless, in several whorls, each whorl enclosed by leaf-like bracts, K (5), C (5), A4. Fruit a berry like a small gooseberry.

* **L. crocothyrsos** Shaw. 8. April. D. Stem with pairs of large kidney-shaped stipules. Fls. yellow. East Himalaya.

L. formosa Wall. 8. June–September. D. Stem without stipules. Fls. purplish, with claret-coloured bracts. Himalaya. (Fig. 59 G.)

LINNAEA BOREALIS L. Twin Flower. ¼. July–August. E. Creeping plant with a woody base. Ls. opposite, ov., ½, rounded and coarsely toothed at apex, the base tapering, hairy. Fls. ½, pink or white, nodding in pairs at the top of a slender stalk, funnel-shaped, K (5), C (5), A4. Fruit yellow, dry, egg-shaped, 1-seeded. North Hemisphere (including Britain). (Fig. 56 J.)

LONICERA. Honeysuckle. Ls. opposite or in threes, short-stalked or stalkless, entire. Fls. in whorls or in pairs in the leaf-axils, 5-parted. Fruit a berry.

(a) Climbing, twining, or creeping

L. Caprifolium L. Perfoliate Woodbine. 20. May–June. D. Stems hairless. Ls. ov., 4, hairless, blunt-ended, glaucous below, upper pairs united at base. Fls. 2, tubular, 2-lipped, yellowish white, in a terminal whorl in a large leafy cup, fragrant. Berry orange-coloured. Europe (including Britain). (Fig. 71 F.)

L. etrusca Santi. 30. June–July. ½ E. Like the above, but the leaves are hairy and the flowers are in stalked heads or spikes. Mediterranean region.

L. flava Sims. 10. May–June. D. Slightly twining. Ls. ov., 2, bright green above, bluish green below, upper pairs united at base. Fls. 1, orange-yellow, fragrant, 2-lipped, in short-stalked whorls. Berry red. South Carolina.

L. Heckrottii Rehd. June–September. D. Stems creeping and slightly twining, hairless. Ls. ov., 2, pointed, glaucous below, the uppermost pairs often united at base. Fls. 1½, purple outside, yellow inside, in scattered whorls forming long spikes. Hybrid.

L. japonica Thunb. (*L. japonica*, var. *Halliana* Nichols., *L. confusa* DC.). 30. June–July. D. or ½ E. Stems hairy. Ls. ov., 3, pointed, downy on both sides. Fls. 1, white, changing to yellow, tubular, 2-lipped, in pairs in the leaf-axils, fragrant. Berry black. Japan. (Fig. 71 H.)

LONICERA—*continued*

Var. *aureo-reticulata* Nichols. Veins yellow, ls. often pinnately lobed.

Var. *flexuosa* Nichols. (*brachypoda* DC.). Stems purple. Fls. reddish outside.

L. Periclymenum L. Common Honeysuckle, Woodbine. 20. June–September. D. Ls. ov., obov., 2½, green above, glaucous below, never united at base. Fls. 2, yellow or red, tubular, 2-lipped, in terminal whorls, fragrant. Berry red. Europe (including Britain). (Fig. 71 E.)

Var. *belgica* Ait. Dutch Honeysuckle. Stems purple, hairless; ls. hairless.

Var. *quercina* West. Oak-leaved Woodbine. Ls. lobed.

Var. *serotina* Ait. Late-flowering Honeysuckle. Fls. dark purple outside.

* **L. sempervirens** L. Trumpet Honeysuckle. 20. June–September. ½ E. Stems hairless, glaucous. Ls. ov., 2½, bright green above, bluish below, uppermost pairs united. Fls. 2, tubular, scentless, orange-scarlet, in terminal whorls. Berry red. South United States. (Fig. 71 G.)

L. tragophylla Hemsl. Chinese Woodbine. June–July. D. Stems hairless. Ls. ov., 4, glaucous and slightly downy below, uppermost pairs united. Fls. 3, yellow, tubular, 2-lipped, in terminal whorls, not fragrant. Berry red. Hupeh province of China.

(*b*) *Evergreen shrubs*

L. nitida Wils. 5. April–May. Stems slender, erect, purplish, hairy. Ls. ov., ¼, glossy green, hairless. Fls. ¼, white, in pairs in the leaf-axils. Berry blue-purple, transparent. China. (Fig. 71 J.)

L. pileata Oliv. 2. May. Stems spreading, purplish, hairy. Ls. ov., 1, blunt-ended, glossy green, hairless. Fls. ¼, yellowish white, in pairs in the leaf-axils. Berry blue-purple, transparent. China. (Fig. 71 K.)

(*c*) *Deciduous shrubs with solid white pith*

(i) Berry black or blue

L. coerulea L. 3. April. Stems brown and flaking. Ls. roundish ov., 2, bright green. Fls. ½, yellowish white, in nodding pairs in the leaf-axils. Berry blue, surrounded by a fleshy cup. North Hemisphere.

L. discolor Lindl. 6. May–June. Ls. ov., lanc., 2, bright green above, glaucous below. Fls. ¼, 2-lipped, in pairs in leaf-axils. Berry black. Kashmir to Afghanistan.

L. involucrata Banks. Twinberry. 3. June. Stems hairless. Ls. ov., 4, bright green, long-pointed. Fls. ½, white, tinged with red, half enclosed by broad bracts. Berry purple-black. West North America.

L. Ledebourii Esch. 9. June. Stems erect, 4-angled, hairless. Ls. ov., 4, hairy. Fls. ¾, yellow and red, on long erect stalk at the top of which are two large reddish bracts. Berry black. California. (Fig. 72 E.)

L. nervosa Maxim. 10. May–June. Stems slender, hairless. Ls. ov., 1½, hairless, with red midrib and veins. Fls. ½, pale pink, 2-lipped, the tube swollen, ovaries distinct. Berry black. North-west China.

L. orientalis Lam. 10. May–June. Stems hairless. Ls. ov., 1, dark green above, glaucous below, ending in a small sharp point. Fls. ¾,

LONICERA—*continued*

2-lipped, in pairs in the leaf-axils, corolla tube red, lobes white, stamens protruding. Berry black. Orient.

L. tomentella Hook. f. & Thoms. 12. June–July. Stems woolly. Ls. ov., oblong, 1½, woolly below. Fls. ½, pinkish white, drooping. Berry blue-black. Himalaya. (Fig. 72 C.)

(ii) Berry red

L. Albertii Regel (*L. spinosa* Jacq., var. *Albertii* Rehd.). 4. June. Stems slender, hairless, spreading. Ls. linear, blunt-ended, bluish green, hairless. Fls. ½, lilac. Berry purplish red. Turkestan. (Fig. 50 L.)

L. alpigena L. Cherry Woodbine. 8. April–May. Stems erect, hairless. Ls. ov., 4, margins hairy. Fls. ½, yellow tinged with red, 2-lipped. Berry ½, red. Alps and Himalaya. (Fig. 73 C.)

L. canadensis Marsh. American Fly Honeysuckle. 3. April. Twigs hairless. Ls. ov., 3, edged with hairs, stalked. Fls. ½, yellowish white tinged with red, nodding, style prominent. East North America.

L. Ferdinandi Franch. 10. June. Stems bristly; the barren ones with leafy disks at each joint. Ls. ov., 4, long-pointed, dull green, hairy. Fls. ¾, yellow, 2-lipped. China. (Fig. 72 J.)

L. fragrantissima Lindl. & Paxt. 8. December–March. ½ E. Stems hairless. Ls. ov., 2, leathery, ending in a bristle-like tip, dark dull green above, glaucous below. Fls. ½, white, very fragrant. China. (Fig. 72 B.)

L. gracilipes Miq. 6. May. Branches spreading. Ls. ov., rounded base, bright green and red-edged above, bluish green below. Fls. ½, pink, solitary, with two unequal awl-shaped bracts. Japan.

Var. *albiflora* Maxim. Fls. white.

L. iberica Bieb. 6. June. Dense bush, with downy twigs. Ls. ov., 1, hairy. Fls. ½, yellowish white, 2-lipped. Caucasus.

L. Maximowiczii Regel. 10. June–July. Stems hairless, purplish. Ls. ov., 2, dark green and hairless above, bright green and downy below. Fls. ½, reddish purple, 2-lipped. Amur region.

Var. *sachalinensis* Schmidt. Fls. dark purple.

L. Myrtillus Hook. f. & Thoms. 4. May. Dense and compact bush. Ls. ov., ½, dark green above, glaucous below, hairless, margins recurved. Fls. ½, pinkish white. Berry orange-red. Himalaya. (Fig. 71 M.)

L. oblongifolia Hook. Swamp Fly Honeysuckle. 3. June. Twigs downy. Ls. oblong, lanc., 2½, blunt-ended, stalkless or nearly so. Fls. 1, erect, yellowish white, 2-lipped, style not prominent. East North America.

L. pyrenaica L. 3. June. Stems erect, hairless. Ls. obov., oblanc., 1, glaucous, hairless. Fls. ½, pink. Pyrenees.

L. rupicola Hook. f. & Thoms. 8. May–June. Very dense bush. Twigs interlacing, hairless, bark peeling. Ls. in threes, ov., 1, hairy below. Fls. ½, pink. Tibet. (Fig. 72 D.)

L. Standishii Carr. 8. November–March. ½ E. Bark peeling; stems warted, bristly. Ls. lanc., 4, pointed, bristly on midrib and margins. Fls. ½, white, very fragrant. China. (Fig. 72 A.)

LONICERA—*continued*

L. syringantha Maxim. 8. May. Stems slender, spreading, hairless. Ls. ov., ¾, dull greyish green, hairless. Fls. ½, lilac. China. (Fig. 72 G.)

L. tangutica Maxim. 1. May–June. Low and spreading; stems hairless. Ls. obov., 1, white below. Fls. ½, yellowish white, tinged with pink, drooping. West China.

L. tatsienensis Franch. 6. May–June. Stems hairless, with reflexed bud-scales. Ls. ov., 2, often deeply lobed. Fls. ½, dark purple. West China.

L. thibetica Bur. & Franch. 6. May–June. Stems purplish, hairy, with peeling bark. Ls. in threes, lanc., 1, dark green above, white-felted below. Fls. ½, lilac. Berry oblong. Tibet. (Fig. 71 L.)

L. vesicaria Komar. 12. May. Twigs stout, bristly. Ls. ov., 2, hairy. Fls. ½, lemon-yellow, 2-lipped, in pairs in the leaf-axils. Corea.

(*d*) *Deciduous shrubs with hollow or brown pith*

L. chrysantha Turcz. 12. June. Stems hairy. Ls. ov., lanc., 4, pointed, hairy. Fls. ½, yellow, the corolla conspicuously swollen at the base. Berry coral-red. Siberia. (Fig. 73 A.)

L. deflexicalyx Batal. 10. June. Stems often horizontal or drooping; branchlets in opposite rows, purplish, hairy. Ls. ov., 3, pointed, hairy. Fls. ½, yellow, 2-lipped. Berry orange-red. China. (Fig. 73 B.)

L. Korolkowii Stapf. 12. June. Ls. ov., 1, bluish green. Fls. ½, pink, 2-lipped. Berry red. Turkestan.

L. Maackii Maxim. 10. May. Stems spreading; branchlets often in two opposite rows. Ls. ov., lanc., 3, long-pointed, tapering base, hairy. Fls. ½, white or yellow, 2-lipped, in a close row on the upper side of the stem. Berry red. Manchuria. (Fig. 72 F.)

L. Morrowii Gray. 6. May–June. Wide-spreading. Ls. ov., 1½. Fls. ½, white turning to yellow, 2-lipped, the upper lip deeply divided. Berry dark red. Japan.

Var. *rosea* Dipp. (*L. bella* Zabel). Fls. pink.

L. quinquelocularis Hardw. 15. June. Stems purplish, hairy. Ls. ov., 2, rounded or short-pointed at end, hairy. Fls. ¾, white or yellow, 2-lipped. Berry white, transparent. Himalaya. (Fig. 73 D.)

L. Ruprechtiana Regel. 10. May–June. Like *L. Morrowii*, but upper lip of fl. divided only about half-way. Berry orange-red. North China.

L. tatarica L. 10. May. Stems hairless. Ls. ov., green above, glaucous below, hairless. Fls. 1, white or pinkish, 2-lipped. Berry red. Siberia. (Fig. 72 K.)

Var. *rosea* Regel. Fls. rosy red.

L. tricosantha Bur. & Franch. 8. June. Ls. ov., 2, grey. Fls. ¾, pale yellow. Berry red. China. (Fig. 71 N.)

L. Xylosteum L. Fly Honeysuckle. 10. May. Stems hairy. Ls. ov. or roundish, 2½, velvety on both sides; stalk ¼, hairy. Fls. ½, yellowish white, 2-lipped, on stalks up to ½. Berry red. Europe (including Britain), North Asia. (Fig. 72 H.)

SAMBUCUS. Elder. Branchlets stout, pithy, warted. Ls. opposite, pinnate; lflts. ov., lanc., 5, toothed. Fls. small, white, 5-parted, in terminal branched clusters. Fruit a berry.

SAMBUCUS—*continued*

S. canadensis L. American Elder. 12. June–July. D. Pith white. Ls. 7-fol. Fl.-clusters slightly convex. Berry black. North America.

Var. *aurea* Cow. Ls. golden yellow.
Var. *maxima* Schwer. Ls. up to 18 long. Fl.-clusters up to 18 across.

S. coerulea Rafin. 30. June–July. D. Pith white. Ls. 5-7-fol., hairless. Fl.-clusters convex. Berry blue-black dusted with white. West North America.

S. melanocarpa Gray. 12. May. D. Pith brown on older shoots. Ls. 5-7-fol. Fls. in hemispherical branched clusters. Berry black. West North America.

S. nigra L. Common Elder. 20. June. D. Pith white. Ls. 3-5-fol. Fls. in large flat-topped branched clusters, heavy-scented. Berry black. The whole plant emits a sickly scent when cut or bruised. Europe (including Britain). (Fig 8 F and H.)

Var. *alba* West. Berry whitish.
Var. *albo-variegata* West. Ls. variegated with white.
Var. *aurea* Sweet. Ls. yellow.
Var. *aureo-variegata* West. Ls. variegated with yellow.
Var. *laciniata* L. Cut-leaved Elder. Lflts. deeply dissected.
Var. *pendula* Dipp. Prostrate or weeping form.
Var. *pyramidalis* Jaeg. Habit narrow and erect.

S. pubens Michx. Red-berried Elder. 12. July. D. Pith brown. Ls. 5-7-fol. Fls. in a loose panicle. Berry red. British Columbia, Vancouver.

S. racemosa L. Red-berried Elder. 12. April–May. D. Like the preceding species, but the flowers open earlier and are in a compact panicle, the lower branches of which are reflexed. Europe and North Asia.

Var. *laciniata* (W. Koch), *plumosa* (Carr.), and *plumosa-aurea* (Schwer.) are forms in which the lflts. are pinnately lobed or dissected, the last named being golden-leaved. (Fig. 8 G.)

SYMPHORICARPUS. Ls. opposite, entire or lobed, short-stalked, often in two opposite rows. Fls. small, white or pink. Fruit a berry.

S. albus Blake (*S. racemosus* Michx.). Snowberry. 10. June–July. D. Ls. nearly circular, 3, often lobed, hairless. Fls. ¼, pink, bell-shaped. Berry ½, white. North America. (Fig. 34 J.)

S. mollis Nutt. 1. June–July. D. Low prostrate shrub. Stems hairy. Ls. nearly circular, 1, sometimes shallowly lobed, hairy. Fls. ¼, pinkish white, solitary or in few-flowered clusters. Berry ¼, white. California. (Fig. 71 D.)

S. occidentalis Hook. Wolfberry. 3. June–July. D. Stiff and upright. Ls. ov., 2, entire. Fls. pinkish, with protruding style and stamens. Berry ½, white. North America. (Fig. 71 DD.)

Var. *Heyeri* Dieck. Ls. thinner and less distinctly veined below (Rehd.).

S. orbiculatus Moench (*S. parvifolius* Desf., *S. vulgaris* Michx.). Coral Berry, Indian Currant. 7. August–September. D. Stems thin,

SYMPHORICARPUS—*continued*

hairy. Ls. ov., 1, hairy. Fls. very small, white, in dense clusters or spikes. Berry purplish red. North America. (Fig. 71 C.)

Var. *variegatus* Schneid. Variegated form.

VIBURNUM. Ls. opposite, simple. Fls. small, white or pinkish, in branched clusters, K (5), C (5), A5, $\bar{G}1$. Fruit a berry.

(*a*) *Ls. palmately lobed*

V. acerifolium L. Dockmackie. 6. June–July. D. Ls. ov., 4, 3-lobed, rounded or heart-shaped base, scattered hairs above, softly downy and with black dots below. Fls. ½, white. Berry red to black. East North America. (Fig. 25 G.)

V. Opulus L. Guelder Rose. 15. June. D. Young stems ribbed. Ls. ov., 4, 3-5-lobed, coarsely and unevenly toothed, dark green above, downy below, two small glands at base of blade, stalk grooved. Fl.-cluster 3 across, marginal fls. larger and sterile. Berry red, drooping. Europe (including Britain). (Figs. 25 F and 26 A.)

Var. *americanum* Ait. (*V. trilobum* Marsh.). Cranberry Bush. Leaf-stalk with larger glands and narrower groove.

Var. *sterile* DC. Snowball Tree. Fls. in closely packed round heads, all sterile. (Fig. 26 B.)

(*b*) *Ls. 3-nerved, leathery, evergreen*

V. cinnamomifolium Rehd. 20. June. Ls. ov., 5, nearly hairless. Fls. white, in loose clusters or panicles. Berry blue-black. China.

V. Davidii Franch. 2. June. Ls. ov., 6, nearly entire, hairless. Fls. white, in stiff clusters. Berry blue. China. (Fig. 65 C.)

(*c*) *Ls. pinnately nerved, evergreen*

V. Burkwoodii Hort. 5. April. See *V. Carlesii* under (*e*) (i).

V. cylindricum Buch.-Ham. (*V. coriaceum* Blume). 50. Twigs warted, hairless. Ls. ov., 8, long-pointed, distantly toothed in outer half, upper surface covered with wax which shows white when the leaf is folded or rubbed. Fls. white, tubular, stamens lilac-coloured, protruding. Berry black. Himalaya, China. (Fig. 63 B.)

V. Harryanum Rehd. 8. July–August. Twigs downy. Ls. roundish, 1, entire, hairless, nearly stalkless. Fls. white. Berry black. China. (Fig. 65 F.)

V. Henryi Hemsl. 10. June–July. Twigs stiff, hairless. Ls. ov., lanc., 5, finely and distantly toothed, bluish green, hairless. Fls. in stiff pyramidal panicles. Berry red to black. China. (Fig. 63 A.)

V. japonicum Spreng. (*V. macrophyllum* Blume). 6. June. Twigs hairless. Ls. ov., 4, finely and distantly toothed at outer end, dark glossy green, hairless. Fls. white, fragrant. Berry red. Japan.

V. macrocephalum Fort. 20. May. Twigs scurfy. Ls. ov., 4, toothed, dull green, hairy. Fls. like those of *V. Opulus* (see (*a*) above), but larger. China.

Var. *sterile* Dipp. Fls. 1½, white, in large round trusses.

V. odoratissimum Ker-Gawl (*V. Awafuki* Hort.). 20. August. Twigs

VIBURNUM—*continued*

warted, hairless. Ls. ov., 8, tapering base, entire, glossy green, leathery, hairless. Fls. white, in broad pyramidal panicles. Berry red to black. China. (Fig. 65 B.)

V. rhytidophyllum Hemsl. 10. May–June. Branchlets covered with bright tawny down. Ls. ov., lanc., 8, entire, wrinkled above, felted or woolly below. Fls. yellowish white, in large flattish trusses. Berry red to black. China. (Fig. 65 D.)

V. Tinus L. Laurustinus. 10. November–May. Branchlets hairless or nearly so, sometimes 4-angled. Ls. ov., 4, dark glossy green above, margins hairy when young, stalk hairy. Fls. white. Berry black. Mediterranean region. (Fig. 65 A.)

V. utile Hemsl. 6. May. Branchlets slender. Ls. ov., lanc., 3, entire, firm, dark glossy green above, white-felted below, stalk very short. Fls. white, in rounded trusses. Berry blue-black. China. (Fig. 65 G.)

(*d*) *Ls. pinnately nerved, deciduous, lateral veins curve aside before reaching margin*

V. Lentago L. Sheepberry. 30. May–June. Twigs reddish, scurfy. Ls. ov., 4, finely and sharply toothed, hairless except for scurf on midrib and veins; stalk winged. Fls. creamy white, fragrant, in stalkless clusters. Berry blue-black, bloomy. North America. (Fig. 64 C.)

V. macrocephalum Fort. See under (*c*).

V. nudum L. Withe Rod. 10. May–June. Twigs slightly scurfy. Ls. ov., 4, minutely and unevenly toothed, dark glossy green above, scurfy or smooth below; stalk slightly winged. Fls. yellowish white, in stalked clusters. Berry blue-black. East North America. (Fig. 64 D.)

V. cassinoides (L.), Appalachian Tea, differs in slight particulars and may be a mere variety.

V. prunifolium L. Black Haw. 30. June. Twigs reddish, hairless. Ls. ov., $3\frac{1}{2}$, minutely toothed, hairless, stalk reddish. Fls. white, in stalkless clusters. North America. (Fig. 64 E.)

V. rufidulum Rafin. Southern Black Haw. 40. June. Twigs rigid, covered with rust-coloured down. Ls. ov., 3, stiff and leathery, dark glossy green above, rusty below. Fls. white. Berry blue. South United States.

(*e*) *Ls. pinnately nerved, deciduous, lateral veins reach margin*

(i) L.-buds without scales

V. alnifolium Marsh. (*V. lantanoides* Michx.). American Wayfaring Tree, Hobble Bush. 10. May–June. Twigs scurfy. Ls. ov., 8, short-pointed, heart-shaped base, unevenly toothed, dark green above, scurfy-downy below. Fls. white, in stalkless clusters; marginal fls. $\frac{3}{4}$, steriles. Berry red to dark purple. East North America.

V. bitchiuense Makino. 10. April–May. Branchlets hairy. Ls. ov., 3, toothed, hairy, stout-stalked. Fls. $\frac{1}{2}$, pink or white, slender-tubed, fragrant. Berry black. Japan. (Fig. 63 E.)

VIBURNUM—*continued*

V. buddleifolium Wright. 6. May–June. Branchlets densely downy. Ls. ov., lanc., 5, pointed, shallowly toothed, rounded or heart-shaped base, dark green and wrinkled above, white-felted or woolly below. Fls. white, funnel-shaped. Berry black. China. (Fig. 63 F.)

V. Carlesii Hemsl. 5. April. Branchlets densely downy. Ls. broadly ov., 3, unevenly toothed, hairy, sometimes unevenly lobed, dull green above, greyish below. Fls. ½, pink or white, slender-tubed, fragrant, in terminal rounded clusters. Berry black. Corea. (Fig. 63 G.)

Very similar is *V. Burkwoodii* (Hort.), practically an evergreen, a cross between this and *V. utile*.

V. cotinifolium D. Don. 12. May. Branchlets grey-felted. Ls. ov., 5, finely toothed or entire, dark green above, grey-felted below. Fls. white or pink, widely funnel-shaped. Berry black. Himalaya. (Fig. 65 E.)

V. Lantana L. Wayfaring Tree. 15. May–June. Branchlets stout and stiff, densely downy or pale-felted. Ls. ov. or roundish, 5, pointed, toothed, hairy, heart-shaped base. Fls. white, in flattish-topped clusters. Berry red to black. Europe (including Britain), North Asia, North Africa. (Fig. 64 B.)

V. Veitchii Wright. 6. May–June. Like the preceding species, but leaves distantly toothed and calyx much more hairy. China.

(ii) Leaf-buds scaly

V. affine Bush. 6. May–June. Branchlets hairless. Ls. ov., 2, heart-shaped base, coarsely toothed. Fl.-clusters 2 across, white. Berry bluish black. North United States.

V. betulifolium Batal. 12. June–July. Branchlets hairless. Ls. ov., 4, coarsely toothed at outer end. Fl.-clusters large and loose. Berry red. China. (Fig. 63 D.)

V. dentatum L. Arrow-wood. 15. June–July. Branchlets hairless. Ls. broadly ov., almost circular, 2, coarsely toothed, glossy. Fl.-clusters 2½ across, hairless. Berry bluish black. North America.

V. dilatatum Thunb. 10. June. Young branchlets very downy. Ls. roundish ov., obov., 5, pointed, distantly toothed, hairy. Fls. ¼, white. Berry ¼, red. China and Japan.

V. erubescens Wall. 20. June. Ls. ov., 3, toothed. Fls. ½, tubular, white tinged with pink, drooping. Berry red to black. Nepal and China.

V. foetens Decne. 10. January–March. Branchlets hairless. Ls. ov., 4, pointed, toothed, parallel-veined, hairless except in vein-axils below, emitting strong odour when rubbed. Fls. ½, white, tubular, fragrant. Berry black, edible. Himalaya.

V. fragrans Bunge. 10. November–April. Like the preceding species, but the leaves are not offensive when rubbed, and the fl.-clusters are stiffer and more fragrant. Berry red, edible. China. (Fig. 64 A.)

According to Bean there is a form in cultivation with 'bronzy young leaves and shoots, and flowers that are pink in bud.'

V. grandiflorum Wall. (*V. nervosum* Don). 12. February–March. Branchlets downy. Ls. ov., 3, dark green and wrinkled above, tapering base, finely and evenly toothed, downy below, stalk red. Fls. ½, white

VIBURNUM—*continued*

tinged with pink, in terminal clusters, fragrant. Berry ½, purplish black, edible. Himalaya.

V. hupehense Rehd. 6. June. Branchlets downy. Ls. ov., 3, coarsely toothed, heart-shaped or straight base, hairy, stalk grooved. Berry red. China.

V. lobophyllum Graebn. 15. June–July. Branchlets dark reddish brown, nearly hairless. Ls. roundish ov., 4, rounded or heart-shaped base, shallowly and somewhat coarsely toothed, dark green above, hairy below, 5–6 pairs veins. Fls. white, in long-stalked flattish clusters. Berry ½, bright red. China. (Fig. 64 J.)

V. molle Michx. 12. May–June. Branchlets hairless; older bark peeling. Ls. roundish, 5, heart-shaped base, coarsely toothed, stipulate. Fls. white, in long-stalked clusters. Berry blue, flattened. North America. (Fig. 64 F.)

V. pubescens Pursh (*V. venosum* Brit.). 12. June–July. Branchlets downy. Ls. roundish, 4, coarsely toothed, rounded or heart-shaped base, hairy, slender-stalked. Fls. white. Berry blue. North America. (Fig. 64 H.)

V. Sieboldii Miq. 10. May–June. Branchlets stiff and spreading. Ls. obov., 5, parallel-veined, coarsely toothed, dark glossy green above. Fls. ¼, creamy white, in long-stalked rounded clusters or panicles. Berry ½, egg-shaped, pink to blue-black. Japan.

V. theiferum Rehd. 12. May–June. Branchlets hairless, grey. Ls. ov., lanc., 6, long-pointed, distantly and sharply toothed, parallel-veined. Fls. white. Berry red. China.

V. tomentosum Thunb. 10. June. Branchlets horizontal, downy. Ls. ov., 4, toothed, hairy. Fls. white, in flat-topped clusters; the outer ones large, with unequal petals. Berry red to black. Japan. (Fig. 64 G.)

Var. *plicatum* Maxim. (*V. plicatum* Thunb.). Japanese Snowball Tree. Fls. 1, in erect round trusses.

V. Wrightii Miq. 10. May. Branches erect. Ls. ov., obov., 5, distantly toothed, point long and abrupt, bright green above, 6–10 pairs parallel veins. Fls. white. Berry red. Japan.

Family 56. **RUBIACEAE.** K4–5, C (4–5), A4–5, $\bar{G}$ (2)

Ls. opposite or whorled, entire, often with triangular stipules on the stem between the leaf-stalks. The petals are usually continued into a tube or funnel below their insertion. Mostly tropical or sub-tropical and containing many products of economic importance, such as coffee berries (from *Coffea arabica*), quinine bark from species of *Cinchona* and *Remijia*, and madder from *Rubia tinctorum*. The timbers of *Adina cordifolia*, known as haldu, imported from India, etc., and opepe (*Sarcocephalus Diderichii*) from Nigeria are yellow, durable, and easily worked and polished. *Gardenia* belongs to this family.

CEPHALANTHUS OCCIDENTALIS L. Button Bush. 6. August–September. D. Stems olive green, shining, hairless. Ls. in threes, ov., 5, tapering at both ends, glossy, hairless. Fls. small, white, in axillary, long-stalked round heads. Fruit dry. North America. (Fig. 67 O.)

COPROSMA. Ls. opposite. Fls. inconspicuous. Fruit a berry.

COPROSMA—*continued*

C. acerosa Cunn. ¼. E. Stems prostrate, wiry, interlacing. Ls. linear, ¾, dark green, hairless. Berry pale transparent blue. New Zealand. (Fig. 50 E.)

* **C. foetidissima** Forst. 15. E. Ls. ov., lanc., 2, slender-stalked, emitting disagreeable smell when bruised. Berry red or yellowish red, transparent. New Zealand. (Fig. 67 N.)

* **C. grandifolia** Hook. f. 15. April–May. E. Ls. obov., 9, dull green, slender-stalked. Berry ¼, orange-red. New Zealand.

* **C. lucida** Forst. 15. E. Ls. obov., 5, leathery and glossy, short-stalked. Berry oblong or pear-shaped, reddish orange. New Zealand. (Fig. 67 M.)

C. Petriei Cheeseman. ¼. E. Stems prostrate. Ls. linear, oblong, ¼, hairy. Berry purple. New Zealand. (Fig. 48 L.)

C. rigida Cheeseman. 15. April. E. Stiff and erect. Ls. obov., oblanc., ¾, stiff and rather leathery, hairless. Berry ¼, oblong or pear-shaped, yellow. New Zealand.

EMMENOPTERYS HENRYI Oliv. 80. June–July. D. Twigs hairless. Ls. opposite, ov., 9, tapering base, entire, rather fleshy, with a velvety sheen, stalk reddish. Fls. 1, white, funnel-shaped, in large terminal panicles; one lobe of the calyx develops into a large white bract. Fruit 1, spindle-shaped, ribbed. China. (Fig. 67 G.)

LEPTODERMIS. Ls. opposite, entire, with a disagreeable smell when crushed. Fls. white or purple, 5-parted, tubular, in axillary clusters. Fruit dry, splitting into five.

L. lanceolata Wall. 3. July–October. D. Ls. ov., lanc., 3. Fls. ½, white, fading to pale yellow, the clusters forming large terminal panicles. Himalaya. (Fig. 67 J.)

L. oblonga Bunge. 4. July–September. D. Ls. lanc., 1, rough above. Fls. ¾, purple. China. (Fig. 67 L.)

L. pilosa Diels. 10. July–September. D. Ls. ov., 1, grey-green, hairy. Fls. ½, lavender-coloured. China. (Fig. 67 K.)

L. Purdomii Hutch. 5. August–September. D. Stems long, slender, wiry. Ls. linear, ½, in clusters at joints, hairless. Fls. ½, pink. China. (Fig. 50 K.)

LUCULIA. Branchlets dotted. Ls. opposite, ov., lanc., 6, with nine or more pairs of veins. Fls. 1½, funnel-shaped, fragrant, in terminal branched clusters. Fruit a capsule with numerous winged seeds.

* **L. gratissima** Sweet. 12. August–September. D. Branchlets downy. Fls. pink. Himalaya.

* **L. Pinceana** Hook. f. 12. June–September. D. Branchlets hairless. Fls. white. Himalaya.

MITCHELLA REPENS L. Partridge Berry. Prostrate. June–July. E. Ls. opposite, ov., ½, hairless. Fls. ½, white or tinged with purple, funnel-shaped, 4-parted, in stalked pairs. Fruit ¼, a red berry. North America. (Fig. 67 C.)

PAEDERIA CHINENSIS Hance (P. TOMENTOSA Maxim.). 18. June–September. D. Climber. Ls. opposite, ov., lanc., 4, downy below. Fls. ½, tubular, white, with purple throat, in axillary and terminal branched clusters. China.

Family 57. **COMPOSITAE.** K (5), C (5), A (5), Ḡ1

The daisy and thistle family; mostly herbaceous. Fls. in composite heads, each head having the appearance of a single flower; sepals reduced to a *pappus* of hairs or bristles; what appear to be sepals are really bracts. Corolla tubular and 5-toothed, or strap-shaped, i.e. flat, with a short tube at the base. The flowers (florets) in one head may be all tubular or all strap-shaped, but in many species the tubular florets are compressed into a central *disk*, while the strap-shaped florets appear on the circumference of the head, forming a *ray*. Stamens united into a tube round the style, which has a forked stigma. Ovary inferior, 1-celled and containing one erect ovule. The fruit is dry and often crowned by the persistent pappus. The family has been divided into numerous tribes spread all over the world. It contains many plants of medicinal value, mostly giving tonics or stimulants, e.g. absinth, wormwood, arnica, chicory, tansy, chamomile, etc.; kitchen-garden plants such as lettuce, endive, and artichoke; and many plants of great beauty, including asters, dahlias, chrysanthemums, sunflowers, cosmos, zinnias, and marigolds.

(I) Pappus None (*Anthemideae*)

ARTEMISIA. Ls. alternate, greyish, strongly aromatic. Fl.-heads small, yellow, without ray florets, in terminal leafy spikes or panicles.

A. Abrotanum L. Southernwood, Lad's Love, Old Man. 3. September. E. Ls. 3, pinnately or 2-pinnately dissected into fine linear lobes. South Europe. (Fig. 36 c.)

A. Absinthium L. Wormwood. 3. July–October. E. Ls. 4, coarsely divided into lanc. or oblong blunt lobes, silky. Fl.-heads numerous, drooping. South Europe. (Fig. 36 b.)

A. tridentata Nutt. Sage Brush. 8. August–September. E. Ls. linear, lanc., 1½, grey-felted, 3-toothed at apex. West United States. (Fig. 51 l.)

Santolina Chamaecyparissus L. Lavender Cotton. 2. July. E. Stem and leaves white. Ls. alternate, 1, pinnately lobed, crowded. Flower-heads ½, yellow, hemispherical, solitary at end of erect slender stalk. South Europe. (Fig. 36 a.)

(II) Pappus of Hairs or Bristles

(i) ray florets with two unequal limbs (*Mutisieae*)

* Mutisia decurrens Cav. 10. Summer. E. Climbing by tendrils. Ls. lanc., 5, entire, ending in a forked tendril, base continued down the stem as a pair of narrow wings. Fl.-heads 4, red or orange, with yellow centre, solitary at end of shoot, long-stalked. Chile. (Fig. 120 k.)

M. ilicifolia (Cav.) has leathery leaves with spiny teeth; *M. Clematis* (L. f.) has pinnate leaves.

(ii) florets all tubular, with white papery bracts (*Inuleae* in part)

CASSINIA (DIPLOPAPPUS). Ls. alternate, ¼, entire, dark green above, yellow below, crowded. Fl.-heads small, white, in terminal branched clusters, without ray florets.

C. fulvida Hook. f. (*Diplopappus ebrysophyllus* Hort.). Golden Bush. 6.

CASSINIA (DIPLOPAPPUS)—*continued*

July. E. Stems clammy. Ls. mustard-yellow below. New Zealand. (Fig. 49 M.)

C. leptophylla R. Br. 4. July–August. E. Stems not clammy. Ls. pale yellow or white below. New Zealand.

OZOTHAMNUS. Evergreen shrubs with angled or ribbed and clammy branchlets, alternate entire leaves and small white flower-heads in rounded branched clusters. Florets all tubular and surrounded by white papery bracts.

O. Antennaria Hook. f. 10. June–July. Branchlets covered with grey or tawny scurf. Ls. oblanc., 1, dark green and smooth above, scurfy below, stalkless or nearly so. Tasmania. (Fig. 120 J.)

* **O. rosmarinifolius** DC. (*Helichrysum rosmarinifolium* DC.). 9. July–September. Ls. linear, 1, dark green and clammy above, pale below, margins recurved. Victoria and Tasmania. (Fig. 51 N.)

(iii) FLORETS ALL TUBULAR, STIGMAS VERY LONG (*Eupatorieae*)

* EUPATORIUM MICRANTHUM Less. (E. WEINMANNIANUM Regel & Koern.). 9. September–November. E. Branchlets slender, hairless. Ls. opposite, ov., lanc., 4, pointed, thin, tapering base, vaguely toothed in outer half. Fl.-heads ¼, white or rose-tinted, fragrant, in flattish branched clusters. Mexico. (Fig. 60 K.)

(iv) BRACTS IN ONE OR TWO ROWS, EXCEPT FOR SCALES AT BASE (*Senecioneae*)

* BRACHYGLOTTIS REPANDA Forst. (SENECIO FORSTERI Schlecht). 20. April. E. Branchlets white-felted. Ls. alternate, ov., 12, pointed, rounded or straight base; teeth large, unequal and lobe-like; dark green above, white-felted below. Fl.-heads small, greenish white, in large terminal panicles up to 16 wide. New Zealand. (Fig. 100 D.)

SENECIO. Evergreen shrubs with thick alternate leaves which are usually felted on one or both sides. Fl.-heads yellow or white, with one row of sepal-like bracts.

(*a*) *Fl.-heads without ray florets*

S. elaeagnifolius Hook. f. (*S. Buchananii* Armstr.). 10. June. Branchlets buff-felted. Ls. ov., 5, entire, leathery, blunt-ended, glossy green above, buff-felted below, stalk grooved. Fl.-heads ½, yellow in terminal panicles. New Zealand. (Fig. 121 B.)

S. rotundifolius Hook. f. 6. June–July. Branchlets grooved, white-felted. Ls. circular, 5, glossy green above, white-felted below, stalk grooved. Fl.-heads ½, white, in close erect clusters. New Zealand.

(*b*) *Fl.-heads with ray florets*

* **S. compactus** Kirk. 3. September. Branchlets white-felted. Ls. ov., 2, entire, blunt-ended, margins wavy. Fl.-heads ¾, yellow, in terminal racemes. New Zealand. (Fig. 121 C.)

* **S. Greyii** Hook. f. 8. June. Branchlets stout, white-felted. Ls. ov., 4, entire, blunt-ended, white-felted below and also on the margins above. Fl.-heads 1, yellow, in terminal panicles. New Zealand. (Fig. 121 D.)

* **S. Haastii** Hook. f. ½. A low spreading plant, white all over. Ls. nearly circular, 5, vaguely round-toothed, woolly. Fl.-heads 1, yellow, in terminal racemes up to 15 high. New Zealand.

SENECIO—*continued*

* **S. Hectori** Buch. 14. July. Branchlets stout, woolly. Ls. lanc., ov., 10, pinnately lobed at base, conspicuously toothed, warted above, grey below. Fl.-heads 2, white, in terminal flattish branched clusters. New Zealand. (Fig. 100 A.)

* **S. Huntii** F. Muell. 20. June–July. Branchlets stout, clammy and downy. Ls. lanc., 4, entire, blunt-ended, rusty-felted below. Fl.-heads ½, yellow, in dense terminal panicles, fifteen to twenty ray florets. Chatham Islands. (Fig. 121 E.)

* **S. laxifolius** Buch. 4. Summer. Branchlets grey, downy. Ls. ov., lanc., entire, blunt-ended, grey down above, white felt below. Fl.-heads 1, yellow, in loose terminal panicles. New Zealand. (Fig. 121 F.)

* **S. Monroi** Hook. f. 6. Branchlets white-felted. Ls. ov., 1, wrinkled or wavy at margin, blunt-ended, dull green above, white-felted below. Fl.-heads ½, yellow, on long, slender, glandular-downy stalks. New Zealand. (Fig. 121 G.)

(v) BRACTS OVERLAPPING IN SEVERAL ROWS, FL.-HEADS OF VARIOUS COLOURS (*Astereae*)

* APLOPAPPUS ERICOIDES DC. (DIPLOPAPPUS ERICOIDES Less.). 5. August. E. Stems erect. Ls. linear, ½, in clusters at each joint. Fl.-heads ½, yellow, in long-stalked terminal branched clusters; ray florets five. California. (Fig. 49 N.)

BACCHARIS. Groundsel Tree. Ls. alternate, obov., oblanc., coarsely toothed, clammy with resin, stalkless or nearly so. Fl.-heads small, white or yellowish white, in panicles, pappus silky.

B. halimifolia L. 12. October. D. Branchlets angular, hairless. Ls. 3, grey-green, resin-dotted, shortly stalked. North America. (Fig. 100 B.)

B. patagonica Hook. & Arn. 9. May. E. Branchlets angled, scurfy and clammy. Ls. 1, deep green, scurfy on both sides, stalkless. South America. (Fig. 100 C.)

* BIGELOVIA GRAVEOLENS Gray (CHRYSOTHAMNUS DRACUNCULOIDES Nutt.). Plumed Golden Rod. 8. October. E. Stems erect, grey. Ls. alternate, linear, 3, crowded, long-pointed, hairless, aromatic. Fl.-heads ¼, yellow, long and narrow, in flattish branched clusters. West North America. (Fig. 51 M.)

* GRINDELIA SPECIOSA Lindl. & Paxt. 3. May–October. E. Young stems sticky and very leafy. Ls. alternate, linear-oblong, 4, tapering base, coarsely toothed, grey-green, gummy, stalkless or nearly so. Fl.-heads 3, yellow, solitary, long-stalked. South America.

MICROGLOSSA ALBESCENS Clarke (AMPHIRAMIS ALBESCENS DC., ASTER CABULICUS Lindl.). 5. July. D. Stems pithy, grey and downy. Ls. alternate, lanc., 5, tapered at both ends, pointed, minutely and distantly toothed, dark green above, grey below. Fl.-heads ¼, bluish purple, with yellow centre, in terminal branched clusters. Himalaya. (Fig. 98 H.)

OLEARIA. New Zealand Daisy Bush. Evergreen shrubs with stiff leathery leaves, usually green above and white, grey, or silvery below. Flower-heads small, white or purplish, in branched clusters.

(*a*) *Ls. opposite or in opposite clusters*

O. odorata Petrie. 10. August. Branchlets slender, cylindrical, wiry.

OLEARIA—*continued*

Ls. linear, 1, blunt-ended, green above, silvery below. Fl.-heads ¼, greyish brown, fragrant. New Zealand. (Fig. 53 F.)

* **O. Solandri** Hook. f. 10. May–June. Branchlets angled, yellowish, downy. Ls. linear, obov., ¼, yellow-felted below. Fl.-heads ¼, solitary from the centre of a leaf-cluster. New Zealand. (Fig. 49 L.)

* **O. Traversii** Hook. f. 15. June. Branchlets 4-angled, silver-felted. Ls. ov., 2, entire, apex ending in minute tip, bright dark green above, silver-felted below. Fl.-heads dull grey, without ray florets. New Zealand. (Fig. 70 D.)

* **O. virgata** Hook. f. 10. May–June. Branchlets slender, wiry, 4-angled, hairless. Ls. linear, oblanc., ¾, white-felted below, stalkless. Fl.-heads yellowish white, in opposite clusters, three to six ray florets. New Zealand. (Fig. 53 E.)

Var. *lineata* Kirk. Branches more pendulous. Leaf-clusters further apart, leaves narrower. Eight to fourteen ray florets (Bean).

(*b*) *Ls. alternate, toothed*

* **O. argophylla** F. Muell. 30. May–June. Branchlets silver-felted. Ls. ov., lanc., 6, shallowly and distantly toothed, silver-felted below. Fl.-heads white, with three to six ray florets. Australia and Tasmania. (Fig. 92 A.)

* **O. chathamica** Kirk. 6. May–June. Ls. lanc., 5, evenly and bluntly toothed, white-felted below, with prominent veins running lengthwise beside the midrib. Fl.-heads 1½, purple. Chatham Islands. (Fig. 99 B.)

* **O. Colensoi** Hook. f. 10. July. Ls. ov., lanc., 6, very leathery, glossy green above, woolly-white below, stout-stalked, the veins netted and prominent below. Fl.-heads 1, brownish purple, in racemes up to 6 long. New Zealand. (Fig. 99 C.)

* **O. erubescens** Dipp. 5. May–June. Branchlets brown, downy. Ls. ov., lanc., very variable in size, ½ to 2, conspicuously toothed, glossy green above, brown-felted below. Fl.-heads white, in cylindrical panicles up to 18 long. Australia. (Figs. 99 H–K.)

* **O. Gunniana** Hook. f. (*O. stellulata* Benth.). 10. May. Branchlets white-felted. Ls. lanc., 1½, rounded at end, coarsely round-toothed, white- or brown-felted below. Fl.-heads 1, white, in erect open-branched clusters, each head with ten to sixteen ray florets. New Zealand. (Fig. 99 L.)

* **O. macrodonta** Baker. 20. June–July. Bark peeling; branchlets angled, downy. Ls. ov., 5, leathery, coarsely toothed, dark glossy green above, silver-felted below. Fl.-heads ½, white, with reddish centre, ten or more ray florets. New Zealand. (Fig. 99 D.)

O. ilicifolia (Hook. f.) is similar, but with narrower leaves and more spreading teeth.

* **O. myrsinoides** F. Muell. 5. May–June. Branchlets angled, silvery. Ls. ov., ½, blunt-ended, silvery and scaly below. Fl.-heads white, in cylindrical panicles up to 12 long. New Zealand.

* **O. nitida** Hook. f. 12. May–June. Branchlets grooved, brown-felted. Ls. ov., 3, distantly toothed, dark glossy green above, silver-felted

OLEARIA—*continued*

below, margins often wavy. Fl.-heads ½, white, with fifteen to twenty ray florets. New Zealand. (Fig. 99 E.)

* **O. semidentata** Decne. 12. May–June. Branchlets slender, white-felted. Ls. linear, lanc., 3, toothed at outer end, dark green and wrinkled above, woolly-white below. Fl.-heads 2, purple, solitary. Chatham Islands. (Fig. 99 F.)

* **O. speciosa** Hutch. 4. June. Ls. ov., lanc., 4, dark glossy green and wrinkled above, brown-felted below, coarsely and unevenly toothed. Fl.-heads 1, white, in loose branched clusters. New Zealand. (Fig. 99 G.)

(*c*) *Ls. alternate, entire*

* **O. albida** Hook. f. 20. July. Branchlets grooved, brown-felted. Ls. ov., 4, blunt-ended, dark green above, white-felted below. Fl.-heads ¼, white, with one to three ray florets. New Zealand. (Fig. 120 O.)

* **O. avicenniaefolia** Hook. f. 20. August–September. Branchlets ribbed, white-felted. Ls. ov., lanc., 4, greyish green above, white- or yellow-felted below, stalk grooved. Fl.-heads ½, white, with two to three ray florets, fragrant. New Zealand. (Fig. 120 L.)

* **O. floribunda** Benth. 6. June. A heath-like plant with minute leaves in alternate clusters. Fl.-heads ½, white, in leafy racemes forming large panicles, each head with three to four ray florets. Australia. (Fig. 49 O.)

* **O. Forsteri** Hook. f. 20. October. Branchlets ribbed, dark brown, scurfy. Ls. ov., 3, rounded or heart-shaped base, margins wavy, glossy green above, white-felted below, stalk grooved. Fl.-heads ¼, dull white, in small axillary panicles, each fl.-head consisting of a solitary tubular floret. New Zealand. (Fig. 120 M.)

* **O. furfuracea** Hook. f. 20. Ls. ov., 4, very leathery, sometimes with a few teeth, glossy green above, silver-felted below. Fl.-heads ½, white, in axillary branched clusters, each head with two to five ray florets. New Zealand. (Fig. 120 Q.)

O. Haastii Hook. f. 9. July–August. Branchlets downy. Ls. ov., 1, rounded at end, glossy green above, white- or tawny-felted below, very shortly stalked. Fl.-heads ½, white, in branched clusters at end of twigs. New Zealand. (Fig. 120 R.)

* **O. lineata** Cockayne. 10. Stems slender, often drooping. Ls. linear, 2, mostly in alternate clusters, white-felted below, margins recurved. Fl.-heads small, in small axillary clusters, each head with eight to fourteen ray florets. New Zealand. (Fig. 153 G.)

* **O. nummularifolia** Hook. f. 10. July. Branchlets slightly downy. Ls. ov., ½, thick and leathery, margins recurved, glossy green above, with yellowish white felt below and closely set on the stem. Fl.-heads ½, white, solitary and erect from the terminal leaf-axils. New Zealand. (Fig. 120 N.)

* **O. oleifolia** Kirk. 9. July–August. Branchlets downy. Ls. lanc., 3, blunt-ended, glossy green above, white-felted below, very shortly stalked. Fl.-heads ½, white, in branched clusters at end of twigs. New Zealand. (Fig. 120 P.)

* PACHYSTEGIA INSIGNIS Cheeseman (OLEARIA INSIGNIS Hook. f.). 6. July.
E. Branches stout, densely hairy. Ls. alternate, broadly ov., 7, entire, blunt-

ended, leathery, dark green above, white-felted below, stout-stalked. Fl.-heads 3, white, with yellow centre, long-stalked, solitary or in 2-5-flowered clusters at end of branchlets, ray florets very numerous. New Zealand. (Fig. 121 A.)

Family 58. **VACCINIACEAE.** K (4–5), C (4–5), A8–10, $\bar{G}$ (4–5)

Low shrubs or woody plants, disliking limestone and chalk. Ls. alternate, without stipules. Fls. small, bell-shaped or urn-shaped, nodding, solitary or in twos or threes, stamens not attached to the corolla, anthers 2-celled, opening by apical pores, ovary inferior. Fruit a berry.

CHIOGENES HISPIDULA Torr. & Gray (C. SERPYLLIFOLIA Salisb.). Creeping Snowberry. May–June. E. Creeping plant. Ls. alternate, roundish, ½, dark green above, pale below with a few reddish bristles. Fls. small, white, bell-shaped, solitary on curved stalks in the leaf-axils. Fruit a white berry. North America. (Fig. 122 Q.)

GAYLUSSACIA. Huckleberry. Ls. alternate, very shortly stalked. Fls. white or red, K (5), C (5), A10. Ovary 10-celled. Fruit a blue or black berry.

- **G. baccata** Koch. Black Huckleberry. 3. June. D. Branchlets sticky. Ls. ov., 1½, entire, very sticky, yellowish green above, resin-dotted below. Fls. ¼, red, urn-shaped, in drooping racemes. Berry black, edible. North America.
- **G. brachycera** Torr. & Gray (*Vaccinium buxifolium* Salisb.). Box Huckleberry. 1. May–June. E. Ls. ov., 1, leathery, toothed, glossy green above. Fls. ¼, white, faintly striped with red, cylindrical, contracted at the mouth, in short-stalked axillary racemes. Berry blue. East United States. (Fig. 100 E.)
- **G. dumosa** Torr. & Gray (*Vaccinium dumosum* Andr.). Dwarf Huckleberry. 2. May–June. D. Ls. ov., lanc., 1½, entire, glossy green. Fls. ¼, cylindrical, white, nodding. Berry black. Newfoundland and East United States.
- **G. frondosa** Torr. & Gray (*Vaccinium frondosum* L.). Dangleberry, Tangleberry, Blue Huckleberry. 6. May. D. Branches spreading, twigs hairless. Ls. ov., blunt-ended, 1½, entire, pale green above, downy and resin-dotted below. Fls. ¼, broadly bell-shaped, greenish purple. Berry blue, edible. East United States.
- **G. ursina** Torr. & Gray (*Vaccinium ursinum* Curt.). Buckberry. 6. May. D. Ls. ov., 3, pointed. Fls. ¼, white or reddish, cylindrical, in few-flowered nodding racemes. Berry black, sweet. Carolina.

OXYCOCCUS. Cranberry. Prostrate shrubs with long wiry creeping stems. Ls. alternate, ov., ½, entire, dark green above, bluish white below. Fls. ¼, pink, corolla deeply divided and bent back revealing the stamens. K (4), C (4), A8. Ovary 4-celled. Fruit a red berry.

- **O. macrocarpus** Pers. (*Vaccinium macrocarpum* Ait.). American Cranberry. September. E. Ls. rounded at end. Fls. in terminal racemes ending in a leafy shoot. East North America. (Fig. 121 J.)
- **O. palustris** Pers. (*Vaccinium Oxycoccus* L.). Cranberry. June. E. Ls. pointed. Fls. in terminal 1-4-flowered clusters. Berry ¼. Northern Hemisphere (including Britain). (Fig. 121 H.)

VACCINIUM. Ls. alternate, very shortly stalked. Fls. small, white or pinkish, the corolla not deeply divided, ovary 4-5-celled. Fruit a berry.

(a) Deciduous

V. arboreum Marsh. Farkleberry. 10. July–August. Ls. ov., 2, pointed, minutely toothed, dark glossy green above, slightly downy below, the margins slightly recurved. Fls. ½, widely bell-shaped, 5-lobed. Berry ¼, black. East United States. (Fig. 100 F.)

V. Arctostaphylos L. Caucasian Whortleberry, Bear's Grape. 10. June. Ls. ov., 4, pointed, finely toothed, dark dull green above, downy below. Fls. ¼, white tinged with red, jointed to the stalk, in axillary racemes. Berry ¼, purple. Caucasus. (Fig. 101 A.)

V. caespitosum Michx. Dwarf Bilberry. 1. May. Stems cylindrical, hairless. Ls. obov., oblanc., 1, toothed, bright green, glossy above. Fls. ¼, white or pink, 5-lobed, solitary, short-stalked, anthers awned. Berry ¼, black, sweet. North America.

V. canadense Kalm. Sour-top, Velvet-leaf. 1. May. Stems very downy. Ls. lanc., 1½, entire, pointed. Fls. ¼, in dense short clusters. Berry ¼, blue-black. East North America. (Fig. 121 N.)

V. corymbosum L. Swamp Blueberry. 12. May. Ls. ov., lanc., 3, tapering at both ends, entire. Fls. ¼. Berry black, with blue bloom. East North America. (Fig. 121 M.)

V. hirsutum Buckl. Hairy Huckleberry. 2. May. Young stems very downy. Ls. ov., 2½, entire, pointed, dark green, downy, short-stalked. Fls. ¼, cylindrical, hairy. Berry ¼, blue-black, hairy. Mountains of North Carolina. (Fig. 121 L.)

V. Myrtillus L. Whortleberry, Bilberry. 1. May. Stems flanged or angled, hairless. Ls. ov., 1, round-toothed, bright green, hairless. Fls. ¼, round, pale pink, anthers awned. Berry ¼, black, with blue bloom. Europe (including Britain). (Fig. 100 G.)

V. pennsylvanicum Lam. Low Blueberry. 1½. April–May. Young stems warted, downy. Ls. lanc., 1½, pointed, minutely toothed, bright green, hairless. Fls. ¼. Berry usually black, with blue bloom, sometimes red or white. East North America. (Fig. 101 E.)

V. praestans Lamb. ½. June. Creeping plant, with upright stems. Ls. ov., 1½, minutely toothed, slender-stalked. Fls. ¼, white tinged with pink, with two narrow bracts below the calyx. Berry red, sweet. Kamschatka.

V. stamineum L. Deerberry. 4. May–June. Ls. ov., 2½, pointed, entire, dark dull green above. Fls. ¼, white, with projecting yellow stamens. Berry ¼, greenish or yellowish. East United States.

V. uliginosum L. Bog Bilberry, Bog Whortleberry. 2. May. Stems cylindrical. Ls. obov. or circular, 1, entire, stalkless. Fls. very small, 4-lobed, in twos or threes on drooping stalks, anthers awned. Berry black, with blue bloom. Northern Hemisphere (including Britain). (Fig. 121 K.)

V. vacillans Kalm. Blue Huckleberry. 3. May. Stems yellowish green, hairless, warted. Ls. ov., obov., 2, minutely toothed or entire, firm, hairless. Fls. ¼, pink, cylindrical, in short clusters. Berry ¼, black, with blue bloom, very sweet. U.S.A.

VACCINIUM—*continued*

(*b*) *Evergreen*

* **V. glauco-album** Hook. f. 4. July. Stems hairless. Ls. ov., 2, stiff and hard, pointed, toothed, green above, blue-white below. Berry ¼, black, with blue bloom. Himalaya. (Fig. 101 D.)

V. Mortinia Benth. Mortina. 4. May. Stems dark, downy. Ls. ov., ½, minutely toothed, pitted below, crowded. Fls. pink. Berry red. South America. (Fig. 101 C.)

V. Myrsinites Lam. Evergreen Blueberry. 1½. April. Ls. obov., ¾, glossy above. Fls. ¼, white, in short racemes. Berry blue-black. South United States.

V. ovatum Pursh. 12. September. Stems purple, downy. Ls. ov., 1, leathery, finely toothed. Fls. white, in short nodding axillary racemes. Berry ¼, black. West North America. (Fig. 101 B.)

V. Vitis-idaea L. Cowberry. ½. May–June. Low-creeping shrub. Stems yellowish green, warted, hairless. Ls. ov., 2, minutely toothed in outer half or entire, firm, hairless. Fls. pink. Berry ¼, red. Northern Hemisphere (including Britain). (Fig. 101 F.)

Family 59. **ERICACEAE.** K4–5, C (4–5) or 4–5, A8–10, $\underline{G}$ (4–5)

As in the preceding family the anthers are 2-celled and open by apical pores, but the ovary is superior. Fruit a capsule or berry. In other respects it is similar to *Vacciniaceae*, which is often included in *Ericaceae*. Both prefer peaty or healthy soils free from lime, though there are notable exceptions, e.g. the winter-flowering heaths and many rhododendrons. *Ericaceae* contains few trees other than *Arbutus*, *Oxydendron*, and the Himalayan *Rhododendron arboreum*. All are highly ornamental, but without economic importance, except that briar pipes are made from the root of *Erica scoparia* (Fr. *bruyère*).

ANDROMEDA POLIFOLIA L. Bog Rosemary. 1½. April. E. Stems thin, wiry, hairless. Ls. alternate, linear, ½, dark green above, felted or glaucous below, margins recurved. Fls. ¼, pink, egg-shaped, in terminal clusters. Fruit an egg-shaped capsule. Northern and Arctic regions. (Fig. 51 B.)

ARBUTUS. Ls. alternate, leathery, toothed, hairless, crowded towards end of branch. Fls. ¼, white or pinkish, pitcher-shaped, in terminal panicles. Fruit a berry.

A. andrachnoides Link. 30. November–January. E. Ls. ov., 4, dark green above, glossy below, stalk short and hairy. Berry ½, red. Hybrid.

A. Menziesii Pursh. Madrona. 100. May. E. Bark smooth, peeling, reddish brown. Ls. ov., oblong, 6, finely toothed or entire, dark green above, grey or white below, stalk short. Fl.-panicles erect. Berry ½, orange-coloured. California. (Fig. 101 H.)

A. Unedo L. Strawberry Tree. 30. October–November. E. Ls. ov., 4, tapering to both ends, sharply toothed, stalk hairy. Fl.-panicles drooping. Berry ¾, orange-red, rough. South Europe and Eire. (Fig. 101 J.)

ARCTERICA NANA Makino (PIERIS NANA Makino). Prostrate. April. E. Stems downy. Ls. in whorls of three, ov., ½, entire, leathery. Fls. ¼, white, in small terminal clusters. Fruit a dry capsule. Japan. (Fig. 72 L.)

ARCTOSTAPHYLOS. Ls. alternate, leathery, entire. Fls. pink, egg-shaped, nodding in terminal clusters. Fruit a red berry.

A. Manzanita Parry. Manzanita. 25. March–April. E. Branchlets

ARCTOSTAPHYLOS—*continued*

downy. Ls. ov., 2, unequal-sided, hard and stiff, greyish green, pitted. Fls. $\frac{1}{4}$. Berry $\frac{1}{2}$. California. (Fig. 122 B.)

A. tomentosa (Lindl.), the Woolly Manzanita, has woolly branchlets and leaves.

A. Uva-ursi Spreng. Red Bearberry. Prostrate. April–June. E. Ls. obov., 1, rounded at end, crowded, often in rosette-like tufts. Fls. very small, white or pinkish, in terminal clusters. Berry $\frac{1}{4}$, red. Northern Hemisphere (including Britain). (Fig. 122 A.)

ARCTOUS ALPINUS Nied. (ARCTOSTAPHYLOS ALPINA Spreng.). Black Bearberry. $\frac{1}{2}$. April–June. D. Ls. obov., $1\frac{1}{2}$, thin, rounded at end, round-toothed towards apex, net-veined. Fls. very small, white or pinkish, in terminal clusters. Berry $\frac{1}{4}$, black. Northern Hemisphere. (Fig. 101 G.)

BRUCKENTHALIA SPICULIFOLIA Reichb. $\frac{1}{2}$. May–June. E. Ls. linear, $\frac{1}{4}$, in whorls of four, sharp-pointed, downy. Fls. small, pink, bell-shaped, in dense terminal spikes, corolla persistent, C (4), A8. Fruit a dry capsule. East Europe and Asia Minor. (Fig. 48 B.) Differs from *Erica* in the stamens, which are attached to the base of the corolla and not to a disk.

CALLUNA VULGARIS Salisb. Ling, Heather. 3. August-September. E. Ls. opposite, minute, scale-like, in four rows, keeled. Fls. purplish pink, in thin terminal spikes, corolla deeply divided into four lobes and shorter than the calyx, both being persistent in fruit, C (4), A8. Fruit a dry capsule. Europe (including Britain). (Fig. 48 P.)

Var. *alba* Sweet. Fls. white, ls. bright green.
Var. *alba aurea* Hort. Fls. white, ls. golden.
Var. *alba pilosa* Hort. Fls. white, ls. greyish.
Var. *Alportii* Kirchn. Tall, fls. crimson.
Var. *argentea* Hort. Fls. purple, ls. silvery.
Var. *aurea* Forbes. Fls. purple, ls. gold.
Var. *coccinea* Don. Fls. red, ls. greyish.
Var. *cuprea* Bean. Tall, fls. purple, ls. red to bronze in winter.
Var. *flore pleno* Hort. Fls. double, pale pink.
Var. *Foxii* Bean. Dwarf cushiony tufts, fls. pale pink.
Var. *Searlei* Bean. Tall loose feathery growth, fls. white.

CASSANDRA CALYCULATA D. Don (CHAMAEDAPHNE CALYCULATA Moench, ANDROMEDA CALYCULATA L.). Leather Leaf. 2. March–April. E. Ls. alternate, ov., $1\frac{1}{2}$, finely toothed in outer half, scurfy or scaly below. Fls. $\frac{1}{4}$, white, bell-shaped, solitary in the leaf-axils, K5, C (5), A10. Fruit a dry capsule. Northern Hemisphere. (Fig. 101 K.)

Var. *nana* Lodd. Dwarf form.

CASSIOPE. Ls. opposite, minute, scale-like, in four rows, keeled. Fls. solitary, white or pinkish, nodding, corolla deciduous, K5, C (5), A10. Fruit a dry capsule.

C. fastigiata D. Don (*Andromeda fastigiata* Wall.). Himalayan Heather. April–May. E. Ls. with silvery margin. Himalaya. (Fig. 48 Q.)

C. tetragona D. Don (*Andromeda tetragona* L.). E. Ls. without silvery margin. Arctic regions.

CLADOTHAMNUS PYROLAEFLORUS Bong. 10. June. D. Branchlets reddish, angular, hairless. Ls. alternate, obov., oblanc., 2, entire, hairless, stalkless or nearly so. Fls. 1, pink, K5, C5, A10, the corolla divided into five separate petals; solitary or in twos or threes at end of shoot. Fruit a dry capsule. West North America. (Fig. 124 F.)

CLETHRA. Ls. alternate, ov., lanc., tapering base, toothed except at base, prominently veined. Fls. white or pinkish, in terminal racemes or panicles, K5, C5, A10, the corolla deeply divided into five separate petals, ovary 3-celled. Fruit a dry capsule.

C. acuminata Michx. White Alder. 20. July–August. D. Ls. 6, long-pointed, with 10–15 pairs of veins, nearly hairless, crowded at end of shoot. Fls. in erect solitary racemes. South-east United States. (Fig. 102 B.)

C. alnifolia L. Sweet Peppermint. 8. August–September. D. Ls. obov., oblanc., 4, short-pointed, with 7–10 pairs of veins, nearly hairless. Fls. fragrant, in several racemes forming a panicle. East North America. (Fig. 102 A.)

* **C. arborea** Ait. Lily-of-the-Valley Tree. 25. August–October. E. Twigs reddish. Ls. oblanc., 6, dark green and smooth above, hairy below; stalk reddish, hairy. Fls. fragrant, in several terminal racemes. Madeira. (Fig. 102 D.)

C. barbinervis Sieb. & Zucc. (*C. canescens* Auct., not Reinw.). 6. July–September. D. Ls. obov., 5, slightly hairy below, 10–15 pairs of veins. Fls. fragrant, in several terminal racemes. China and Japan.

* **C. Delavayi** Franch. 40. August–September. D. Ls. lanc., bright green above, very downy below, 10–15 pairs of veins. Fls. ½, in one-sided solitary terminal racemes, calyx red. China. (Fig. 102 L.)

C. Fargesii Franch. 8. August–September. D. Ls. ov., oblong, 4, nearly hairless, 10–15 pairs of veins. Fls. in several terminal racemes. Differs from *C. barbinervis* in the hairy staminal filaments and more pointed sepals. China.

C. tomentosa Lam. 8. August–September. D. Ls. obov., dark green and rough above, pale and woolly-felted below, with 7–10 pairs of veins. Fls. fragrant, in one or more terminal racemes. South-east United States. (Fig. 102 C.)

DABOECIA CANTABRICA Koch (MENZIESIA POLIFOLIA Juss.). St. Dabeoc's Heath. 1. May–September. E. Ls. alternate, lanc., ½, entire, dark glossy green above, white-felted below. Fls. ½, rosy purple, egg-shaped, in terminal racemes, K4, C (4), A8, corolla deciduous. Fruit a dry capsule. Ireland, West France, Spain, Portugal, Azores. (Fig. 48 C.)

Var. *alba* Dipp. Fls. white.
Var. *bicolor* Dipp. Some fls. white, some purple.

ELLIOTTIA RACEMOSA Muhl. 20. July–August. D. Ls. alternate, ov., lanc., 4, entire, thin, hairy below; stalk slender and swollen at the base, nearly concealing the bud. Fls. ½, white, fragrant, in terminal racemes or panicles, K4, C (4), A8, petals recurved and nearly separate. Fruit unknown (increases by root suckers). Georgia. (Fig. 122 D.)

ENKIANTHUS. Branches in whorls. Ls. alternate or whorled, ov., finely toothed. Fls. ¼, bell-shaped, in drooping clusters, K5, C (5), A10. Fruit a dry capsule.

ENKIANTHUS—*continued*

E. campanulatus Nichols. 20. May. D. Fls. creamy yellow veined with red. Japan. (Fig. 55 G.)

Var. *albiflorus* Makino (*pallidiflorus* Craib). Fls. nearly white.

Var. *Palibinii* Bean. Fls. red.

E. cernuus Makino. 15. May. D. Fls. white, corolla lobes toothed. Japan.

Var. *rubens* Makino. Fls. deep red.

E. deflexus Schneid. (*E. himalaicus* Hook. f.). 20. May. D. Like *E. campanulatus*, but with larger and showier flowers and hairy ovary and style. Himalaya, West China.

E. chinensis (Franch.) has salmon-red flowers.

E. perulatus Schneid. (*E. japonicus* Hook. f.). 6. May. D. Fls. white, corolla lobes entire. Fruit-stalks straight. Japan.

EPIGAEA REPENS L. May Flower. ½. May. E. A creeping shrub with hairy rooting stems. Ls. alternate, roundish ov., 3, leathery, distantly toothed, with short bristles on both sides. Fls. ½, white or pinkish, bell-shaped, in terminal heads. Fruit a dry capsule. North America. (Fig. 102 E.)

ERICA. Heath, Heather. Ls. usually whorled, linear, ¼ or less, blunt-ended, margins recurved. Fls. small, pink, white, or purple, egg-shaped, K (4), C (4), A8, the corolla persistent. Fruit a dry capsule.

(*a*) *Ls. mostly alternate*

E. lusitanica Rudolphi. 12. February–May. E. Fls. white, fragrant. Spain and Portugal. (Fig. 48 F.)

(*b*) *Ls. in whorls of three*

E. arborea L. Tree Heath. 20. March–May. E. Branchlets with branched hairs. Fls. white, fragrant. Mediterranean region.

E. ciliaris L. Fringed Heath. 1. June–October. E. Ls. hairy, whitish below. Fls. rosy red, in terminal spikes. South-west Europe (including Cornwall and Dorset). (Fig. 48 J.)

E. cinerea L. Scotch or Grey Heath, Bell Heather. 1½. July–September. E. Ls. hairless. Fls. bright purple, in terminal clusters. West Europe (including Britain). (Fig. 48 G.)

E. scoparia L. Besom Heath. 10. May–June. E. Fls. greenish. Central France.

E. Veitchii Bean. 20. March–May. Like *E. arborea*, but the branchlets have simple hairs. Hybrid.

(*c*) *Ls. in whorls of four or more*

E. australis L. Spanish Heath. 6. May. E. Young stems very downy. Fls. purplish red, in small clusters. Spain.

E. carnea L. ½. February–May. E. Young stems hairless. Ls. hairless. Fls. rosy red, with projecting anthers of a darker colour, solitary or in pairs in the leaf-axils. Europe. (Fig. 48 E.)

Var. *alba* Zabel (*E. herbacea* Auct., not L.). Fls. white.

E. darleyensis Bean. 2. November–May. E. Like *E. carnea*, but growing taller. Hybrid.

ERICA—*continued*

E. Mackayi Hook. 2. July–August. E. Ls. ov., oblong, hairless above. Fls. pink, in terminal clusters, ovary hairless. Ireland and Spain.

E. mediterranea L. 10. April–May. Like *E. carnea* and *E. darleyensis*, but with a single upright main stem. South-west France and Spain.

E. terminalis Salisb. (*E. stricta* Ait.). 9. June–September. E. Ls. minutely downy. Fls. pink, in terminal clusters. South Europe.

E. Tetralix L. Cross-leaved Heath. 1½. June–September. E. Ls. hairy, white below, arranged in the form of a cross. Fls. pink, in dense terminal clusters, ovary hairy. Europe (including Britain). (Fig. 48 H.)

Var. *mollis* Bean. Ls. greyish white.

E. vagans L. Cornish Heath. 2½. August–September. E. Ls. hairless. Fls. pinkish purple, in long terminal spikes. South-west Europe (including Cornwall). (Fig. 48 D.)

GAULNETTYA WISLEYENSIS (March.) Rehd. 1½. June. E. Ls. 1, dark green, minutely round-toothed. Fls. ¼, white, in terminal and axillary racemes. A cross between *Gaultheria* and *Pernettya*.

GAULTHERIA. Branchlets zigzagged. Ls. alternate, ov., stiff, toothed, stalk red and hairy. Fls. ¼, pinkish white, egg-shaped, K (5), C (5), A10. Fruit a berry.

G. Miqueliana Takeda (*G. pyroloides* Miq.). 1. May–June. E. Ls. ov., 1, toothed, crowded at end of shoot. Fls. in racemes. Berry ½, white or pinkish. Japan.

G. procumbens L. Creeping Wintergreen, Checkerberry, Partridge Berry. ½. July–August. E. Roots creeping and sending up thin erect stems with a small cluster of leaves at the top. Ls. ov., 1, minutely toothed. Fls. solitary. Berry ¼, red. North America. (Fig. 102 N.)

G. Shallon Pursh. Shallon. 6. May–June. E. Spreading by underground stems. Branchlets reddish, bristly. Ls. ov., 4, pointed, toothed. Fls. in clammy racemes, each flower in the axil of a hooded bract. Berry ¼, black, hairy, juicy. West North America. (Fig. 102 M.)

G. trichophylla Royle. ½. June. E. Aromatic. Ls. ov., oblong, ½, glossy, hairless except on margins, crowded. Fls. pink, bell-shaped, solitary. Berry ½, blue. Himalaya.

G. Veitchiana Craib. 3. May–June. E. Branchlets hairy. Ls. ov., oblong, 3, minutely toothed, dark green and wrinkled above, hairy on veins below. Fls. white, in racemes. Berry ½, dark blue. China.

KALMIA. Mountain Laurel. Ls. crowded radially at end of branches, ov., lanc., entire. Fls. saucer-shaped, in branched or unbranched clusters, K (5), C (5), A10. Fruit a dry egg-shaped capsule.

K. angustifolia L. Sheep Laurel. 4. June. E. Ls. opposite or in threes, ov., 2, bright green above, hairless, short-stalked. Fls. ¼, pink, in rounded clusters. North America.

K. cuneata Michx. 4. June. E. Ls. opposite, obov., 2. Fls. ½, white, slender-stalked, in few-flowered axillary clusters. North America.

K. latifolia L. Calico Bush. 10. June. E. Ls. alternate, ov., lanc., 5, glossy green above, stalk red. Fls. ¾, white to deep rose. North America. (Fig. 124 G.)

K. polifolia Wangh. (*K. glauca* Ait.). 2. April. E. Ls. opposite or in

KALMIA—*continued*
threes, ov., 1½, dark glossy green above, white below. Fls. ½, rosy purple, in flattish clusters. North America.

LEDUM. Ls. alternate, entire. Fls. ½, white, with separate spreading petals, K5, C5, A5–11, in terminal clusters. Fruit a dry capsule.

L. glandulosum Nutt. 3. May. E. Ls. lanc., 1½, dark green above, bluish green below. North America.

L. columbianum (Piper) is practically the same.

L. groenlandicum Oed. (*L. latifolium* Ait.). Labrador Tea. 2. May. E. Stem and lower side of leaves rusty-felted. Ls. ov., lanc., 2, blunt-ended, midrib not visible below. North America.

L. palustre L. Wild Rosemary, Marsh Ledum. 4. May. E. Stem and lower side of leaves rusty-felted. Ls. linear, 1, midrib visible below. Arctic regions. (Fig. 52 A.)

LEIOPHYLLUM BUXIFOLIUM Ell. Sand Myrtle. 1½. May–June. E. Ls. opposite and alternate, ov., ½, entire, leathery, glossy, hairless. Fls. ¼, white or pinkish, with separate spreading petals, K5, C5, A10, in crowded terminal clusters. East North America. (Fig. 67 F.)

LEUCOTHOE. Ls. alternate, lanc., finely toothed, short-stalked. Fls. ¼, white, bell-shaped, in racemes or panicles, K (5), C (5), A10. Fruit a dry capsule.

(*a*) *Deciduous*

L. racemosa Gray (*Andromeda racemosa* L.). 6. June. Branchlets slender, erect, downy. Ls. 2, firm, short-pointed, shallowly round-toothed, downy on veins below. Fls. in erect 1-sided racemes. North America. (Fig. 102 J.)

L. recurva Gray (*Andromeda recurva* Buckl.). 5. May–June. Branchlets spreading. Ls. 4, thin but firm, short-pointed. Fls. in curved racemes. Virginia to Alabama.

(*b*) *Evergreen*

L. axillaris D. Don (*Andromeda axillaris* Lam.). 6. April–May. Branches arching. Ls. 4, short-pointed, distantly toothed, glossy above. Fls. in axillary racemes. South-east United States. (Fig. 102 F.)

L. Catesbaei Gray (*Andromeda Catesbaei* Walt.). 6. May. Branchlets slender, arching, zigzagged. Ls. 5, leathery, long-pointed, closely spine-toothed, a few hairs below. Fls. in axillary racemes. South-east United States. (Fig. 102 G.)

L. Davisiae Torr. 3. May. Branchlets stout, erect, hairless. Ls. 2, firm, short-pointed, minutely toothed, hairless. Fls. in terminal panicles. North America. (Fig. 102 H.)

LOISELEURIA PROCUMBENS Desv. (AZALEA PROCUMBENS L.). ½. June. E. Ls. opposite, ov., ¼, entire, whitish below, margins recurved. Fls. ¼, white or pinkish, erect, bell- or star-shaped, in terminal clusters, K5, C (5), A5. Fruit a dry capsule. North America, North Asia, North Europe (including Scottish Highlands). (Fig. 48 K.)

LYONIA LIGUSTRINA DC. (ANDROMEDA LIGUSTRINA Muhl., XOLISMA LIGUSTRINA Brit. & Br.). Male-berry. 8. July. D. Branchlets zigzagged. Ls. alternate, ov., lanc., 3, entire, pointed, downy on both sides, prominently veined, very shortly stalked. Fls. very small, round, dull white, in few-flowered terminal racemes, K (5), C (5), A10. Fruit a dry capsule. North America. (Fig. 122 E.)

MENZIESIA PILOSA Juss. 6. May. D. Bark peeling, branchlets hairy. Ls. alternate, ov., 2, entire, thin, with scattered hairs. Fls. $\frac{1}{4}$, white, bell-shaped, in few-flowered clusters at end of short side shoots, A8–10. Fruit a dry capsule. East North America. (Fig. 124 D.)

M. glabella (Gray) has obov. leaves and small egg-shaped 4-parted flowers. North America.

OXYDENDRON ARBOREUM DC. (ANDROMEDA ARBOREA L.). Sorrel Tree. 50. August–September. D. Branchlets hairless. Ls. alternate, ov., lanc., 6, minutely toothed, thin, hairless or nearly so. Fls. $\frac{1}{4}$, white, bell-shaped, in terminal panicles, K5, C (5), A10. North America. (Fig. 102 K.)

PERNETTYA MUCRONATA Gaud. Prickly Heath. 5. May–June. E. Stems suckering freely; branchlets wiry. Ls. alternate, ov., $\frac{3}{4}$, spiny-pointed, toothed, leathery. Fls. $\frac{1}{4}$, white, bell-shaped, nodding, solitary in the l.-axils, K (5), C (5), A10. Fruit a berry, $\frac{1}{2}$, white, pink, lilac, crimson, purple, or black. South America. (Fig. 103 A.)

P. pumila (Hook.) is smaller, being only a few inches high. Ls. $\frac{1}{4}$, blunt-ended. Berries white or pink. South Chile and Falkland Is.

PHYLLODOCE. Low heath-like shrubs. Ls. alternate, linear, $\frac{1}{2}$, blunt-ended, toothed, crowded, margins recurved. Fls. bell- or egg-shaped, slender-stalked, solitary or in terminal clusters, K (4–6), C (4–6), A8–12. Fruit a dry capsule.

P. Breweri Hell. 1. May. E. Fls. $\frac{1}{2}$, purple, broadly bell-shaped. California.

P. coerulea Bab. $\frac{3}{4}$. May. E. Fls. $\frac{1}{4}$, bluish purple, egg-shaped. Alpine regions of Northern Hemisphere. (Fig. 48 A.)

P. empetriformis D. Don. $\frac{3}{4}$. May. E. Fls. $\frac{1}{4}$, reddish purple, egg-shaped, solitary in the terminal l.-axils. West North America.

P. nipponica Makino. $\frac{3}{4}$. May. E. Fls. $\frac{1}{4}$, pinkish white, bell-shaped, solitary in the terminal leaf-axils. Japan.

PIERIS. Ls. alternate. Fls. white, pitcher-shaped, usually in terminal panicles or racemes, K5, C (5), A10. Fruit a dry capsule. In *Pieris* proper the anthers have reflexed awns; species without awns are sometimes referred to a separate genus, XOLISMA.

(a) Ls. entire

P. lucida Rehd. (*Andromeda coriacea* Ait.). Fetter Bush. 6. June. E. Branchlets angled. Ls. ov., obov., 3, glossy green, margins recurved. Fls. $\frac{1}{4}$, white to pink. South-east United States.

P. Mariana Benth. & Hook. f. (*Andromeda Mariana* L.). Stagger Bush. 6. June. D. Branchlets hairless. Ls. ov., lanc., 3, thin but stiff, hairless, veins prominent below. Fls. $\frac{1}{2}$, nodding, in lateral racemes. East United States. (Fig. 122 G.)

* **P. ovalifolia** D. Don (*Andromeda ovalifolia* Wall.). 20. June. D. Branchlets hairless. Ls. ov., 5, firm, conspicuously veined, hairless or nearly so. Fls. $\frac{1}{4}$, nodding, in one-sided terminal and axillary racemes. Himalaya. (Fig. 122 F.)

PIERIS—*continued*

(*b*) *Ls. toothed*

P. floribunda Benth. & Hook. f. (*Andromeda floribunda* Pursh). 6. March–April. E. Branchlets stiff, hairy. Ls. lanc., 3, minutely toothed, glossy green above, hairy. Fls. ¼, in erect panicles. South-east United States. (Fig. 103 E.)

P. formosa D. Don (*Andromeda formosa* Wall.). 20. May. E. Branchlets hairless. Ls. lanc., 7, leathery, glossy, minutely toothed, hairless. Fls. ¼, nodding, in drooping panicles, sepals green. Himalaya, China. (Fig. 103 D.)

P. Forrestii Harr. 10. April. E. Branchlets hairless, reddish. Ls. lanc., 3, hairless, bronze to scarlet when young. Fls. ½, fragrant, in drooping panicles, sepals pale green to whitish. Upper Burma and China.

P. japonica D. Don (*Andromeda japonica* Thunb.). 10. March–April. E. Branchlets brown, rough with scars of fallen ls., often opposite or whorled. Ls. ov., lanc., 3, hairless, crowded radially at end of shoot. Fls. ¼, in drooping racemes. Japan. (Fig. 103 C.)

P. taiwanensis Hayata. 6. March–April. E. Branchlets yellowish green, hairless. Ls. lanc., 1½, finely round-toothed, pale green below, bronze when young. Fls. ¼, nodding. Formosa.

RHODODENDRON. Shrubs or small trees with conspicuous pointed, many-scaled buds, the terminal one usually in the centre of a group of radiating leaves. Ls. alternate, entire. Fls. showy, funnel-shaped or bell-shaped, solitary or in pairs or terminal clusters; ovary 3-10-celled, with a long style. Fruit a dry splitting capsule. A large genus containing an immense number of species and hybrids, of which there is not space to list more than a small fraction.

(I) Deciduous or Half Evergreen; Stamens usually five

(Azalea Section)

R. azaleoides Desf. 6. June–July. ½ E. Branchlets downy and sticky. Ls. oblanc., 3, dark glossy green above, glaucous below, hairless. Fls. 1, white tinged with lilac, fragrant, in terminal clusters. Hybrid.

R. indicum Sweet (*Azalea indica* L.). Indian Azalea. 6. May. Young shoots bristly. Ls. ov., obov., 3, bristly. Fls. 2, red, solitary or in pairs, anthers purple. China and Japan. (Fig. 122 H.)

R. japonicum Suringar (*R. molle* Sieb. & Zucc.). Japanese Azalea. 8. April–May. Ls. lanc., 4, dark green, slightly hairy. Fls. 3, pink or red, in clusters appearing before the ls. Japan. (Fig. 122 K.)

R. luteum Sweet (*Azalea pontica* L.). 10. May. Buds with sharply pointed scales. Ls. lanc., 5, hairy on margins and midrib below. Fls. 1½, yellow, in crowded clusters. Caucasus. (Fig. 122 J.)

R. molle Don (*R. sinense* Sweet, *Azalea mollis* Blume). Chinese Azalea. 8. April–May. Branchlets soft-felted. Ls. lanc., 4, velvety-felted below. Fls. 3, yellow, in clusters appearing before the leaves. China. (Fig. 122 N.)

R. occidentale Gray (*Azalea occidentalis* Torr. & Gray). 8. June. Ls. ov., lanc., 4, glossy green above, with scattered hairs. Fls. 3, white, with

RHODODENDRON—*continued*

yellow blotch, in terminal clusters appearing before the leaves. West North America. (Fig. 122 P.)

R. quinquefolium Bisset & S. Moore. 3. April–May. Ls. 1½, in whorls of five at end of shoot. Fls. 1½, white or pinkish, solitary or in pairs, stamens ten. Japan. (Fig. 70 K.)

Var. *roseum* Rehd. (R. *pentaphyllum* Maxim.). Fls. deep pink.

R. Rhodora Gmel. (*Rhodora canadensis* L.). 4. April. Ls. ov., lanc., 2, bristly above and on margins, downy or hairless below. Fls. 1, rosy purple, 2-lipped, in lateral and terminal clusters, stamens ten. East North America. (Fig. 122 O.)

R. rhombicum Miq. (*Azalea rhombica* Kuntze). 4. April. Ls. diamond-shaped, 1½, dark dull green. Fls. 1½, purple, solitary or in pairs. Japan.

R. speciosum Sweet (*Azalea speciosa* Willd.). 6. May. Branchlets hairy. Ls. ov., 1½, slightly hairy. Fls. 2, scarlet, with yellow blotch, slender-tubed, the stamens projecting far beyond the petals. South-east United States.

R. Vaseyi Gray. 15. April–May. Ls. ov., 4, green on both sides, scattered. Fls. 1, pink, spotted with orange, in terminal clusters appearing before the leaves, stamens seven. Carolina.

R. viscosum Torr. (*Azalea viscosa* L.). Swamp Honeysuckle. 8. June. Ls. obov., 2, margins bristly. Fls. 1, white or pink, covered with sticky hairs, in clusters. North America. (Fig. 122 M.)

(II) Evergreen, Stamens usually ten or more (Rhododendron Section)

(*a*) *Ls. with small scurfy scales on under surface*

R. ambiguum Hemsl. 6. May. Ls. lanc., 1½, dark green above, blue-grey below. Fls. 1, primrose-yellow, stamens eight. West China.

R. Anthopogon D. Don. 2. April. Branchlets hairy. Ls. ov., 1½, glossy green above, brown below, aromatic when crushed. Fls. 1, sulphur-yellow, in small terminal clusters, stamens five to eight. Himalaya. (Fig. 122 L.)

* **R. arboreum** Sm. 40. February–March. Ls. lanc., 7, silvery below. Fls. 2, blood-red, in terminal hemispherical heads. Himalaya. (Fig. 123 C.)

Var. *album* Hort. Fls. white, ls. rust-coloured below.

The parent of many tall hybrids in various shades of red and pink.

R. arbutifolium Rehd. 4. May. Ls. lanc., 2, dull dark green above, with minute glistening silvery scales below. Fls. 1, rose-coloured. Hybrid.

R. calostratum Balf. & Ward. 1. May. Ls. ov., ¾, edged with bristles. Fls. 1, pink or purple, in terminal pairs. Upper Burma.

R. cephalanthum Franch. 3. April. Ls. ov., ¾. Fls. ½, white, stamens five. West China.

R. cinnabarinum Hook. f. 10. May. Ls. ov., 4, metallic green above. Fls. 1½, dull red, funnel-shaped, drooping, in terminal heads. East Himalaya. (Fig. 123 A.)

R. concinnum Hemsl. May. Ls. 2, dark green above. Fls. 1, rosy purple, in few-flowered clusters. West China.

RHODODENDRON—*continued*

R. dauricum L. 6. January–February. Ls. ov., 1, rounded at end, dark glossy green above. Fls. 1, rosy purple, saucer-shaped, solitary or in pairs. Manchuria.

R. Davidsonianum Rehd. & Wils. 6. May. Ls. lanc., 2, scurfy with brown scales below. Fls. 1, pink, solitary or in few-flowered clusters. West China.

R. ferrugineum L. Rose des Alpes, Alpenrose. 3. June. Ls. lanc., 1½, glossy green above, rusty below. Fls. ½, red, in terminal clusters. Alps. (Fig. 123 B.)

R. flavidum Franch. 2. April. Branchlets scaly. Ls. ov., ¾, rounded base, dark green, scaly on both sides. Fls. 1, yellow, in terminal few-flowered clusters. West Szechuen.

R. glaucum Hook. f. 6. May. Ls. ov., lanc., 3, dark dull green above, scaly white or brown below, margins recurved. Fls. 1, rosy red, in terminal clusters. East Himalaya.

R. Hanceanum Hemsl. 4. March. Ls. lanc., 4, hard, slender-pointed, dark green and scaly above and below. Fls. 1, white or yellow, funnel-shaped, corolla deeply lobed. China.

R. hippophaeoides Balf. & W. W. Sm. 4. April. Ls. narrow-oblong, 1, grey beneath, giving acrid odour when crushed (Bean). Fls. ¾, bluish purple, saucer-shaped, in terminal clusters. Yunnan.

R. hirsutum L. Rose des Alpes, Alpenrose. 3. June. Like R. *ferrugineum*, but stem and leaves bristly. Alps.

R. impeditum Balf. & W. W. Sm. May. Ls. oblanc., ½, metallic green above, crowded at end of shoot. Fls. ¾, bright purplish blue. Yunnan.

R. intricatum Franch. 1. April. Ls. roundish ov., ¼, dark green, both sides covered with glistening scales. Fls. ½, lilac, borne in profusion. West China.

R. lepidotum Wall. 2. June. Ls. ov., lanc., 1½, dotted with tiny scales. Fls. 1, rosy crimson, spotted, saucer-shaped, solitary or in few-flowered clusters. Himalaya.

R. moupinense Franch. 3. March. Branchlets hairy. Ls. ov., 1½, leathery, ending in a minute point, dark green above, pale below. Fls. 2, white or pink, with purple or yellow spots, usually in 3-flowered clusters. China. (Fig. 123 E.)

R. myrtilloides Balf. & Ward. ½. May. Branchlets warted. Ls. obov., ½. Fls. ½, reddish purple, bell-shaped, solitary on long stalks. North-east Burma.

R. Nobleanum Lindl. See under (*b*) below.

R. orthocladum Balf. & Forrest. 2. April. A twiggy bush with small scaly leaves and numerous pale lilac flowers. Yunnan.

R. polylepis Franch. 6. May. Ls. narrowly lanc., 3, dark green above. Fls. 1, purplish pink, with brown spots, in 2-4-flowered terminal clusters. China.

R. praecox Carr. 4. March. Ls. ov., 2, dark glossy green, bristly above. Fls. 2, rosy purple. Hybrid. (Fig. 123 D.)

R. prostratum W. W. Sm. Prostrate. April. Ls. ov., ½, blunt-ended, reddish below. Fls. 1, rosy purple, saucer-shaped, solitary or in pairs. China.

RHODODENDRON—*continued*

R. racemosum Franch. 6. April–May. Ls. ov., 1, white below dotted with brown scales. Fls. 1, pink, in axillary and terminal clusters. West China.

R. radicans Balf. & Forrest. $\frac{1}{4}$. May. Ls. oblanc., $\frac{1}{2}$. Fls. $\frac{3}{4}$, purple, solitary. South-east Tibet.

R. rubiginosum Franch. May. Ls. 2, dark green above, rusty below. Fls. 1, pink, in few-flowered terminal clusters. Yunnan.

R. spiciferum Franch. 2. April–May. Ls. lanc., 1, dark green and wrinkled above, margins recurved. Fls. $\frac{3}{4}$, rosy pink, in terminal clusters. China.

R. yunnanense Franch. 12. May. Ls. lanc., 3, bright green above, hairy on margins, slightly scaly on both sides. Fls. $1\frac{1}{2}$, pink, with brown spots, in few-flowered clusters. China.

(*b*) *Ls. felted or woolly on under surface*

R. brachycarpum Don. 6. June. Branchlets downy. Ls. narrow-oblong, 4, base rounded, stout-stalked. Fls. 2, creamy white flushed with pink, in large round trusses. Japan.

R. campanulatum D. Don. 12. April–May. Bark peeling; branchlets hairless. Ls. ov., 5, green above, reddish brown below. Fls. 2, pale purplish pink or lilac, in loose clusters. Himalaya. (Fig. 123 F.)

R. caucasicum Pall. 2. April–May. Ls. ov., 4, dark green above, red below, stalk short. Fls. 2, yellowish white or pale lilac, in terminal clusters. Caucasus.

Var. *sulphureum* Hort. Fls. sulphur-yellow.

* **R. coriaceum** Franch. 25. March. Ls. oblanc., 10, dark green above, grey-white below. Fls. 1, white or rose-tinted, with crimson blotch, in loose trusses, stamens ten to fourteen. China.

R. Falconeri Hook. f. 30. March–April. Ls. ov., lanc., 12, thick, strongly veined, dark green and wrinkled above, rusty below. Fls. 2, corolla 8-10-lobed, creamy white, with dark purple blotch at base, stamens twelve to sixteen. Himalaya. (Fig. 123 H.)

R. fictolacteum Balf. 30. April–May. Ls. lanc., 8, dark green above, red below, stalk felted. Fls. 2, white, corolla 7-8-lobed, in large trusses, stamens fourteen to sixteen. China. (Fig. 123 J.)

R. floccigerum Franch. 5. April. Ls. lanc., 3, pointed, tapering base, green above, rusty-woolly below. Fls. 1, red to yellowish red, with black anthers. Yunnan.

R. fulgens Hook. f. 12. February–March. Ls. ov., 4, red below. Fls. 1, blood-red, in hemispherical trusses. East Himalaya.

R. fulvoides Balf. & Forrest. 20. April. Young shoots brown-felted. Ls. ov., 8, leathery, dark green above, yellow below, midrib prominent. Fls. 1, white or pink, with crimson blotch, in round trusses. China.

R. fulvum Balf. & W. W. Sm. 20. April. Like R. *fulvoides*, but leaves red below. China.

R. haematodes Franch. 6. May. Ls. obov., 2, reddish brown below. Fls. $1\frac{1}{2}$, scarlet, in terminal clusters. China.

R. Hodgsonii Hook. f. 20. Bark peeling. Ls. lanc., 12, very leathery, dark green and glossy above, red below, stalk very thick. Fls. 2, rosy

RHODODENDRON—*continued*

lilac, corolla 8-10-lobed, in round trusses, stamens fifteen to twenty. East Himalaya.

R. insigne Hemsl. & Wils. 6. May. Ls. lanc., 4, dark green above, pale green below. Fls. 1, pink, in few-flowered terminal clusters. Yunnan.

R. Nobleanum Lindl. 15. January–March. Ls. lanc., 6, thin, brown below. Fls. 1½, bright rose, in hemispherical trusses. Hybrid. (Fig. 123 G.)

R. Smirnowii Trautv. 4. May. Ls. narrow-oblong, 4, tapering base, dark green above, white- or brown-felted below. Fls. 3, bright purplish rose, the petals with frilled margins. South Caucasus.

(*c*) *Ls. with scattered hairs or bristles*

* **R. ciliatum** Hook. f. March–April. Ls. ov., 4. Fls. 2, pink, in few-flowered clusters. East Himalaya. (Fig. 124 A.)

R. mucronatum Don (*R. ledifolium* Don, *Azalea ledifolia* Hook.). 6. May–June. Ls. lanc., 2½, hairy all over. Fls. 2, white, solitary or in pairs or threes. China and Japan.

R. obtusum Planch. (*R. amoenum* Planch., *Azalea amoena* Lindl.). 4. April–May. Ls. ov., 1, dark glossy green. Fls. ¾, rosy purple to orange-red; stamens five. Japan. (Fig. 123 K.)

Var. *album* Schneid. Fls. white.

Var. *Kaempferi* Wils. (*R. Kaempferi* Planch.). Fls. red, sepals large.

R. pulchrum Sweet. 6. May. Ls. ov., 2. Fls. 1½, bright carmine, in pairs at end of shoots. Hybrid.

(*d*) *Ls. hairless and smooth*

R. barbatum Wall. 20. March. Ls. lanc., 9, pointed, dark dull green above, pale green below. Fls. 1½, blood-red, in hemispherical trusses. Himalaya.

R. calophytum Franch. 30. April. Ls. obov., oblanc., 8. Fls. 2½, white or pink, with dark crimson blotch, in rounded trusses, stamens sixteen to twenty-two. West China and Tibet.

R. campylocarpum Hook. f. 8. May. Ls. ov., 4, fine-pointed, dark glossy green above, blue-white below. Fls. 3, pale yellow, bell-shaped, slightly fragrant, in loose terminal clusters. East Himalaya.

R. catawbiense Michx. 10. June. Ls. ov., lanc., 6, dark glossy green above, pale green or whitish below. Fls. 2½, lilac, in large clusters. South-east United States.

R. croceum Balf. & W. W. Sm. 20. May. Ls. ov., 4, heart-shaped base, pale green below. Fls. 3, yellow, with crimson blotch, in 7-8-flowered clusters. China. (Fig. 124 B.)

R. decorum Franch. 12. April–May. Ls. ov., lanc., 6, thick, grey-green above, glaucous below. Fls. 2, white to pink, spotted with green, corolla 5-7-lobed, stamens twelve to sixteen. West China.

R. discolor Franch. 18. June–July. Ls. lanc., 8, dark green above, whitish below. Fls. 3, white or purplish; corolla funnel shaped, 6-7-lobed, stamens twelve to sixteen. Central China.

R. Forrestii Balf. ¼. April. Creeping plant with small round leaves and solitary deep crimson flowers. South-east Tibet, West China.

RHODODENDRON—*continued*

R. Fortunei Lindl. 12. May. Ls. ov., oblong, 8, pale green above, glaucous below; stalk stout, purple. Fls. 3, white or pinkish, corolla 5-7-lobed, in loose terminal clusters, stamens fourteen to sixteen. China.

* **R. Griffithianum** Wight (*R. Aucklandii* Hook. f.). 15. Stems smooth, cinnamon-coloured. Ls. lanc., 9, pale green above, glaucous below. Fls. 4, white or pinkish, widely bell-shaped, slightly fragrant, in loose clusters, stamens ten to sixteen. East Himalaya.

R. norbitonense W. W. Sm. 6. May. Ls. narrowly ov., 2, dark green above. Fls. 2, creamy yellow, in round trusses, anthers pale violet. Hybrid.

Var. *Broughtonianum* Rehd. (*R. Broughtonii aureum* Hort.). Young stems and leaves downy. Fls. primrose-yellow, spotted brown.

R. orbiculare Decne. (*R. rotundifolium* David). 6. April–May. Branches stout, purplish, glandular. Ls. broadly heart-shaped, almost circular, 5, stiff, dark green above, white below, stalk purple. Fls. 2, rosy red, bell-shaped, stamens fourteen. West China.

R. ponticum L. 15. May–June. Ls. lanc., 9, dark glossy green above, pale green below. Fls. 2, purple, in terminal heads. Spain, Portugal, Asia Minor, naturalized in Britain. (Fig. 124 C.)

* **R. sino-grande** Balf. & W. W. Sm. 30. Young shoots stout, silvery. Ls. ov., 16, dull green above, silvery below. Fls. 2, white, with crimson blotch, corolla 10-lobed, in large terminal clusters, stamens eighteen. China.

R. Souliei Franch. 8. May. Young shoots purplish, clammy. Ls. ov., 3, heart-shaped base, blunt-ended, glaucous and metallic. Fls. 3, white or pink, saucer-shaped, corolla 5-6-lobed, in terminal clusters, stamens eight to ten. China.

R. Thomsonii Hook. f. 12. April. Ls. roundish ov., 4, dark green above, blue-white below. Fls. 2, blood-red, bell-shaped, in loose clusters. East Himalaya. (Fig. 123 L.)

R. Wardii W. W. Sm. 20. May. Ls. ov., 3, dark green above, glaucous below, heart-shaped base. Fls. 2, yellow, in terminal clusters, the flower-buds tinged with red. South-east Tibet and China.

RHODOTHAMNUS CHAMAECISTUS Reichb. (RHODODENDRON CHAMAECISTUS L.). 1. April. E. Ls. ov., ½, edged with conspicuous bristles, closely set on branches. Fls. 1, pink, petals spreading, in terminal few-flowered clusters, K5, C (5), A10. Fruit a woody capsule. Austrian Alps. (Fig. 124 H.)

THERORHODION CAMTSCHATICUM Small (RHODODENDRON CAMTSCHATICUM Pall.). ½. May–June. D. Spreading by underground suckers. Ls. ov., 2, bristly below and conspicuously so on the margins, stalkless. Fls. 1½, crimson, solitary or in pairs on an erect leafy stem, petals spreading, K (5), C (5), A10. Fruit a dry capsule. North Asia and Alaska. (Fig. 124 J.)

TRIPETALEIA PANICULATA Sieb. & Zucc. (ELLIOTTIA PANICULATA Benth. & Hook.). 6. July–August. D. Branchlets reddish brown, angled. Ls. alternate, ov., 2, entire, hairless or nearly so, short-stalked. Fls. ½, white or pinkish, K3, C3, A6, the corolla divided into three distinct petals, in terminal panicles or racemes. Fruit a small capsule. Japan. (Fig. 124 E.)

ZENOBIA PULVERULENTA Poll. (Z. SPECIOSA D. Don, ANDROMEDA PULVERULENTA Bartr.). 6. June–July. D. Ls. ov., 2, shallowly and distantly toothed, blunt-ended, hairless, usually covered with white bloom. Fls. ¼, white, bell-shaped, drooping at end of long stalks in axillary clusters, K (5), C (5), A10. Fruit a dry round capsule with a long, persistent style. South-east United States. (Fig. 103 B.)

Family 60. **EPACRIDACEAE.** K5, C (5), A5, G (5)

Low heath-like shrubby plants differing from the two previous families in the stamens, in which the anthers are 1-celled and open by longitudinal slits. Fruit a berry.

Leucopogon Fraseri A. Cunn. Australian Beard Heath. 1. E. Ls. alternate, linear, lanc., ½, sharp-pointed, glossy above, veined below. Fls. ½, white, solitary in the leaf-axils. Fruit ¼, a dry, oblong, yellowish orange berry. Australia. (Fig. 122 C.)

Family 61. **DIAPENSIACEAE.** K (5), C (5), A (5), G (3)

Prostrate shrubby plants. Stamens attached to the base of the corolla or joined into a tube; anthers 2-celled, opening by longitudinal slits. Fruit a dry capsule.

Diapensia lapponica L. ¼. June–July. E. Ls. opposite, obov., ½, entire, crowded in rosette-like tufts. Fls. ¾, white, bell-shaped, solitary on a stalk up to 1 long. Alpine and Arctic regions of Northern Hemisphere. (Fig. 67 E.)

Pyxidanthera barbulata Michx. Flowering Moss. Creeping. April–May. E. Ls. alternate, oblanc., ¼, slightly hairy near base. Fls. ½, white or pink, bell-shaped, stalkless. East North America. (Fig. 49 B.)

Family 62. **PLUMBAGINACEAE.** K (5), C (5), A5, G1

Shrubby or herbaceous. Ls. alternate, without stipules. Fls. regular, the calyx angled or winged and often coloured; stamens attached to the corolla; ovary 1-celled, containing one basal ovule, styles five. Fruit a dry capsule. Statice, thrift, and sea lavender belong to this family.

CERATOSTIGMA. Leadwort, Shrubby Plumbago. Ls. alternate, entire, covered with forward-pointing hairs or bristles. Fls. bright blue, in terminal heads. Fruit a dry capsule.

- **C. Griffithii** Clarke. 3. August–September. D. Ls. obov., 1, short-pointed, dull green, with purplish margins. Fls. ½. Himalaya. (Fig. 124 M.)
- **C. minus** Stapf. 3. August–October. D. Ls. obov., 1, blunt-ended, bristly below and on margins. Fls. ½, in terminal and axillary heads, calyx red. West China.
- **C. Willmottianum** Stapf. 4. July–November. D. Ls. diamond-shaped, long-pointed. Fls. ¾. China.

Family 63. **MYRSINACEAE.** K (5), C (5), A5, G1

Trees or shrubs with gland-dotted leaves. No stipules. Fls. regular, style one; ovary 1-celled, with one or more ovules. Fruit a berry.

* Ardisia japonica Blume. 1. August–September. E. Ls. whorled, ov., 3, tapered at both ends, toothed, glossy green, hairless. Fls. ½, white, star-shaped,

solitary or in few-flowered clusters in the leaf-axils. Berry $\frac{1}{4}$, red or white. China and Japan. (Fig. 103 G.)

MYRSINE AFRICANA L. Summer. E. Branchlets angled, downy. Ls. alternate, ov., $\frac{3}{4}$, tapered at base, toothed in outer half, glossy green, hairless, closely set on the branches. Fls. very small, pale brown, unisexual, in stalkless axillary clusters. Berry $\frac{1}{4}$, pale blue, 1-seeded. Himalaya, South Africa, Azores. (Fig. 103 F.)

Family 64. **SAPOTACEAE.** K (5), C (5), A5, $\underline{G}$ (10)

Hard-wooded trees or shrubs with milky or gummy sap. Ls. alternate, entire, without stipules. Style one. Ovary with five or more cells. Fruit a berry. In many tropical members of the family the seeds, and sometimes the flowers, are fleshy or oily, giving economic products, such as vegetable soap and butter. The sapodilla is the fruit of *Sapota achras*, a West Indian tree.

BUMELIA LYCIOIDES Gaertn. f. (SIDEROXYLON LYCIOIDES L.). Southern Buckthorn. 20. August–September. D. Twigs hairless, spiny. Ls. alternate, ov., lanc., 4, entire, thin and firm, hairless, with a pale thin conspicuous midrib, slender-stalked. Fls. very small, white, in hemispherical axillary clusters. Fruit $\frac{1}{2}$, a black berry. South United States. (Fig. 124 L.)

Family 65. **EBENACEAE.** K (3–7), C (3–7), A ∞, $\underline{G}$ (2–16)

Hard-wooded trees and shrubs. Ls. alternate, entire, without stipules. Fls. small, unisexual, stamens numerous, styles two or more, ovary several-celled. Fruit a berry. Ebony is the wood of various species of *Diospyros*. Persimmon is used for the heads of golf clubs.

DIOSPYROS. No terminal bud. Ls. ov., tapered at both ends. Fls. white, 4-lobed, the sexes on different trees, the female solitary. Fruit a large juicy berry with persistent calyx.

D. Kaki L. f. Chinese Persimmon, Kakee. 50. June. D. Ls. 8, glossy above, downy below. Fruit round or egg-shaped, 3, yellow. Japan.

D. Lotus L. Date Plum. 50. June. D. Ls. 5, dark glossy green above, hairless or nearly so. Fls. $\frac{1}{4}$. Fruit round, $\frac{3}{4}$, yellow or purplish. Temperate Asia. (Fig. 124 K.)

D. virginiana L. Persimmon. 100. May–June. D. Ls. 5, glossy green above, hairless or nearly so. Fls. $\frac{1}{2}$. Fruit 1, round or pear-shaped, yellow, with red cheek. U.S.A.

Family 66. **STYRACEAE.** K (4–5), C (4–5), A8–∞, $\bar{G}$ (2–5)

Trees and shrubs with star-shaped hairs. Ls. alternate, entire, without stipules. Fls. usually bisexual, style one, ovary 2-5-celled. Storax is a gum resin obtained from the stem of *Styrax officinale*, a Mediterranean tree, and benzoin from *Styrax Benzoin*, a native of the Moluccas.

HALESIA. Snowdrop Tree, Silver Bell Tree. Ls. ov., pointed, minutely and distantly toothed. Fls. white, drooping in axillary clusters on the old wood, K (4), C (4), A8–16, $\bar{G}$. Fruit dry, pear-shaped, winged.

H. carolina L. 30. May. D. Bark peels off in small scales. Ls. 4, downy

HALESIA—*continued*

below with star-shaped hairs. Fls. $\frac{3}{4}$. Fruit up to $1\frac{1}{2}$, 4-winged. South-east United States. (Fig. 104 A.)

H. diptera Ell. 15. May. D. Ls. 5, nearly hairless. Fls. $\frac{3}{4}$, deeply lobed. Fruit $1\frac{1}{2}$, 2-winged. South-east United States. (Fig. 104 B.)

H. monticola Sarg. 100. May. D. Ls. 5, nearly hairless. Fls. 1. Fruit 2, 4-winged. South-east United States. (Fig. 104 C.)

PTEROSTYRAX HISPIDA Sieb. & Zucc. (HALESIA HISPIDA Mast.). Asagara, Epaulette Tree. 40. June–July. D. Twigs hairless. Ls. ov., 8, tapering base, pointed, minutely toothed, downy below or nearly hairless. Fls. $\frac{1}{4}$, white, fragrant, in drooping axillary panicles, K (5), C (5), A10, $\bar{G}$. Fruit $\frac{1}{2}$, dry, spindle-shaped, 5-10-ribbed, calyx persistent. China and Japan. (Fig. 104 D.)

SINOJACKIA REHDERIANA Hu. 12. May. D. Ls. narrowly ov., 2, glossy, minutely and distantly toothed. Fls. $\frac{1}{2}$, white, K (5), C (5), A10; filaments forming a tube round the style. China.

STYRAX. Buds with one outer scale. Ls. ov., minutely toothed, very shortly stalked. Fls. 1, white, in racemes or clusters at end of short side twigs, K (5), C (5), A10, $\underline{G}$. Fruit egg-shaped, enclosed in persistent calyx.

S. americana Lam. American Storax. 8. June–July. D. Ls. ov., lanc., 3, wedge-shaped base, nearly hairless. Fls. in few-flowered racemes. Fruit $\frac{1}{4}$. South-east United States.

S. Hemsleyana Diels. 30. June. D. Ls. obov., 5, nearly hairless. Fls. in many-flowered racemes. China.

S. japonica Sieb. & Zucc. 25. June–July. D. Ls. ov., 3, distantly toothed, hairless except for tufts in vein-axils. Fls. hanging vertically in few-flowered clusters. Fruit $\frac{1}{2}$. China and Japan. (Fig. 104 G.)

S. Obassia Sieb. & Zucc. 30. June. D. Ls. roundish ov., 8, toothed in outer half, downy below, stalk swollen. Fls. drooping, in many-flowered racemes. Fruit $\frac{3}{4}$, velvety. Japan. (Fig. 104 E.)

S. Shiraiana Makino. 20. June–July. D. Ls. roundish ov., 3, coarsely toothed in outer half, the stalks of the upper ones sheathing. Fls. with a corolla tube longer than the lobes. Fruit $\frac{1}{2}$. Japan.

SYMPLOCOS PANICULATA Wall. (S. CRATAEGOIDES Buch.-Ham.). 30. May. D. Branches slender, spreading. Ls. ov., 3, pointed, sharply toothed, conspicuously veined and downy below. Fls. $\frac{1}{4}$, white, fragrant, in dense terminal or axillary panicles, K (5), C (5), A ∞, $\bar{G}$ (2), stamens in five bundles. Fruit $\frac{1}{4}$, egg-shaped, blue, containing a 1-seeded stone. Himalaya to Japan. (Fig. 103 J.)

Family 67. **OLEACEAE.** K (4), C (4–6) or 0, A2, $\underline{G}$ (2)

Trees and shrubs with usually opposite leaves and no stipules. The flowers have a four-lobed calyx and two stamens, the corolla being 4-6-lobed. Ovary 2-celled. The most useful members of the family are the Ash (*Fraxinus* spp.) and the Olive (*Olea europaea*). Ash timber is white, tough, and elastic. Olive wood is hard and brown, with black streaks. Many others, e.g. lilac, jasmine, forsythia, and privet, are highly ornamental.

ABELIOPHYLLUM DISTICHUM Nakai. 3. May. D. Twigs with chambered pith. Ls. opposite, ov., 3, entire, hairy, short-stalked, in two opposite rows. Fls. $\frac{1}{4}$, white, in small axillary racemes. Fruit 1, flat, winged. Corea. (Fig. 70 C.)

CHIONANTHUS. Fringe Tree. Ls. opposite or sub-opposite, ov., entire, tapering base. Fls. white, with four strap-shaped petals; in loose panicles. Fruit a dark blue 1-seeded berry.

C. retusa Lindl. Chinese Fringe Tree. 30. June. D. Ls. ov., 4, pointed, blunt, or notched at end. Petals $\frac{3}{4}$. China and Japan.

C. virginica L. Fringe Tree. 30. June. D. Ls. ov., oblong, 8, pointed. Petals 1 long. East United States. (Fig. 69 A.)

FONTANESIA PHYLLYREOIDES Labill. 10. June. D. Twigs 4-angled. Ls. opposite, ov., lanc., 2, entire, pointed, hairless. Fls. very small, greenish white, in terminal panicles. Fruit $\frac{1}{4}$, dry, flat, winged, 2-seeded. Asia Minor. (Fig. 69 B.)

FORESTIERA ACUMINATA Poir. (ADELIA ACUMINATA Michx.). 25. April–May. D. Ls. opposite, ov., lanc., 3, finely and distantly toothed at outer end, wedge-shaped base, light green, short-stalked. Fls. very small, greenish, without petals, appearing before the leaves in small clusters or racemes, often unisexual. Fruit $\frac{1}{2}$, a narrow-oblong dark purple berry. U.S.A.

FORSYTHIA. Golden Bell. Branchlets 4-angled, hollow or with chambered pith, hairless. Ls. opposite, simple or 3-fol., ov., lanc., toothed in outer half, hairless. Fls. 1, yellow, solitary or in pairs in the leaf-axils, appearing before the leaves. Fruit a dry capsule.

F. intermedia Zabel. 10. March–April. D. Branches arching or spreading; pith solid at joints, often chambered between. Ls. simple or 3-fol., 5. Hybrid.

Var. *densiflora* Koehne. Fls. densely crowded on branches.

Var. *spectabilis* Koehne. Larger, deeper yellow, and more numerous flowers.

F. ovata Nakai. 3. March–April. D. Branches spreading, yellowish, pith chambered. Ls. simple, ov., 2. Fls. appear earlier than in the other species. Corea.

F. suspensa Vahl. 10. March–April. D. Branches arching, drooping or rambling; pith solid at joints, never chambered between. Ls. 4, mostly simple. China. (Fig. 60 A.)

F. viridissima Lindl. 8. March–April. D. Branches stiff, green, erect, with chambered pith. Ls. simple, lanc., 6. China.

FRAXINUS. Ash. Buds usually black or scurfy brown. Ls. opposite, pinnate; lflts. toothed. Fls. small, in panicles. Fruit dry, 1-winged, 1-seeded.

(a) Fls. white, 4-petalled, in terminal panicles appearing after leaves. (Flowering Ash Section)

F. Bungeana DC. 20. May. D. Buds black. Ls. 5-fol.; lflts. broadly ov., 1, hairless, the lowest pair scarcely smaller than the others. North China.

F. longicuspis Sieb. & Zucc. 20. May. D. Buds reddish. Ls. 5-fol.; lflts. narrowly ov., 2, hairless, the lowest pair much smaller than the others. Ls. turn purple in autumn. Japan.

F. Mariesii Hook. f. 20. June. D. Buds grey. Ls. 5-fol.; lflts. ov., 3, distantly and shallowly toothed, stalkless, lowest pair much the smallest; common stalk grooved, swollen and purple at base. Fruit 1, deep purple in July. Central China. (Fig. 8 C.)

F. Ornus L. Manna Ash. 65. May. D. Buds brown. Ls. 7-9-fol.;

FRAXINUS—*continued*

lflts. ov., 4, short-pointed, shallowly round-toothed, common stalk grooved. Fruit 1. Asia Minor. (Fig. 8 B.)

F. Paxiana Ling. 65. June. D. Buds rusty-downy. Ls. 7-9-fol.; lflts. lanc., 6, distantly and shallowly round-toothed, long-pointed, hairless, stalkless, lowest pair scarcely smaller; common stalk grooved. Fruit 1. China.

F. Spaethiana Ling. 50. June. D. Ls. 5-9-fol.; lflts. ov., lanc., unequal-sided at base, coarsely round-toothed, long-pointed, hairless, stalkless; common stalk slightly grooved on upper side, very much swollen at base and clasping stem. Fruit 1½. Japan.

(*b*) *Fls. without petals, in small lateral panicles appearing before leaves*

F. americana L. White Ash. 120. April. D. Twigs shining dark green or brownish. Ls. 5-9-fol.; lflts. lanc., 6, distantly toothed in outer half or entire, long-pointed, whitish below, stalked; common stalk yellowish white, not grooved. Fruit 2, wing starts at end of seed, calyx persistent. North America.

F. angustifolia Vahl. Narrow-leaved Ash. 70. April. D. Buds dark brown. Ls. 9-13-fol.; lflts. lanc., 3, jaggedly toothed, hairless, stalkless; common stalk grooved. Fruit 1, without calyx. South Europe and North Africa.

F. caroliniana Mill. Water Ash, Swamp Ash. 50. April. D. Buds light brown. Ls. 5-7-fol.; lflts. ov., 2. Fruit 1½, winged to base of seed, with calyx. South United States.

F. excelsior L. Common Ash. 140. April. D. Twigs greenish, buds black or dark brown. Ls. 9-13-fol.; lflts. lanc., 4, evenly and distantly toothed, stalkless; common stalk deeply grooved. Fruit 1, without calyx. Europe (including Britain) and North Africa. (Fig. 8 A.)

Var. *argenteo-variegata* West. Ls. variegated with white.

Var. *asplenifolia* Kirchn. Lflts. linear.

Var. *aurea* Willd. Twigs yellow.

Var. *aurea-pendula* Loud. Branches drooping, twigs yellow.

Var. *aureo-variegata* West. Ls. variegated with yellow.

Var. *diversifolia* Ait. (*F. monophylla* Desf.). One-leaved Ash. Ls. ov., often simple.

Var. *pendula* Ait. Weeping Ash. Branches drooping.

F. pennsylvanica Marsh. Red Ash. 50. May. D. Twigs densely downy. Ls. 5-9-fol.; lflts. narrowly ov., lanc., 4, toothed or entire, downy below. Fruit 1½, with calyx. East North America.

Var. *lanceolata* Sarg. (*F. lanceolata* Borkh.). Green Ash. Twigs and leaves hairless.

F. profunda Bush. Pumpkin Ash. 100. May. D. Twigs woolly. Ls. 7-fol.; lflts. lanc., 7, downy below. Fruit 2, calyx persistent. East United States.

F. quadrangularis Michx. Blue Ash. 100. May. D. Twigs 4-angled or 4-winged, hairless. Ls. 7-11-fol.; lflts. ov., lanc., 3, yellowish green. Fls. bisexual. Fruit oblong, 1½, notched at end, without calyx. U.S.A.

FRAXINUS—*continued*

F. rotundifolia Mill. 12. April–May. Twigs purplish, buds brown. Ls. 5-9-fol.; lflts. round, 1, toothed. Fruit 1, without calyx. South Europe, West Asia.

JASMINUM. Jasmine. Ls. or lflts. entire. Fls. yellow or white, rarely pink, corolla tubular, with four to nine spreading lobes, solitary or in pairs or branched clusters. Fruit a black berry.

(a) Ls. opposite, simple; fls. pink

J. Beesianum Diels & Forrest. 3. June–July. D. Semi-climber. Branchlets green, angular. Ls. ov., 2, pointed, slightly downy on both sides. Fls. ¾, solitary or in 2-3-flowered clusters, sepals linear. China. (Fig. 69 C.)

A cross between this and *J. officinale* is *J. stephanense* (Lem.), which has pale pink flowers and compound as well as simple leaves.

(b) Ls. opposite, compound

J. nudiflorum Lindl. Winter Jasmine. 15. November–February. D. Rambler. Branchlets angled, long, slender and drooping. Ls. 3-fol., short-stalked; lflts. ov., 1, rough or hairy near margins, stalkless. Fls. ¾, yellow, 6-lobed, solitary in the leaf-axils, sepals linear. China and Japan. (Fig. 1 F.)

J. officinale L. Common Jasmine, Jessamine. 20. June–October. D. Climber. Stems very slender, angled, hairless. Ls. pinnate, 5-9-fol.; lflts. ov., 2, downy near margins, lateral ones stalkless. Fls. ¾, white, fragrant, 4-5-lobed, in terminal branched clusters, sepals linear. Persia and North-west India. (Fig. 9 A.)

Var. *affine* Royle (*J. grandiflorum* Hort.). Larger fls., with purple tinge.
Var. *foliis aureis* Hort. Ls. golden yellow.

* **J. primulinum** Hemsl. Primrose Jasmine. 10. January–March. E. Rambler. Ls. 3-fol.; short-stalked; lflts. lanc., 3, dark glossy green, short-stalked. Fls. 1½, yellow, 6-10-lobed, solitary; sepals short, lanc. China. (Fig. 1 G.)

(c) Ls. alternate, compound

J. floridum Bunge. 6. July–September. ½ E. Branchlets angled. Ls. 3-5-fol.; lflts. ov., 1. Fls. yellow, in terminal many-flowered clusters, sepals long and awl-shaped. China.

J. fruticans L. 15. June–September. ½ E. Branchlets angled. Ls. 3-fol.; lflts. lanc., ½, edged with small hairs. Fls. ½, yellow, calyx bell-shaped, 5-lobed; in 3-5-flowered clusters at end of side twigs. Mediterranean region.

J. Giraldii Diels. 8. May–June. E. Branchlets angled. Ls. 3-fol.; lflts. lanc., terminal one up to 4 long, lateral ones much smaller, wrinkled above, downy below. Fls. ¾, yellow, not fragrant, in terminal branched clusters, sepals triangular. China.

J. humile L. Italian Jasmine. 6. June–July. ½ E. Branchlets angled. Ls. 5-9-fol.; lflts. ov., lanc., 1, hairless. Fls. ½, yellow, calyx teeth shorter than calyx tube. South-east Europe.

JASMINUM—*continued*

J. Parkeri Dunn. 1. June. E. Branchlets grooved. Ls. 3-fol. or pinnate; lflts. 1, stalkless. Fls. $\frac{3}{4}$, yellow, fragrant. North-west Himalaya.

J. revolutum Sims. 6. June–August. $\frac{1}{2}$ E. Branchlets slightly angled. Ls. 3-fol. or pinnate, terminal lflts. 2, dull dark green above. Fls. 1, yellow, fragrant, numerous. North-west Himalaya. (Fig. 12 B.)

J. Wallichianum Lindl. 6. June–August. $\frac{1}{2}$ E. Like *J. revolutum*, but ls. 7-13 fol.; lflts. lanc., 1. Nepal.

LIGUSTRUM. Privet. Ls. opposite, entire, short-stalked. Fls. small, white, tubular, in conspicuous terminal panicles. Fruit a black berry.

(*a*) *Tube of corolla scarcely longer than lobes*

L. japonicum Thunb. Japanese Privet. 8. July–September. E. Ls. ov., 4, very glossy, blackish green, veins raised, margin and midrib reddish. Fls. in large panicles up to 8 long. China and Japan.

Var. *coriaceum* Lav. Ls. roundish ov., 2, blunt or notched at apex. Fl.-panicles up to 3 long.

L. lucidum Ait. 30. August–October. E. Ls. ov., 6, long-pointed, glossy green above, hairless, veins sunk, margins translucent. Fls. in large panicles up to 8 long. China. (Fig. 70 B.)

Var. *aureo-variegatum* Hort. Ls. variegated with yellow.

L. Quihoui Carr. 6. September–October. $\frac{1}{2}$ E. Branchlets downy. Ls. ov., $1\frac{1}{2}$, blunt-ended, hairless. Fls. in large panicles up to 8 long. China.

L. sinense Lour. Chinese Privet. 20. July. D. or $\frac{1}{2}$ E. Branchlets densely downy. Ls. ov., 3, pale green, thin, blunt or notched at apex. Fl.-panicles up to 4 long. China. (Fig. 70 H.)

L. vulgare L. Common Privet. 10. June–July. D. or $\frac{1}{2}$ E. Ls. ov., lanc., 2, hairless. Fl.-panicles up to 2 long. Europe (including Britain) and North Africa. (Fig. 70 A.)

Var. *aureum* Jaeg. Ls. yellow.

Var. *glaucum* Mouillef. Ls. bluish green with white margin.

Var. *leucocarpum* Sweet. Berries white.

Var. *variegatum* Loud. Ls. variegated with white or yellow.

Var. *xanthocarpum* Don. Berries yellow.

(*b*) *Tube of corolla much longer than lobes*

L. Delavayanum Hariot. 6. June. E. Branchlets downy. Ls. ov., 1, pointed, dark glossy green above. Fls. in a cylindrical panicle, anthers violet. West China.

L. Henryi (Hemsl.) is similar, but with larger leaves and flowers.

L. ionandrum Diels. 10. June. E. Branchlets greyish, downy. Ls. ov., 1, hairless. Fl.-panicles dense, up to 1 long, stamens violet. China. (Fig. 70 E.)

L. obtusifolium Sieb. & Zucc. 10. July. $\frac{1}{2}$ E. Branches spreading or arching. Ls. ov., 2, pointed or blunt. Fls. in drooping panicles up to 1 long. Japan.

L. ovalifolium Hassk. 15. July. E. Branchlets hairless. Ls. ov., 2, glossy green, hairless. Fl.-panicles up to 4 long. Japan. (Fig. 70 G.)

Var. *argenteum* Hort. Ls. bordered with white.

LIGUSTRUM—*continued*

Var. *aureum* Bean. Golden Privet. Ls. yellow except in middle.

Var. *variegatum* T. Moore. Ls. variegated with pale yellow.

OLEA. Ls. opposite, pitted. Fls. small, white, in axillary racemes. Fruit $\frac{3}{4}$, egg-shaped, oily, containing one hard stone.

* **O. europaea** L. Olive. 40. May. E. Ls. ov., lanc., 3, entire, leathery, dark dull green above, silvery or pale green below, sometimes downy on both sides. South Europe and West Asia. (Fig. 69 D.)

* **O. fragrans** Lour. 50. May. E. Ls. ov., 6, finely toothed or entire, bright yellowish green below. Fls. very fragrant. Japan. (Fig. 59 J.)

OSMANTHUS. Ls. opposite, mostly spine-toothed, hairless. Fls. small, white or yellowish, fragrant, in small clusters. Fruit a dark blue berry.

O. Aquifolium Sieb. 20. September–October. E. Ls. ov., $2\frac{1}{2}$, holly-like with two to four large spiny teeth on each side, glossy green above. Fls. $\frac{1}{4}$, in short-stalked axillary clusters. Japan. (Fig. 54 B.)

Var. *purpureus* Nichols. Young stems black; ls. purple.

Var. *variegatus* Moore. Ls. bordered with white or yellow.

O. armatus Diels. 15. September. E. Ls. lanc., 6, long-pointed, base rounded or heart-shaped, coarsely spine-toothed, prominently net-veined. Fls. $\frac{1}{4}$, in axillary clusters. China. (Fig. 54 C.)

O. Delavayi Franch. 10. April–May. E. Ls. ov., 1, sharply toothed, minutely dotted below. Fls. $\frac{1}{2}$, tubular, with four spreading lobes, in terminal and axillary clusters. China. (Fig. 54 D.)

O. Forrestii Rehd. 20. E. Ls. ov., lanc., 6, dull green, upper entire, lower spine-toothed, dotted with black on both sides, net-veined. Fls. $\frac{1}{2}$, produced abundantly in axillary clusters. Yunnan.

O. Fortunei Carr. 20. September. E. Ls. ov., 4, holly-like with six to ten spiny teeth on each side. Fls. $\frac{1}{4}$, very fragrant, in axillary clusters. Hybrid. (Fig. 54 A.)

O. serrulatus Rehd. 12. April–May. E. Ls. lanc., 4, base tapering, finely toothed, leathery, dotted below. Fls. $\frac{1}{2}$, in axillary clusters. China. (Fig. 59 K.)

OSMAREA BURKWOODII Hort. April. E. Ls. ov., $1\frac{1}{2}$, pointed, toothed, leathery, dark glossy green. Fls. $\frac{1}{2}$, ivory-white, fragrant, in terminal and axillary clusters. A cross between *Osmanthus Delavayi* and *Phillyrea decora*.

PARASYRINGA SEMPERVIRENS W. W. Sm., LIGUSTRUM SEMPERVIRENS Ling, SYRINGA SEMPERVIRENS Franch.). 6. June–July. E. Ls. opposite, broadly ov. or circular, $1\frac{1}{2}$, leathery, glossy, hairless. Fls. small, white, tubular, in terminal spikes. Fruit splitting into two. China. (A genus intermediate between privet and lilac.) (Fig. 70 L.)

PHILLYREA. Jasmine Box. Ls. opposite, hairless, short-stalked. Fls. small, white or greenish, in axillary clusters, stamens protruding beyond the corolla. Fruit a blue-black berry.

P. angustifolia L. 10. May. E. Ls. linear, 2, entire, dark green, hairless, pitted below. Mediterranean region. (Fig. 52 M.)

P. decora Boiss. & Bal. 10. April. E. Ls. ov., lanc., 5, entire, very hard and firm, with bevelled edges. Mediterranean region. (Fig. 70 J.)

P. latifolia L. 30. April–May. E. Ls. ov., sharply toothed. Mediterranean region. (Fig. 60 J.)

SYRINGA. Lilac. Ls. opposite, entire, lobed, or pinnate. Fls. small, lilac, purple, or white. Fruit an oblong leathery capsule.

(*a*) *Tube of corolla scarcely longer than calyx*

S. amurensis Rupr. 12. June. D. Ls. broadly ov., 4, bright green above, hairless and net-veined below, rounded or straight base. Fls. white, in loose panicles up to 6 long, stamens much longer than corolla. China, Japan, and Manchuria.

S. japonica Decne. Japanese Lilac. 30. June–July. D. Ls. ov., 6, bright green above, downy below, rounded or heart-shaped base. Fls. white, in panicles up to 12 long, stamens scarcely longer than corolla. Japan.

S. pekinensis Rupr. 12. June. D. Ls. ov., lanc., 4, dark green above, pale green below, base rounded. Fls. white, in loose panicles up to 6 long, stamens scarcely longer than corolla. China.

Var. *pendula* Dipp. Branches drooping.

(*b*) *Tube of corolla much longer than calyx*

(i) Panicles from terminal buds

S. emodi Wall. Himalayan Lilac. 15. June. D. Twigs dark olive-green spotted with white. Ls. ov., 8, tapering base, whitish below. Fls. white or purplish, in panicles up to 6 long, not fragrant. Himalaya. (Fig. 69 F.)

Var. *variegata* Hort. Ls. margined with yellow.

S. Josikaea Jacq. f. Hungarian Lilac. 9. June. D. Ls. ov., 4, dark green above, whitish below, tapering base. Fls. deep violet, slightly scented, in narrow panicles up to 6 long. Transylvania.

S. reflexa Schneid. 9. June. D. Ls. ov., lanc., 8, tapering base. Fls. deep pink, in narrow drooping panicles up to 8 long. China.

S. Komarowi (Schneid.) is similar, but has purple flowers.

S. villosa Vahl. 10. May–June. D. Ls. ov., lanc., 6, rounded or tapering base, with scattered hairs below. Fls. lilac-rose, in large terminal and axillary panicles up to 10 long. China. (Fig. 69 H.)

S. tomentella (Bur. & Franch.) is similar, but the leaves are downy below.

S. Wolfii Schneid. 12. June. D. Ls. ov., 3, tapering base, upper surface raised between veins, bristly on margins and midrib below. Fls. pink. North China.

(ii) Panicles from lateral buds, usually in pairs at end of shoot

S. chinensis Willd. Rouen Lilac. 15. May. D. Ls. ov., lanc., 3, tapering at the base. Fls. purplish, in long drooping panicles. Hybrid.

Var. *alba* Rehd. Fls. white.

S. Julianae Schneid. 6. May. D. Twigs hairy. Ls. ov., 1½, with a broadly tapering base, dark green and downy above, hairy below. Fls. lilac, fragrant, in panicles up to 4 long. China.

S. Meyeri Schneid. 3. May. D. Twigs slightly 4-angled, downy. Ls. ov., 1, with 2-3 pairs veins. Fls. violet, in dense panicles up to 3 long. North China.

SYRINGA—*continued*

S. microphylla Diels. Small-leaved Lilac. 5. June. D. Ls. roundish ov., 1, downy on both sides. Fls. lilac, in erect panicles up to 6 long. North China.

S. oblata Lindl. 12. April–May. D. Twigs stout, hairless. Ls. round or kidney-shaped, heart-shaped base, hairless. Fls. lilac, in dense broad panicles up to 5 long. North China.

S. persica L. Persian Lilac. 6. May. D. Ls. lanc., 2, tapering base. Fls. purple, in small panicles up to 3 long. Afghanistan. (Fig. 69 G.)

Var. *alba* West. Fls. white.

Var. *laciniata* Vahl. Ls. cut into parallel lobes. (Fig. 34 E.)

S. pinnatifolia Hemsl. Pinnate Lilac. 8. May. D. Ls. pinnate; lflts. ov., lanc., 1½, stalkless, the terminal ones often attached to the common stalk by a part of the blade. Fls. white, in small panicles up to 3 long. China. (Fig. 8 E.)

S. pubescens Turcz. 6. May. D. Twigs thin, slightly 4-angled, downy. Ls. ov., 1½, downy on veins below. Fls. pale lilac, fragrant, in dense panicles up to 4 long. North China.

S. velutina Komar. 10. June. D. Twigs and ls. downy. Ls. ov., 3, long-pointed. Fls. lilac, slender-tubed, fragrant, in downy panicles up to 4 long. Corea.

S. vulgaris L. Common Lilac. 20. May. D. Ls. ov., 6, rounded or heart-shaped base, hairless. Fls. lilac, fragrant, in panicles up to 8 long. East Europe. (Fig. 69 E.)

Var. *alba* West. Fls. white, winter buds yellowish green. A taller and faster growing tree.

Var. *purpurea* West. Fls. purple, winter buds brown.

Many other varieties in cultivation, with flowers of varying shades of colour, from white to deep crimson.

Family 68. APOCYNACEAE. K (5), C (5), A5, G̲ (2)

Woody plants with milky juice, often climbing or trailing. Ls. opposite, entire, hairless, the midrib and veins rather broad. Fls. showy, twisted in bud. Fruit of two dry pods joined together.

* MANDEVILLA SUAVEOLENS Lindl. 12. June–September. D. Climber. Stems hollow, hairless. Ls. ov., 3, long-pointed, with tufts of white down in the vein-axils beneath, long-stalked. Fls. 1½, white, funnel-shaped, fragrant, in branched axillary clusters. Fruit 12, of two narrow cylindrical seed-pods, seeds bearded. Argentine. (Fig. 76 D.)

TRACHELOSPERMUM. Climbers with hairy stems. Ls. glossy dark green, blunt-ended. Fls. 1, fragrant, in terminal branched clusters. Pods long.

* **T. asiaticum** Nakai (*T. divaricatum* Kanitz, *T. crocostemon* Stapf). 15. July–August. E. Ls. ov., 2. Fls. with erect sepals. Pods nearly parallel. East Asia.

* **T. jasminoides** Lem. (*Rhynchospermum jasminoides* Lindl.). 12. July–August. E. Ls. lanc., 3. Fls. with reflexed sepals. Pods spreading. China and Japan. (Fig. 77 D.)

VINCA. Periwinkle. Barren stems trailing, flowering ones erect. Ls. ov., glossy, hairless. Fls. blue. Pods 2, cylindrical.

V. major L. Greater Periwinkle. 2. April. E. Ls. 3. Fls. 1½, with linear sepals. Europe (including Britain) and West Asia. (Fig. 77 A.)

V. minor L. Lesser Periwinkle. ½. April. E. Ls. 2, narrow. Fls. 1, with lanc. sepals. Europe (including Britain) and West Asia.

Var. *argenteo-variegata* West. Ls. blotched with white.

Var. *aureo-variegata* West. Ls. blotched with yellow.

Family 69. **ASCLEPIADACEAE.** K (5), C (5), A (5), G̲2

Like the previous family, but the stamens are usually united and the pollen glued together in masses. Ls. opposite, entire. The seed-pods are large and contain seeds with tufted hairs.

* ARAUJIA SERICOFERA Brot. (PHYSIANTHUS ALBENS Mart.). 20. July. E. Ls. ov., lanc., 4, pointed, square-cut at base, pale green above, minutely felted below. Fls. ½, white, fragrant, tubular, with spreading lobes, in few-flowered racemes at joints of stem. Fruit 5 × 3, grooved. Brazil. (Fig. 76 H.)

MARSDENIA ERECTA R. Br. (CYNANCHUM ERECTUM L.). 20. July. D. Ls. ov., 2, heart-shaped base, pointed, pale glaucous green. Fls. ¼, white, fragrant, in terminal and axillary branched clusters. Fruit 3, cone- or spindle-shaped, pointed. Asia Minor. (Fig. 76 E.)

METAPLEXIS JAPONICA Makino (M. STAUNTONII Roem. & Schultz). 20. July–September. D. Ls. ov., 4, heart-shaped base. Fls. ½, pinkish, bell-shaped, with reflexed sepals. Fruit 4, spindle-shaped. China and Japan.

PERIPLOCA GRAECA L. Silk Vine. 30. July–August. D. Ls. ov., 4, the veins parallel and ending in a marginal vein. Fls. 1, greenish outside, brownish purple inside, in branched clusters at end of short side shoots. Seed-pods 5, in pairs usually joined at ends. South-east Europe and Orient. (Fig. 76 F.)

Family 70. **LOGANIACEAE.** K (4–5), C (4–5), A4–5, G̲ (2)

Woody plants with usually opposite and stipulate leaves. Stamens as many as petals and alternate with them. Ovary 2-celled.

BUDDLEIA. Butterfly Bush. Branchlets usually ribbed or angled. Ls. usually opposite, short-stalked. Fls. small, tubular or bell-shaped, in small clusters grouped together in spikes or panicles. Fruit a dry capsule containing many small seeds.

(*a*) *Ls. alternate*

B. alternifolia Maxim. 20. June. D. Branchlets arching or drooping. Ls. lanc., 4, pointed, tapering base, dull dark green above, glaucous below. Fls. lilac-purple, in clusters on old wood. China. (Fig. 125 A.)

(*b*) *Ls. opposite; branchlets winged at angles*

B. japonica Hemsl. 6. July–August. D. Branchlets 4-angled. Ls. lanc., 8, minutely and distantly toothed, dark green above, tawny-felted below. Fls. pale lilac, in terminal drooping spikes. Japan.

B. Lindleyana Fort. 6. July–August. D. Branchlets 4-angled, hairless. Ls. ov., lanc., 4, tapering base, coarsely toothed, hairless. Fls. purplish violet, in erect spikes. Japan. (Fig. 57 B.)

BUDDLEIA—*continued*

(*c*) *Ls. opposite; branchlets not winged*

* **B. auriculata** Benth. 8. August–September. D. Branchlets cylindrical. Ls. ov., lanc., 3, distantly toothed in outer half, bright green and somewhat wrinkled above, white- or rusty-felted below, about five pairs of veins. Fls. orange-yellow, in axillary racemes at end of shoots. South Africa. (Fig. 57 D.)

B. Colvilei Hook. f. & Thoms. 40. June–September. D. Branches arching or drooping, covered with reddish wool when young. Ls. lanc., 10, shallowly toothed, tapered at both ends, dark green above, felted below. Fls. crimson, in large terminal panicles. East Himalaya. (Fig. 57 G.)

B. Davidii Franch. (*B. variabilis* Hemsl.). 15. June–September. D. Branchlets 4-angled, downy. Ls. lanc., 12, long-pointed, finely toothed, white-felted below. Fls. lilac or purple, with orange eye, in long narrow spikes up to 12 long on young wood. China. (Fig. 57 F.)

Var. *magnifica* Rehd. & Wils. Fl.-spikes violet-purple, up to 30 long; corolla lobes reflexed.

Var. *Veitchiana* Rehd. Like above, but corolla lobes erect. Comes into flower a little earlier (Bean).

Var. *Wilsoni* Rehd. Fls. rosy lilac, with deep orange centre, corolla lobes erect.

* **B. Fallowiana** Balf. & W. W. Sm. 8. August–September. D. Young stems white-felted. Ls. lanc., 8, long-pointed, wedge-shaped base, shallowly toothed, white-felted below. Fls. pale lilac, in long terminal panicles. China.

* **B. Farreri** Balf. & W. W. Sm. 10. May. D. Young stems white-felted. Ls. ov., lanc., 12, unevenly toothed, straight or heart-shaped base, dull dark green above, white-felted or woolly below. Fls. rose-lilac, in clusters on old wood. China. (Fig. 57 E.)

B. globosa Lam. Orange Ball Tree. 15. June. ½ E. Young stems tawny-felted. Ls. lanc., 8, tapered at both ends, round-toothed, dark green and wrinkled above, tawny-felted below. Fls. orange-yellow, in balls ¾ diameter. South America. (Fig. 57 H.)

In *B. Weyeriana* (Weyer), a hybrid, the flower-balls are tinged with pink or purple.

B. nivea Duthie. 9. July–August. D. Young stems covered with white wool. Ls. ov., lanc., 10, rounded at base, coarsely toothed, white-felted below. Fls. pale purple, in terminal spikes. West China.

* **B. officinalis** Maxim. 9. April. D. Branchlets cylindrical, grey-woolly. Ls. lanc., 4, long-pointed, tapered at both ends, toothed or entire, white or tawny below. Fls. lilac, with orange eye, fragrant, in panicles. China.

B. paniculata Wall. 15. June–September. D. Like *B. Farreri*, but leaves lanc., 4, and flowers lilac, with white throat, fragrant, in pyramidal panicles up to 3 long. Himalaya.

* **B. salvifolia** Lam. South African Sage Wood. 15. July. ½ E. Branchlets covered with white or reddish down. Ls. lanc., 3, minutely round-toothed, dull green and wrinkled above, white- or brown-felted below.

BUDDLEIA—*continued*

Fls. white or pale lilac, woolly, in terminal panicles on young wood. South Africa. (Fig. 57 c.)

* Desfontainea spinosa Ruiz & Pav. 10. July–October. E. Branches smooth and shining. Ls. opposite, ov., 2, leathery and glossy, the margins armed with sharp triangular spines. Fls. 1½, funnel-shaped, red, with yellow lobes. South America. (Fig. 54 G.)

Family 71. BORAGINACEAE. K (5), C (5), A5, G̲ (2)

Mostly herbaceous. Ls. alternate, entire, without stipules and generally very hairy. Fls. usually in curved spikes or racemes, the youngest flower being at the top. Ovary 4-cleft, with a single style usually rising from the base between the sections of the ovary. Fruit typically of four hard nutlets. Forget-me-not, borage, and anchusa are well-known herbaceous plants.

EHRETIA. Ls. ov., 7, toothed. Fls. ¼, white, in terminal panicles, style terminal. Fruit berry-like.

E. Dicksonii Hance (*E. macrophylla* Thunb.). 20. June–July. D. Ls. hairy. Himalaya.

E. thyrsiflora Nakai (*E. acuminata* Hemsl.). 20. June–July. D. Ls. hairless or nearly so. North India, China and Japan. (Fig. 104 L.)

Lithospermum diffusum Lag. (L. prostratum Loisel.). Gromwell. ½. May. E. Stems slender, trailing, bristly. Ls. linear-oblong, ¾, blunt-ended, bristly. Fls. ½, blue, funnel-shaped, stalkless, in terminal spikes. Europe. (Fig. 52 J.)

Moltkia petraea Boiss. (Lithospermum petraeum A. DC.). 2. June. ½ E. Stems erect, hairy. Ls. linear, 1, hairy. Fls. ¼, violet-blue, tubular, in crowded terminal clusters. Dalmatia. (Fig. 51 E.)

Family 72. CONVOLVULACEAE. K (5), C (5), A5, G̲ (2)

Mostly twining or prostrate herbs with showy trumpet-shaped or funnel-shaped flowers twisted or pleated in bud. Ovary 2-4-celled, styles one or two. Fruit a few-seeded capsule.

* Convolvulus Cneorum L. (C. argenteus Lam.). 3. May–August. E. Whole plant covered with silky hairs. Ls. alternate, lanc., 2, entire, tapered at base. Fls. 1½, white or pinkish, trumpet-shaped, in a terminal cluster. Fruit a pod splitting into four. South Europe. (Fig. 125 D.)

Family 73. SOLANACEAE. K (5), C (5), A2–5, G̲ (2)

Ls. alternate, without stipules. Fls. usually regular in shape or nearly so, with a 2-celled ovary and one style. Fruit many-seeded. Tobacco is the leaf of several species of *Nicotiana*, a native of America, potato the underground tuber of *Solanum tuberosum*, from South America, and tomato the berry of *Lycopersicum esculentum*, also from South America. Belladonna and hyoscyamine are drugs obtained from British members of the family.

CESTRUM. Ls. lanc., 5, short-stalked. Fls. fragrant at night, in axillary or terminal panicles, tubular. Fruit a berry cupped in the persistent calyx.

CESTRUM—*continued*

* **C. elegans** Schlecht. (*C. fasciculatum* Miers). 8. June–July. D. Rambler. Ls. hairy. Fls. ¾, rosy crimson. Mexico. (Fig. 125 K.)

Var. *Newelli* Bailey. Fls. larger.

* **C. Parqui** L'Hérit. (*C. virgatum* Ruiz & Pav.). Willow-leaved Jessamine. 8. June–July. D. Ls. hairless. Fls. 1, yellowish green. Chile. (Fig. 125 L.)

FABIANA. False Heath. Ls. minute, scale-like, completely covering the branchlet. Fls. ¾, tubular, solitary at end of side shoots. Fruit a capsule.

* **F. imbricata** Ruiz & Pav. 8. June. E. Narrow habit of growth. Fls. white. South America. (Fig. 49 C.)

* **F. violacea** Hort. 12. June. E. Spreading habit of growth. Fls. pale mauve or pale blue. South America.

LYCIUM. Box Thorn. Ramblers. Branches with a few spines. Ls. alternate or in clusters, ov., lanc., short-stalked. Fls. ½, solitary or in few-flowered clusters in the leaf-axils. Fruit a red berry.

L. chinense Mill. (*L. barbatum* Hort.). Chinese Box Thorn, Cottage Tea Tree. May–July. D. Ls. 4. Fls. purple. China. (Fig. 125 E.)

L. pallidum Miers. Fremont's Box Thorn. June–July. D. Ls. 2. Fls. greenish white. South United States.

SOLANUM. Ls. entire or lobed. Fls. blue, purple, or white, with conspicuous yellow stamens forming a cone in the centre; solitary or in branched clusters in the leaf-axils. Fruit a berry.

* **S. crispum** Ruiz & Pav. Potato Tree. 10. June–September. ½ E. Climber. Ls. ov., lanc., 5, pointed, with a tapering or rounded base. Fls. 1, blue. Chile. (Fig. 125 B.)

S. Dulcamara L. Woody Nightshade, Bittersweet. 8. July. D. Rambler. Ls. ov., 4, heart-shaped at base, often 3-fol. or 3-lobed, pointed, bright green. Fls. deep purple, drooping. Berry red. Europe (including Britain). (Fig. 125 F.)

* **S. jasminoides** Paxt. Climber. 10. July–September. ½ E. Ls. deeply lobed or pinnate, 3. Fls. pale blue or white. Brazil. (Fig. 12 C.)

S. valdiviense Dunal. 8. May. D. Climber. Ls. ov., lanc., 2, pointed. Fls. ½, pale purple or white. Chile.

* STREPTOSOLEN JAMESONII Miers. 6. June–July. D. Ls. ov., 2, thin, rough above, downy below. Fls. 1, orange-red, tubular, twisted; stamens four, two long and two short; in terminal clusters. Fruit a capsule. South America. (Fig. 125 C.)

Family 74. **SCROPHULARIACEAE.** K (4–5), C (4–5), A2–5, $\underline{G}$ (2)

In all the shrubby members of the family described below the leaves are opposite and without stipules. Fls. slightly irregular to very irregular in shape, often 2-lipped; stamens typically four, two long and two short, but only two in *Veronica*; ovary 2-celled, with a single terminal style. Fruit usually a many-seeded capsule (few-seeded in *Veronica*). Well-known garden members are antirrhinum, foxglove, calceolaria, mullein, alonsoa, collinsia, toadflax, and nemesia. Digitalin is obtained from the foxglove.

* BOWKERIA GERRARDIANA Harvey. 10. August. E. Stems hairy. Ls. in

threes, ov., lanc., 7, toothed, long-pointed, downy, stalkless. Fls. ¾ (like calceolaria), white, 2-lipped, in 2-10-flowered branched clusters. South Africa. (Fig. 55 A.)

CALCEOLARIA. Ls. ov., toothed. Fls. ½, 2-lipped, pouched, in terminal branched clusters.

* **C. integrifolia** L. 4. July–August. E. Branchlets velvety. Ls. ov., 3, tapered at both ends, minutely round-toothed, dull green and wrinkled above, grey-felted below. Fls. yellow. Chile. (Fig. 56 O.)

* **C. violacea** Cav. 6. July–August. ½ E. Branchlets minutely downy. Ls. ov., 1, pointed, coarsely and unevenly toothed, hairy. Fls. pale violet, helmet-shaped. Chile.

* FREYLINIA CESTROIDES Colla. 12. October–November. E. Ls. linear, 5, hairless, midrib prominent below. Fls. ½, creamy yellow, tubular, in terminal panicles. South Africa. (Fig. 50 H.)

* MIMULUS AURANTIACUS Curt. (DIPLACUS GLUTINOSUS Nutt.). 6. June–August. E. Stems clammy. Ls. lanc., 4, tapered at base, minutely toothed in outer half, glossy above, slightly downy below, short-stalked or stalkless. Fls. 1, yellow or orange, trumpet-shaped, solitary in leaf-axils. Seed-pod ½, slender, ribbed. California. (Fig. 62 J.)

PAULOWNIA. Foxglove Tree. Ls. ov., 12, heart-shaped base, sometimes 3-5-lobed, hairy or downy, long-stalked. Fls. large, like a foxglove, in large terminal panicles. Fruit a dry egg-shaped pointed capsule containing numerous winged seeds.

P. Fargesii Franch. 70. June. D. Twigs and leaf-stalks clammy. Ls. downy below. Fls. 3, pale lilac, with yellow in throat. China.

P. tomentosa C. Koch (*P. imperialis* Sieb. & Zucc.). 50. May–June. D. Ls. velvety above, woolly below. Fls. 2, purple. Japan. (Fig. 26 C.)

PENTSTEMON. Beard Tongue. Semi-herbaceous. Ls. toothed, stalkless or nearly so. Fls. large, tubular, 2-lipped, in terminal racemes or panicles. Fruit a dry capsule.

* **P. cordifolius** Benth. 2. July–August. E. Ls. heart-shaped, 2, coarsely toothed. Fls. 1½, scarlet, in large panicles. California. (Fig. 56 K.)

* **P. heterophyllus** Lindl. 5. July–September. D. Ls. linear, lanc., 2, tapering base. Fls. 1, purple, in narrow racemes. California. (Fig. 52 O.)

P. Menziesii Hook. f. 1. May–June. D. Ls. ov., ¾, finely toothed, blunt-ended, tapering base. Fls. 1, purple. California. (Fig 56 L.)

P. Scouleri Dougl. 1½. July–August. D. Ls. linear, lanc., 2, pointed, tapered at both ends, toothed. Fls. 1, lilac-purple, in 5-11-flowered racemes. West North America. (Fig. 52 N.)

PHYGELIUS CAPENSIS E. Mey. Cape Figwort. 6. September. D. Semi-herbaceous. Stems erect, stout, angled, very pithy, hairless. Ls. ov., 5, blunt-toothed, hairless; leaf-stalk 1, with a pair of small wings at the base. Fls. 1, scarlet, tubular, in large erect terminal panicles. South Africa. (Fig. 57 A.)

VERONICA (HEBE). Shrubby Speedwell. Stem conspicuously ringed with the scars of fallen leaves. Ls. in four distinct rows, very shortly stalked or stalkless. Fls. small, blue, purple, or white, in terminal or axillary spikes or racemes, K (4), C (4), A2. Fruit a dry flattened 2-lobed capsule.

VERONICA (HEBE)—*continued*

(*a*) *Ls. minute, scale-like*

V. cupressoides Hook. f. (*V. salicornioides* Hook. f.). 3. July–August. E. L.-pairs distinct. Fls. pale blue, in small heads. New Zealand. (Fig. 49 J.)

V. Hectori Hook. f. 2. July–August. E. L.-pairs overlapping, completely concealing the stem. Fls. white or pinkish, in small terminal heads. New Zealand. (Fig. 49 Q.)

V. loganioides Armstr. $\frac{3}{4}$. June–July. E. Young stems hairy. Ls. keeled, often toothed, dull green, hairless. Fls. white, in a terminal 1-3-branched raceme; fl.-stalks and sepals hairy. New Zealand.

V. lycopodioides Hook. f. 2. June–July. E. Ls. keeled, giving a 4-sided appearance to the branchlet. Fls. white, with large blue stamens, in small terminal heads. New Zealand. (Fig. 49 K.)

(*b*) *Adult leaf* 1 *inch or less in length*

V. amplexicaulis Armstr. 3. July–August. E. Ls. heart-shaped, 1, not keeled, blunt-ended, green or glaucous, crowded. Fls. $\frac{1}{4}$, white, stalkless, in axillary spikes. New Zealand. (Fig. 66 K.)

V. anomala Armstr. 5. July–August. E. Ls. lanc., pointed. Fls. $\frac{3}{4}$, white or pinkish, in a cluster of spikes at end of shoot. New Zealand. (Fig. 66 J.)

V. Balfouriana Hook. f. 3. July. E. Stems erect, purplish. Ls. ov., $\frac{3}{4}$, pale glossy green. Fls. $\frac{1}{2}$, purplish blue, in axillary racemes. New Zealand.

V. buxifolia Benth. 4. June–August. E. Ls. ov., $\frac{1}{2}$, pointed, keeled, dark glossy green. Fls. $\frac{1}{4}$, white, in closely packed clusters at end of shoot. New Zealand. (Fig. 66 L.)

V. carnosula Hook. f. 1. July–August. E. Ls. ov., $\frac{1}{2}$, pointed, keeled, dark glossy green. Fls. $\frac{1}{4}$, white, in a terminal cluster of dense spikes. New Zealand.

V. Colensoi Hook. f. 2. July–August. E. Ls. ov., lanc., pointed, greyish green, 3-nerved, occasionally toothed, crowded. Fls. $\frac{1}{4}$, white, in axillary racemes. New Zealand. (Fig. 66 G.)

V. elliptica Forst. (*V. decussata* Ait.). 15. July–August. E. Ls. ov., 1, minutely pointed, keeled, downy white on margins, rounded or straight base. Fls. $\frac{1}{2}$, white, with purple lines, in 4-12-flowered racemes up to $1\frac{1}{2}$ long. Falkland Islands.

V. glauco-coerulea Armstr. $\frac{1}{2}$. June–August. E. Stems downy. Ls. ov., $\frac{1}{2}$, grey or glaucous. Fls. $\frac{1}{4}$, blue-purple, stalkless, in axillary or branched spikes. New Zealand.

V. pinguifolia Hook. f. 3. July–August. E. Ls. ov., blunt-ended, concave, grey-green. Fls. $\frac{1}{4}$, white, in axillary spikes. New Zealand. (Fig. 66 D.)

V. procumbens Clarke. 1. May–June. E. Ls. $\frac{1}{2}$, spoon-shaped, crowded, glaucous. Fls. $\frac{1}{4}$, white, in terminal clusters. New Zealand.

V. Traversii Hook. f. 6. July. E. Ls. lanc., pointed, tapering base, dull pale green. Fls. $\frac{1}{4}$, white, in axillary racemes. New Zealand. (Fig. 66 E.)

V. vernicosa Hook. f. 2. June–August. E. Ls. ov., 1, pointed, dark glossy green, 3-nerved. Fls. $\frac{1}{4}$, white, racemes in pairs. New Zealand.

VERONICA (HEBE)—*continued*

(*c*) *Adult leaf more than* 1 *inch long*

V. angustifolia A. Rich. 5. July–September. E. Ls. linear, 3, pointed, often directed downwards. Fls. ¼, white tinged with lilac, the racemes in axillary pairs. New Zealand. (Fig. 50 J.)

* **V. Hulkeana** F. Muell. 6. May–June. E. L.-pairs somewhat distant. Ls. ov., 2, coarsely toothed, dark glossy green. Fls. ¼, lilac, in large terminal panicles. New Zealand. (Fig. 59 L.)

V. salicifolia Forst. f. 10. June–August (in mild districts throughout the year). E. Ls. lanc., 5, pointed, pale green. Fls. ¼, bluish purple, in cylindrical racemes. New Zealand. (Fig. 66 F.)

Var. *serrulata* Hort. Ls. distantly toothed. Many other varieties in cultivation.

V. speciosa R. Cunn. 5. July–September. E. Branches stout, spreading. Ls. ov., 4, blunt-ended, concave. Fls. ¼, dark reddish purple, in axillary racemes. New Zealand. (Fig. 66 H.)

Many varieties in cultivation.

Family 75. **GESNERACEAE.** K (5), C (5), A4, G̱ (2)

Mostly tropical plants with simple opposite leaves without stipules. Fls. tubular, 2-lipped; stamens typically four, two long and two short; ovary 1-celled, style one. Fruit a berry or capsule; seeds numerous, minute.

* MITRARIA COCCINEA Cav. Mitre Flower. Prostrate or climbing. May–June. E. Stems slender, downy. Ls. ov., 1, pointed, toothed, dark glossy green above, short-stalked. Fls. 1, scarlet, solitary on slender downy stalk. Fruit an egg-shaped berry. Chile. (Fig. 56 H.)

Family 76. **BIGNONIACEAE.** K (3–5), C (5), A4, G̱ (2)

Ls. opposite, often compound, without stipules. Fls. tubular or trumpet-shaped; stamens typically four, two long and two short; ovary 2-celled (1-celled in *Eccremocarpus*), style one. Fruit a capsule with winged seeds.

BIGNONIA CAPREOLATA L. Cross Vine. 50. June. E. Climber. Ls. 2-fol.; common stalk ½, ending in a tendril; lflts. lanc., 5, pointed, entire, heart-shaped base, deep green, hairless. Fls. 1, orange-red, in axillary clusters. Fruit 6, slender, flattened. South-east United States. (Fig. 6 C.)

CAMPSIS (TECOMA). Climbing by aerial roots which occur in tufts at the joints. Ls. pinnate; lflts. ov., 3, toothed, stalkless. Fls. 3, orange-red, trumpet-shaped, in terminal clusters or panicles. Seed-pod 4, elongated, with numerous winged seeds.

C. chinensis Voss (*Tecoma grandiflora* Loisel.). 30. August–September. D. Aerial roots few or none. Lflts. hairless. Fls. in terminal drooping panicles. China and Japan.

C. radicans Seem. (*Tecoma radicans* Juss., *Bignonia radicans* L.). Trumpet fls. 30. August–September. D. Aerial roots numerous. Lflts. hairy on midrib and veins below. Fls. in terminal clusters. North America. (Fig. 9 C.)

CATALPA. Ls. large, opposite or in threes, ov., pointed, 3-5-nerved at base, often lobed, long-stalked. Fls. large, bell-shaped, with five spreading lobes, in large terminal panicles. Seed-pod cylindrical, narrow, up to 24 long.

C. bignonioides Walt. Indian Bean Tree. 50. July. D. Ls. 8, short-pointed, with an unpleasant smell when crushed. Fls. 1½, white spotted with yellow and purple. East United States. (Fig. 25 E.)

C. Fargesii Bur. 30. July. D. Ls. 6, long-pointed, hairy below, not odorous when crushed. Fls. 1½, pinkish, spotted with brown and red. China.

C. ovata Don. 30. July. D. Ls. 8, short-pointed, 3-5-lobed. Fls. yellowish white. Japan.

C. speciosa Warder. Western Catalpa. 100. July. D. Ls. 12, long-pointed. Fls. 2, spotted with yellow and purple. U.S.A.

ECCREMOCARPUS SCABER Ruiz & Pav. Climber. June–September. D. Stems herbaceous, ribbed, hairless. Ls. 2-pinnate, the main stalk ending in a tendril; lflts. ov., 1, unevenly toothed or lobed, hairless. Fls. 1, orange-red, tubular, nodding, in 7-12-flowered racemes. Seed-pod 1½, egg-shaped, flattened on one side; seeds flat, winged. Chile. (Fig. 21 D.)

* PITHECOCTENIUM MURICATUM Moc. ex DC. Climbing by tendrils. Stems ribbed. Ls. 3-fol. or the middle lflt. replaced by a tendril; lflts. ov., 2, pointed, rounded or slightly heart-shaped base. Fls. 1, trumpet-shaped, white, with yellow throat, in terminal many-flowered racemes. Fruit oblong, 5, prickly. Mexico. (Fig. 1 H.)

Family 77. GLOBULARIACEAE. K (5), C (5), A4, G̲1

Only one genus, *Globularia*. Ls. alternate. Fls. in a head. Ovary 1-celled, containing one hanging ovule.

GLOBULARIA CORDIFOLIA L. Globe Daisy. ¼. May–August. Ls. obov., 1, toothed or notched at apex, mostly spreading radially at ground level. Fls. small, blue, 2-lipped, in round heads ½ across on the top of an erect stalk. Alps, Tyrol, and mountains of South Europe. (Fig. 103 H.)

Family 78. VERBENACEAE. K (4–5), C (4–5), A4, G̲ (2)

Ls. opposite or in whorls on 4-edged branchlets, without stipules. Fls. tubular; ovary 2-4-celled. Fruit a berry or capsule. Teak is the wood of *Tectona grandis*, a native of India, Burma, and Siam.

CALLICARPA. Ls. 5, ov., lanc., toothed, pointed, base tapering. Fls. small, 4-parted, in axillary branched clusters. Fruit ¼, a violet berry.

C. americana L. French Mulberry. 6. May–July. D. Ls. hairy. Fls. bluish, stalkless. Virginia to Texas.

C. Giraldiana Hesse. 6. July. D. Ls. slightly downy. Fls. lilac, flower-stalks longer than the leaf-stalks. China.

C. japonica Thunb. Murasaki. 5. August. D. Ls. hairless. Fls. pale pink; flower-stalks longer than the leaf-stalks. Japan and Corea. (Fig. 62 G.)

CARYOPTERIS. Young stems grey-felted. Ls. opposite, short-stalked, covered with grey-white down on lower surface. Fls. small, 4-parted, in axillary branched clusters. Fruit ¼, a violet berry.

CARYOPTERIS—*continued*

C. Mastacanthus Schauer (*C. incana* Miq.). Blue Spiraea. 8. September. D. Ls. ov., 3, tapering base, coarsely toothed, dull green above, grey-white below. China and Japan.

C. mongolica Bunge. 3. July–August. D. Ls. linear, 1½, entire, greyish green, downy on both sides. Mongolia. (Fig. 50 F.)

C. tangutica Maxim. 3. September–October. D. Ls. ov., 1½, with four rounded lobe-like teeth on each side. (Fig. 34 L.)

* CITHAREXYLUM. Fiddle Wood. Several species in cultivation. Ls. lanc., toothed or entire, hairless, short-stalked. Fls. small, K (5), C (5), A4, in long terminal racemes or spikes. South America. (Fig. 77 C.)

CLERODENDRON. Ls. large and flexible, ov., 9. Fls. in terminal branched clusters or panicles, K (5), C (5), A4. Fruit a berry enclosed in a persistent calyx.

C. foetidum Bunge. 6. August–September. D. Ls. heart-shaped, short-pointed, coarsely toothed, with an unpleasant smell when crushed. Fls. purplish red, fragrant. China. (Fig. 62 D.)

C. trichotomum Thunb. 12. July–September. D. Ls. ov., long-pointed, entire or toothed, downy below, sometimes 2-3-lobed towards apex. Fls. 1, white, fragrant, petals narrow-oblong, sepals reddish. Berry bright blue to black, in a crimson calyx. China and Japan. (Fig. 62 E.)

Var. *Fargesii* Rehd. (*C. Fargesii* Dode). Ls. smaller, sepals green (Rehd.)

DIOSTEA JUNCEA Miers (BAILLONIA JUNCEA Benth.). 20. June. D. Branches tall, slender, rush-like. Ls. ov., lanc., ¾, toothed, the pairs some distance apart on the stem. Fls. ¼, pale lilac, tubular, in short axillary and terminal racemes. Fruit a berry enclosed in the persistent calyx. Chile. (Fig. 62 H.)

* LIPPIA CITRIODORA Kunth (ALOYSIA CITRIODORA Ortega). Lemon-scented Verbena. 15. August. D. Ls. in threes, lanc., 4, entire, pointed, margins hairy, lemon-scented. Fls. small, pale purple, in terminal panicles. South America. (Fig. 66 A.)

* RAPHITHAMNUS CYANOCARPUS Miers (CITHAREXYLUM CYANOCARPUM C. Gay). 25. April. E. Young stems bristly, with axillary spines. Ls. opposite or in threes, ov., ¾, pointed, entire, dark green above. Fls. ½, pale blue, solitary or in pairs in leaf-axils on old wood. Fruit a bright blue berry. Chile. (Fig. 54 L.)

VITEX. Ls. digitate, long-stalked; lflts. grey-felted below. Fls. small, purple or white, in axillary or terminal spikes or branched clusters. Fruit a berry surrounded by the persistent calyx.

* **V. Agnus-castus** L. Chaste Tree. 10. September–October. D. Lflts. linear, lanc., 6, entire, dark green above. Fls. pale violet, tubular, in long spikes, corolla 5-lobed. Mediterranean region. (Fig. 5 D.)

Var. *alba* West. Fls. white.

* **V. Negundo** L. 15. September–October. D. Lflts. ov., lanc., toothed in the middle. Fls. purple, in panicles. India and China. (Fig. 5 H.)

Var. *incisa* Clarke. Lflts. deeply cut into narrow segments A smaller shrub, with smaller flower-panicles and berries.

Family 79. **LABIATAE.** K (5), C (5), A2–4, G̲ (2)

Branchlets usually quadrangular. Ls. opposite, without stipules. Fls. usually irregular in shape and 2-lipped, in the axils of the upper ls. forming whorls, spikes, or panicles; stamens typically four, two long and two short, rarely two. Ovary 4-cleft, with a single style arising from the base between the four sections of the ovary. Fruit of four nutlets enclosed in the persistent calyx. A large family containing many aromatic and culinary herbs, such as mint, sage, thyme, lavender, hyssop, balm, bergamot, basil, tulsi, patchouli, etc.

* BALLOTA FRUTESCENS Woods. Shrubby Horehound. 1. July–August. E. Stems slender, with a pair of spines at each joint. Ls. ov., 1, 3-9-lobed or merely toothed, dull green, downy on both sides, slender-stalked. Fls. ½, white, in pairs or threes in the leaf-axils. Riviera. (Fig. 54 H.)

* COLQUHOUNIA COCCINEA Wall. 10. August–October. D. Ls. ov., lanc., 8, toothed, dull green and downy above, grey-felted below. Fls. 1, red or orange, 2-lipped, in whorls in terminal spikes and panicles. Himalaya. (Fig. 56 P.)

ELSHOLTZIA. Branchlets cylindrical. Ls. lanc., 6, long-pointed, tapering base, toothed in the middle, smelling like mint. Fls. arranged in whorls in terminal spikes, stamens four. Nutlets egg-shaped or oblong.

* **E. polystachya** Benth. 8. August–October. E. Fls. white. Himalaya. (Fig. 61 O.)

E. Stauntonii Benth. 8. September–October. E. Fls. purplish pink. China. (Fig. 61 N.)

HYSSOPUS OFFICINALIS L. Hyssop. 2. August–September. E. Stems square. Ls. linear, 1½, minutely toothed, green, gland-dotted on both sides. Fls. ½, bluish purple in axillary whorls; stamens four, protruded. South Europe. (Fig. 50 A.)

LAVANDULA. Lavender. Young stems square. Ls. narrow, 2, entire, grey-green and downy, margins recurved. Fls. ¼, grey-blue or purple, in whorls in terminal spikes, stamens four.

L. Spica Cav. 4. July–September. E. Ls. slightly broadened towards the end. Fls. grey-blue. Mediterranean region.

Var. *alba* Sweet. Fls. white.

Var. *latifolia* L. f. Ls. broader and flat.

L. Stoechas L. 2. May–June. E. Flowering stems leafy to the top. Fls. deep purple, in a compact terminal spike surrounded by a cluster of bracts. S. W. Europe, North Africa.

L. vera DC. 4. July–September. E. Ls. not broadened towards the end. Fls. grey-blue. Mediterranean region. (Fig. 50 D.)

* LEONOTIS LEONURUS R. Br. 4. Summer. E. Branchlets 4-angled, downy, and deeply grooved. Ls. lanc., 3, toothed in outer half, aromatic, tapering base, downy on both sides, dotted with oil glands below, margins recurved, very shortly stalked. Fls. ¼, scarlet, in whorls. South Africa.

PEROWSKIA ATRIPLICIFOLIA Benth. Russian Sage. 5. August–September. E. Stems cylindrical, long, stiff and erect, white-felted. Ls. ov., lanc., 1½, greyish green, unevenly toothed in outer half. Fls. ¼, violet-blue, in opposite spikes forming a large terminal panicle covered with white powdery down, stamens two. Central Asia. (Fig. 56 D.)

PHLOMIS FRUTICOSA L. Jerusalem Sage. 6. June. E. Stems square, stout, grey-felted. Ls. ov., 5, dull green, wrinkled, prominently net-veined, minutely round-toothed. Fls. 1, yellow, hooded, in crowded axillary whorls. South Europe. (Fig. 56 B.)

PROSTRANTHERA. Mint Bush. Fls. ½, bell-shaped, in terminal racemes or panicles.

* **P. lasianthos** Labill. 20. April–May. E. Ls. ov., lanc., sharply toothed, hairless. Fls. white, tinged with pink or purple. Australia. (Fig. 56 G.)

* **P. rotundifolia** R. Br. 12. April–May. E. Stems very slender, grey-felted. Ls. roundish ov., ½, entire or round-toothed at end, dark glossy green, hairless, gland-dotted. Fls. purple. Tasmania. (Fig. 56 F.)

ROSMARINUS OFFICINALIS L. Rosemary. 7. March–May. E. Ls. linear, 2, entire, blunt-ended, dark green above, white-felted below, margins recurved. Fls. ½, pale violet, in 2-3-flowered clusters in the leaf-axils. Europe and Asia Minor. (Fig. 50 C.)

SALVIA. Sage. Branchlets square. Ls. greyish green, round-toothed, downy on both sides. Fls. in pairs or whorls in terminal erect racemes, stamens two.

* **S. Grahami** Benth. 4. June–July. E. Ls. ov., 3, smelling like black currant. Fls. 1, red to purple, in pairs in terminal racemes. Mexico. (Fig. 56 C.)

* **S. Greggii** Gray. 4. June–July. E. Ls. lanc., 1½. Fls. 1, red to purple, in pairs or threes in terminal racemes. Mexico.

S. officinalis L. Garden Sage. 2. July. E. Ls. ov., 3, much wrinkled. Fls. ¾, purple, in whorls in terminal racemes. South Europe. (Fig. 56 A.)

Var. *alba* Alef. Fls. white.
Var. *purpurea* Bean. Stems and ls. reddish.

SATUREIA MONTANA L. Winter Savory. 1. August. ½ E. Stems erect. Ls. linear, 1, entire, pointed, pitted on both sides, stalkless. Fls. ½, purple or whitish, in terminal leafy panicles. South Europe. (Fig. 50 B.)

TEUCRIUM. Germander. Stems square. Upper lip of flower deeply cleft, stamens protruding.

T. Chamaedrys L. ¾. July–September. E. Stems hairy. Ls. ov., 1, coarsely toothed. Fls. ½, purple or rose, in whorls of four in loose terminal spikes. Europe and West Asia. (Fig. 56 E.)

* **T. fruticans** L. 8. July–September. E. Stems white-felted. Ls. ov., lanc., 1½, entire, dark green above, white-felted below, the pairs somewhat distant on the stem. Fls. pale purple, in erect leafy racemes. South Europe. (Fig. 66 B.)

T. montanum L. ½. June–August. E. Stems tufted, prostrate, white-felted. Ls. linear, lanc., ½, grey-woolly below. Fls. ½, yellow, in heads. South Europe.

THYMUS. Thyme. Prostrate shrubs only a few inches high. Ls. ½ or less, entire, dotted with oil glands. Fls. small, lilac or purple, in erect racemes or spikes.

T. Chamaedrys Fries. Common Thyme. ¼. May–July. E. Ls. ov., ½, blunt-ended. Fls. ½, rosy purple, in elongated spikes. Europe (including Britain). (Fig. 49 F.)

T. Serpyllum L. Wild Thyme. ¼. May–July. E. Ls. ov., ¼, blunt-

THYMUS—*continued*

ended, with long white hairs below and on the margins. Fls. ¼, rosy purple, in rounded heads. Europe (including Britain), North Africa, West Asia. (Fig. 49 H.)

In *T. ovatus* (Mill.), a less common plant, the whorls of flowers are in several tiers, and the leaves have few or no hairs.

T. vulgaris L. Garden Thyme. 1. May–July. E. Ls. lanc., ½, grey, downy, margins recurved. Fls. ½, lilac, in terminal spikes. South Europe. (Fig. 49 G.)

SUB-CLASS III. MONOCHLAMYDEAE

Perianth not differentiated into distinct sepals and petals, usually small and inconspicuous, sometimes absent. The sub-class being largely artificial is rejected by modern botanists, but is retained here in deference to custom.

Family 80. **CHENOPODIACEAE.** P2–5, A=P, G̲1

Ls. usually alternate, without stipules. Fls. small, in clusters, spikes or panicles; stamens opposite the petals; ovary 1-celled, styles two or three. Fruit of a single seed enclosed in the persistent sepals. Among well-known plants belonging to this family are beet, spinach, and orach.

ATRIPLEX. Ls. alternate, entire, usually scurfy or mealy. Fls. unisexual, in terminal spikes.

A. canescens James. Grey Sage Brush, Orach. 3. July. E. Ls. linear, 2, greyish green, fleshy. Fls. yellowish. West North America. (Fig. 51 G.)

A. Halimus L. Tree Purslane. 8. June. ½ E. Ls. ov. or diamond-shaped, 2½, pointed, silvery grey. Fls. greenish. South Europe. (Fig. 125 G.)

CAMPHOROSMA MONSPELIACUM L. 2. July. E. Stems woolly, giving a camphor-like smell when crushed. Ls. awl-shaped, ¼, hairy. Mediterranean region. (Fig. 49 P.)

EUROTIA CERATOIDES C. A. Meyer. 4. July. D. Branches long, slender, whitish. Ls. lanc., 2, pointed, 3-veined, grey-white to green. Fls. with yellow protruding stamens and linear woolly bracts. Caucasus and Asia Minor. (Fig. 125 H.)

SUAEDA FRUTICOSA Forssk. Shrubby Goosefoot. 4. June. ½ E. Stems erect, hairless. Ls. linear, ¼, cylindrical, fleshy, bluish green. North Temperate regions. (Fig. 51 K.)

Family 81. **PHYTOLACCACEAE.** P4–5, A4–5, G̲1–∞

Ls. alternate, without stipules. Fls. small, inconspicuous, ovary of several carpels. Fruit various.

ERCILLA VOLUBILIS A. Juss. (BRIDGESIA SPICATA Hook. & Arn.). 20. March–April. E. Climbs by aerial roots which form adhesive disks on the stem. Ls. ov., 1½, fleshy, bright green, margins crinkled. Fls. ¼, dull white or pinkish, in short dense spikes at end of side shoots. Fruit of two or more carpels. South America. (Fig. 125 J.)

Family 82. **POLYGONACEAE.** P3–6, A6–9, G (3)

Stem with swollen joints and clasped by stipules above the leaf-bases. Ls. alternate, with sheathing stipules. Fls. small, in clusters, spikes or panicles; sepals sometimes coloured, stamens opposite to them; ovary 1-celled, styles two to three. Fruit a small nut enclosed in the persistent sepals. To this family belong docks, sorrel, rhubarb, and buckwheat.

ATRAPHAXIS. Goat Wheat. July–August. D. The genus includes several low, rather unattractive shrubs with slender stems clasped by transparent stipular sheaths. Ls. ov., lanc., usually small, with wavy margins, hairless. Fls. small, pinkish white. *A. Billardieri* (Spach) is a low shrub, often spiny, with very small leaves and small clusters of rosy pink flowers. *A. Muschketowi* (Krassn.) grows up to 8 feet, with leaves up to 2 inches long. *A. spinosa* (L.) has whitish spiny branches and flowers with four sepals. Central Asia. (Figs. 125 N and O.)

BRUNNICHIA CIRRHOSA Banks. 25. July–August. D. Climber with slender grooved stems; sheath very short; branchlets end in tendrils. Ls. ov., 6, straight or heart-shaped base, entire, dark green, hairless. Fls. very small, greenish white, in large panicles. South United States. (Fig. 125 P.)

MUEHLENBECKIA COMPLEXA Meissn. Climbing or prostrate shrub. September. D. Dense masses of wiry interlacing stems; sheath very small. Ls. fiddle-shaped, $\frac{3}{4}$, dull green, hairless. New Zealand. (Fig. 125 M.)

POLYGONUM BALDSCHUANICUM Regel. 40. August–October. D. Climber. Stem slender, grey, hairless. Ls. heart-shaped, 4, pale green, hairless. Fls. $\frac{1}{4}$, pinkish white, in large panicles. Fruit 2-angled. Central Asia. (Fig. 125 Q.)

Family 83. **ARISTOLOCHIACEAE.** P (3), A (6), $\bar{G}$ (4–6)

Mostly tropical plants with flowers having a curiously shaped perianth adapted to catch small insects for pollination purposes. Ovary inferior, 3-6-celled. Fruit a capsule.

ARISTOLOCHIA. Dutchman's Pipe, Birthwort. Climbers. Ls. heart-shaped, 5-7-nerved at base. Fls. large, yellowish green, U-shaped, solitary on a slender stalk. Fruit 3, 6-ribbed.

A. moupinensis Franch. 15. June. D. Ls. 4, leathery, downy below. China. (Fig. 126 B.)

A. Sipho L'Hérit. 30. June–July. D. Ls. 10, hairless. U.S.A. (Fig. 126 A.)

Family 84. **MONIMIACEAE.** P (6–12), A6–12, G several

Mostly tropical or sub-tropical aromatic trees and shrubs with opposite or whorled leaves without stipules. Fls. small, unisexual, in clusters, racemes or panicles. Fruit of several to many 1-seeded carpels, fleshy or dry.

* LAURELIA SERRATA Philippi. 50. April. E. Young stems square. Ls. ov., 5, tapered at both ends, coarsely toothed, dark glossy green, hairless, aromatic, short-stalked. Fls. small, yellowish green. Seeds with tufts of fine hairs. Chile. (Fig. 60 C.)

Family 85. **LAURACEAE.** P (4–6), A8–∞, G̲1

Aromatic trees and shrubs inhabiting the milder parts of the world. Ls. alternate (often close together), without stipules. Fls. small, inconspicuous, usually bisexual, ovary 1-celled. Fruit a berry. East African camphorwood, greenheart, and Queensland walnut are valuable imported timbers.

* CINNAMOMUM CAMPHORA Nees & Eberm. Camphor Tree. 60. April. E. Ls. ov., 6, long-pointed, tapering base, leathery, glossy, hairless, the lowest pair of veins often so strongly developed as to make the leaf appear 3-nerved. Fls. greenish white, in long-stalked panicles up to 3 long. China and Japan. (Fig. 126 C.)

LAURUS. Laurel, Sweet Bay. Ls. ov., lanc., 4, pointed, leathery, glossy. Fls. greenish yellow, 4-parted, in small axillary clusters. Fruit a black shining berry.

* **L. canariensis** Webb & Berth. 60. April. E. Branchlets downy, purplish. Ls. hairy below, conspicuously veined. Canary Islands and Azores.

L. nobilis L. Poet's Laurel. 60. May. E. Branchlets and leaves hairless. Ls. often turn brown at the top and usually have glands in the vein-axils, margins often wavy. Mediterranean region. (Fig. 126 D.)

Var. *angustifolia* Hort. Ls. narrow.

Var. *undulata* Mill. L.-margins conspicuously wavy.

LINDERA BENZOIN Blume (BENZOIN AESTIVALE Nees). Spice Bush. 12. April. D. Ls. obov., 5, thin, margins hairy, with a very pungent spicy smell. Berry dark red or purple. U.S.A. (Fig. 126 F.)

L. megaphylla Hemsl. is a Chinese laurel with large shining evergreen leaves.

LITSAEA (TETRANTHERA). Fls. unisexual, in 2-6-flowered heads which, in bud, are enclosed by several large bracts. Anthers 4-celled.

* **L. geniculata** Benth. & Hook. f. Pond Spice. 6. February–March. D. Branchlets zigzagged. Ls. ov., 2. Berry red. South-east United States.

* **L. japonica** Mirb. 60. April. E. Ls. ov., lanc., 6, bright glossy green above, midrib and veins below covered with brown down, crowded at end of shoot. Berry black. Japan. (Fig. 126 F.)

SASSAFRAS OFFICINALE Nees & Eberm. (S. VARIIFOLIUM Kuntze). Ague Tree. 90. May. D. Ls. ov., 6, 3-nerved, glossy green above, often with a conspicuous lobe on one or both sides. Fls. in branched clusters or racemes. Berry bluish black, with a red fleshy stalk. U.S.A. (Figs. 31 G and 126 H.)

UMBELLULARIA CALIFORNICA Nutt. Californian Laurel or Spice Tree. 100. April. E. Ls. lanc., 5, dark green and glossy above, hairless. Fruit 1, egg- or pear-shaped, green changing to purplish. California. (Fig. 126 J.)

Family 86. **PROTEACEAE.** P (4), A4, G̲1

Trees and shrubs of the southern hemisphere. Ls. alternate or in clusters, leathery, without stipules. Fls. bisexual, 4-parted, generally showy; ovary 1-celled, with a long, often persistent style. Fruit a nut, pod, or capsule, containing one to many seeds. The imported timber known as 'silky oak' is the wood of *Cardwellia sublimis*, a native of Australia.

* EMBOTHRIUM COCCINEUM Forst. Fire Bush. 30. May. E. Ls. ov., lanc., 4, entire, hairless. Fls. 1½, crimson-scarlet, tubular, the four lobes afterwards curling back and exposing the long erect style. Fruit a pod containing two rows of seeds. Chile. (Fig. 126 G.)

GREVILLEA. Stems downy. Ls. linear and pointed, with recurved margins. Fruit a capsule containing two winged seeds. (*G. robusta* (Cunn.) is commonly known as Silky Oak and can often be grown out of doors for a time. It has deeply cut leaves and orange-coloured flowers in one-sided racemes. A tall tree in Australia.)

* **G. rosmarinifolia** A. Cunn. 7. February–June. E. Ls. 2, dark grey-green above, silvery white below. Fls. 1, red, in terminal racemes. Australia. (Fig. 51 D.)

* **G. sulphurea** A. Cunn. 7. May–June. E. Ls. 1, prickly pointed, pale below, almost hairless. Fls. 1, pale yellow, in terminal and axillary racemes. Australia.

* GUEVINA AVELLANA Mol. Chilean Nut. 40. August. E. Branchlets stout, downy. Ls. alternate, pinnate or 2-pinnate; lflts. ov., up to 7 long, rounded or straight at base, sharply toothed, leathery and glossy. Fls. ivory-white, in axillary racemes. Fruit ¾, a hard nut, finally black; seeds edible. Chile. (Fig. 20 A.)

* HAKEA SALIGNA Knight. April–May. E. Ls. ov., lanc., 6, blunt-ended or with a minute point, the veins very indistinct. Fls. small, white, in dense axillary clusters. Fruit 1, beaked, 2-seeded, seeds with a terminal wing. Australia. (Fig. 119 F.)

LOMATIA. Branchlets downy. Ls. leathery. Fruit a pod containing two rows of seeds.

* **L. ferruginea** R. Br. 30. April–May. E. Branchlets covered with reddish brown velvety down. Ls. pinnate; lflts. 3, deeply and pinnately lobed, dark green above, fawny below. Fls. ½, red and yellow, in axillary panicles. South America. (Fig. 20 B.)

* **L. obliqua** R. Br. 12. E. Ls. ov., 4, blunt-ended, coarsely round-toothed, glossy green above, tawny below, stalk brown. Fls. not seen. South America. (Fig. 104 H.)

* TELOPEA TRUNCATA R. Br. Tasmanian Waratah. 25. June. E. Branchlets stout, covered with brown down. Ls. oblanc., 4, entire, or toothed near apex, leathery, dull green above, glaucous below, crowded. Fls. 1, crimson, in terminal heads up to 3 across, style long and curved. Seed-pod 2, cylindrical, curved, seeds in two rows. Tasmania. (Fig. 127 J.)

Family 87. **THYMELEACEAE.** P (4–5), A2–10, $\underline{G}1$

Shrubs or woody plants with alternate entire leaves without stipules. Fls. with a tubular 4-5-lobed perianth and two to ten stamens inserted on the perianth tube; ovary 1-celled, style one. Fruit a berry.

DAPHNE. Buds small. Ls. obov., oblanc., stalkless, often crowded at end of shoot. Fls. small, with a petal-like perianth, in terminal or axillary clusters, P (4), A8, style short and knobbed.

DAPHNE—*continued*

(*a*) *Fls. in axillary clusters*

D. Burkwoodii Burk. 3. May. D. Ls. oblanc., greyish green. Fls. ½, pinkish white. Hybrid.

D. collina Sm. See under (*b*).

* **D. Genkwa** Sieb. 4. May. D. Ls. lanc., 2, silky-hairy below. Fls. ½, lilac. China and Japan.

D. Houtteana Lindl. Purple-leaved Daphne. 4. April. ½ E. Ls. oblanc., 4, purple. Fls. pale lilac. Hybrid.

D. Laureola L. Spurge Laurel. 4. February–March. E. Stems hairless. Ls. oblanc., 4, dark green, thick and firm, hairless. Fls. yellowish green, in stalkless clusters on old wood. Berry egg-shaped, bluish black, poisonous. Europe (including Britain), North Africa, West Asia. (Fig. 127 A.)

D. Mezereum L. Mezereon. 5. February–March. D. Stem with hairs. Ls. oblanc., 3, greyish green, hairless. Fls. purplish red, fragrant. Berry red. Europe and Siberia. (Fig. 127 D.)

Var. *alba* West. Fls. white.

Var. *grandiflora* Dipp. Fls. larger. October–February.

D. pontica L. 3. April. E. Stem hairless. Ls. obov., 3, pointed, glossy green, hairless. Fls. yellowish green, long-tubed, fragrant, in stalked axillary pairs. Asia Minor. (Fig. 127 C.)

(*b*) *Fls. in terminal heads*

D. alpina L. 1. May–June. D. Stems downy. Ls. oblanc., 1½, grey-green, downy on both sides. Fls. white, fragrant. Berry yellowish red. Alps.

D. altaica Pall. 1. May–June. D. Like *D. alpina*, but hairless. Siberia.

D. Blagayana Frey. 1. March–April. E. Ls. obov., 1½, hairless, in rosette-like tufts at end of twigs. Fls. ½, creamy white, very fragrant. Berry pinkish white. Mountains of East Europe. (Fig. 127 B.)

D. Cneorum L. Garland Flower. ½. May. E. Trailing plant with slender stems. Ls. oblanc., 1, greyish green, hairless, in rosette-like tufts. Fls. rosy pink. Berry yellowish brown. South Europe. (Fig. 127 E.)

D. collina Sm. 3. May. E. Stems silky-hairy. Ls. obov., 1½, blunt-ended, dark glossy green above, hairy below. Fls. purplish rose fragrant, silky-felted. Italy and Asia Minor. (Fig. 127 F.)

Var. *neapolitana* Lindl. Ls. nearly hairless below.

D. Giraldii Nitsche. 1½. June. D. Hairless. Ls. oblanc., 1½, crowded at end of shoot. Fls. yellow. Berry red. North China.

D. hybrida Lindl. (*D. Dauphinii* Hort.). 4. May. E. Ls. lanc., 3, glossy green, hairless. Fls. ½, reddish purple, very fragrant, hairy. Hybrid.

* **D. odora** Thunb. (*D. japonica* Sieb. & Zucc.). 6. April–July. E. Stems hairless. Ls. lanc., 3, dark green, hairless. Fls. ½, rosy purple, very fragrant. China and Japan. (Fig. 127 G.)

D. oleoides Schreb. 3. April–May. E. Stems downy. Ls. obov., 1, downy, dotted with white below. Fls. white or pale lilac. Berry red. South Europe.

DAPHNE—*continued*

D. petraea Leyb. (*D. rupestris* Facch.). ½. June. E. Ls. oblanc., ½, hard and leathery, crowded, dark green. Fls. pink, fragrant. South Tyrol. (Fig. 127 H.)

D. retusa Hemsl. 3. May. E. Twigs covered with yellow hairs. Ls. oblanc., 2, notched at end, margins recurved, hairless. Fls. ¾, white inside, purple outside. Berry red. West China.

D. striata Tratt. ½. May. E. Like *D. Cneorum*, but stems hairless and flowers streaked. Alps.

D. tangutica Maxim. 5. March–April. E. Twigs stout, greyish. Ls. oblanc., 2, notched at apex, bright green. Fls. ½, white tinged with rose-purple. Berry red. North-west China.

DIRCA PALUSTRIS L. Leatherwood. 6. March–April. D. Stems jointed, very flexible (can be twisted round and round without breaking), buds downy. Ls. ov., 3, pale green above, glaucous below. Fls. pale yellow, in 2-3-flowered clusters in joints of old wood; stamens eight, protruded. Berry pale green or reddish. China. (Fig. 127 L.)

* EDGEWORTHIA PAPYRIFERA Zucc. (E. CHRYSANTHA Lindl.). 6. February–March. D. Stems olive-green, very tough and flexible (see *Dirca*). Ls. lanc., 5, dull green above, greyish below, with silky hairs when young. Fls. ½, yellow, silky-hairy, P4, A8, style long; in round terminal heads. China. (Fig. 127 K.)

PIMELEA. Ls. opposite, ov., entire. Fls. ¼, tubular, in compact heads surrounded by ov. bracts, P (4), A2, G1. Fruit a berry.

* **P. ferruginea** Labill. 2. June. E. Ls. ½, margins recurved. Fls. pink. Australia.

* **P. ligustrina** Labill. 6. June. E. Fls. white. Australia.

Family 88. ELAEAGNACEAE. P (4), A4–8, G1

Shrubs or small trees covered with brown or silvery scales. Ls. entire, without stipules. Fls. in leaf-axils; ovary 1-celled, style one, with a knobbed stigma. Fruit a berry enclosed by the persistent perianth.

ELAEAGNUS. Ls. alternate, short-stalked. Fls. 4-parted.

(*a*) *Deciduous*

E. angustifolia L. (*E. hortensis* Bieb.). Oleaster, Bohemian Olive. 20. July–August. Branches silvery, spiny. Ls. lanc., 3, dull green above, silvery below. Fls. ¼, bell-shaped, silver outside, yellow within, solitary or in 2-3-flowered clusters. Berry silvery. Mediterranean region. (Fig. 127 O.)

E. argentea Pursh. Silver Berry. 12. May. Branches brown. Ls. ov., 2½, silvery white on both sides. Fls. ½, drooping, silvery outside, yellow within, in few-flowered clusters. Berry silvery. North America. (Fig. 127 R.)

E. multiflora Thunb. (*E. longipes* Gray). 10. April–May. Branches brown. Ls. ov., 2½, green and hairy above, silvery below and dotted with brown scales. Fls. ½, solitary or in few-flowered clusters. Berry orange-coloured, edible. China and Japan.

E. umbellata Thunb. 20. May–June. Branches brown, often thorny. Ls. lanc., 4, bright green above, silvery below. Fls. ½, funnel-shaped,

ELAEAGNUS—*continued*

silvery outside, creamy white within, in few-flowered clusters. Berry red. Himalaya, China, and Japan. (Fig. 127 N.)

(b) Evergreen

E. glabra Thunb. 20. October–November. Rambler. Branches glistening brown. Ls. ov., 2½, long-pointed, glossy green above, glistening silvery below. Fls. funnel-shaped, brown outside, white within. Berry grey or rusty. China and Japan. (Fig. 127 P.)

E. macrophylla Thunb. 12. October–November. Branchlets silvery white. Ls. ov., 4, dark glossy green above, silvery below. Fls. ½, very fragrant, nodding, in 4-6-flowered clusters. Berry red. Japan and Formosa.

E. pungens Thunb. 15. October–November. Twigs brown, spiny. Ls. ov., 4, dark glossy green above, dull white dotted with brown below, leathery, rounded base, margins wavy. Fls. ½, drooping, silvery white, in few-flowered clusters. Berry red. China and Japan. (Fig. 127 Q.)

Var. *aurea* Serv. Ls. margined with yellow.

Var. *aureo-variegata* Bean. Ls. yellow in middle.

Var. *reflexa* Rehd. Less spiny; ls. brown-scaly below, margins not wavy.

HIPPOPHAE RHAMNOIDES L. Sea Buckthorn. 40. April. D. Twigs often spine-tipped; young parts silvery. Ls. alternate, linear, 3, dark green above, silvery below. Fls. very small, in small axillary clusters on old wood, sexes on different trees. Berry ¼, orange-coloured. Europe (including Britain) and Temperate Asia. (Fig. 51 A.)

SHEPHERDIA ARGENTEA Nutt. Buffalo Berry. 12. February–March. D. Ls. opposite, lanc., 2, round-ended, silvery below. Berry ¼, scarlet. North America. (Fig. 54 K.)

Family 89. LORANTHACEAE. P (3–4), A3–4, $\bar{G}1$

Shrubby parasites on the branches of trees. Ls. opposite, entire, without stipules. Ovary 1-celled. Fruit a 1-seeded berry.

VISCUM ALBUM L. Mistletoe. March–April. E. Parasite on apple and poplar trees, but will grow on almost any tree. Branches green, dividing into two at each joint. Ls. lanc., 4, round-ended, yellowish green, stalkless. Fls. inconspicuous, in the forks of the stem. Berry ¼, white. Europe (including Britain) and North Asia. (Fig. 76 G.)

According to Rehder the American Mistletoe, *Phoradendron flavescens* (Nutt.), differs in the leaves being 3-5-nerved and the flowers in axillary spikes. *Loranthus europaeus* (L.), a continental plant growing on oak and chestnut, has brown twigs and thin deciduous leaves.

Family 90. BUXACEAE. Male fl. P4, A4; female P6, $\underline{G}$ (3)

Evergreen trees and shrubs. Fls. unisexual, the sexes on different plants; ovary 3-celled. Fruit a 3-horned capsule. Box wood is yellow, hard, and heavy, without much tendency to warp or split, so that it is suitable for mathematical and musical instruments, printing blocks, and chessmen.

BUXUS. Box. Young branchlets square. Ls. opposite, ov., 1, entire, rounded or notched at end. Fls. yellowish green, in axillary clusters. Fruit a dry 3-horned capsule.

B. balearica Lam. Balearic Box. 30. April–May. Ls. leathery, glossy, dark green above, pale below. Balearic Islands.

B. microphylla Sieb. & Zucc. 2. April–May. Ls. obov., with tapering base. China.

B. sempervirens L. Common Box. 30. April. Ls. ov., thick and glossy, dark green above, pale green below. Europe (including Britain). North Africa, and North Asia. (Fig. 67 H.)

Var. *argentea* Hort. Ls. with white border.
Var. *aurea* Loud. Ls. partly or wholly yellow.
Var. *aurea pendula* Hort. Golden Weeping Box.
Var. *pendula* Hort. Green weeping form.
Var. *suffruticosa* Loud. Edging Box. Dwarf, ls. obov.

PACHYSANDRA. Mountain Spurge. Low shrubs not exceeding 1 foot. Stems erect, fleshy. Ls. alternate, ov., coarsely and unevenly toothed, 3-nerved at base, crowded at end of stem. Fls. small, unisexual, in erect spikes, the females at the base. Fruit a 3-horned capsule.

P. procumbens Michx. Alleghany Spurge. April. ½ E. Stems downy. Ls. 3, with hairs. South-east United States. (Fig. 104 K.)

P. terminalis Sieb. & Zucc. April. E. Stems hairless. Ls. 2, hairless. Japan. (Fig. 104 J.)

SARCOCOCCA. Low evergreen shrubs. Ls. alternate, entire, pointed, leathery and glossy, 3-nerved at base, hairless. Fls. small, unisexual, in axillary racemes or clusters, the females at the base. Fruit ¼, a berry.

S. Hookeriana Baill. 6. February–March. Ls. lanc., 3, long-pointed, tapering base. Berry round, black. West Himalaya.

S. humilis Stapf. 1½. February–March. Ls. lanc., 3, with a prominent nerve parallel to each margin. Berry round, blue-black. China. (Fig. 128 C.)

S. ruscifolia Stapf. 2. February–March. Ls. ov., 2½, long-pointed. Fls. white, fragrant, in few-flowered clusters. Berry round, crimson. China. (Fig. 128 B.)

S. saligna Muell.-Arg. (*S. pruniformis* Lindl.). 3. March–May. Ls. lanc., 5, long-pointed, with a marginal vein. Berry egg-shaped, purple. Himalaya. (Fig. 128 A.)

Family 91. EUPHORBIACEAE. P4–10 or 0, A1–∞, G̲ (3)

Fls. small, green or greenish yellow, unisexual; ovary 2-3-celled. In *Euphorbia* the flowers appear to be bisexual, but in reality each stamen is a separate male flower, indicated by the joint in the filament. Crotons, the castor-oil plant, tapioca, manihot (cassava), and Para rubber (*Hevea brasiliensis*) belong to this family. The last named is the chief source of natural rubber and was introduced to the East Indies through the agency of Kew Gardens.

ANDRACHNE COLCHICA Fisch. & Mey. 3. June–September. D. Stems erect, very slender, hairless. Ls. alternate, ov., ¾, entire, rounded at base, hairless, crowded. Fls. ¼, yellowish green, the male in axillary clusters, the female solitary in the leaf-axils, P5+5, A5. Fruit 1/4, a dry pale-brown capsule. Caucasus. (Fig. 128 D.)

DAPHNIPHYLLUM MACROPODUM Miq. 12. May. E. Branchlets hairless. Ls. alternate, lanc., 8, entire, pointed, dark green above, glaucous below, crowded radially at end of shoot, stalk reddish. Fls. small, pale green, aromatic, in axillary racemes on old wood, P3–8. Fruit 1/4, a blue-black berry. China and Japan. (Fig. 128 G.)

EUPHORBIA WULFENII Hoppe. Shrubby Spurge. 5. April–May. E. Stems erect, unbranched, downy, fleshy and filled with milky juice. Ls. alternate, linear, 5, entire, pointed, blue-green, crowded radially on upper part of stem. Fls. 1/2, greenish yellow, in large terminal panicles. Dalmatia. (Fig. 52 H.)

SECURINEGA. Stems hairless. Ls. alternate, ov., 2, dull green, hairless. Fls. greenish yellow, P5, A5, the male in axillary clusters, the female solitary. Fruit 1/4, a dry greenish capsule.

- **S. flueggeoides** Muell.-Arg. 5. August. D. Branchlets brown. Japan. (Fig. 128 E.)
- **S. ramiflora** Muell.-Arg. 5. August. D. Branchlets green. East Asia.

Family 92. **ULMACEAE.** P4–9, A4–9, G (2)

Trees with alternate stipulate leaves that are usually unequal-sided at the base. Fls. small; stamens as many as the perianth segments and opposite them; ovary 1-celled. Fruit a 1-seeded nut or berry. Elm timber lasts well under water or when completely buried in the ground and is therefore used for ship-building, dock construction, well kerbs, and coffins.

APHANANTHE ASPERA Planch. 60. D. Ls. ov., 4, evenly toothed, 3-nerved at base, parallel-veined, rough on both sides. Fls. very small, unisexual. Fruit 1/4, a black-purple berry. China and Japan. (Fig. 105 A.)

CELTIS. Nettle Tree. Bark grey and smooth. Ls. alternate, toothed, 3-nerved at base, rough on both sides, unequal-sided at base. Fls. small, greenish, unisexual. Fruit a berry.

- **C. australis** L. 70. May. D. Ls. lanc., long-pointed. Berry reddish brown. Mediterranean region. (Fig. 105 B.)
- **C. caucasica** Willd. 20. May. D. Twigs downy. Ls. ov., lanc., 5, short-pointed, coarsely toothed. Berry reddish brown. Caucasus. (Fig. 105 C.)
- **C. laevigata** Willd. Mississippi Hackberry. 100. May. D. Bark warted. Ls. ov., lanc., 3, long-pointed, teeth few or none. Berry orange-red to purplish black. South United States.
- **C. occidentalis** L. Sugarberry, Hackberry. 120. May. D. Ls. ov., 4, long-pointed, sharply toothed in outer half, rounded base. Berry purple. North America. (Fig. 105 D.)

PLANERA AQUATICA Gmel. Water Elm. 35. April–May. D. Ls. ov., 3, unevenly toothed, pinnately nerved, rough above, scurfy and downy below, very shortly stalked. Fruit 1/2, an irregularly ribbed 1-seeded nut. U.S.A. (Fig. 105 E.)

PTEROCELTIS TATARINOWII Maxim. 50. D. Bark grey, peeling off in long flakes. Ls. ov., 3, long-pointed, unevenly toothed, 3-nerved at base, rough above. Fruit 1/2, winged, slender-stalked. China. (Fig. 105 F.)

ULMUS. Elm. Ls. ov., double-toothed, parallel-veined, unequal-sided at base. Fls. small, green or reddish, bisexual, usually appearing before the leaves in small clusters in the axils of the leaf-scars on the previous year's growth. Fruit flat, winged, 1-seeded.

(a) Ls. smooth above

U. alata Michx. Wahoo Elm. 50. March. D. Twigs with two opposite corky wings. Ls. narrowly ov., 1½, stiff. Fls. drooping, slender-stalked. Wing of fruit narrow, with two incurved beaks. South United States.

U. laevis Pall. European White Elm. 100. March. D. Bark smooth in saplings. Buds long and pointed. Ls. obov., 4. Fls. drooping, slender-stalked. Seed in centre of wing. Central Europe to West Asia.

U. nitens Moench (*U. foliacea* Gilib., *U. carpinifolia* Gleditsch). Smooth-leaved Elm, Feathered Elm. 100. February–March. D. Branches drooping at ends; branchlets often corky. Ls. ov., 4, long-pointed, stalked. Fls. erect, in thick clusters. Seed close to notch of wing. Europe (including Britain). (Fig. 105 G.)

Var. *pendula* Henry. Weeping form.

U. parvifolia Jacq. Chinese Elm. 50. September–October. D. Bark smooth. Ls. ov., 1½, leathery. Fls. erect. Seed in centre of wing. China.

U. serotina Sarg. Red Elm. 70. September. D. Twigs corky. Ls. oblong, 2½, glossy above. Fls. in drooping racemes. Wing of fruit ov., hairy, deeply notched. South United States.

U. stricta Lindl. Cornish Elm. 100. February–March. D. Tall narrow tree. Ls. ov., 2. Fls. erect. Seed close to notch of wing. Cornwall, Devon, Somerset, Brittany. (Fig. 105 K.)

Var. *Wheatleyi* Bean. Guernsey or Jersey Elm. Narrower or pyramidal tree with stiffer and more erect branches and stiff shining dark-green leaves remaining on the tree very late in the season.

(b) Ls. rough above

U. americana L. American or White Elm. 120. March. D. A wide-spreading tree with ashy-grey bark. Ls. ov., obov., 6. Fls. slender-stalked, drooping, with white stigmas. Fruit ov., obov., ½, fringed with hairs. North America. (Fig. 105 H.)

U. fulva Michx. Slippery Elm. 70. March. D. Twigs reddish orange, with large downy buds. Ls. obov., 6. Fls. in thick erect clusters. Wing of fruit nearly circular, with a reddish downy seed in the middle. North America.

U. glabra Huds. (*U. montana* With.). Wych Elm. 125. February–March. D. A wide-spreading and rather open tree with stringy bark, which is smooth in saplings. Ls. ov., obov., 7, nearly stalkless. Fls. with red stigma. Fruit 1, seed in centre of wing. North Europe (including Britain). (Fig. 105 M.)

Var. *Camperdownii* Rehd. Round-headed weeping form.

U. japonica Sarg. Japanese Elm. 70. March. D. Like the Common or English Elm (see below), but the leaves are obov. and larger. Japan.

U. major Sm. (*U. hollandica* Mill.). Dutch Elm. 120. February–March.

ULMUS—*continued*

D. Branches often drooping. Bark rough in saplings. Ls. ov., 5, nearly smooth above. Fruit 1, seed close to notch. Natural cross between *U. glabra* and *U. nitens*.

U. minor Mill. (*U. Plotii* Druce). East Anglian or Lock Elm. 90. February–March. D. Twigs interlacing. Ls. ov., 2½. Fls. with pink stigmas. Fruit ½, seed close to notch. East and Central England, and Hampshire. (Fig. 105 L.)

U. procera Salisb. (*U. campestris* L.). Common or English Elm. 150. February–March. D. A tall tree with erect or spreading branches, corky branchlets, and hairy twigs. Buds small, downy. Bark of saplings rough. Suckers freely. Ls. ov., 3½. Fls. reddish, erect, stigmas white. Fruit ½, seed close to notch of wing. South England. (Fig. 105 J.)

Var. *Louis Van Houttei* Rehd. Ls. yellow.

Var. *variegata* Hort. Ls. variegated with white.

Var. *viminalis* Loud. Ls. 2, long-pointed. A slender narrow-headed tree with drooping branchlets.

U. racemosa Thomas (*U. Thomasi* Sarg.). Rock Elm, Cork Elm. 100. April. D. Branchlets corky; buds large, pointed, and downy. Ls. ov., 3. Fls. in drooping racemes. Seed in centre of wing. North America.

U. vegeta Lindl. Huntingdon Elm, Chichester Elm. 100. March. D. Branches ascending. Ls. 6, stalked. Fruit ¾, seed in centre of wing. Natural hybrid. (Fig. 105 M.)

Zelkova carpinifolia Koch (Z. crenata Spach). 100. April–May. D. Bark smooth. Trunk short, dividing into a large number of ascending branches. Ls. ov., 3, rounded or heart-shaped base, coarsely and more or less evenly toothed, with scattered hairs above. Fruit ¼, not winged. Caucasus. (Fig. 106 A.)

Z. serrata (Makino) has more sharply toothed leaves, with a long point; it is a native of Japan.

Family 93. **MORACEAE.** P3–4, A3–4, G1

Stems with milky juice. Ls. alternate, stipulate. Fls. unisexual; ovary 1-celled. Fruit fleshy, composed of many 1-seeded carpels borne on a fleshy development of the flower-bearing axis. An important family, to which belong hops, mulberries, figs, rubber trees (*Ficus elastica*), the Indian banyan, bread-fruit, and the West African timber known as iroko or African teak.

BROUSSONETIA. Paper Mulberry. Ls. ov., 8, toothed, long-pointed, 3-5-nerved and rounded at base, often lobed. Fls. ½, white, in clusters or catkins, the sexes on different trees. Fruits in a rounded head, 1 across.

B. Kazinokii Sieb. 15. May. D. Ls. with few hairs, stalk less than 1. Fls. in clusters. Japan.

B. papyrifera Vent. 30. May. D. Ls. woolly below, stalk more than 1. Fls. in long drooping catkins. China, Japan, South Sea Islands. (Fig. 28 E.)

Cudrania tricuspidata Bur. (C. triloba Hance, Maclura tricuspidata Carr., Vaniera tricuspidata Hu). Silkworm Thorn. 20. July. D. Branches thorny, hairless. Ls. ov., 4, entire or shallowly 3-lobed near apex, rounded at base, dark green above, slightly downy below. Fls. green, crowded into little balls in the leaf-axils, the sexes on different trees. Fruit 1, red, egg-shaped, hard and shiny. China. (Fig. 127 M.)

FICUS CARICA L. Fig Tree. 30. May. D. Ls. ov., 8, 3-5-lobed, palmately nerved, heart-shaped base, rough above. Fls. produced inside a pear-shaped receptacle which enlarges and becomes the fruit. West Asia. (Fig. 28 C.)

MACLURA POMIFERA Schneid. (M. AURANTIACA Nutt.). Osage Orange, Bow Wood. 50. June. D. Branches spiny. Ls. ov., lanc., 4, entire, pointed, rounded at base, slender-stalked. Fls. green, in round clusters, the sexes on different trees. Fruit 4, round, yellowish green, rough. South United States. (Fig. 128 F.)

Var. *inermis* Schneid. Without spines.

MORUS. Mulberry. Ls. 8, pointed, toothed, often lobed, heart-shaped and 3-5-nerved at base. Fls. small, in short drooping catkins in the leaf-axils. Fruit a composite mass of fleshy carpels.

M. alba L. White Mulberry. 45. May. D. Ls. light green, with few hairs. Fruit cluster 1, white or pinkish. Temperate and sub-tropical Asia.

M. nigra L. Common Mulberry. 30. May. D. Ls. dark green above, pale and downy below. Fruit cluster 1, dark red. Orient. (Figs. 28 F. and 106 B.)

M. rubra L. Red Mulberry. 60. May. D. Ls. with a straight or slightly heart-shaped base, downy below. Fruit cluster 1, dark purple. U.S.A.

Family 94. **URTICACEAE.** P4–5, A4–5, $\underline{G}1$

The nettle family. Fls. small, unisexual; the stamens as many as the perianth segments and opposite them; ovary 1-celled, containing one erect ovule. Hemp and hashish are obtained from *Cannabis sativa*, an Asiatic herb.

* DEBREGEASIA LONGIFOLIA Wedd. (D. VELUTINA Gaud.). 12. May–June. D. Stems very tough. Ls. alternate, lanc., 6, long-pointed, toothed, 3-nerved at base, dark green above, white below. Fls. small, yellow, in fleshy heads. Fruit $\frac{1}{4}$, fleshy, bright orange-yellow, edible. India. (Fig. 106 C.)

Family 95. **PLATANACEAE.** P3–8, A3–8, $\underline{G}3$–8

The plane tree family, containing only one genus.

PLATANUS. Plane. Trees with smooth bark peeling off in thin large flakes. Ls. alternate, ov., 10, palmately lobed, stipulate. Fls. unisexual, in dense round heads. Fruit burr-like.

P. acerifolia Willd. London Plane. 100. May. D. Ls. shallowly lobed, the lobes longer than broad and coarsely toothed. Usually two fruiting heads on one stalk. Hybrid. (Fig. 30 B.)

P. occidentalis L. Button Wood. 150. May. D. Ls. shallowly lobed, the lobes broader than long and coarsely toothed. One fruiting head at the end of each stalk. North America. (Fig. 30 C.)

P. orientalis L. Oriental Plane. 100. May. D. Ls. deeply lobed, the lobes longer than broad and scarcely toothed. Several fruiting heads at the end of each stalk. South-east Europe and West Asia. (Fig. 30 A.)

Family 96. LEITNERIACEAE. Po, A3–12, G1

LEITNERIA FLORIDANA Chap. Corkwood. 10. April. D. Trunk swollen at base; buds woolly. Ls. alternate, ov., lanc., 7, entire, pointed, tapering base, bright green above, paler below, covered with minute velvety down. Fls. unisexual, in axillary catkins appearing before the leaves, the sexes on different trees. Fruit $\frac{3}{4}$, a light olive-brown berry. South United States. (Fig. 128 M.)

Family 97. JUGLANDACEAE. P4, A3–40, $\bar{G}$ (2)

Trees with alternate and usually aromatic leaves without stipules. Fls. unisexual, the male in long drooping catkins, the female solitary or in small clusters or racemes, styles two. Fruit a large 1-seeded nut. Hickory and walnut wood are much in demand.

CARYA. Hickory. Twigs with solid pith. Ls. pinnate; lflts. toothed. Fruit a smooth nut enclosed in a splitting husk.

C. alba Koch (*C. tomentosa* Nutt.). Mocker Nut. 100. June. D. Bark ridged. Twigs hairy; buds large, with overlapping scales. Lflts. ov., lanc., 7, hairy below, fragrant when crushed; leaf-stalk hairy. Fruit $1\frac{1}{2}$, pear- or egg-shaped, light brown, thick-stalked, kernel sweet. East North America. (Fig. 11 C.)

C. cordiformis Koch (*C. amara* Nutt.). Bitter Nut. 100. June. D. Bark light brown, rough. Twigs hairless at maturity; buds bright yellow, the scales not overlapping. Lflts. lanc., 6. Fruit $1\frac{1}{2}$, egg-shaped; nut compressed, grey, thin-shelled, kernel bitter. North America.

C. glabra Sweet (*C. porcina* Nutt.). Pig Nut. 90. June. D. Bark smooth, dark grey. Twigs hairless; buds small, with overlapping scales. Lflts. ov., lanc., 7, the terminal one the largest, hairless. Fruit 1, pear-shaped, slightly winged towards apex, nut thin-shelled, kernel bitter. East North America.

C. laciniosa Loud. King Nut, Big Shellbark Hickory. 120. June. D. Bark shaggy. Ls. 5-7-fol.; lflts. lanc., the terminal one the largest. Fruit $2\frac{1}{2}$, 4-ribbed above middle, nut thick-shelled, kernel sweet. U.S.A.

C. myristiciformis Nutt. Nutmeg Hickory. 100. June. D. A tree with dark brown bark and yellow scaly young twigs. Lflts. ov., 4, silvery white below. Fruit $1\frac{1}{2}$, elongated, nut scarcely compressed. South United States.

C. ovata Koch. Shellbark Hickory, Shagbark Hickory. 100. June. D. Bark light grey and shaggy. Twigs bright reddish brown; buds large, with overlapping scales. Lflts. five, ov., lanc., 7, margins fringed with hairs. Fruit 2, pear- or egg-shaped, white; nut thin-shelled, kernel sweet. East North America.

* **C. Pecan** Engl. & Graebn. Pecan. 150. June. D. Bark deeply furrowed; buds yellow and downy. Lflts. lanc., 6. Fruit 2, egg-shaped or oblong, kernel sweet. South United States.

JUGLANS. Walnut. Twigs with chambered pith. Ls. pinnate, fragrant when rubbed. Fruit a rough nut enclosed in a green non-splitting husk.

J. californica S. Wats. (*J. Hindsii* Rehd.). 40. May. D. Lflts. lanc., coarsely and sharply toothed, downy. Nut $1\frac{1}{2}$, round, thick-shelled, faintly grooved. California.

JUGLANS—*continued*

J. cathayensis Dode. Chinese Bitternut. 50. May. D. Ls. very long (up to 3 feet); lflts. ov., obov., finely toothed, rounded or slightly heart-shaped at base. Nut 1½, egg-shaped, strongly ridged, the ridges broken and spiny, thick-shelled, kernel small. China.

J. cinerea L. Butternut. 80. May. D. Twigs reddish or purplish brown. Lflts. lanc., 4, toothed in outer half. Fruit large and sticky, nut prominently ridged. North America.

J. nigra L. Black Walnut. 100. May. D. Lflts. ov., 6, toothed. Fruit 2, round, ridged. North America. (Fig. 11 F.)

J. regia L. Common Walnut. 100. May. D. Lflts. ov., entire. Fruit 2, egg-shaped, nut wrinkled. Caucasus to Himalaya. (Fig. 11 G.)

Var. *laciniata* Loud. Lflts. pinnately dissected.

J. Sieboldiana Maxim. 70. May. D. Lflts. ov., 6, finely toothed. Fruit 2, round or egg-shaped, clammy, nut wrinkled. Japan.

* PLATYCARYA STROBILACEA Sieb. & Zucc. 30. June. D. Twigs with solid pith, bright yellowish or reddish brown. Ls. pinnate; lflts. ov., lanc., 4, slightly curved, double-toothed, stalkless. Catkins erect. Fruit a winged nut. China. (Fig. 17 B.)

PTEROCARYA. Wing Nut. Bark deeply furrowed. Twigs with chambered pith; buds stalked. Ls. pinnate; lflts. lanc., 5, toothed, unequal-sided at base. Fruit a winged nut, in long drooping spikes.

P. fraxinifolia Spach (*P. caucasica* E. A. Mey.). Caucasian Wing Nut. 100. June. D. Common leaf-stalk not winged. Fruit ¾, wings circular. Caucasus. (Fig. 11 E.)

P. stenoptera DC. (*P. sinensis* Hort.). 60. June. D. Common leaf-stalk winged. Fruit ¾, wings oblong or lanc., forming a V. China. (Fig. 11 D.)

Family 98. **MYRICACEAE.** P0, A2–16, $\underline{G}1$

Trees or shrubs with alternate, aromatic and resin-dotted ls. without stipules. Fls. unisexual, in catkins, the sexes on different plants; ovary 1-celled, two to each catkin scale, styles two. Fruit a berry or nut.

MYRICA. Ls. toothed or lobed, sometimes entire. Fls. small, in male and female catkins.

M. asplenifolia L. (*Comptonia asplenifolia* Ait.). Sweet Fern. 4. April–May. D. Stems downy. Ls. linear, 4, pinnately lobed, dark green, downy. Fruit-cluster burr-like. North America. (Fig. 36 G.)

M. californica Cham. Californian Wax Myrtle. 15. May–June. E. Ls. lanc., 4, leathery, glossy green, toothed. Fruits small, round, thinly coated with white wax. California. (Fig. 106 E.)

M. carolinensis Mill. Bayberry. 10. March–April. D. Ls. oblanc., 4, blunt-toothed towards apex, or entire. Fruit thickly coated with white wax. U.S.A.

M. cerifera L. Wax Myrtle. 40. March–April. ½ E. Ls. lanc., thin, 3, toothed towards apex, glossy green above. Fruits small, round, thickly coated with white wax, in clusters on old wood. U.S.A. (Fig. 106 F.)

M. Gale L. Sweet Gale, Bog Myrtle. 4. March–April. D. Ls. oblanc., 2,

MYRICA—*continued*

toothed towards apex, dark glossy green. Fruit small, 3-pointed, resin-dotted, in dense catkins up to ½ long. Northern Hemisphere (including Britain). (Fig. 106 D.)

Family 99. **BETULACEAE.** P4 or 0, A2–4, Ḡ (2)

Trees or shrubs with alternate, stipulate, and usually straight-veined leaves. Fls. unisexual, the male in catkins; the female in catkins, spikes, or clusters; ovary 2-celled, two to three ovaries to each catkin scale, styles two. Fruit a 1-seeded nut. The wood of alder and birch is used for turnery, plywood, and cheap furniture. Hornbeam wood is hard and heavy. Hazel is made into wattle hurdles, thatching spars, and crate rods for packing pottery. Birch bark can be used for canoes, primitive roofing, and for writing on. All make good charcoal.

ALNUS. Alder. Each male flower with four stamens. The female catkins become woody cones in fruit.

(*a*) *Buds stalked*

A. cordata Desf. Italian Alder. 80. March. D. Twigs angled, hairless. Ls. broadly ov., 4, pointed, straight or heart-shaped base, finely and evenly toothed, veins curved back, dark glossy green above, hairless except for tufts in vein-axils below. South Europe. (Fig. 106 H.)

A. subcordata (C. A. Mey.) is similar, but with downy twigs and larger, broader ls.

A. glutinosa Gaertn. Common Alder. 90. January–February. D. Wood yellow when freshly cut. Twigs clammy, hairless; buds violet-coloured. Ls. broadly obov. or circular, 4, coarsely toothed, rounded or notched at end, dark glossy green and clammy above, pale green below. Europe (including Britain), North Africa, North and West Asia. (Fig. 106 G.)

Var. *imperialis* Kirchn. Ls. cut into linear lobes. (Fig. 34 F.)

Var. *laciniata* Willd. Ls. deeply and pinnately lobed. (Fig. 34 G.)

A. hirsuta Turcz. 70. D. Ls. broadly ov., 4, pointed, coarsely toothed or lobed, dark green above, downy below. North-east Asia.

A. incana Moench. Grey Alder, Speckled Alder. 70. D. Ls. ov., 4, pointed, double-toothed and slightly lobed, glaucous or grey-green below. Cones stalkless or nearly so. North temperate regions. (Fig. 106 K.)

Var. *aurea* Schelle. Ls. yellow.

Var. *glauca* Hort. Ls. blue-green below.

Var. *incisa* Bean. Ls. deeply lobed, lobes toothed.

Var. *pendula* Call. Weeping form.

A. japonica Sieb. & Zucc. Japanese Alder. 80. February. D. Ls. lanc., 5, tapered at both ends, finely toothed, dark glossy green above, pale green below. Japan.

A. maritima Nutt. Sea-side Alder. 20. September. D. Twigs reddish brown. Ls. obov., 3, pointed, rounded base, finely and distantly toothed, dark green and glossy above, pale green below. North America.

ALNUS—*continued*

A. nepalensis D. Don. 50. October–December. D. Bark silvery grey. Twigs hairless. Ls. ov., 4, pointed, shallowly toothed or entire, glaucous below. Male catkins drooping, up to 8 long. West Himalaya.

A. nitida Endl. Himalayan Alder. 100. September. D. Bark dark brown. Ls. ov., 6, long-pointed, coarsely toothed or almost entire, glossy green above, pale green below, 8–12 pairs veins. Male catkins erect. Himalaya. (Fig. 106 J.)

A. orientalis Decne. 50. January. D. Ls. ov., 3, rounded or heart-shaped base, coarsely and unevenly toothed, glossy green, hairless except for tufts in vein-axils below. Cones large. Orient.

A. rubra Bong. (*A. oregona* Nutt.). Oregon Alder. 50. February. D. Young shoots angled, hairless. Ls. ov., 6, margins recurved, 10–15 pairs parallel veins, dark green above, pale greyish below, edged with small toothed lobes, the stalk and veins red or yellow. West North America. (Fig. 106 L.)

A. rugosa Spreng. Smooth Alder. 25. D. Ls. obov., 3, wedge-shaped base, pointed or rounded at end, finely and evenly toothed, green below. North America.

(*b*) *Buds not stalked*

A. crispa Pursh. American Green Alder. 10. D. Ls. ov., 2, pointed, rounded base, finely toothed, clammy when young, with 5–10 pairs veins. East North America.

A. firma Sieb. & Zucc. 30. March. D. Twigs hairless. Ls. ov., 4, pointed, finely and doubly toothed, with 12–26 pairs veins. Japan.

A. Maximowiczii Call. 30. D. Ls. narrowly ov., 3, the margins fringed with long teeth, 12–15 pairs veins. Cones large. Japan.

A. pendula Matsumara (*A. multinervis* Hort.). 25. March. D. Ls. lanc., 4, long-pointed, sharply and unevenly toothed, with twelve or more pairs of veins. Cones nodding. Japan.

A. sinuata Rydb. Sitka Alder. 30. D. Ls. ov., 4, pointed, with a rounded or broadly wedge-shaped base, sharply toothed and vaguely lobed. West North America.

A. viridis DC. European Green Alder. 6. March. D. Like *A. crispa*, but smaller. Mountains of Europe.

BETULA. Birch. Ls. ov., usually pointed, sharply and unevenly toothed, straight-veined. The female catkins appear in spring at the end of short shoots, the male in autumn in the leaf-axils of long shoots and hanging on the tree throughout winter; stamens two. Nut minute, winged.

(*a*) *Ls. with three to seven pairs lateral veins*

B. japonica Sieb. Japanese White Birch. 85. April. D. Bark white, twigs warted. Ls. ov., 3, teeth bluntish and nearly even, 5–7 pairs lateral veins, slender-stalked. Japan.

B. nana L. Dwarf Birch. 4. April. D. Twigs erect, not warted, minutely downy. Ls. circular, ½, round-toothed, dark glossy green above, net-veined below, 2–4 pairs lateral veins, very shortly stalked. North Europe (including Britain), North Asia, North America, Greenland. (Fig. 107 A.)

BETULA—*continued*

B. pubescens Ehrh. (*B. alba* L., sub-species *pubescens* Loud.). White Birch, Swedish Birch. 70. April. D. Bark white (even in young trees), peeling off in papery layers. Twigs downy, not warted, erect or horizontal. Ls. ov., 2½, pointed, slender-stalked. Europe (including Britain) and North Asia. (Fig. 107 C.)

B. verrucosa Ehrh. (*B. alba* L., sub-species *verrucosa* Wallr., *B. pendula* Roth). Silver Birch. 70. April. D. Bark brown in saplings, white on older trees, peeling off in papery layers. Twigs hairless, warted, drooping. Ls. ov., 2½, long-pointed, slender-stalked. Europe (including Britain) and North Asia. (Fig. 107 B.)

Var. *laciniata* Hort. Ls. deeply lobed; lobes lanc., toothed, long-pointed. (Fig. 34 H.)

Var. *purpurea* Hort. Ls. purple.

Var. *Youngii* Schneid. Twigs very slender and drooping.

(*b*) *Ls. with seven or more pairs lateral veins*

B. albo-sinensis Burk. 100. D. Bark orange-red, peeling off in thin sheets. Ls. ov., 2, double-toothed, dark yellowish green above. China.

B. costata Trautv. 100. D. Bark greyish brown, peeling off in papery layers. Ls. ov., 2½, firm, finely double-toothed, dark green above, pale green below. Female catkins egg-shaped. North-east Asia.

B. Ermannii Cham. 60. April. D. Bark dull white, peeling off in thin sheets. Ls. triangular, 3, coarsely and unevenly toothed. Japan.

B. lenta L. Cherry Birch. 80. April. D. Trunk dark reddish brown, not peeling. Young bark aromatic. Ls. narrowly ov., 4, heart-shaped base. North America.

B. luminifera Winkl. 60. D. Trunk dull yellow, not peeling. Ls. ov., 4, sharply and unevenly toothed. Female catkins solitary. Nut broadly winged. China.

B. lutea Michx. Yellow Birch. 100. April. D. Bark yellowish brown. Ls. narrowly ov., 4, pointed, double-toothed, dull green, with twelve pairs of lateral veins. North America. (Fig. 107 D.)

B. Maximowicziana Regel. 100. April. D. Bark orange-coloured; twigs warted, hairless. Ls. heart-shaped, 6, pointed, with 10–12 pairs lateral veins. Male catkins 4, female 2 long, in pairs or racemes. Nut with broad wings. Japan. (Fig. 107 F.)

B. Medwediewi Regel. 100. April. D. Twigs stout, with large and sticky buds. Ls. ov., 4, sharply toothed, dark green above. Female catkins cylindrical. Nut with a very narrow wing. Caucasus.

B. nigra L. River Birch, Red Birch. 90. April. D. Bark grey or brown, peeling; twigs downy, warted. Ls. ov., 3, pointed, glossy green above, glaucous white below, slender-stalked. East United States. (Fig. 107 E.)

B. papyrifera Marsh. Paper Birch or Canoe Birch. 100. April. D. Bark very white and smooth; twigs warted. Ls. ov., 3, long-pointed, dotted with small black glands below, 6–10 pairs lateral veins. North America. (Fig. 107 G.)

Var. *occidentalis* Sarg. Bark reddish brown.

B. utilis D. Don. Himalayan Birch. 60. April. D. Trunk and branches

BETULA—*continued*

creamy white; twigs downy. Ls. ov., 3, rounded at base, pointed, dark green above, pale green and downy below, 9–12 pairs lateral veins. Himalaya. (Fig. 107 H.)

CARPINUS. Hornbeam. Trunk fluted, smooth-barked; buds pointed, many-scaled. Ls. ov., pointed, double-toothed, parallel-veined, equal-sided at base or nearly so, usually in two opposite rows. Male catkins drooping, appearing in spring from lateral buds on previous year's wood; female catkins erect at end of young shoots. Fruit a nut at the base of a 3-lobed leaf-like bract, in drooping spikes.

C. Betulus L. Common Hornbeam. 80. April. D. Buds thin, pointed. Ls. 3. Fruiting bracts 3-5-nerved at base. Europe (including Britain) and West Asia. (Fig. 107 J.)

Var. *asplenifolia* Hort. (*laciniata* Hort.). Fern-leaved Hornbeam. Ls. deeply double-toothed, almost lobed.

Var. *columnaris* Spaeth. Narrow form.

Var. *pendula* Kirchn. Weeping form.

C. caroliniana Walt. American Hornbeam. 40. April. D. Buds egg-shaped. Ls. 4. Fruiting bracts 5-7-nerved at base. East North America. (Fig. 107 K.)

C. cordata Blume. 40. April. D. Ls. heart-shaped, 4, unevenly toothed, with numerous parallel veins in deep grooves. Japan.

C. japonica (Blume) is similar, but the leaves are smaller, narrower, and less heart-shaped.

CORYLUS. Hazel. Buds rounded. Ls. ov., pointed, unevenly toothed, heart-shaped base, folded in bud. Male catkins drooping, appearing in clusters in late autumn ('lambs' tails'); female flowers very small, bud-like, with red stigmas protruding. Nuts formed in clusters, each nut enclosed in persistent bracts.

C. americana Marsh. American Hazel. 10. February. D. Like Common Hazel (see below), but the fruiting bracts are longer than the nut. East North America.

C. Avellana L. Common Hazel. 20. February. D. Ls. 4, often slightly lobed, stalk short and hairy. Nut ¾, nearly as long as bracts. Europe (including Britain) and West Asia. (Fig. 108 A.)

Var. *laciniata* Hort. Ls. deeply lobed.

Var. *purpurea* Bean. Ls. purple.

C. chinensis Franch. Chinese Hazel. 100. D. Ls. 6, not lobed, stalk up to 1 long. Fruiting bracts longer than nut and recurved at ends. China.

C. Colurna L. Turkish Hazel. 80. February. D. Ls. 6, often lobed, stalk up to 1 long. Nut ¾, bracts deeply divided into linear recurved lobes. South-east Europe to Himalaya. (Fig. 108 B.)

C. mandshurica Maxim. Manchurian Hazel. 20. D. Ls. 6, lobed near apex. Fruiting bracts bristly, up to 2 long. Manchuria and North China.

C. maxima Mill. Filbert. 20. February. D. Ls. 5. Nut 1, set in bracts twice as long as itself, the bracts downy but not bristly. South Europe. (Fig. 108 C.)

Var. *atropurpurea* Dipp. Ls. dark purple.

C. tibetica Batal. Tibetan Hazel. 25. D. Twigs hairless, spotted; buds

CORYLUS—*continued*

pointed. Ls. broadly ov., obov., 4, long-pointed. Fruiting bracts spiny. China and Tibet.

OSTRYA. Hop Hornbeam. Bark rough. Buds pointed, many-scaled. Ls. ov., 4, pointed, double-toothed, parallel-veined, rounded at base. Male catkins drooping, appearing in autumn. Nut ribbed, enclosed in bladder-like bracts, in drooping spikes.

O. carpinifolia Scop. 60. April. D. Nut egg-shaped. South Europe and Asia Minor.

O. virginiana Koch. Ironwood. 50. April. D. Nut spindle-shaped. North America. (Fig. 107 L.)

OSTRYOPSIS DAVIDIANA Decne. 10. April. D. Ls. broadly ov., 3, double-toothed, shallowly lobed, heart-shaped base, scattered hairs above, downy and dotted with red glands below, short-stalked. Male catkins ½, drooping, appearing in autumn in joints of old wood; female erect, appearing in spring at end of young shoots. Nut enclosed in a conical 3-pointed bract. China. (Fig. 108 F.)

Family 100. **FAGACEAE.** P (4–7), A4–∞, Ḡ (3)

Trees with alternate stipulate leaves and small unisexual flowers which are solitary or in stalked heads or slender catkin-like spikes. Ovary 3-celled, styles three. Fruit of one or more 1-seeded nuts enclosed in a husk.

CASTANEA. Chestnut. Trees with furrowed and often twisted bark. Ls. oblong to lanc., sharply toothed, straight-veined, the veins ending in teeth. Flowering spikes long, slender, and erect, mostly of male flowers with a few female at the bottom. Fruit of one or more reddish brown 1-seeded nuts enclosed in a prickly husk. Chestnut wood is strong and durable, resembling that of oak without the silver grain, and is used for much the same purposes.

C. crenata Sieb. & Zucc. Japanese Chestnut. 30. July. D. Twigs hairy. Ls. 5, somewhat round-toothed. Two to three nuts in each husk. Japan.

C. dentata Borkh. (*C. americana* Rafin.). American Chestnut. 100. June–July. D. Ls. 8, sharply and coarsely toothed, base wedge-shaped, hairless. Two to three nuts in each husk. North America.

C. mollissima Blume. Chinese Chestnut. 60. July. D. Twigs hairy. Ls. 5, sharply toothed, downy below and without scaly glands. Two to three nuts in each husk. China.

C. pumila Mill. Chinquapin. 12. July. D. Twigs hairy. Ls. 4, hairy below. One nut in each husk. North America.

C. sativa Mill. (*C. vesca* Gaertn.). Spanish or Sweet Chestnut. 100. June–July. D. Twigs hairless except when young. Ls. 9, evenly and sharply toothed, with scaly glands near the veins below. One to three nuts in each husk. Europe (including Britain), North Asia, North Africa. (Fig. 108 D.)

Var. *heterophylla* Bean. Ls. variously shaped and marked.

CASTANOPSIS CHRYSOPHYLLA DC. Golden Chestnut. 100. July. D. Ls. lanc., 3, entire, pointed, tapered at both ends, dark glossy green above, golden scurf below. Catkins 1, erect. Husk 1½, prickly, enclosing one pale brown edible nut. California and Oregon. (Fig. 128 L.)

FAGUS. Beech. Bark smooth, grey. Buds long and pointed. Ls. ov., parallel-veined, dark glossy green above, the margins fringed with white hairs when young. Male flowers in long-stalked, drooping heads; the female solitary or in pairs, surrounded by bracts. Fruit of two smooth triangular nuts enclosed in a 4-lobed woody husk covered with thick bristles. Beech wood is white or pale brown and not durable out of doors, though it makes good furniture, block flooring, shoe heels and trees, mangle rollers and carpenters' tools.

F. grandifolia Ehrh. (*F. americana* Sweet). American Beech. 100. April–May. D. Ls. 4, coarsely toothed, with 9–12 pairs lateral veins. East North America.

F. sylvatica L. Common Beech. 100. April–May. D. Ls. 3, vaguely toothed or entire, with 5–9 pairs lateral veins. Europe (including Britain) and Asia Minor. (Fig. 108 E.)

Var. *cuprea* Loud. Copper Beech. Ls. coppery red.

Var. *heterophylla* Loud. Fern-leaved Beech. Ls. deeply and pinnately lobed. (Fig. 34 D.)

Var. *pendula* Loud. Weeping form.

Var. *purpurea* Ait. Ls. deep purple.

Var. *purpurea pendula* Rehd. Weeping Purple Beech.

NOTHOFAGUS. Southern Beech. Ls. small (2 or less). Fls. solitary or in few-flowered clusters. Fruit of three smooth triangular nuts in a 4-winged husk.

N. antarctica Oerst. Antarctic Beech. 120. May. D. Twigs downy. Ls. ov., 1, rounded at end, straight or heart-shaped and unequal-sided at base, minutely toothed, often lobed. South America. (Fig. 34 N.)

N. betuloides Oerst. 120. May. E. Twigs clammy. Ls. ov., 1, minutely and evenly toothed, crowded on branch. South America.

* **N. cliffortioides** Hook. f. Mountain Beech. 50. E. Ls. ov., ½, entire, net-veined, hairless, in two regular rows. New Zealand. (Fig. 128 N.)

N. Dombeyi Blume. 100. May. E. Twigs downy. Ls. ov., 1, unevenly toothed, prettily net-veined, rounded base, in two opposite rows. South America. (Fig. 108 G.)

N. fusca Oerst. New Zealand Red Beech. 100. E. Ls. broadly ov. or circular, 1, coarsely toothed, with a straight or tapering base. New Zealand.

N. obliqua Blume. Roblé Beech. 100. May. D. Twigs hairless. Ls. ov., lanc., 3, double-toothed or shallowly lobed, hairless, unequal-sided at base, with 8–11 pairs veins. South America. (Fig. 34 O.)

QUERCUS. Oak. April–May. Ls. usually toothed or pinnately lobed. Male catkins usually drooping, in clusters; female flowers few and inconspicuous. Fruit a 1-seeded nut (acorn) enclosed in a cup. Not all oaks give good timber. The best is that of the common English oak (*Q. Robur*) and Durmast oak (*Q. petraea*). The American red oaks (*Q. borealis*, *rubra*, and *Shumardii*) and white oaks (*Q. alba*, *lyrata*, *montana*, and *Prinus*) are imported, as also the Japanese oak (*Q. mongolica*). Imported oak from Central Europe comes from varieties of common oak. The timber of Holm oak is good, but not that of Turkey oak.

(a) *Evergreen oaks*

(i) Male catkins erect (*LITHOCARPUS*)

Q. densiflora Hook. & Arn. Tanbark Oak. 70. Young shoots woolly.

QUERCUS—*continued*

Ls. ov., 4, stiff and leathery, with 12–14 pairs parallel veins, each ending in a sharp tooth, dark glossy green above, white-felted or glaucous below. Acorns solitary or in pairs. California and Oregon. (Fig. 109 E.)

Q. edulis Makino (*Q. glabra* Sieb. & Zucc.). 30. Young shoots hairless. Ls. lanc., oblanc., 6, entire, tapered at both ends, blunt-ended, leathery and glossy, yellowish green above, dull greyish below, with 9–11 pairs parallel veins. Acorns in threes on spikes up to 3 long. Japan. (Fig. 128 J.)

(ii) Male catkins drooping

Q. acuta Thunb. 40. Ls. ov., 5, leathery, entire, dark glossy green above, dull yellowish below, margins wavy, 8–10 pairs lateral veins. Acorns crowded on a spike, cup downy. Japan. (Fig. 128 H.)

Q. agrifolia Née. Encena or Live Oak. 80. Twigs densely downy. Ls. ov. or roundish, 2, spine-toothed, hard, dark glossy green above, hairless except for tufts in vein-axils below. Acorns solitary or in pairs. California. (Fig. 108 H.)

Q. alnifolia Poech. Golden Cyprus Oak. 12. Ls. broadly obov. or circular, 1½, dark glossy green above, yellowish below. Acorn 1, cup with recurved scales. Cyprus.

Q. chrysolepis Liebm. Maul Oak. 50. Young shoots downy. Ls. ov., 2, spine-toothed in young plants, glossy green above, yellow and downy below in first year, with 4–10 pairs parallel veins, very shortly stalked. Acorns solitary or in pairs. California and Oregon. (Fig. 109 C.)

Q. coccifera L. Kermes Oak, Grain Tree. 12. Ls. ov., 1½, leathery, spine-toothed, dark green above, hairless. Acorn cup with reflexed spiny scales. Mediterranean region. (Fig. 109 B.)

Q. Ilex L. Holm Oak, Common Evergreen Oak. 90. Bark grey, nearly smooth; twigs downy. Ls. ov., lanc., 3, entire, or sometimes vaguely toothed or even spine-toothed in young trees, dark green above, white- or tawny-felted below when young. Acorns ½, solitary or in small clusters on a short stalk. Mediterranean region. (Fig. 109 A.)

Q. myrsinaefolia Blume (*Q. bambusaefolia* Fort.). Bamboo-leaved Oak. 50. Ls. lanc., 4, long-pointed, tapering base, distantly toothed, glossy above, somewhat glaucous below. Acorns in short spikes, cup hairless. Japan. (Fig. 109 G.)

Q. Suber L. Cork Oak. 60. Bark thick and corky. Twigs downy. Ls. ov., 2½, toothed, dark glossy green above, grey-felted below. Acorns solitary or in pairs on short stalk. The tree yields cork. South Europe and North Africa. (Fig. 109 D.)

Q. virginiana Mill. Live Oak. 60. Like Holm oak, but leaves usually blunt-ended. South United States.

(b) Deciduous oaks

(i) Stipules long and persistent

Q. castaneaefolia C. A. Mey. Chestnut-leaved Oak. 100. Twigs downy. Ls. lanc., 7, strongly parallel-veined, the veins ending in coarse teeth, dark glossy green above, dull grey and minutely downy below. Acorn cup with reflexed downy scales. Caucasus. (Fig. 109 F.)

QUERCUS—*continued*

Q. Cerris L. Turkey Oak. 120. Twigs downy. Ls. ov., lanc., 5, teeth or lobes triangular and pointed, dark green and rough above, greyish green below, thin and firm. Acorn cup covered with narrow recurved scales. South Europe and Asia Minor. (Fig. 32 C.)

Q. Lucombeana Sweet. Lucombe Oak. 100. ½ E. Ls. ov., 5, unequal-sided at base, parallel-veined, sharply toothed, glossy green above, grey-felted below. Acorn more than half enclosed in cup. Hybrid between Cork oak and Turkey oak.

Q. macranthera Fisch. & Mey. 60. Twigs hairy. Ls. obov., 5, with numerous rounded lobes, dark green above, grey and hairy below. Caucasus and Persia.

(ii) Ls. entire

Q. imbricaria Michx. Shingle Oak. 60. Twigs hairless. Ls. ov., 6, dark green above, red in autumn. Acorn small and round. North America.

Q. laurifolia Michx. Laurel Oak. 60. Like the preceding species, but the under side of the leaf is downy. Virginia to Louisiana.

Q. Phellos L. Willow Oak. 100. Bark smooth and grey. Ls. lanc., 5, tapering base, pale green, yellow in autumn. Acorn very small, in a shallow cup. U.S.A. (Fig. 128 K.)

(iii) Teeth or lobes ending in a sharp point

Q. borealis Michx. Red Oak. 60. Like *C. coccinea* (see below), but leaves less deeply lobed. North America.

Q. coccinea Muenchh. Scarlet Oak. 80. Bark smooth; twigs hairless and warted; buds hairy at tip. Ls. ov., lanc., 6, deeply lobed, the lobes oblong or triangular and coarsely toothed near apex, small brown tufts in vein-axils below, long-stalked, scarlet in autumn. North America. (Fig. 33 B.)

Q. Shumardii (Buckl.) is similar, but with larger tufts in the vein-axils.

Q. falcata Michx. Spanish Oak. 80. Twigs hairy. Ls. obov., 8, deeply lobed, the lobes pointed and entire or obscurely toothed, dark green above, grey or tawny below. Acorn small and round. South United States.

Q. glandulifera Blume (*Q. serrata* Thunb.). 30. Twigs hairless. Ls. lanc., 6, sharply toothed, with 12–16 pairs parallel veins, pale green, hairless except for tufts in vein-axils below. Acorn broad, about two-thirds enclosed in cup, stalkless. China and Japan.

Q. ilicifolia Wangh. Scrub Oak. Spreading shrub with hairy twigs. Ls. obov., 3, usually 4-lobed, dark green above, white below. Acorn half enclosed in shallow cup. East United States.

Q. Libani Oliv. Lebanon Oak. 30. Ls. lanc., 3, sharply toothed, with 9–12 pairs veins, downy on veins below. Acorn broad, about two-thirds enclosed in cup, stalked. Asia Minor.

Q. Lucombeana Sweet. See (i) above.

Q. macrolepis Kotschy (*Q. Aegilops* L.). Valonia Oak. 80. Twigs covered with yellowish down. Ls. ov., 4, lobes triangular and pointed, dark glossy green above, grey below, base rounded or heart-shaped. Acorn very large (up to 2 across). South Europe and Asia Minor.

QUERCUS—*continued*

Q. marilandica Muenchh. Black Jack. 50. Ls. broadly ov., 6, base rounded, 3-5-lobed at apex, dark glossy green above, at first brownish and hairy below, becoming green and nearly hairless. East United States. (Fig. 33 D.)

Q. nigra L. Water Oak. 80. Twigs hairless. Ls. often crowded at end of short twigs, obov., lanc., 4, pale green on both sides, lobed or unlobed, occasionally entire, hairless except for tufts of down in the vein-axils below, stalk very short. South United States.

Q. palustris Muenchh. Pin Oak. 100. Bark smooth. Twigs hairless; warted; buds hairless. Ls. ov., 6, glossy, deeply lobed, the lobes oblong or triangular and toothed near apex, large brown tufts in vein-axils below, long-stalked, red in autumn. U.S.A. (Fig. 33 A.)

Q. rubra Du Roi. Red Oak. 100. Bark smooth, grey. Twigs hairless, warted. Ls. ov., 9, deeply lobed, the lobes obliquely triangular and entire or with a few teeth, the terminal lobe long and narrow; dull green above, greyish and downy below, with brown tufts in the vein-axils, long-stalked. Acorn cup very shallow. North America. (Fig. 32 D.)

Q. velutina Lam. Black Oak. 80. Twigs downy, buds hairy. Ls. ov., 12, deeply lobed, the lobes triangular and entire or with a few teeth, dark green and glossy above, pale and downy below, red in autumn. Acorn solitary, half enclosed in cup. North America. (Fig. 34 A.)

(iv) Teeth or lobes blunt, or with a minute point

Q. alba L. White Oak. 100. Twigs hairless. Ls. obov., 6, deeply lobed, bright green above, somewhat glaucous below, purple in autumn. Acorn about one quarter enclosed in cup, which has thickened scales. North America.

Q. bicolor Willd. Swamp White Oak. 60. Ls. obov., 6, shallowly lobed, dark green above, white or grey below, orange or red in autumn. Acorn slender-stalked. North America.

Q. canariensis Willd. (*Q. Mirbeckii* Dur.). 100. Ls. ov., obov., 6, coarsely blunt-toothed, slightly heart-shaped base, glossy above, woolly below at first, becoming hairless. Acorn cluster on short stalk. Spain, Portugal, North Africa.

Q. Frainetto Tenore (*Q. conferta* Kit.). Hungarian Oak. 100. Ls. obov., 6, deeply cut into six to ten oblong lobes, dark green above, greyish green and downy below, very shortly stalked. Acorns stalkless. Italy to Hungary. (Fig. 32 E.)

Q. lanuginosa Thuill. 50. Bark rough and corky. Twigs downy. Ls. ov., 4, with 4–6 rounded lobes on either side, dark green and hairless above, downy below. Acorn small and almost entirely enclosed in cup. South-east Europe to West Asia.

Q. lobata Née. Valley Oak. 60. Twigs downy. Ls. obov., 2½, 7-11-lobed, dark green above, grey-woolly below. Acorn nearly stalkless. California.

Q. lusitanica Lam. Lusitanian Oak. 50. Twigs downy. Ls. obov., 5, with 8–10 pairs short lobes, bright green above, downy and greyish below. South Europe.

QUERCUS—*continued*

Q. lyrata Walt. Overcup Oak. 100. Ls. 7, deeply lobed, the terminal lobes the largest, dark green above, white or grey below. Acorn small, almost entirely enclosed in the cup. South United States.

Q. macrocarpa Michx. Burr Oak. 50. Ls. obov., 10, tapering base, 5-7-lobed, the terminal lobe much the largest, dark glossy green above, minutely felted below. Acorn cup with thread-like scales forming a fringe. North America. (Fig. 33 C.)

Q. mongolica Fisch. Japanese Oak. 100. Twigs hairless. Ls. obov., 6, coarsely blunt-toothed, dark green above, with 7–10 pairs parallel veins; clustered at end of twig. Acorn small, half enclosed in cup. Japan.

Var. *grosseserrata* Rehd. & Wils. Ls. smaller, with more pointed lobes.

Q. montana Willd. Chestnut Oak. 60. Ls. lanc., 6, coarsely toothed, yellowish green above, with 10–15 pairs parallel veins, orange in autumn. East North America.

Q. obtusa Willd. (*Q. rhombica* Sarg.). 100. Ls. lanc., 4, with one, two, or three irregular lobes, turning scarlet in autumn. U.S.A.

Q. petraea Liebl. (*Q. sessiliflora* Salisb.). Durmast Oak, Sessile Oak. 80. Twigs downy. Ls. ov., 5, deeply lobed, lobes rounded, dark green above, greyish and somewhat downy below, tapering or rounded base without 'ears,' stalk more than ½ long. Acorn cluster on short stalk. Europe (including Britain) and West Asia. (Fig. 32 B.)

Q. Prinus L. Basket Oak. 100. Bark pale grey and scaly. Ls. obov., oblanc., 6, coarsely and evenly toothed, with 10–14 pairs parallel veins, bright green and glossy above, grey and downy below, crimson in autumn. U.S.A.

Q. pyrenaica Willd. (*Q. Toza* DC.). 50. Twigs downy. Ls. obov., 6, deeply lobed, dark green above, yellowish and downy below, base rounded. South Europe.

Q. Robur L. (*Q. pedunculata* Ehrh.). Common English Oak. 80. Twigs hairless. Ls. ov., 4, shallowly lobed, the lobes rounded, dark green above, greyish below, with small 'ears' at junction with stalk, stalk less than ½. Acorn cluster on long slender stalk. Europe (including Britain) and Asia. (Fig. 32 A.)

Var. *concordia* Lem. Golden Oak. Ls. yellow.

Var. *filicifolia* Lem. Fern-leaved Oak. Ls. cut into narrow slender lobes, base tapering.

Var. *purpurescens* DC. Purple Oak. Ls. purplish.

Q. Turneri Willd. 50. ½ E. Ls. obov., 2½, shallowly and distantly toothed, rounded or heart-shaped base, dark green above. Acorn slender-stalked. Cross between common oak and Holm oak.

Family 101. SALICACEAE. Po, A2–30, G̲ (2)

The poplar and willow family. Trees and shrubs with alternate stipulate leaves. Fls. unisexual, in catkins, the sexes on different trees; ovary 1-celled. Fruit a dry splitting capsule containing seeds with tufts of silky hairs.

POPULUS. Poplar. The twigs have terminal buds, which are resinous and have several scales. Ls. usually broadest below the middle, long-stalked. Catkins drooping, the male with 8–30 stamens in the axil of each scale. Poplar

POPULUS—*continued*
wood is white, soft, and not durable; it burns badly and does not splinter, which makes it suitable for match-sticks and wagon bottoms.

(*a*) *Ls. white- or grey-felted below* (*White Poplars*)

P. alba L. White Poplar, Silver Poplar, Abele. 60. February–March. D. Bark smooth, young branchlets white-felted. Ls. ov., 3, palmately 3-5-lobed. Europe and North and West Asia. (Fig. 28 D.)

P. canescens Sm. Grey Poplar. 100. March. D. Bark smooth at first, becoming rough, often with rows of black diamond-shaped marks. Ls. roundish ov., 4, coarsely and unevenly toothed. West Europe (including Britain). (Fig. 109 H.)

(*b*) *Ls. with clear translucent border* (*Black Poplars*)

P. angulata Ait. Carolina Poplar. 100. March. D. Twigs angular or ribbed, hairless; buds greenish. Ls. ov., 7, heart-shaped or straight base, margins hairy, teeth small and curved; stalk flattened, with glands at base. East United States. (Fig. 110 A.)

P. berolinensis Dipp. 100. March. D. Like Lombardy Poplar (see below), but ls. whitish underneath and stalk not flattened. Hybrid between Lombardy Poplar and *P. laurifolia*.

P. Eugenei Simon-Louis. 150. D. Tall and narrow tree with hairless twigs and small, sticky buds. Ls. ov., 3, long-pointed, coarsely toothed, margins hairy. Hybrid. (Fig. 110 C.)

P. Fremontii S. Wats. (*P. Wislizenii* Sarg.). 100. Like *P. nigra* (see below), but the leaves have no hairs on the margins. California.

P. generosa Henry. D. Buds large and sticky. Ls. ov., 12; teeth even, curved and gland-tipped; glands at base of leaf-stalk. Hybrid. (Fig. 110 F.)

P. marilandica Bosc. 100. March. D. Like *P. serotina* (see below), but twigs cylindrical, and coming into leaf earlier. Hybrid.

P. monilifera Ait. (*P. canadensis* Michx., *P. deltoidea* Marsh.). Canadian Black Poplar, Necklace Poplar, Cottonwood. 100. D. Ls. ov., 5, heart-shaped base, long-pointed, teeth large and curved, margins hairy, green on both sides; stalk flattened, with glands at base. East North America. (Fig. 110 B.)

P. nigra L. Black Poplar. 100. March. D. Twigs cylindrical, hairless, buds sticky. Ls. usually diamond-shaped or triangular, 4, shallowly round-toothed, no glands at base, stalk flattened. North Asia. (Fig. 109 J.)

Var. *italica* Du Roi. Lombardy Poplar. Tall and narrow.

P. regenerata Henry. 100. D. Like Black Italian (see below), but coming into leaf earlier. Hybrid.

P. robusta Schneid. 150. D. Twigs stout, angled, buds brown and sticky. Ls. ov., 7, round-toothed, stalk flattened. A very fast-growing tree. Hybrid.

P. serotina Hartig. Black Italian Poplar. 100. D. Twigs green, hairless, slightly angled. Ls. ov., triangular, 6, with glands at base. Male catkins red, no female. A fast-growing tree with a broad, fan-shaped crown. Hybrid. (Fig. 109 K.)

Var. *aurea* Henry (*Van Geertii* Hort.). Ls. yellow.

POPULUS—*continued*

(*c*) *Ls. without clear translucent border; stalk flattened* (*Aspens*)

P. grandidentata Michx. Large-toothed Aspen. 75. February. D. Twigs stout, covered with grey down when young; buds grey, hairy. Ls. ov., 4, with coarse undulating teeth, dark green above, grey below when young. East North America.

P. tremula L. Common Aspen. 50. February. D. Twigs hairless, buds bright brown. Ls. broadly ov., 2, coarsely and unevenly blunt-toothed, greyish green. Europe (including Britain), North Africa, North Asia. (Fig. 110 D.)

P. tremuloides Michx. American Aspen. 100. February. D. Twigs reddish brown, hairless. Ls. broadly ov., 2, finely toothed, dark glossy green above. North America. (Fig. 110 E.)

(*d*) *Ls. without clear translucent border; stalk not or slightly flattened* (*Balsam Poplars*)

P. angustifolia James. Willow-leaved Poplar. 60. D. Twigs cylindrical; buds long-pointed, sticky. Ls. lanc., 5, tapering base, minutely and evenly round-toothed, green on both sides. North America. (Fig. 110 H.)

P. candicans Ait. (*P. balsamifera* Du Roi, *P. tacamahaca* Mill.). Balm of Gilead, Balsam Poplar, Cottonwood. 50. February–March. D. Buds large and sticky. Ls. ov., 5, somewhat coarsely round-toothed, straight or heart-shaped base, dark green above, whitish below. North America. (Fig. 110 G.)

P. lasiocarpa Oliv. 60. D. Twigs stout, downy. Ls. heart-shaped, 12, shallowly round-toothed, green below, the stalk and chief veins red. China.

P. laurifolia Ledeb. 50. March. D. Like *P. trichocarpa* (see below), but the leaves are lanc. and the twigs yellowish grey. Siberia.

P. Maximowiczii Henry. 100. D. Twigs cylindrical, downy. Ls. ov., 4, dark green and wrinkled above, white below, the point twisted. North-east Asia, Japan.

P. szechuanica Schneid. 100. D. Twigs angled. Ls. heart-shaped, 9, finely toothed, greyish below, stalk and chief veins red. China. (Fig. 110 K.)

P. trichocarpa Torr. & Gray. Black Cottonwood. 200. D. Ls. ov., 8, finely toothed, dark green above, white and net-veined below. West North America. (Fig. 110 J.)

P. Wilsonii Schneid. 80. D. Twigs stout, cylindrical, hairless. Ls. heart-shaped, 9, minutely toothed, dull pale green above, greyish below. China.

P. yunnanensis Dode. 100. D. Like *P. trichocarpa*, but leaves lanc. and twigs yellowish grey. China.

SALIX. Willow. Each leaf-bud with a single scale. Ls. short-stalked. The twigs are usually very tough and without a terminal bud. Catkins erect; stamens usually two to five, rarely more. Willow wood is white, soft, and not durable, but can be used for cart bottoms, packing-cases, and artificial limbs. One species is valuable for cricket bats. The young branchlets can be used for basket making.

SALIX—*continued*

(*a*) *Adult leaves hairy or downy below*

S. alba L. White Willow. 80. May. D. Branches drooping at ends; twigs olive-brown, at acute angle. Ls. lanc., 3½, finely toothed, silky-hairy below. Stamens two. Europe (including Britain), Asia, North Africa. (Fig. 111 A.)

Var. *argentea* Wimm. Silver Willow. Ls. of intense silvery colour.

Var. *britzensis* Hort. Twigs red.

Var. *coerulea* Syme. Cricket Bat Willow. 100. Branches erect. Ls. becoming hairless and blue-grey below in late summer.

Var. *Russelliana* Sm. Bedford Willow. A cross with *S. fragilis* (q.v.). Ls. silky below.

Var. *vitellina* Stokes. Golden Willow. Twigs yellow.

S. Arbuscula L. 3. May. D. Ls. ov., lanc., 2, deep green above, grey below, toothed or entire. Stamens two. Europe (including Scottish mountains) and North Asia. (Fig. 111 B.)

S. aurita L. Round-eared Willow. 6. April. D. Twigs downy, buds brown or green. Ls. obov., 2, vaguely toothed, dark green and wrinkled above, grey-woolly below, with a pair of broad stipules at the base of the leaf-stalk. Stamens two. Europe (including Britain) and North Asia. (Fig. 111 C.)

S. Bockii Diels. 10. October. D. Young twigs covered with grey down. Ls. obov., ½, deep green above, blue-white below, entire or slightly toothed. Stamens two. China.

S. Caprea L. Goat Willow, Sallow, Pussy Willow, 'Palm.' 25. March–April. D. Branchlets downy, buds yellow. Ls. ov., 4, vaguely toothed, dark green and slightly wrinkled above, grey-woolly below. Stamens two. Europe (including Britain) and North Asia. (Fig. 111 D.)

Var. *pendula* Th. Lang. Kilmarnock Weeping Willow.

S. cinerea L. Grey Willow. 10. March–April. D. Twigs and buds covered with grey down. Ls. ov., 3½, entire or vaguely toothed, dull grey and slightly hairy above, grey-woolly below. Stamens two. Often mistaken for the previous species, but can be distinguished by the smaller and narrow grey leaves and the grey downy buds. Europe (including Britain) and North Asia. (Fig. 111 H.)

S. incana Schrank (*S. rosmarinifolia* Gouan). 12. April–May. D. Buds yellow. Ls. linear, 5, dark green above, white-felted below, margins recurved. Stamens two. Europe. (Fig. 53 A.)

S. jessoensis Seem. Japanese Willow. 80. May. D. Like *S. alba*, but the branches do not droop at the ends and the twigs are light brown and hairy. Ls. white below. Japan.

S. lanata L. Woolly Willow. 3. May. D. Twigs woolly. Ls. roundish ov., 2, entire, silvery on both sides, stipules large. Europe (including Scotland) and North Asia. (Fig. 128 O.)

S. Lapponum L. Lapland Willow. 4. April–May. D. Twigs dark brown, downy. Ls. ov., lanc., 3, entire, white or grey below, stipules small or absent. North Europe (including Scotland) and North Asia. (Fig. 128 Q.)

S. myrsinifolia Salisb. (*S. Andersoniana* Sm.). 10. April–May. D. Like

SALIX—*continued*

S. phylicifolia (see (*b*) below), but the twigs and leaves are more downy and the ovary hairless. Europe (including Britain). (Fig. 111 O.)

S. repens L. Creeping Willow. 1. April–May. D. Creeping by underground stems. Branchlets silky. Ls. lanc., 1, entire or faintly toothed, dull grey-green above, silvery below. Stamens two. Europe (including Britain) and North Asia. (Fig. 128 P.)

Var. *argentea* Syme. Ls. silver-grey on both sides.

S. viminalis L. Common Osier. 20. March–April. D. Ls. linear, 6, entire, dark dull green above, silvery grey below, midrib prominent. Stamens two. Europe (including Britain) and Asia. (Fig. 53 F.)

This is the best willow for basket making, and many varieties are cultivated for that purpose. *S. mollissima* (Sm.), with broader lanc. leaves, is a hybrid with *S. Caprea*.

(*b*) *Adult leaves hairless, green below*

S. amygdalina L. (*S. triandra* L.). Almond-leaved Willow. 30. April–May. D. Twigs angled or furrowed. Ls. lanc., 4, toothed. Stamens three. Europe (including Britain) and North Asia. (Fig. 111 K.)

S. fragilis L. Crack Willow. 90. April–May. D. Bark corrugated. Twigs at angle of sixty degrees or more, brittle at base, hairless. Ls. lanc., 7, toothed, long-pointed. Stamens two. Europe (including Britain) and North Asia. (Fig. 111 E.)

Var. *bullata* Spaeth. Compact round bush.

S. herbacea L. Dwarf Willow. Prostrate. June. D. Creeping by partly underground rooting stems. Branchlets slender, angled. Ls. roundish ov., ½, rounded or notched at end, finely toothed, net-veined. Stamens two. Mountains of Europe (including Britain).

S. Meyeriana Rostk. 50. March–April. D. Branchlets wine-coloured. Ls. ov., oblong, 4, finely toothed, glossy green above, pale bluish green and somewhat glaucous below. Catkins pinkish, stamens four. Natural hybrid.

S. myrsinites L. Whortle Willow. 1. May. D. Ls. ov., 1, finely toothed, with 6–10 pairs parallel veins. Stamens two. Europe (including mountains of Scotland and Ireland) and North Asia. (Fig. 111 F.)

S. pentandra L. Bay Willow. 50. May. D. Twigs brown, hairless, buds yellow. Ls. ov., lanc., 4, finely toothed, dark glossy green above, midrib yellow. Stamens five or more. Europe (including Britain) and North Asia. (Fig. 111 J.)

S. phylicifolia L. Tea-leaved Willow. 10. April–May. D. Twigs bright chestnut brown. Ls. ov., 3, slightly toothed or entire, glossy green above, often glaucous below. Stamens two. Europe (including Britain). (Fig. 111 G.)

S. rubra Huds. 20. April. D. Ls. linear, lanc., 6, toothed, long-pointed. Stamens two. Europe (including Britain). (Fig. 53 C.)

(*c*) *Adult leaves hairless, blue-grey or whitish below*

S. babylonica L. Weeping Willow. 50. March–April. D. Branches drooping, yellowish, hairless. Ls. lanc., 4, long-pointed, finely toothed. Stamens two. China. (Fig. 111 L.)

SALIX—*continued*

S. blanda Anders. (*S. pendulina* Wendl.), the Wisconsin Weeping Willow, and *S. elegantissima* (Koch), the Thurlow Weeping Willow, appear to be forms of this, usually with broader leaves and more spreading habit.

S. coerulea Sm. (*S. alba* L., var. *coerulea* Syme). Cricket Bat Willow. See *S. alba* under (*a*). Easily distinguishable by its olive-green twigs all growing erect at a narrow angle. A cross between *S. alba* and *S. fragilis*.

S. daphnoides Vill. Violet Willow. 40. March. D. Twigs plum-coloured, downy, brittle. Ls. lanc., 4½, leathery, dark glossy green above, blue below, finely toothed. Europe, Siberia, Himalaya. (Fig. 111 P.)

S. discolor Muhl. Canadian Pussy Willow. 25. March–April. D. Twigs purplish brown. Ls. lanc., 5, toothed, bright green above, blue-white below. Stamens two. Canada. (Fig. 111 M.)

S. magnifica Hemsl. 20. D. Ls. broadly ov., 6, entire or nearly so, dull bluish green above, resembling magnolia. China.

S. nigricans Sm. Dark-leaved Sallow. 12. April. D. Twigs downy. Ls. ov., 4, toothed, dark dull green above, bluish below. Stamens two. Europe (including Britain). (Fig. 111 N.)

S. purpurea L. Purple Osier. 18. April. D. Twigs glossy, purple on the sunny side. Ls. linear, lanc., 3, minutely toothed at outer end, glossy green above, bluish below, often opposite. Stamen one or with a forked filament. Europe (including Britain) and Central Asia. (Fig. 53 B.)

S. reticulata L. ½. May–June. D. Ls. roundish ov., 1, entire, dark green and wrinkled above, white and net-veined below. Stamens two. Europe (including Scottish Highlands) and Labrador. (Fig. 128 R.)

S. Salamonii Carr. 60. D. Branches drooping (not so much as in *S. babylonica*). Ls. lanc., 5, finely toothed, persisting to December. Female catkins only. Hybrid.

S. viridis Fries. 80. May. D. Twigs at angle of sixty degrees or more. Ls. lanc., 5, toothed, dark glossy green above, glaucous below. Natural hybrid.

S. vitellina L. (*S. alba* L., var. *vitellina* Stokes). Golden Willow. See *S. alba* under (*a*). A conspicuous object in the winter landscape with its bright golden yellow branches.

Family 102. **EMPETRACEAE.** P4–6, A2–3, $\underline{G}$ (2–9)

An anomalous family of low evergreen heath-like shrubs. Ls. alternate or in whorls, linear, ½, blunt-ended, glossy green, margins recurved, crowded on the stems. Fls. small, inconspicuous, unisexual, purple; ovary with spreading divided stigmas. Fruit a berry. The affinities of the family are obscure, but it appears to be allied to *Euphorbiaceae*.

COREMA ALBUM Don. Portuguese Crowberry. 2. April–May. Young stems very downy. Ls. usually in threes. Fls. in terminal heads. Berries ¼, white, in clusters, 3-seeded. Portugal. (Fig. 48 N.)

EMPETRUM NIGRUM L. Crowberry. 1. March. Ls. usually in fours. Fls. in the leaf-axils. Berries ¼, black, in clusters, 6-9-seeded. North temperate (including Britain) and Arctic regions. (Fig. 48 M.)

CLASS II. MONOCOTYLEDONS

Only one leaf appears first when the seed germinates. The leaves which follow do not usually have a network of branching veins. There is no clear distinction of bark, wood, and pith. The parts of the flower are usually in threes, or a multiple of three.

Family 103. **MUSACEAE.** P3+3, A5, Ḡ (3)

The banana family. Stems not woody, but formed by the leaf-stalks. Ls. alternate. Fls. unisexual, enclosed by green bracts. The banana is the fruit of *Musa sapientum*, a native of the West Indies, but cultivated in the Canary Islands, India, etc. Manila hemp is prepared from *Musa textilis*.

* MUSA BASJOO Sieb. Japanese Banana. 9. Summer. E. Ls. oblong, very large (up to nine feet by two), with numerous parallel veins springing at right angles from the midrib; crowded at the top of an erect tapering stem formed by the remains of leaf-stalks. Fls. yellow, in a terminal drooping spike. Fruit 4×1, 3-angled, banana-like. Japan.

Family 104. **AMARYLLIDACEAE.** P3+3, A3+3, Ḡ (3)

The daffodil and snowdrop family. Not true shrubs. Distinguished by the six stamens and inferior 3-celled ovary. The following two genera are often referred to a separate family, *Agavaceae*. The genus *Agave* yields valuable fibres such as sisal.

* AGAVE AMERICANA L. Century Plant. 12. E. Ls. linear, lanc. or awl-shaped, 12×3, thick and fleshy, toothed, spine-tipped, dull grey-green, crowded radially in a tuft at or near ground level. Fls. 2, white, in a large panicle at top of an erect stalk 8 to 12 feet high; the plant dies after flowering. Arizona to Mexico. (Fig. 38 H.)

* BESCHORNERIA YUCCOIDES Koch. 6. June. E. Ls. lanc., 24×3, entire, sharp-pointed, glaucous, margins minutely toothed, crowded radially in a tuft at or near ground level. Fls. 2, green, drooping, in few-flowered clusters from the axils of red bracts, the whole being borne on a stout erect red stalk up to 6 feet high. Fruit 2, fig-shaped. Mexico. (Fig. 38 J.)

Family 105. **LILIACEAE.** P3+3, A3+3, G̲ (3)

A very large family of herbaceous plants or soft-wooded shrubs, including many garden favourites such as lilies, hyacinths, tulips, onions, leeks, and garlic. Differs from the previous family in the superior ovary.

ASPARAGUS APHYLLUS L. (A. HORRIDUS Hort.). Rambling or shrubby. Summer. E. Ls. absent, their place being taken by alternate clusters of awl-shaped green spines. Fls. small, greenish. Fruit a black berry. Mediterranean region. (Fig. 38 K.)

CORDYLINE. Club Palm. Ls. linear, entire, crowded palm-like at top of main stem or branches, green, firm, upper erect, lower drooping. Fls. small, creamy white, in large much-branched panicles. Fruit a berry. Very similar

CORDYLINE—*continued*
is *Dracaena Draco*, the Dragon Tree of Teneriffe. The resin known as Dragon's Blood is obtained from *Dracaena Cinnabari*.

* **C. australis** Hook. f. Cabbage Tree. 40. E. Stem branches after reaching flowering stage. Ls. 36×3. Berry white. New Zealand. (Fig. 39 A.)

* **C. indivisa** Kunth (*C. Hectori* Colenso). 25. E. Stem unbranched. Ls. 72×6. Berry purplish blue. New Zealand.

DANAEA RACEMOSA Moench (D. LAURUS Medic.). Alexandrian Laurel. 4. June–July. E. Ls. ov., lanc., 4, entire, bright green on both sides, hairless, stalkless. Fls. small, white or greenish yellow, in small terminal racemes. Fruit a berry, ¼, red. Asia Minor. (Fig. 38 A.)

* LAPAGERIA ROSEA Ruiz & Pav. Chilean Bell Flower. 15. June–October. E. Climber. Ls. alternate, ov., 4, entire, pointed, heart-shaped or rounded base, dark glossy green, stiff and leathery, 3-5-nerved, short-stalked. Fls. 3, crimson or white, bell-shaped, drooping, solitary or in few-flowered clusters in the terminal leaf-axils. Fruit 2, egg-shaped, 3-sided. Chile. (Fig. 38 B.)

*PHILESIA MAGELLANICA Gmel. (P. BUXIFOLIA Lam.). Pepino. 3. September–October. E. Branchlets angled, hairless. Ls. alternate, lanc. or oblong, 1½, entire, stiff, dark green above, grey-green below, with green midrib, margins recurved, terminated by a beak which is often yellow. Fls. 2, rosy red, solitary at end of shoot. Fruit a berry. South Chile. (Fig. 38 C.)

PHORMIUM. Ls. long, linear or awl-shaped, entire, pointed, green, keeled, very rough, rising in a tuft at ground level. Fls. 2, in a large panicle.

* **P. Colensoi** Hook. f. Mountain Flax. 5. Summer. E. Ls. 60×2, pale green. Fls. yellow or yellowish red. Seed vessel twisted. New Zealand. (Fig. 40 A.)

Var. *variegatum* Hort. Variegated form.

* **P. tenax** Forst. New Zealand Flax. 9. Summer. E. Ls. 108×5, dark green, margins red or orange-coloured. Fls. red. Seed vessel not twisted. New Zealand.

Var. *alpinum* Hort. Dwarf.
Var. *purpureum* Hort. Ls. purple.
Var. *variegatum* Hort. Ls. striped with yellow.
Var. *Veitchii* Hort. Ls. with broad yellow stripe down middle.

RUSCUS. Stems green. Ls. alternate, entire, pointed, set in vertical plane (are really leaf-like branches), stiff and leathery. Fls. ¼, solitary or in few-flowered clusters in centre of ' leaf.' Fruit a red berry.

R. aculeatus L. Butcher's Broom. 3. March–April. E. Stems grooved, branched. Ls. ov., 1½, spine-tipped. Fls. white. Europe (including Britain). (Fig. 38 F.)

R. hypoglossum L. 1½. March–April. E. Stems unbranched. Ls. ov., lanc., 4, not spine-tipped. Fls. yellowish, in axil of leaf-like bract on the upper surface of the ' leaf.' South Europe. (Fig. 38 G.)

R. hypophyllum L. 1. March–April. E. Stems unbranched. Ls. ov., 2½, not spine-tipped. Fls. white, in small cluster in axil of minute bract on upper surface of the ' leaf.' South-west Europe and North Africa.

SMILAX. Climbers with prickly stems. Ls. alternate, entire, pointed, palmately veined, hairless, a pair of tendrils at base of leaf-stalk. Fls. small,

SMILAX—*continued*

greenish yellow or white, unisexual. Fruit a berry. Sarsaparilla is obtained from the roots of various species.

S. aspera L. Rough Bindweed. August–September. E. Stems zigzagged, angled. Ls. ov., 4, heart-shaped base, often prickly on margins and midrib below. Fls. in terminal and axillary racemes. Berry red. Mediterranean region. (Fig. 38 D.)

S. hispida Muhl. Hag Brier. June. D. Stems very bristly. Ls. ov., 6, often with a straight or tapering base. Fls. in axillary clusters, stalk of cluster longer than leaf-stalk. Berry black. North America.

S. lanceolata L. June. E. Ls. lanc., 3, tapering base. Berry dark red. North America.

S. megalantha Wright. May. E. Ls. ov., 4, glaucous below. Berry large, bright coral-red. China.

S. rotundifolia L. Horse Brier. June. D. Stems 4-angled, with a few short prickles between the joints. Ls. nearly circular, 3, heart-shaped base. Fls. in axillary clusters, stalk of cluster not longer than leaf-stalk. Berry bluish black. North America. (Fig. 38 E.)

YUCCA. Ls. long, linear or awl-shaped, pointed, glaucous, crowded radially in a tuft at the top of a short stem which is often so short as to be scarcely visible. Fls. large, white, bell-shaped, drooping, in large erect terminal panicles or racemes. Fruit a capsule.

(*a*) *Ls. flaccid, recurving*

Y. flaccida Haw. July–August. E. Stem not rising above ground level. Ls. 20×1, with marginal threads. Panicle up to 6 feet high. South-east United States.

Y. recurvifolia Salisb. 8. August–September. E. Ls. 36×2, spine-tipped. Panicle up to 3 feet high. South United States. (Fig. 38 M.)

(*b*) *Ls. stiff*

Y. filamentosa L. July–August. E. Stem not rising above ground level. Ls. 30×2, margins with curly threads. Panicle up to 6 feet high. South United States.

Y. glauca Nutt. July–August. E. Stem not rising above ground level. Ls. 30×½, margins white. Panicle narrow (racemose), up to 4 feet high. South United States.

Y. gloriosa L. Adam's Needle. 8. August–September. E. Ls. 24×3, spine-tipped. Panicle up to 4 feet high. South United States. (Fig. 38 L.)

Family 106. PALMAE. P3+3, A3+3, G̲ (3) or 3

Ls. large, usually digitate or pinnate and clustered at the top of the stem. Fls. small, often unisexual, in large panicles among or below the leaves. Fruit a berry. Palms yield coconuts, coir, dates, sago, betel-nut, palm oil, rattan canes, toddy, arrack, etc. Only *Trachycarpus Fortunei* is really hardy in this country.

CHAMAEROPS HUMILIS L. Dwarf Fan Palm. 8. Summer. E. Ls. digitate, 18, greyish green. Mediterranean Region.

* JUBAEA SPECTABILIS H. B. K. Wine Palm. 50. E. Trunk bare, with

numerous small vertical cracks. Ls. pinnate, up to 15 feet long; lflts. up to 2 feet long. Chile. (Fig. 17 A.)

TRACHYCARPUS FORTUNEI Wendl. (CHAMAEROPS EXCELSA Mart.). Chusan Palm. 30. Summer. E. Stem erect, covered by dark stiff fibres. Ls. 30, palmately dissected into narrow segments, dark green; stalk 2-edged, toothed; crowded radially at and near top of stem. Fls. small, yellow, in large panicles near top of stem. Berry ½, blue-black. Japan. (Fig. 6 B.)

Family 107. **GRAMINEAE.** Po, A1–6, G1

Stems jointed, usually hollow. Ls. alternate, linear or lanc., pointed, usually entire, the base continued into a split sheath which envelops the stem. Fls. in spikes, racemes, or panicles, composed of small spikelets, each containing one or more flowers (*florets*). Each spikelet is made up of several alternate scales or bracts, the outer (glumes) being empty, the inner (paleas) bearing florets. Anthers long and hanging loose. Ovary with feathery stigmas. The grasses are of great economic importance, yielding the majority of our cereals; wheat, barley, oats, rye, maize (corn), rice, cane sugar, and animal fodder. Bamboos are put to many uses in tropical countries, including the manufacture of paper. Paper is also made from many grasses.

ARUNDINARIA. Hardy Bamboo. Stems straight, cylindrical, with whorled branchlets; sheath open on one side and usually deciduous. The plant flowers very rarely, after which it dies. Stamens usually three; those with six stamens are sometimes referred to a separate genus, *Sasa.*

(*a*) *Stems purplish brown*

A. anceps Mitf. Ringal. 15. E. Stems erect, arching at top. Sheath mottled inside, hairy on margin. Ls. 4×½. North-west Himalaya. (Fig. 40 B.)

A. auricoma Mitf. 4. E. Stems very thin. Ls. 8×1, rounded or heart-shaped at base, striped with yellow. Japan. (Fig. 40 C.)

A. marmorea Makino. 5. E. Stems solid, erect, clasped by persistent mottled sheaths. Ls. 5×½, apex constricted about ½ inch from top. Japan.

A. nitida Mitf. 10. E. Stems arching at top. Ls. 3×¼, with tapering base. China. (Fig. 40 G.)

A. palmata Bean. 8. E. Ls. 12×3, spreading palm-like from end of branch. Japan. (Fig. 40 D.)

(*b*) *Stems green or yellow*

A. angustifolia De Lahaie. 6. E. Stems erect, very thin. Ls. 6×¾, rounded at base, bristle-toothed on one margin, sheath with tuft of erect hairs at top. Japan.

* **A. falcata** Nees. Ringal. 10. E. Young stems covered with bloom. Ls. 4×½, curved, without cross veinlets, rows of transparent dots between veins. Himalaya. (Fig. 40 E.)

* **A. Falconeri** Benth. Ringal. 25. E. Stems purple at joints, sheath purple. Ls. 4×½, no cross veinlets. Himalaya.

ARUNDINARIA—*continued*

A. fastuosa Makino. 25. E. Stems stout, erect; sheaths up to 9×4, glazed inside. Ls. 8×1, tapering base. Japan. (Fig. 40 J.)

A. Fortunei A. & C. Rivière. 3. E. Stems very slender, sheaths persistent. Ls. 7×1, rounded base, striped with white, hairy on both sides. Japan.

A. graminea Makino. 10. E. Stems slender, very hollow; branchlets in dense whorls at top. Ls. 9×½, tapering base. Japan. (Fig. 40 H.)

A. japonica Sieb. & Zucc. (*Sasa japonica* Makino). 15. E. Stems erect, very hollow; sheath with long tail-like point. Ls. 12×2, long-pointed. Japan. (Fig. 40 F.)

A. Ragamowskii Pfitzer (*Sasa tessellata* Makino, *Bambusa tessellata* Munro). 3. E. Stem sheaths covering several joints. Ls. 18×4. China.

A. Simonii A. & C. Rivière. 18. E. Stems very hollow; sheaths rather persistent, hairy on margins, very glazed inside. Ls. 12×1, long-pointed, bright green above, glaucous on one side of midrib below. China.

Var. *Chino* Makino. 4. Ls. 6×½, dark green mottled with dull yellow.

ARUNDO DONAX L. Great Reed. 10. July–August. E. Stems hollow. Ls. awl-shaped, 24×1½, long-pointed, drooping, in two opposite rows, base of blade clasping stem. Fls. in erect silky panicles up to 24 long. Mediterranean region, India, etc. (Fig. 39 D.)

BAMBUSA. Bamboo. Not distinguishable from *Arundinaria* except in the flower, which is rarely seen and has six stamens, the lower florets being imperfect (perfect in *Arundinaria*). The two hardy species given below are, however, clearly distinguishable.

B. disticha Mitf. (*Sasa disticha* Camus). 2. E. Stems slender, zigzagged. Ls. 2×¼, in two opposite rows. Japan. (Fig. 40 K.)

B. quadrangularis Fenzl. 30. E. Stem 4-sided, with rounded corners. Ls. 8×1, margins bristly. China and Japan.

CORTADERIA ARGENTEA Stapf (GYNERIUM ARGENTEUM Nees). Pampas Grass. 14. August–October. E. Ls. 60×¼, arising in a dense tuft from or near ground level, rough to the touch owing to the midrib and margins being finely toothed. Fls. in several erect plume-like silvery panicles rising from centre of tuft; spikelet with two or more florets. South America. (Fig. 39 B.)

EULALIA JAPONICA Trin. (MISCANTHUS SINENSIS Anders.). 6. E. Stems herbaceous, green. Ls. linear, 12×1, entire, green, with white midrib. Fls. in large purplish brown panicles, erect at first but later bending over. Japan.

Var. *variegata* Beal. Ls. striped with white.

Var. *zebrina* Beal. Ls. with cross-bars of yellow or white.

PHYLLOSTACHYS. Hardy Bamboo. Stems woody, zigzagged, flattened above the joints. Like *Arundinaria* and *Bambusa*, the plant flowers very rarely, after which it dies; stamens three. (Fig. 40 L.)

(*a*) *Stems yellow*

P. aurea A. & C. Rivière. 15. E. Stems stiff, erect, a swollen band below each joint. Ls. 4×1. Japan.

P. Castillonis Mitf. 10. E. Stems very hollow, dark green on flattened parts. Ls. 5×¾, usually striped with yellow. Japan.

P. mitis A. & C. Rivière. 20. E. Stems arching. Ls. 5×¾. Japan.

PHYLLOSTACHYS—*continued*

(*b*) *Stems not yellow*

P. flexuosa A. & C. Rivière. 8. E. Stems green, then black; margin of sheath not hairy. Ls. $4 \times \frac{1}{2}$. Japan.

P. Henonis Mitf. 15. E. Stems very hollow, arching outwards. Ls. $3 \times \frac{1}{2}$, tufted. Japan.

P. nigra Munro. 20. E. Stems very hollow, green at first, then black; margin of sheath hairy. Ls. tufted, $3 \times \frac{1}{2}$. Japan.

P. Quilioi A. & C. Rivière. 20. E. Stem-sheaths conspicuously mottled. Ls. 8×1, in tufts. Japan.

P. viridi-glaucescens A. & C. Rivière. 20. E. Stems very hollow, arching, branched from base; sheaths striped with purple. Ls. 5×1. China.

CLASS III. GYMNOSPERMS

Mostly trees and shrubs usually with linear or scale-like leaves. Fls. small, unisexual, solitary or in separate catkin-like or cone-like structures; ovules attached to an open carpellary scale without ovary, style, or stigma. The timber is known to the trade as softwood—a somewhat misleading term—and can usually be identified by the absence of large pores in the spring wood when a fresh specimen is examined through a lens. Gymnosperms yielded ninety-four per cent of the timber imports into Great Britain before the second world war. Families 109 and 110 are commonly known as conifers, but the typical woody cone is not found in *Taxaceae* and *Juniperus*.

Family 108. **GNETACEAE.** P2–4, A2–8, G1

Ls. minute and opposite, or none. Fls. with a perianth of small bracts or scales.

EPHEDRA. Shrubby Horse-tail. Branchlets green, opposite or whorled, slender, rush-like. Ls. distant, opposite or whorled, usually minute, united at base, and often reduced to a mere sheath. Fls. small, yellow, in small racemes from the joints. Fruit usually a berry.

(a) Ls. minute, scale-like

E. distachya L. (*E. vulgaris* Rich.). 4. A spreading mass of bright green cylindrical upright branches. Berry red. Europe and Asia Minor. (Fig. 37 J.)

E. Gerardiana Wall. 2. Like above, but dwarfer. Not more than four flowers in the male raceme. Himalaya.

(b) Ls. awl-shaped

E. foliata C. A. Mey. 30. Climbing or prostrate. Ls. 1. Berry red or whitish. Arabia, Persia, Turkestan.

E. trifurca Torr. 3. Stems rigid, spiny. Ls. ½. Fruit dry, with winged bracts. South United States. (Fig. 37 K.)

Family 109. **TAXACEAE**

Resinous trees and shrubs with linear or scale-like leaves. Fls. without a perianth, the sexes usually on different trees. Fruit fleshy, usually 1-seeded.

CEPHALOTAXUS. Main branches whorled in young trees; branchlets opposite. Ls. alternate, linear, pointed, with two broad grey bands below, usually in two rows. Male flowers yellowish, in leaf-axils on lower side of branch. Fruit 1, egg-shaped.

C. drupacea Sieb. & Zucc. Cow's Tail Pine. 12. E. Ls. 2, abruptly pointed, directed upward forming a V-shaped trough. Fruit green. Japan. (Fig. 41 A.)

Var. *fastigiata* Pilger. Erect habit; ls. not in two rows.
Var. *pedunculata* Miq. Ls. up to 2½.

C. Fortunei Hook. 20. E. Ls. 3, long-pointed, horizontal. Fruit brown. China. (Fig. 41 B.)

DACRYDIUM. Ls. scale-like, awl-shaped, or linear. Fruit a fleshy cone containing one seed.

* **D. cupressinum** Soland. Rimu. 80. E. Branches long, thin, and drooping. Ls. of younger trees awl-shaped, $\frac{1}{4}$, completely covering the stem; scale-like on older trees. The timber is valuable and used for house building. New Zealand. (Fig. 41 H.)

* **D. Franklinii** Hook. f. Huon Pine. 100. E. Branches arching. Ls. minute, scale-like, keeled, giving 4-sided shape to branchlet. Tasmania.

* PHYLLOCLADUS TRICHOMANIOIDES D. Don. 50. E. Bark thick, black outside, reddish inside. Branches whorled. Ls. alternate, ov., 1, toothed or lobed, in two opposite rows giving a rather fern-like appearance to the branchlet. Fruit fleshy, enclosing a nut-like seed. New Zealand. (Fig. 34 M.)

PODOCARPUS. Ls. alternate, linear, pale green below. Fruit a 1-seeded berry on a short stalk (hence the name). Several species from New Zealand and East Africa give good timbers, e.g. matai, totara, podo, New Zealand white pine, etc.

P. alpina R. Br. 4. E. Branchlets whorled. Ls. $\frac{1}{2}$, blunt-ended. Fruit $\frac{1}{4}$, red. Victoria and Tasmania. (Fig. 41 D.)

P. andina Poepp. (*Prumnopitys elegans* Philippi). Plum-fruited Yew. 50. E. Ls. $\frac{1}{2}$, flattened, in two ranks, dull grey-green below. Fruit $\frac{3}{4}$, yellowish white. Chile. (Fig. 41 G.)

P. macrophylla D. Don. 30. E. Ls. $4\times\frac{1}{2}$, abruptly pointed or blunt, tapering at both ends, midrib prominent below. Fruit $\frac{1}{4}$, green or purplish. China and Japan.

P. saligna D. Don (*P. chilina* Rich.). 30. E. Ls. $4\times\frac{1}{4}$, fine-pointed, tapering at both ends. Fruit $\frac{1}{4}$. Chile. (Fig. 41 C.)

* **P. Totara** A. Cunn. Totara. 80. E. Ls. 1, stiff, sharp-pointed. Fruit $\frac{1}{2}$, red. New Zealand. (Fig. 41 E.)

SAXEGOTHEA CONSPICUA Lindl. Prince Albert's Yew. 40. E. Branchlets whorled. Ls. alternate, linear, 1, indistinctly 2-ranked. Fruit $\frac{1}{2}$, a small fleshy cone with several seeds. South America. (Fig. 41 F.)

TAXUS BACCATA L. Yew. 40. E. Bark peeling; branchlets alternate. Ls. alternate, linear, 1, dark green above, bright green below, 2-ranked. Fruit $\frac{1}{4}$, a red fleshy cup containing one seed. Europe (including Britain), West Asia, Himalaya. (Fig. 41 J.)

Var. *fastigiata* Loud. Irish Yew. Stems and branchlets erect. Ls. $1\frac{1}{2}$, not 2-ranked, but spreading radially.

T. canadensis Marsh. Canada Yew or Ground Hemlock is a low shrub with pointed and keeled bud scales.

TORREYA. Main branches whorled in young trees; branchlets opposite. Ls. alternate, linear, sharp-pointed, with two narrow grey bands in grooves below, 2-ranked. Fruit a dryish egg-shaped 1-seeded berry.

T. californica Torr. (*T. Myristica* Hook.). Californian Nutmeg. 70. E. Two-year-old branchlets brown. Ls. 2 or more. Fruit $1\frac{1}{2}$, green streaked with purple. California.

T. grandis Fort. 70. E. Two-year-old branchlets green. Ls. 1. Fruit 1, green. China.

T. nucifera Sieb. & Zucc. 30. E. Two-year-old branchlets brown. Ls. 1. Fruit 1, green. Japan. (Fig. 41 K.)

TORREYA—*continued*

T. taxifolia Arn. Stinking Cedar. 30. E. Two-year-old branchlets green. Ls. 1, evil smelling when crushed. Fruit 1, green streaked with purple. Florida.

Family 110. PINACEAE

Resinous trees with linear, awl-shaped, or scale-like leaves. Male and female flowers usually on same tree. Fruit a cone with several or many scales, usually woody (fleshy in *Juniperus*), the seeds attached to the scales.

ABIES. Silver Fir. Tall narrow evergreen trees with pointed crowns. Bark greyish white or greyish green; branches whorled in young trees, the main branchlets opposite. Ls. alternate, linear, generally with two white bands below; spirally arranged on leading shoots, usually 2-ranked on older ones; they leave round scars when they fall. Male catkins drooping; female erect, egg-shaped. Cones woody, erect, the scales dropping off, leaving the central axis on the branch. The timber is imported as Whitewood; it is soft, white, and contains no resin, being suitable for food boxes. Canada balsam is obtained from *A. balsamea*.

(a) Ls. all radially arranged

A. cephalonica Loud. Grecian Fir. 100. Ls. 1, flattened, long- and sharp-pointed. Cone cylindrical, 6×1½, the bracts protruding and bent downwards. Mountains of Greece.

A. Pinsapo Boiss. Spanish Fir. 100. Ls. ¾, short-pointed or blunt. Cone cylindrical, 5×1½, bracts not protruding. Mountains of Spain. (Fig. 41 M.)

Var. *glauca* Beiss. Ls. blue-grey.
Var. *pendula* Beiss. Branches drooping.

(b) Ls. in two approximately horizontal rows

A. alba Mill. (*A. pectinata* DC.). Common Silver Fir. 120. Twigs grey, downy; buds not resinous. Ls. 1, glossy green, notched at apex. Cone 6×2, reddish brown. Europe. (Fig. 42 A.)

A. grandis Lindl. Giant Fir. 250. Twigs olive green, hairless; buds small, resinous. Ls. 2, glossy green, blunt-ended, not grooved above. Cone 4×2, cylindrical, bright green. West North America. (Fig. 41 N.)

A. Lowiana Murr. 200. Ls. 2, bluish or greyish green, grooved above. South Oregon to California.

A. sibirica Ledeb. Siberian Fir. 100. Like *A. alba*, but buds resinous and leaves directed forward. Cone 3, with toothed scales. North Asia.

Var. *nephrolepis* Mayr. Ls. and cones smaller.

A. venusta Koch (*A. bracteata* Nutt.). Santa Lucia Fir. 150. Buds spindle-shaped, light brown, not resinous. Ls. 2 or more, rigid, sharp-pointed. Cone 4×2, egg-shaped, purplish brown, bracts spine-tipped. California. (Fig. 41 L.)

(c) Ls. in two rows with V-shaped trough between

A. balsamea Mill. Balsam Fir. 60. Twigs grey, smooth, with scattered hairs; buds small, egg-shaped or round, resinous. Ls. 1, slightly notched at apex, grey below. Cone 3×1, dark purple or olive-green. Canada. (Fig. 42 B.)

ABIES—*continued*

A. cilicica Carr. See under (*d*).

A. Delavayi Franch. 100. Twigs reddish brown; buds round, resinous. Ls. 1, curved, grey below, margins recurved. Cone $2\frac{1}{2}\times\frac{3}{4}$, purplish black. China.

A. firma Sieb. & Zucc. 120. Ls. 1, pale green (white bands indistinct). Cone 5×2, bracts protruding. Japan. (Fig. 42 D.)

A. Forrestii Craib. 65. Twigs reddish brown; buds small, egg-shaped, resinous. Ls. 2, notched at apex, white below. Cone $3\frac{1}{2}\times 1\frac{1}{2}$, dark blue. China.

A. homolepis Sieb. & Zucc. (*A. brachyphylla* Maxim.). Nikko Fir. 100. Twigs grey, deeply grooved; buds egg-shaped or round, resinous. Ls. 1, slightly notched at apex, white below. Cone $4\times 1\frac{1}{2}$, bracts hidden. Japan. (Fig. 42 C.)

A. Nordmanniana Spach. See under (*d*).

A. numidica Carr. Algerian Fir. 70. Twigs brown, glossy, hairless; buds large, egg-shaped, not resinous. Ls. $\frac{3}{4}$, dark glossy green above, with grey patch near apex, white below. Cone $5\times 1\frac{1}{2}$, bracts hidden. Algeria.

A. Pindrow Spach. 120. Twigs grey, hairless; buds large, resinous. Ls. $2\frac{1}{2}$, curved, directed forward, with faint grey lines below. Cone 4×2, cylindrical, deep purple when young. Himalaya.

A. spectabilis Spach (*A. Webbiana* Lindl.). Himalayan Fir. 200. Twigs reddish brown, downy, deeply grooved; buds large, round, resinous. Ls. 2, deeply notched at apex, dark glossy green above, white below. Cone 6×3, cylindrical, violet-purple when young. Himalaya. (Fig. 42 F.)

(*d*) *Ls. in two rows without, or with indistinct, V-shaped trough between; straight or nearly so*

A. amabilis Forbes. 250. Twigs grey, downy; buds round, resinous. Ls. $1\frac{1}{2}$, dark green above, vividly blue-white below. Cone $6\times 2\frac{1}{2}$, purple. West North America. (Fig. 42 G.)

A. cilicica Carr. Cilician Fir. 100. Twigs greyish brown, hairless or nearly so; buds rough, egg-shaped, not resinous. Ls. 1, stiff and crowded, directed outward, dark green above, grey below, not notched at apex. Cone 8×2, bracts hidden. Asia Minor.

A. Fraseri Poir. Southern Balsam Fir. 70. Twigs grey, hairy; buds small, very resinous. Ls. $\frac{3}{4}$, dark green above, white below, blunt and notched at end. Cone 2, purple, bracts protruding and reflexed. South-east United States.

A. holophylla Maxim. Manchurian Fir. 150. Twigs grey, hairless; buds slightly resinous. Ls. 1, bright green above, the grey bands below often indistinct. Cone 4×2, bracts hidden. Manchuria.

A. Mariesii Mast. 80. Twigs reddish brown, very downy; buds round, resinous, purple. Ls. $\frac{3}{4}$, yellowish green above, white below. Cone 4×2, bracts hidden. Japan.

A. Nordmanniana Spach. Caucasian Fir. 200. Twigs grey; buds egg-shaped, not resinous. Ls. 1, stiff and crowded, dark green and grooved above, grey below. Cone 6×2, reddish brown, bracts protruding and bent downward. Caucasus. (Fig. 42 E.)

ABIES—*continued*

A. numidica Carr. See (*c*) above.

A. Veitchii Lindl. 70. Twigs brown, downy; buds round, resinous. Ls. 1, notched at apex, white below, all directed forward. Cone 2×1, cylindrical, blue-purple to brown. Japan. (Fig. 42 II.)

(*e*) *Ls. in two rows without V-shaped trough between; much curved, some white on upper as well as lower side*

A. magnifica Murr. Red Fir. 200. Ls. 1½, 4-angled, not grooved above, not notched at apex. Cone 8×4, purple to brown, bracts not protruding. Oregon to California. (Fig. 43 A.)

Var. *argentea* Beiss. Ls. bluish white.
Var. *glauca* Beiss. Ls. glaucous.

A. nobilis Lindl. 200. Ls. 1, flattish, grooved above, notched at apex. Cone 10×3, cylindrical, brown-purple, bracts protruding and bent back. Washington to North California. (Fig. 42 K.)

Var. *glauca* Beiss. Ls. bluish green.

(*f*) *Ls. irregularly arranged*

A. concolor Lindl. & Gord. 100. Twigs hairless or nearly so; buds large, round, resinous. Ls. 3, glaucous green. Cone 4×1½, plum-coloured to brown, bracts not protruding. Colorado. (Fig. 43 C.)

Var. *violacea* Beiss. Ls. bluish.

A. lasiocarpa Nutt. Rocky Mountain Fir. 90. Twigs grey, downy; buds small, egg-shaped. Ls. 1½, much crowded, pointing forward and upward, pale bluish green. Cone 4×2, cylindrical, bracts not protruding. West North America. (Fig. 43 B.)

Var. *arizonica* Lemmon. Bark white and corky.

(*g*) *Ls. mostly erect on upper side of shoot*

A. koreana Wils. Korean Fir. 60. Ls. 1, white below, broadest towards apex. Cone 2½×1, purple. Korea. (Fig. 42 J.)

ARAUCARIA. Main branches whorled, twigs opposite. Ls. alternate, awl-shaped. Male catkins in clusters at end of branches. Cones falling when ripe. Parana Pine is the timber of *Araucaria brasiliensis*; Kauri Pine of *Agathis australis*, an allied genus from the North Island of New Zealand.

A. araucana Koch (*A. imbricata* Pav.). Chile Pine, Monkey Puzzle. 80. E. Ls. 2×1, leathery, spine-tipped, overlapping spirally, green on both sides, very crowded. Cone 6; seeds 1½, conical, wingless, edible. Chile. (Fig. 43 E.)

* **A. excelsa** R. Br. Norfolk Island Pine. 150. E. Bark peeling. Ls. on young branchlets ½, spreading; on older branchlets ¼, incurved. Cone 4; seeds 1, winged. Norfolk Island and Pacific. (Fig. 43 F.)

ATHROTAXIS. Branches alternate. Ls. alternate, scale-like or awl-shaped, closely and spirally arranged. Male and female catkins on same tree. Cones small.

* **A. cupressoides** D. Don. Tasmanian Cedar. 40. E. Ls. minute, scale-like, blunt-ended except on the oldest branches where they are sharp-

ATHROTAXIS—*continued*

pointed and much larger, closely pressed to stem. Cone ¼. Tasmania. (Fig. 43 K.)

* **A. laxifolia** Hook. Tasmanian Cedar. 30. E. Ls. minute, scale-like, with incurved points, free from stem. Cone ½. Tasmania. (Fig. 43 H.)

* **A. selaginoides** D. Don. King William Pine. 100. E. Ls. awl-shaped, ½, sharp-pointed, keeled, with two white bands below. Cone 1. Tasmania. (Fig. 43 J.)

* CALLITRIS OBLONGA Rich. Cypress Pine. 25. E. Ls. minute, scale-like, in threes on slender feathery branches. Cone 1×¾, egg-shaped, 6-scaled, seeds winged. Tasmania. (Fig. 43 L.)

CEDRUS. Cedar. Strongly resinous. Branches alternate. Ls. linear, alternate and spirally arranged on leading shoots, in clusters on older shoots, persistent for several years. Male catkins 2, cylindrical, erect; female ½, egg-shaped, purple. Cones erect, purple when young; scales fan-shaped, horizontal and closely packed like the leaves of a book, falling and leaving the central axis on the branch. The timber is strongly scented, easily worked and very durable, but not particularly strong.

C. atlantica Manetti. Atlas Cedar. 120. Leading shoot stiff and erect. Ls. 1. Cone 3×2, cylindrical. North Africa. (Fig. 44 B.)

Var. *glauca* Carr. Ls. silvery.

C. Deodara Laws. Deodar. 250. Leading shoot and branches drooping. Ls. 2. Cone 4×3, egg-shaped. Himalaya. (Fig. 44 A.)

Var. *argentea* Nels. Ls. bluish or silvery white.

Var. *aurea* Nels. Ls. yellow.

C. Libani Barrelier (*C. libanotica* Link). Cedar of Lebanon. 120. Leading shoot arching, branches horizontal or slightly drooping. Ls. 1. Cone 5×2½, cylindrical. Mountains of Syria. (Fig. 44 C.)

Var. *glauca* Rehd. Ls. bluish white.

Var. *nana* Loud. Dwarf compact form.

C. brevifolia (Henry), a native of Cyprus, has much shorter glaucous needles, and cones 3×2.

CHAMAECYPARIS. Small-coned Cypress. Ls. opposite, of two kinds: (1) juvenile form, linear or awl-shaped, sometimes found on parts of older plants; (2) adult form, scale-like and closely pressed to stem. Branchlet systems flattened. Cones ½ or less, woody; scales peltate and touching at their edges, with central boss, each one usually with 2–4 seeds.

* **C. formosensis** Matsumara (*Cupressus formosensis* Henry). Formosan Cypress. 150. E. Branches horizontal. Ls. pointed, without white markings. Cone ½, egg-shaped. According to Dallimore it is like *C. nootkatensis* (see below), but branchlet systems of a paler green and often tinged with bronze. Formosa. (Fig. 44 G.)

C. Lawsoniana Parl. (*Cupressus Lawsoniana* Murr.). Lawson's Cypress. 200. E. Scale ls. pointed, with small glands on back and vague white markings (as if edged with white). Male flowers red, at end of branchlets. Cone ¼. The timber is imported under the name of Port Orford Cedar. West North America. (Fig. 44 B.)

Var. *Allumii* Beiss. Tall and thin, with grey leaves.

CHAMAECYPARIS—*continued*

Var. *argentea* Gord. Silvery.

Var. *Boskoop Triumph* Hort. Blue-grey.

Var. *erecta viridis* Waterer. Narrow, branchlets all erect, foliage bright green.

Var. *Fletcheri* Hort. Slow-growing blue-grey form, with leaves all juvenile.

Var. *filiformis* Beiss. Long drooping cord-like branches. (Fig. 44 J.)

C. nootkatensis Sudw. (*Cupressus nutkaensis* Spach, *Thuyopsis borealis* Carr.). Nootka Cypress. 120. E. Scale ls. long-pointed, without glands or white markings. Branchlet systems in a somewhat vertical plane. Cone ½. The timber is imported under the name of Yellow Cedar. South-west Alaska to Oregon. (Fig. 44 L.)

Var. *glauca* Beiss. Ls. glaucous.

Var. *lutea* Beiss. Young shoots yellow.

C. obtusa Endl. (*Cupressus obtusa* Koch, *Retinospora obtusa* Sieb. & Zucc.). Hinoki Cypress. 120. E. Scale ls. blunt, without glands on back but with X- and Y-shaped white markings. Cone ¼. Japan. (Fig. 44 M.)

Var. *aurea* Beiss. Young shoots yellow.

Var. *lycopodioides* Mast. Dwarf. Branchlet systems not quite flat.

C. pisifera Endl. (*Cupressus pisifera* Koch, *Retinospora pisifera* Sieb. & Zucc.). Sawara Cypress. 100. E. Scale ls. sharply pointed, with white markings on back; juvenile leaves usually present on parts of older trees. Cone ¼. Japan. (Fig. 44 N.)

Var. *aurea* Carr. Young shoots yellow.

Var. *filifera* Beiss. Branches long and cord-like.

Var. *plumosa* Mast. Ls. all juvenile. (Fig. 44 O.)

Var. *plumosa argentea* Hort. Ls. all juvenile, creamy white.

Var. *plumosa aurea* Hort. Ls. all juvenile, yellow.

Var. *squarrosa* Mast. Ls. all juvenile, silvery; outline of bush very irregular. (Fig. 44 P.)

C. thyoides Brit. (*Cupressus thyoides* L.). White Cedar. 50. E. Scale ls. very small, dark green, with large glands on back and with either X-shaped or no white markings. Cone very small, ¼ or less. East North America.

CRYPTOMERIA JAPONICA D. Don. Japanese Cedar. 150. E. Bark reddish brown, peeling. Ls. alternate, awl-shaped, ¾, curved inward. Male catkins ¼, terminal. Cone ½, round, at end of branches. Japan. (Fig. 44 D.)

Var. *elegans* Mast. Ls. 1, spreading, turning brown in winter.

CUNNINGHAMIA LANCEOLATA Hook. (C. SINENSIS R. Br.). 150. E. Ls. alternate, linear, 2, flat, pointed, margins finely toothed, green above, two white bands below, 2-ranked. Cone roundish, 1½, cone-scales toothed. China. (Fig. 44 F.)

CUPRESSOCYPARIS LEYLANDII (A. B. Jacks.) M. L. Green. E. Ls. opposite, scale-like, long-pointed, without glands or white markings, the branchlet systems flattened. Cone round, ¾, woody; scales peltate, with central boss. Cross between *Chamaecyparis nootkatensis* and *Cupressus macrocarpa*.

CUPRESSUS. Big-coned Cypress. Ls. opposite, juvenile awl-shaped, adult scale-like and closely pressed to stem. Cone round, ¾ or more, woody; scales peltate and touching at their edges, with central boss, each scale usually with five or more seeds.

C. arizonica Greene. Arizona Cypress. 40. E. Bark peeling in thin papery flakes. Scale ls. pointed, with conspicuous glands and often white on the back, very closely pressed to stem. Cone 1. Arizona. (Fig. 44 R.)

C. funebris Endl. Chinese Weeping Cypress. 70. Bark smooth; branches ascending or horizontal, with long drooping ends; branchlet systems flattened. Scale ls. pointed, furrowed on the back, without white markings. Cone ⅜. West China. (Fig. 44 K.)

C. Goveniana Gord. 20. E. Like *C. macrocarpa* (see below), but much smaller. Foliage orange-scented when bruised. Male flowers and cones produced in great abundance, the ground beneath becoming yellow with pollen. South California.

C. lusitanica Mill. Cedar of Goa. 50. E. Branchlets 4-sided. Scale ls. sharply pointed, free at tip. Cone ⅜. Mexico.

C. Macnabiana Murr. 30. E. Like *C. arizonica*, but branchlets stouter and scale ls. blunter. California.

C. macrocarpa Hartw. Monterey Cypress. 90. E. Branchlet systems radially arranged, bright fresh green. Scale ls. swollen at tip. Cone 1½. Bay of Monterey (California). (Fig. 44 S.)

Var. *fastigiata* Carr. Branchlets erect.

Var. *lutea* Dicks. Ls. yellow.

C. sempervirens L. Italian Cypress. 150. E. Branchlet systems radially arranged, dark dull green. Scale ls. not swollen at tip, very small. Cone 1. South Europe and North Persia.

Var. *stricta* Ait. (*fastigiata* Beiss., *pyramidalis* Targ.). Branchlets erect; a thin narrow tree.

C. torulosa D. Don. Himalayan Cypress. 150. E. Branches drooping. Scale ls. triangular, blunt-ended, with two small glands on either side. Cone ¾, with more than five seeds to each scale. Himalaya.

FITZROYA CUPRESSOIDES Johnst. (F. PATAGONIA Hook. f.). 50. E. Ls. in whorls of three or four, linear, ¼, blunt-ended, with two white bands on upper side. Cone ¼, round, at end of branchlets. South America. (Fig. 44 T.)

* FOKIENIA HODGINSII Henry & Thomas. 50. E. Ls. scale-like, in fours on flattened 3-pinnate branchlet systems. Cone 1, round, 12-16-scaled, seed with two unequal wings. Fukien province of China. (Fig. 44 V.)

GLYPTOSTROBUS PENSILIS Koch (G. SINENSIS Henry). Chinese Deciduous Cypress. 100. D. Like *Taxodium* (see page 343), but cone scales elongated and not peltate. According to Henry it 'is readily distinguished from *Taxodium* in all stages of growth by the numerous stomatic white dots on the branchlets of the first, second, and third year.' China.

JUNIPERUS. Juniper. Ls. opposite or in threes, awl-shaped or scale-like. Cones fleshy, berry-like. The timber of *J. virginiana* is pinkish and easy to work, being useful for pencils and house-fittings. The berries of the common juniper are used for flavouring gin.

JUNIPERUS—*continued*

(a) Ls. awl-shaped and needle-like, in threes, spreading, jointed at base

J. communis L. Common Juniper. 30. E. Ls. ½, sharp-pointed, with one grey band above. Berry ¼, blue-black. Europe (including Britain), Asia, North America. (Fig. 44 W.)

Var. *aurea* Nichols. Young shoots yellow.

Var. *suecica* Ait. Swedish Juniper. Tall and narrow, with bluish leaves and nodding branchlets.

J. drupacea Labill. Syrian Juniper. 60. E. Branchlets triangular. Ls. ¾, sharp-pointed, with two white bands above. Berry 1, brown. Greece and Asia Minor.

J. formosana Hayata. 40. E. Branches drooping at ends. Ls. ¾, 1-banded and grooved above. Berry ¼, brown. Japan.

J. macrocarpa Sibth. Large-berried Juniper. 12. E. Ls. ¾, 2-banded above. Berry ½, brown. Spain to Syria.

J. Oxycedrus L. Prickly Juniper. 30. E. Ls. ½, stiff, 2-banded, tapering to a sharp point from the middle. Berry ½, reddish brown. Mediterranean region.

J. rigida Sieb. & Zucc. 30. E. Branches drooping at ends. Ls. ¾, 2-banded and not grooved above. Berry ¼, dark brown. Japan.

(b) Ls. awl-shaped and needle-like, in threes, directed upward, not jointed at base

J. procumbens Sieb. Creeping Juniper. E. Ls. ¼, bluish grey, with one green band above. Japan.

J. recurva Buch.-Ham. Himalayan Juniper. 40. E. Usually a low shrub with long creeping stems. Ls. ¼, bluish grey, without green band above. Berry ¼, brown to purple. Himalaya. (Fig. 44 Y.)

J. squamata Buch.-Ham. 2. E. Like *J. recurva*, but leaves bright green. Himalaya.

(c) Ls. mostly scale-like

J. chinensis L. Chinese Juniper. 60. E. Bark twisted, peeling in long strips. In the male tree the lower branches are furnished with 2-banded needle-like leaves in threes; in the female the leaves are scale-like except on small side shoots and lower branches. Berry ¼, white with bloom when ripe. China. (Fig. 44 K.)

Var. *albo-variegata* Veitch. Shoots creamy white at tips.

Var. *aurea* Young. Young shoots yellow.

Var. *glauca* Hort. Ls. bluish grey.

Var. *Sargentii* Henry. Prostrate form.

J. excelsa Bieb. Grecian Juniper. 40. E. Bark peeling in long strips; branches curved up at ends. Needle ls. in opposite pairs, 2-banded, rarely present on adult trees. Berry ¼, dark brown, with blue bloom. Greece and Asia Minor.

J. horizontalis Moench. 1. E. Bluish green, creeping. Berry ¼, pale blue, drooping. North America.

JUNIPERUS—*continued*

J. occidentalis Hook. Western Juniper. 50. E. Bark bright cinnamon-red, scaly. Scale ls. in threes, closely pressed to stem, grey-green, minutely toothed. Berry $\frac{1}{4}$, bluish black, bloomy. West North America.

J. pachyphloea Torr. Alligator Juniper. 50. E. Bark dark brown, scaly. Scale ls. in pairs, bluish green, minutely toothed. Berry $\frac{1}{2}$, reddish brown, bloomy. Arizona and New Mexico.

J. phoenicea L. f. Phoenicean Juniper. 18. E. Branchlets tufted at ends. Scale ls. in threes, minutely toothed; needle ls. in threes, 2-banded. Berry $\frac{1}{4}$, yellowish or reddish brown. Mediterranean region.

J. Sabina L. Savin. 6. E. Dark green, spreading; strongly aromatic when bruised. Needle ls. in opposite pairs, 1-banded. Berry $\frac{1}{4}$, dark brown, covered with blue bloom. Central and South Europe. (Fig. 44 zz.)

J. scopulorum Sarg. 30. E. Trunk dividing near base; bark reddish brown, shreddy. Scale ls. sharp-pointed, closely pressed to stem, yellowish green or glaucous. Berry $\frac{1}{4}$, bright blue. West North America.

J. thurifera L. Incense Juniper, Spanish Juniper. 40. E. Needle ls. in opposite pairs, 2-banded; scale ls. minutely toothed. Berry $\frac{1}{4}$, blue. Spain and North Africa.

J. virginiana L. Red or Pencil Cedar. 100. E. Bark reddish brown, peeling in strips. Needle ls. in opposite pairs, 1-banded. Scale ls. pointed, in opposite pairs. Berry $\frac{1}{4}$, blue, ripe in one season. North America. (Fig. 44 z.)

Var. *glauca* Carr. Silver Juniper.

KETELEERIA. Like *Abies*, but adult leaves keeled on both sides and pale green below; buds with keeled scales. Ls. on young trees up to $2\frac{1}{2}$, spiny-pointed. Cones 8×2, erect, the scales not being shed.

K. Davidiana Beiss. 100. E. Twigs yellowish grey, hairy. China and Formosa. (Fig. 43 D.)

K. Fortunei Carr. 80. E. Twigs orange-red, hairless. South-east China.

LARIX. Larch. Branches alternate. Ls. linear, deciduous, in clusters on old shoots, spirally arranged on leading shoots, pale green. Male flowers solitary, yellow, round or cylindrical; female catkins round, red or purple, erect. Cones small, woody. The timber is strong, and durable in the open.

L. decidua Mill. (*L. europea* DC.). European Larch. 150. Twigs yellowish grey, hairless. Ls. $1\frac{1}{2}$, bright green, soft. Female catkins purple. Cone $1\frac{1}{2}$. Europe. (Fig. 45 A.)

L. eurolepis Henry. Hybrid Larch. Twigs yellow. Other characters variable, following one parent or the other, but growing faster when young than European larch. Natural hybrid between *L. decidua* and *L. leptolepis*.

L. Gmelinii Pilger (*L. dahurica* Turcz.). Dahurian Larch. 100. Twigs yellowish or reddish, usually downy. Ls. $1\frac{1}{2}$, flattened. Cone 1, glossy and hairless. North-east Asia.

L. Griffithii Hook. f. Sikkim Larch. 60. Branchlets long and drooping, twigs reddish brown. Ls. 1, obtuse. Female catkins purple. Cone 3×1; bracts lanc., exceeding scales. East Himalaya.

LARIX—*continued*

L. laricina Koch (*L. americana* Michx.). Tamarack. 80. Twigs reddish brown. Ls. 1, obtuse, bluish green. Cone $\frac{3}{4}$, egg-shaped. East North America.

L. leptolepis Sieb. & Zucc. (Gord.), (*L. Kaempferi* Sarg.). Japanese Larch. 100. Twigs reddish brown. Ls. $1\frac{1}{2}$, flat, obtuse, with two white bands below giving the underside a bluish appearance. Female catkins red. Cone 1×1, scales recurved at apex. Japan.

L. occidentalis Nutt. Western Larch. 200. Bark reddish; twigs orange-brown. Ls. $1\frac{1}{2}$, pale green, sharply pointed, keeled below. Cone $1\frac{1}{2} \times \frac{3}{4}$, with long-pointed protruding upright bracts. West North America. (Fig. 45 B.)

L. pendula Salisb. Weeping Larch. Branches drooping, twigs pinkish. Cone with long, protruding upright bracts. East North America.

L. Potaninii Batal. Chinese Larch. 100. Like *L. occidentalis*, but bark grey and leaves keeled on both sides. China.

L. sibirica Ledeb. Siberian Larch. 150. Like *L. decidua*, but leaves up to 2 in. long and cone scales incurved at apex.

LIBOCEDRUS DECURRENS Torr. Incense Cedar. 120. E. A tall narrow tree with erect branches, dense foliage, and rounded top. Bark chocolate colour, scaling off in small rectangles. Branchlet systems flattened, green on both sides, set in a vertical plane. Ls. in fours, scale-like, with long tapering bases, dark green. Cone $\frac{3}{4}$, erect, elongated, 4-scaled, seeds winged. West North America. (Fig. 44 U.)

PICEA. Spruce. Tall narrow evergreen trees with pointed crowns. Bark scaly, grey or greenish, often with a bronze or pinkish tinge; branches whorled in young trees, the main twigs opposite. Ls. alternate, linear, leaving small pegs on the twigs when they fall. Male catkins in leaf-axils at end of shoots, yellow or red; female terminal, green or purple. Cones hanging. The timber of several species has been imported in large quantities under the name of white deal or whitewood, as wood pulp for the manufacture of newsprint, and as scaffolding and ladder poles. Silver Spruce, used in aircraft construction, oar making, tent poles, etc., is the timber of *P. sitchensis*.

(a) Ls. flattened or distinctly 2-edged, with grey lines on one side only

P. brachytyla Pritz. 80. Ls. on upper side of shoot only, $\frac{3}{4}$, dark green above, bluish grey below. Cone 4×2, scales not toothed. China.

P. Breweriana Wats. Weeping Spruce. 100. End twigs hang perpendicularly. Ls. 1, radially arranged. Cone 3, light orange-brown, scales rounded and entire. West North America. (Fig. 45 G.)

P. jezoensis Carr. (*P. ajanensis* Fisch.). Yeddo Spruce. 150. Ls. on upper side of shoot only, 1, blunt, dark green above, vividly blue-white below. Cone 2×1, scales toothed. Japan.

P. Omorika Bolle. Serbian Spruce. 100. Buds enclosed by a ring of awl-shaped scales. Ls. 1, thick, directed at different angles on central upper part of shoot. Cone 2, egg-shaped, scales toothed. South-west Yugoslavia. (Fig. 45 C.)

P. sitchensis Carr. (*Abies Menziesii* Lindl.). Sitka Spruce. 200. Twigs

PICEA—*continued*

very stiff, yellowish brown, hairless. Ls. 1, stiff and prickly pointed on young trees, radially arranged, green on one side, silvery on the other. Cone 4×1, blunt, pale brown. West North America. (Fig. 45 F.)

(*b*) *Ls. quadrangular in section, grey lines on both sides*

P. Abies Karst. (*P. excelsa* Link). Common Spruce, Norway Spruce, Christmas Tree. 120. Ls. ½, vaguely 2-ranked, deep green. Cones 5×2, cylindrical, tapering at top; scales triangular, jagged at apex. Europe. (Fig. 45 E.)

Var. *argentea spica* Rehd. Young shoots creamy white.

P. asperata Mast. 100. Twigs yellowish grey. Ls. ¾, radially arranged, leaving large pegs. Cone 4×1½, scales entire. China.

P. bicolor Mayr (*P. Alcockiana* Carr.). 80. Ls. ½, very crowded, bright glossy green. Cone 3×1½, scales slightly toothed. Japan.

P. Engelmannii Engelm. 100. Branches drooping; twigs downy. Ls. 1, radially arranged. Cone 2×1, tapering at top; scales toothed, cut off square at apex. West North America. (Fig. 45 L.)

P. glauca Voss (*P. alba* Link). White Spruce, Canadian Spruce. 100. Twigs hairless. Ls. ¾, with pale bluish green bloom. Cone 2, cylindrical; scales very thin, nearly entire. North America. (Fig. 45 D.)

P. Glehnii Mast. Saghalin Spruce. 120. Terminal winter buds with ring of scales at base. Ls. ½, deep green, blunt. Cone 3, violet coloured when unripe; scales rounded, entire. Japan and Saghalin.

P. likiangensis Pritz. 100. Twigs brown, bristly, with prominent leaf-pegs. Ls. 2-ranked, ½, horny-pointed. Cone 2, egg-shaped, with rounded wavy scales. China.

P. Mariana B. S. P. (*P. nigra* Link). Black Spruce. 30. Branches densely twiggy; twigs covered with reddish down. Ls. ½, slightly curved, dark bluish green. Cone 1. North America. (Fig. 45 H.)

P. obovata Ledeb. Siberian Spruce. 100. Like *P. Abies*, but cones smaller (3) and cone scales rounded and entire. North-east Russia and Siberia.

P. orientalis Carr. 100. Ls. ¼, dark glossy green, pressed close to twig. Cone 2, scales toothed. Asia Minor and Caucasus. (Fig. 45 J.)

P. polita Carr. Tiger-tail Spruce. 120. Twigs creamy yellow, hairless. Ls. 1¾, sabre-like, stiff and prickly, curved and hollowed, glossy, radially arranged. Cone 4, scales minutely toothed. Japan. (Fig. 45 M.)

P. pungens Engelm. 100. Twigs hairless; bud scales recurved at tip. Ls. radially arranged, 1, stiff, spine-tipped. Cone 4×1, scales coarsely toothed. U.S.A.

Vars. *argentea* Beiss and *glauca* Regel. Ls. blue-white.
Var. *pendula* Beiss. Blue weeping form.

P. rubra Link (*P. rubens* Sarg.). Red Spruce. 100. Twigs glandular-hairy, terminal winter bud with a ring of scales at the base. Ls. ½, glossy green. Cone oblong, 1½, purplish green when unripe; scales rounded, entire. North America.

P. Smithiana Boiss. (*P. Morinda* Link). Himalayan Spruce. 120. Branches

PICEA—*continued*

drooping. Ls. 2, prickly pointed, radially arranged and directed forward. Cone 6×2; scales rounded, entire. West Himalaya. (Fig. 45 K.)

P. Wilsonii Mast. 60. Twigs hairless, light grey, almost smooth. Ls. ½, 2-ranked, stout. Cone 2; scales round, entire. West China.

PINUS. Pine. Branches whorled in young trees, twigs opposite. Ls. linear, in bundles of two to five. Male catkins yellow or red, clustered at the base of either the terminal or lateral young shoots; female egg-shaped, borne at the end of lateral young shoots. Fruit a woody cone; cone scales thickened and bossed at outer end, opening when ripe and allowing the winged seeds to escape. The timber is yellow or red, resinous, strong, and absorbs creosote well.

(*a*) *Two leaves in each bundle*

P. Banksiana Lamb. Jack Pine, Banksian Pine. 80. E. Buds thickly coated with resin. Ls. 1½, bright green, curved and often twisted. Cone 1½, curved. East North America. (Fig. 45 N.)

P. contorta Dougl. Beach Pine. 30. E. Twigs orange-brown. Ls. 2, dark green, rigid, twisted. Cone 2×¾, unequal sided. West North America. (Fig. 45 P.)

Var. *Murrayana* Engelm. (*P. Murrayana* Balf.). Lodge-pole Pine. Ls. 3, lighter green.

P. echinata Mill. (*P. mitis* Michx.). Short-leaf Pitch Pine. 120. Bark light red. Ls. 4, dark bluish green. Cone 2×1, egg-shaped or conical, each scale with a small prickle.

P. halepensis Mill. Aleppo Pine. 50. E. The tree has a bare thin appearance. Twigs pale grey, the buds without resin. Ls. 4, very slender, bluish green. Cone 3×1, stalked, in clusters, remaining on the tree for several years. Mediterranean region.

P. koraiensis Sieb. & Zucc. Siberian Pine. 100. Bark grey; twigs yellowish, woolly. Ls. 4, straight, dark green, rough-edged. Cone 4, yellowish. East Asia.

P. leucodermis Ant. Bosnian Pine. 90. E. Twigs greyish white; buds without resin. Ls. 4, bright green, erect and rigid. Cone 3×1, egg-shaped, yellow or light brown. Yugoslavia.

P. Mugo Turra (*P. montana* Mill.). Mountain Pine. 80. E. Usually a low shrub. Densely branched and therefore useful for shelter. Ls. 3, dull pale green, crowded. Cone 2, glossy, very hard, with pyramidal scales. Alps. (Fig. 45 Q.)

Var. *pumilio* Willk. (*Mughus* Zenari). Dwarf. Cone 1½.

Var. *uncinata* Willk. 80. Cone scales hooked.

P. muricata D. Don. Bishop Pine. 90. E. Twigs orange-brown; buds cylindrical, coated with resin. Ls. 6, stiff, blunt, concave, rough-edged. Cone 3, unequal sided, scales hooked. California. (Fig. 46 A.)

P. nigra Arnold (*P. Laricio* Poir.). 150. E. Buds cylindrical, thickly coated with resin; twigs light brown, covered with long narrow plates. Ls. 6, dark green, curved and twisted in young plants, minutely toothed. Cone 3×1, egg-shaped, glossy. Central Europe to West Asia. (Fig. 45 S.)

Var. *calabrica* Schneid. Corsican Pine. Crown narrow.

PINUS—*continued*

Var. *nigricans* Parl. (*austriaca* Loud.). Crown broader and foliage greener and denser (cannot be seen through). Cone scale with radiating cracks (Henry).

P. Pinaster Ait. (*P. maritima* Lam.). Cluster Pine, Maritime Pine. 120. E. Bark deeply furrowed. Twigs yellowish brown; buds without resin, scales free at tip, recurved and edged with silvery threads. Ls. 8. Cone 5 × 2, pointed, yellowish brown, in clusters remaining on the tree for several years. Mediterranean region. (Fig. 46 B.)

P. Pinea L. Stone Pine. 100. E. Old trees have a broad umbrella-shaped crown. Buds ½, scales curly, pointed, edged with silvery threads. Ls. 5. Cone 4 × 3, roundish egg-shaped, not pointed, glossy, pale brown; seed about the size of a hazel nut, wingless or nearly so, edible. Mediterranean region. (Fig. 45 R.)

P. resinosa Ait. Red Pine. 70. E. Branches drooping; buds conical, resinous. Ls. 6, dark glossy green, rough-edged, densely crowded, bundle sheath ¾. Cone egg-shaped, 2 × 1, pale shining brown. East North America.

P. sylvestris L. Scots Pine, Scotch Fir, Redwood. 100. E. Crown flattens out in old trees. Bark reddish, scaly, peeling off in upper part of tree. Buds with little resin, scales free at tip. Ls. 3, stiff, bluish green. Cone 2½, conical. Europe (including Britain) and North Asia. (Fig. 45 O.)

The timber is imported as redwood, red or yellow deal, or red fir.

P. Thunbergii Parl. Japanese Black Pine. 100. E. Bark dark grey; twigs yellow; buds white, not resinous. Ls. 3, stout, sharp-pointed, bright green. Cone 2 × 1, each scale with a small prickle. Japan.

(b) Three ls. in each bundle

P. Bungeana Zucc. Lace-bark Pine. 80. E. Bark smooth, ashy grey, peeling like the plane tree. Ls. 3, rigid, bright pale green, rough-edged. Cone 2 × 1, scales hooked, seeds wingless. China.

P. Coulteri D. Don. Big-cone Pine. 80. E. Twigs very thick, with the leaves clustered at the end; buds resinous. Ls. 12, minutely toothed, grey-green. Cone 12 × 6, polished; scales thick, with strong hooked spines. California. (Fig. 46 E.)

P. palustris Mill. Southern Pitch Pine. 120. E. An important timber- and turpentine-producing tree. Bark light brown, peeling in thin scales; branches ascending, with the ls. in tufts at the end of the twigs; buds whitish, not resinous. Ls. 16, dark green. Cone 8 × 2, each scale with a short hook. South-east United States.

P. ponderosa Dougl. Western Yellow Pine. 200. E. Crown narrow, open, and tufted; lower branches drooping; twigs shining reddish brown; buds resinous. Ls. 12, 3-sided, densely crowded at end of branches on older trees. Cone 6 × 2, narrowly egg-shaped, scale with short hooked prickle. West North America. (Fig. 46 F.)

Var. *Jeffreyi* Vasey (*P. Jeffreyi* Grev.). Buds not resinous. Ls. 8, bluish.

P. radiata D. Don (*P. insignis* Dougl.). Monterey Pine. 120. E. Bark

PINUS—*continued*

rough. Buds resinous. Ls. 6, thin, bright green, clustered at end of branches on older trees, often in pairs. Cone 5×3, unequal sided, bright brown, boss of scale diamond-shaped with minute prickle in centre. California. (Fig. 46 L.)

P. rigida Mill. Northern Pitch Pine. 80. E. Trunk with numerous small shoots in addition to the larger branches. Twigs pale brown, hairless; buds cylindrical, resinous. Ls. 4, rough-edged. Cone 1 to 3, round or conical, scales ending in short prickle. East North America. (Fig. 46 C.)

P. Sabiniana Dougl. Digger Pine. 50. E. Young twigs blue-white, with the leaves clustered at the end. Ls. 12, bluish green, drooping. Cone 10×6, very resinous, scales hooked. California.

P. Taeda L. Loblolly Pine, Pitch Pine. 120. E. Bark bright reddish brown, thick; branches spreading or ascending; buds resinous. Ls. 9, bright green. Cone 4×2, each scale with a short hooked spine. The tree is tapped for turpentine. East United States.

(c) Five ls. in each bundle

P. aristata Engelm. Bristle-cone Pine, Hickory Pine. 50. E. Often a prostrate shrub. Twigs light orange, hairless. Ls. 1½, dark green, with conspicuous white lines. Cone 3×2, egg-shaped, scales with hooked bristles. California. (Fig. 46 D.)

P. Armandi Franch. 60. E. Twigs greyish green. Ls. 6, bright green, minutely toothed. Cone 8×3, narrowly egg-shaped, seeds wingless. China.

P. Ayacahuite Ehrenb. Mexican White Pine. 100. E. Like *P. excelsa* (see below), but cones much longer (up to 18). Mexico.

P. Cembra L. Arolla Pine, Cembran Pine. 100. E. Densely branched and very leafy. Twigs covered with shaggy reddish brown hairs. Ls. 3, bright green, smooth-edged, crowded. Cone 3×2, egg-shaped, not spiny. Alps. (Fig. 46 K.)

P. excelsa Wall. Bhutan Pine, Blue Pine. 150. E. Bark smooth and silver-grey on young trees. Twigs glaucous green, hairless. Ls. 6, thin, drooping, bluish green, rough-edged. Cone 8×1½, hanging, slightly curved. Himalaya. (Fig. 46 H.)

P. flexilis James. Limber Pine. 60. E. Twigs long, slender, and downy, can be bent double without breaking. Ls. 3, rigid, dark green. Cone 4×1½. Rocky Mountains. (Fig. 46 G.)

P. Lambertiana Dougl. Sugar Pine. 200. E. Bark smooth, ashy grey, full of resin. Buds ¼, blunt-ended. Ls. 4, bluish green, rough-edged, spirally twisted, with white lines on back, clustered at end of branch. Cone 20×3, hanging. West North America. (Fig. 46 M.)

P. Montezumae Lamb. Rough-barked Mexican Pine. 100. E. Bark thick and rough. Ls. 6, erect, glaucous green; sheath 1, persistent. Cone 6×2½, scale with short hooked prickle. Mexico.

P. monticola D. Don. Western White Pine. 125. E. Twigs downy. Ls. 4, rigid, blunt, twisted, white on one side, rough-edged. Cone 8×1, curved towards tip. West North America.

P. parviflora Sieb. & Zucc. Japanese White Pine. 40. E. Twigs minutely

PINUS—*continued*

downy; buds ¼. Ls. 2. Cone 3×¾, in whorls in great profusion. Japan. (Fig. 46 J.)

P. Peuke Griseb. Macedonian Pine. 100. E. Narrow tree, with green, glossy, and hairless twigs. Ls. 4, crowded, stiff, rough-edged. Cone 5×1½. Balkan Mountains.

P. Strobus L. Weymouth Pine, Yellow Pine. 80. E. Bark smooth and silvery on young trees. Twigs with tufts of hairs at first below the insertion of the ls., not glaucous. Ls. 5, light green or bluish green, drooping, rough-edged. Cone 8×1, curved. East North America.

PSEUDOLARIX AMABILIS Rehd. (P. FORTUNEI Mayr). Golden Larch. 100. D. Branches whorled. Ls. linear, 2, pale green, in clusters at end of short curved side shoots; alternate and spirally arranged on leading shoots. Male flowers yellow, in clusters at end of short side shoots; female solitary. Cone 2, roundish egg-shaped, woody, falling to pieces when ripe. China. (Fig. 47 B.)

PSEUDOTSUGA. Douglas Fir. Tall evergreen trees with pointed crowns. Bark grey or greenish, smooth on young trees, thick and furrowed later. Branches whorled, but not so regularly as in the spruces and silver firs. Terminal winter buds long, narrow, and pointed. Ls. alternate, linear, 1, spirally arranged, imperfectly 2-ranked on older twigs, leaving raised scars when they fall. Male fls. solitary in the leaf-axils; female terminal on short branchlets. Fruit a woody cone, 2×1, hanging; each scale with a protruding 3-pronged bract. The timber is strong and imported under the name of Oregon Pine or British Columbian Pine.

P. japonica Beiss. Japanese Douglas Fir. 100. Twigs yellowish, hairless. Ls. notched at apex. Japan.

P. taxifolia Brit. (*P. Douglasii* Carr.). Oregon Douglas Fir. 250. Twigs reddish brown, downy; buds bright chestnut brown, beech-like, not resinous. Ls. green on upper side. West North America. (Fig. 47 A.)

Var. *glauca* Schneid. (*P. glauca* Mayr). Colorado Douglas Fir. 150. Buds coated with resin. Ls. covered with bluish grey bloom. Colorado.

SCIADOPITYS VERTICILLATA Sieb. & Zucc. Umbrella Pine. 100. Ls. linear, 4, grooved below, in whorls. Male flowers in terminal racemes; female solitary, terminal. Cone 3×2, scales with recurved margins. Japan. (Fig. 47 C.)

SEQUOIA. Tall narrow evergreen trees with pointed crowns and a uniform outline. Bark reddish, thick, soft, and spongy. Ls. alternate, awl-shaped or linear, the lower part adhering to the stem. Fruit a woody cone with diamond-shaped scales.

S. gigantea Decne. (*Wellingtonia gigantea* Lindl.). Mammoth Tree. 300. Ls. awl-shaped, ½, pointed. Cone 3×2. California. (Fig. 47 E.)

S. sempervirens Endl. Redwood. 300. Ls. linear, lanc., ¾, 2-ranked except on leading shoots where they are similar to those of the preceding species. Cone 1×½. The timber is strong and durable and much more useful than that of *S. gigantea*. California. (Fig. 47 D.)

Var. *adpressa* Carr. Ls. ¼, white-tipped.

* TAIWANIA CRYPTOMERIOIDES Hayata. 150. E. Ls. in young trees alternate, awl-shaped, ½, spine-tipped, keeled on both sides; in older trees scale-like, closely

pressed to stem. Cone ½, egg-shaped, terminal, with numerous rounded overlapping scales (Bean). Formosa. (Fig. 47 G.)

TAXODIUM DISTICHUM Rich. Deciduous Cypress, Swamp Cypress, Bald Cypress. 100. D. Trunk buttressed at base. In wet places the roots send up hollow protuberances known as 'knee roots.' Ls. alternate, linear, ½, 2-ranked, the whole shoot falling off in autumn; ls. spirally arranged on leading shoots. Male flowers in terminal drooping panicles; female scattered near end of previous year's wood. Fruit a leathery round or egg-shaped cone, 1½, scales peltate. South United States. (Fig. 47 M.)

T. *ascendens* (Brongn.), the Pond Cypress, is a smaller tree, with erect branches and smaller, adpressed ls.

* TETRACLINIS ARTICULATA Mast. Alcerce. 50. E. Like the cypresses and *Thuya*, but the cones have only four scales. North Africa. (Fig. 47 N.)

THUYA. Arbor-vitae. Foliage similar to *Chamaecyparis* (see page 332). Fruit a woody cone, usually elongated, with six to ten pairs of non-peltate overlapping scales.

T. occidentalis L. White Cedar. 60. E. Branchlet systems dark green above, pale green below, turning brown in winter, no white markings but glands prominent; central axis flattened, with the leaf-pairs close together. Cone ¼ to ½. East North America. (Fig. 47 R.)

Var. *aurea* Nichols. Young shoots yellow.

Var. *ericoides* Beiss. (*Retinospora dubia* Carr.). A dwarf shrub with all juvenile leaves.

T. orientalis L. (*Biota orientalis* Endl.). 40. E. Branchlet systems in vertical plane, with the same shade of green on both sides. Ls. very small, with small depressed glands on the lower surface, closely pressed to stem. Cone ¾, egg-shaped, scales hooked, seeds wingless. China. (Fig. 47 Q.)

Var. *aurea* Dauv. Branches tipped with yellow in summer.

T. plicata D. Don (*T. gigantea* Nutt., *T. Lobbii* Hort.). Western Red Cedar. 200. E. Branchlet systems in horizontal plane. Ls. aromatic, with white markings and small glands on back; central axis not flattened, the leaf-pairs sharp-pointed and somewhat distant. Cone ½. The timber is exceptionally durable. Alaska to North California. (Fig. 47 S.)

Var. *pyramidalis* Bean. Tall and narrow.

Vars. *variegata* Hort. and *zebrina* Hort. Yellow interspersed with green.

T. Standishii Carr. (*T. japonica* Maxim., *Thuyopsis Standishii* Gord.). Japanese Arbor-vitae. 25. E. Bark twisted. Branchlet systems in horizontal planes. Ls. with white markings on back but no glands, not aromatic; the leaf-pairs on central axis not distant. Cone ¼, oblong. Japan. (Fig. 47 P.)

THUYOPSIS DOLABRATA Sieb. & Zucc. (THUYA DOLABRATA L. 50. E. Branchlets in opposite rows in a horizontal plane. Ls. with brilliant and clearly defined white markings on the back. Cone ¾, egg-shaped, each scale 3-5-seeded. Japan. (Fig. 47 O.)

Var. *variegata* Fort. Ls. variegated with creamy white.

TSUGA. Hemlock Spruce. Branches alternate. Ls. alternate, linear, flat, blunt, usually 2-ranked, with two white lines below. Male flowers solitary, round, in the leaf-axils; female at the end of lateral shoots. Fruit a small woody drooping cone. The timber contains no resin; that of Western Hemlock has recently been imported in large quantities.

(*a*) *Ls. minutely toothed*

T. canadensis Carr. Eastern Hemlock. 100. E. Usually an irregular-shaped tree in Britain, with several stems and a broad crown. Winter buds egg-shaped, pointed. Ls. ½, the white lines with clearly defined edges. Cone ¾. East North America. (Fig. 47 J.)

T. dumosa Sarg. (*T. Brunoniana* Carr.). Himalayan Hemlock. 120. E. Winter buds round. Ls. 1, very white below, the lines with clearly defined edges. Cone 1. East Himalaya.

T. heterophylla Sarg. (*T. Albertiana* Sénécl.). Western Hemlock. 200. E. A tree with a straight stem, narrow crown, and pendulous leading shoot and branches. Winter buds round. Ls. ¾, the white lines with diffuse or broken edges. Cone ¾. East North America. (Fig. 47 J.) One of the most graceful conifers, and as it stands a lot of shade it is suitable for underplanting.

(*b*) *Ls. entire*

T. caroliniana Engelm. Carolina Hemlock. 50. E. Twigs hairy on upper side. Ls. ½. Cone 1½, scales ov., oblong. South-east United States.

T. chinensis Pritz. Chinese Hemlock. 150. E. Twigs downy. Ls. 1, broad, notched at apex, with broad white bands below. Cone 1, scales round. West China.

T. diversifolia Mast. (*T. Sieboldii* Carr.). Japanese Hemlock. 100. E. Twigs hairless. Ls. ½, notched at apex, with narrow white bands below. Japan. (Fig. 47 L.)

T. Mertensiana Sarg. (*T. Pattoniana* Sénécl.). Mountain Hemlock. 100. E. Ls. radially arranged, 1, rounded or keeled above, with white lines on both sides. Cone 3×¾. West North America. (Fig. 47 K.)

Var. *argentea* Sudw. (*glauca* Hort.). Ls. bluish white.

* WIDDRINGTONIA WHYTEI Rendle. Milanji Cedar. 100. E. Main branches whorled. Ls. in young trees alternate, awl-shaped, 1; in older trees opposite, scale-like, closely pressed to stem. Cone woody, 1×½, egg-shaped, 4-scaled, seeds winged. South Africa. (Fig. 47 F.)

Family 111. GINKGOACEAE

A curious family consisting of only one genus and species of very ancient origin, traces having been found in the coal measures. The ovule has a rudimentary ovary. The pollen grain produces an intermediate structure as in ferns and sexual reproduction is by spermatazoids as in cycads.

GINKGO BILOBA L. (SALISBURIA ADIANTIFOLIA Sm.). Maidenhair Tree. 100. D. Twigs stout, rigid, and jointed. Ls. alternate or in clusters, fan-shaped, 3, notched or jagged, long-stalked. Male catkins 1, short stalked; female flowers long-stalked; the sexes on different trees. Fruit 1, egg-shaped, yellowish green, with a fleshy outer and a bony inner coat, rarely seen in Britain. China. (Fig. 27 B.)

CLASS IV. CRYPTOGAMS

Flowerless and seedless plants; reproduction by spores.

Family 112. FILICES

Spores minute, produced in conspicuous spore-cases on the leaf, usually on the under side. The spore on germination produces an intermediate structure of cells on which the sexual cells are developed.

* DICKSONIA ANTARCTICA Labell. Tree Fern. 30. E. Trunk covered with matted rootlets. Ls. 2-pinnate, 6 feet by 2 feet, spreading palm-like from the top of the stem, crozier-like when opening. Australia and Tasmania. (Fig. 22 D.)

AUTHORS' NAMES

Arr., Aiton
Aitch., Aitchison
Alef., Alefeld
Anders., Anderson
Andr., Andrews
André
Ant., Antoine
Armstr., Armstrong
Arn., Arnott
Arnold
Ashe
Asso
Auct., Auctorum, of various authors
Audub., Audubon

Bab., Babington
Bailey
Baill., Baillon
Baker
Bal., Balansa
Balf., Balfour
Ball
Banks
Barbier
Barrelier
Bartl., Bartling
Bartr., Bartram
Batal., Batalin
Baumg., Baumgarten
Bausch
Beadle
Beal
Bean
Beauv., Beauvois
Bedd., Beddome
Beiss., Beissner
Benth., Bentham
Berg., Berger
Bernh., Bernhardi
Berth., Berthelot
Bess., Besser
Bieb., Bieberstein
Bigel., Bigelow
Bisset
Blake
Blume
Bois
Boiss., Boissier
Bolle
Bong., Bongard
Booth
Borkh., Borkhausen
Bosc
Br., Brown
Brandegee
Brit., Britton
Brongn., Brongniart
Brot., Brotero
B. S. P., Britton, Sterns, Poggenberg
Buch., Buchanan
Buch.-Ham., Buchanan-Hamilton
Buckl., Buckley
Buerg
Bunge
Bur., Bureau
Burk., Burkill
Bush

Call., Callier
Camus
Carr., Carrière
Carruthers
Cav., Cavanilles
Cham., Chamisso
Chap., Chapman
Cheeseman
Chitt., Chittenden
Choisy
Clarke
Cockayne
Colebr., Colebrooke
Colenso
Colla
Cow., Cowell
Craib
Crantz
Crép., Crépin
Cunn., Cunningham
Curt., Curtis

Dall., Dallimore
Dauv., Dauvesse
David
DC., De Candolle
Decne, Decaisne
De Lahaie
Delavay
Déségl., Déséglise
Desf., Desfontaines
Desr., Desrousseaux
Desv., Desvaux
Dicks., Dickson
Dieck
Diels
Dietr., Dietrich
Dipp., Dippel
Dodd
Dode
Don, G. Don
Dougl., Douglas
Druce
Dryand., Dryander
Du Caill., Du Caillaud
Dum.-Cours., Dumont de Courset
Dumort., Dumortier
Dunal

Dunn
Dur., Durieu
Durazz., Durazzino
Du Roi
Duthie

Eastw., Eastwood
Eberm., Ebermaier
Eckl., Ecklon
Ehrenb., Ehrenberg
Ehrh., Ehrhart
Ell., Elliott
Ellis
Endl., Endlicher
Engelm., Engelmann
Engl., Engler
Esch., Eschscholtz

Facch., Facchini
Fedde
Fenzl
Fern., Fernald
Fisch., Fischer
Focke
Foëx
Forbes
Forrest
Forssk., Forsskal
Forst., Forster
Fort., Fortune
Franch., Franchet
Frey., Freyer
Fries
Fritsch
Fouc., Foucaud

Gaertn., Gaertner
Gaertn. f., Gaertner filius
Gaud., Gaudin
Gay
Gibbs
Gilib., Gilibert
Gill., Gillies
Gleditsch
Gmel., Gmelin
Gord., Gordon
Gouan
Graebn., Graebner
Gray
Green
Greene
Grev., Greville
Griseb., Grisebach

Hance
Hardw., Hardwicke
Hariot
Harms
Harr., Harrow
Hartig
Hartw., Hartweg
Harvey
Hassk., Hasskarl
Haw., Haworth
Hayata

Hayne
H. B. K., Humboldt, Bonpland, Kunth
Hedl., Hedlund
Hell., Heller
Hemsl., Hemsley
Henry
Hérincq
Herrm., Herrmann
Hesse
Hitch., Hitchcock
Hook., Hooker
Hook. f., Hooker filius
Hoppe
Hort., hortorum (of gardeners)
Host
Hu
Huds., Hudson
Hughes
Hutch., Hutchinson

Jacks., Jackson
Jacq., Jacquin
Jaeg., Jaeger
James
Johnst., Johnston
Jouin
Juss., de Jussieu

Kalm
Kanitz
Karst., Karsten
Ker-Gawl, Ker (formerly Gawler)
Kern., Kerner
Kipp., Kippist
Kirchn., Kirchner
Kirk
Kit., Kitaibel
Knight
Koch
Koehne
Koern., Koernicke
Koidz., Koidzumi
Komar., Komarov
Korsh., Korshinsky
Kotschy
Krassn., Krassnov
Kunth
Kuntze
Kurz

L., Linnaeus
L. f., Linnaeus filius
Labill., Labillardière
Lag., Lagasca
Lam., Lamarck
Lamb., Lambert
Lang
Lauche
Lav., Lavallée
Laws., Lawson & Son
Laxm., Laxmann
Ledeb., Ledebour
Lem., Lemaire
Lemmon
Less., Lessing

Leyb., Leybold
L'Hérit., L'Héritier
Liebl., Lieblein
Liebm., Liebmann
Lindl., Lindley
Ling., Lingelsh
Link
Lodd., Loddiges
Lois
Loisel., Loiseleur
Loud., Loudon
Lour., Loureiro

Maack
Mairet
Makino
Manetti
March., Marchant
Marsh., Marshall
Mart., Martius
Mast., Masters
Matsumara
Maxim., Maximowicz
Mayr
Med., Medic., Medicus
Meissn., Meissner
Melv., Melville
Merc., Mercier
Mey., Meyer
Michx., Michaux
Miers
Mill., Miller
Miq., Miquel
Mirb., Mirbel
Mitf., Freeman-Mitford
Moc., Mocino
Moehl
Moench
Mol., Molino
Moore
Morren
Mouillef., Mouillefert
Muell., Mueller
Muell.-Arg., Mueller Argovinensis
Muenchh., Muenchhausen
Muhl., Muhlenberg
Munro
Murr., Murray

Nakai
Nash
Naud., Naudin
Née
Nees
Neilr., Neilreich
Nels., Nelson
Nichols., Nicholson
Nied., Niedenzu
Nitsche
Nutt., Nuttall

Oed., Oeder
Oerst., Oersted
Oliv., Oliver
Ortega
Osborn
Otto

Pall., Pallas
Parl., Parlatore
Parry
Pav., Pavon
Pax
Paxt., Paxton
Pers., Persoon
Petrie
Pfitzer
Philippi
Pilger
Piper
Planch., Planchon
Poech
Poepp., Poeppig
Pohl
Poir., Poiret
Poll., Pollich
Pourr., Pourret
Presl
Pritz., Pritzel
Pursh

Rafin., Rafinesque
Raoul
Red., Redouté
Regel
Rehd., Rehder
Reichb., Reichenbach
Reinw., Reinwardt
Rendle
Retz., Retzius
Rich., Richard
Rivière
Roem., Roemer
Rolfe
Rostk., Rostkovius
Roth
Rouy
Roxb., Roxburgh
Royle
Rudolphi
Ruiz
Rupr., Ruprecht
Rydb., Rydberg

St. Hil., Saint-Hilaire
Salisb., Salisbury
Santi
Sarg., Sargent
Savi
Schauer
Scheale
Schelle
Schlecht., Schlechtendal
Schleich., Schleicher
Schmidt
Schneid., Schneider
Schott
Schrad., Schrader
Schrank
Schreb., Schreber

Schrenk
Schultz
Schwarz
Schwer., Schwerin
Scop., Scopoli
Seem., Seemann
Sénécl., Sénéclauze
Ser., Seringe
Serv., Servettez
Sesse
Shaw
Sibth., Sibthorp
Sieb., Siebold
Simonkai
Simon-Louis
Sims
Sm., J. E. Smith
Small
Soland., Solander
Soul., Soulange
Spach
Spaeth
Sprague
Spreng., Sprengel
Stapf
Steud., Steudel
Stev., Steven
Stokes
Sudw., Sudworth
Suringar
Sweet
Swingle
Syme
Szys., Szyszylowicz

Takeda
Tanaka
Targ., Targione-Tozzetti
Tenore
Thomas
Thoms., Thomson
Thory
Thouin
Thuill., Thuillier
Thunb., Thunberg
Tobl., Tobler
Torr., Torrey
Tratt., Trattineck
Trautv., Trautvetter
Trel., Trelease
Trin., Trinius
Turcz., Turczaninov
Turra
Turrill

Vahl
Van Houtte
Van Tieghem
Vasey
Veitch
Vent., Ventenat
Vill., Villars
Vilm., Vilmorin
Vitm., Vitman
Voss

Wahl., Wahlenberg
Wahlb., Wahlberg
Waldst., Waldstein
Wall., Wallich
Wallr., Wallroth
Walp., Walpers
Walt., Walter
Wangh., Wangenheim
Ward
Warder
Ware
Waterer
Wats., Watson
Webb
Wedd., Weddell
Weihe
Weld., Welden
Wendl., Wendland
West., Weston
Weyer
Wheeler
Wieg., Wiegand
Wight
Willd., Willdenow
Willk., Willkomm
Wils., Wilson
Wimm., Wimmer
Winkl., Winkler
With., Withering
Witte
Wittm., Wittmack
Wood
Woods
Wright

Young

Zabel
Zenari
Zeyh., Zeyher
Zucc., Zuccarini

LIST OF REFERENCE BOOKS

Bean's *Trees and Shrubs Hardy in the British Isles.*
Beissner's *Handbuch der Nadelholzkunde.*
Bentham and Hooker's *British Flora.*
Bentham and Mueller's *Flora Australiensis.*
Bicknell's *Flowering Plants and Ferns of the Riviera.*
Botanical Register, 33 vols. of coloured plates.
Boulton's *A Dictionary of Wood.*
Brandis's *Indian Trees.*
Britton and Brown's *Illustrated Flora of the Northern States and Canada.*
Butcher and Strudwick's *Further Illustrations of British Plants.*
Cheeseman's *Illustrations of the New Zealand Flora.*
Collett's *Flora Simlensis.*
Curtis's *Botanical Magazine*, coloured plates from 1793 to the present day.
Dallimore and Jackson's *Handbook of the Coniferae.*
Dippel's *Handbuch der Laubholzkunde.*
Elwes and Henry's *The Trees of Great Britain and Ireland.*
Fitch and Smith's *Illustrations of the British Flora.*
Flore des Serres, 23 vols. of coloured plates.
Gardener's Chronicle (weekly).
Gardening Illustrated (weekly).
Gilbert-Carter's *Our Catkin-bearing Plants.*
Harvey and Sonder's *Flora Capensis.*
Hegi's *Flora von Mittel-Europa.*
Henderson's *Timber.*
Hooker's *Flora of British India.*
Hooker's *Icones Plantarum.*
Kerner and Oliver's *The Natural History of Plants.*
Kirk's *Forest Flora of New Zealand.*
Kirk's (J. W. C.) *British Garden Flora.*
Le Maout and Decaisne's *Descriptive and Analytical Botany.*
Loudon's *Arboretum et Fruticetum Britannicum.*
Moggridge's *Flora of Mentone.*
Moss and Hunnybun's *Cambridge British Flora*, vols. ii and iii only.
Nomenclature of Hardwoods (British Standards Institution).
Nomenclature of Softwoods (British Standards Institution).
Rehder's *Manual of Cultivated Trees and Shrubs Hardy in North America.*
Reichenbach's *Icones Florae Germanicae*, 20 vols. of coloured plates.
Robinson's *English Flower Garden.*
Sargent's *Manual of the Trees of North America.*
Sibthorp's *Flora Graeca*, 10 vols. of coloured plates.
Siebold and Zuccarini's *Flora Japonica*, 151 coloured plates.
Sowerby's *English Botany*, 12 vols. of coloured plates.
Veitch's *Manual of Coniferae.*
Wettstein's *Handbuch der Systematische Botanik.*
Willis's *Flowering Plants and Ferns.*
Zimmer's *Popular Dictionary of Botanical Names and Terms.*

INDEX

(Latin synonyms in italics)